INTERNATIONAL SERIES OF MONOGRAPHS ON
PURE AND APPLIED MATHEMATICS
GENERAL EDITORS: I. N. SNEDDON AND S. ULAM

VOLUME 8

OPERATIONAL CALCULUS

OTHER TITLES IN THE SERIES
ON PURE AND APPLIED MATHEMATICS

Vol. 1. *Introduction to Algebraic Topology*
by A. H. WALLACE

Vol. 2. *Circles*
by D. PEDOE

Vol. 3. *Analytical Conics*
by B. SPAIN

Vol. 4. *Integral Equations*
by S. MIKHLIN

Vol. 5. *Problems in Euclidean Space: Application of Convexity*
by H. G. EGGLESTON

Vol. 6. *Homology Theory on Algebraic Varieties*
by A. H. WALLACE

Vol. 7. *Methods Based on the Wiener-Hopf Technique for the Solution of Partial Differential Equations*
by B. NOBLE

OPERATIONAL CALCULUS

by

JAN MIKUSIŃSKI
PROFESSOR OF THE UNIVERSITY OF WARSAW

PERGAMON PRESS
LONDON • NEW YORK • PARIS • LOS ANGELES

PAŃSTWOWE WYDAWNICTWO NAUKOWE • WARSZAWA

PERGAMON PRESS LTD.
4 & 5 Fitzroy Square, London W. 1.

PERGAMON PRESS INC.
122 East 55th Street, New York 22, N. Y.
P.O. Box 47715, Los Angeles, California

PERGAMON PRESS, S.A.R.L.
24 Rue des Écoles, Paris, Ve

Library of Congress Card Number 59-11340

Translated from the second Polish edition,
volume 30 of Monografie Matematyczne, 1957

Printed in Poland

FOREWORD

There have been four editions of this book so far: the first in Polish (Warsaw 1953), the second in Russian (Moscow 1954), the third in German (Berlin 1957) and the fourth in Polish (Warsaw 1957). The present edition, in English, is the fifth. It has been enlarged by the addition of an Appendix of 112 pages, containing:

1° The proofs of theorems omitted in the earlier editions (the reader will thus be spared the trouble of studying original papers scattered over various periodicals).

2° New results in the operational calculus obtained since the publication of the first edition.

3° A discussion of the relations between the operational calculus and other branches of mathematics (such as abstract algebra, the theory of distributions and the Banach spaces).

4° Problems as yet unsolved.

The operational calculus had been known as early as the beginning of the nineteenth century, but its development and popularization was due to the later work of Heaviside, who applied it widely to problems in electricity.

In this book operators are introduced algebraically as a kind of fractions. They are a generalization of the concept of number: operations on them are performed in the same way as operations on numbers. This treatment is simpler and more general than that presented in other books (which base their exposition on the Laplace transform) and can be understood by readers who are not acquainted with the theory of analytic functions.

The book is a methodical presentation of a theory published by the author in the years 1950-1957 together with applications. It is written in such a manner as to be of use both to an engineer, who regards the operational calculus merely as a tool in his work, and to the reader who is interested in proofs of theorems and mathematical problems for their own sake.

I have been greatly assisted in preparing this book by Mr. S. Drobot, who collaborated with me in writing the chapter on the statics of beams, by Mr. C. Ryll-Nardzewski, with whom I discussed certain parts of the book in detail, and by Mr. M. Warmus, who read through the first edition of the book, worked out the solutions of the problems and checked the calculations. I am also indebted to Mr. S. Gładysz, Mr. W. Nowacki and Mrs. H. Pidek-Łopuszańska for their numerous valuable suggestions. The drawings have been made by Mr. S. Gutek.

Jan Mikusiński

PART ONE

OPERATIONAL ALGEBRA

CHAPTER I

THE CONCEPT AND PROPERTIES OF A CONVOLUTION OF CONTINUOUS FUNCTIONS

§ 1. Definition of convolution. The starting point of the theory presented in this book is the concept of convolution (or resultant) (¹). The *convolution* of functions $a(t)$ and $b(t)$ is the function $c(t)$ defined by the integral

$$c(t) = \int_0^t a(t-\tau)b(\tau)\,d\tau.$$

EXAMPLE 1. $a(t) = t^2,\ b(t) = e^t;$

$$c(t) = \int_0^t (t-\tau)^2 e^\tau d\tau = \int_0^t (t^2-2t\tau+\tau^2)e^\tau d\tau$$

$$= t^2\int_0^t e^\tau d\tau - 2t\int_0^t \tau e^\tau d\tau + \int_0^t \tau^2 e^\tau d\tau$$

$$= t^2(e^t-1)-2t(te^t-e^t+1)+(t^2e^t-2te^t+2e^t-2)$$

$$= 2e^t-t^2-2t-2.$$

EXAMPLE 2. $a(t) = b(t) = \sin t;$

$$c(t) = \int_0^t \sin(t-\tau)\sin\tau\,d\tau$$

$$= \int_0^t (\sin t\cos\tau - \cos t\sin\tau)\sin\tau\,d\tau$$

$$= \sin t\int_0^t \cos\tau\sin\tau\,d\tau - \cos t\int_0^t \sin^2\tau\,d\tau$$

$$= \sin t\cdot\tfrac{1}{2}\sin^2 t - \cos t(\tfrac{1}{2}t-\tfrac{1}{2}\sin t\cos t) = \tfrac{1}{2}(\sin t - t\cos t).$$

(¹) In other languages the convolution has the following names: *splot* in Polish, *свёртка* in Russian, *produit de composition* in French, *Faltung* in German.

Exercises. Find the convolutions of the following pairs of functions:

(α) $a(t) = 1 - at$, $b(t) = e^{at}$; (β) $a(t) = e^{at}$, $b(t) = 1 - at$;

(γ) $a(t) = 1$, $b(t) = \sqrt{1+t}$; (δ) $a(t) = \sqrt{1+t}$, $b(t) = 1$;

(ε) $a(t) = \operatorname{sh} t$ [1], $b(t) = \sin t$; (ζ) $a(t) = \sin t$, $b(t) = \operatorname{sh} t$.

§ 2. Class $\mathcal{C}$. Functions that are defined and continuous in the interval $0 \leqslant t < \infty$ will play a particularly important part in the operational calculus; we shall denote the class of those functions by the letter $\mathcal{C}$. Functions of class $\mathcal{C}$ may have real or complex values.

The functions considered in § 1 all belong to class $\mathcal{C}$; they have real values. The function e^{it} is an example of a function of class $\mathcal{C}$ with complex (not real) values. The function $1/t$ does not belong to class $\mathcal{C}$ because it is discontinuous at the point $t = 0$.

If $a(t)$ and $b(t)$ are functions of class $\mathcal{C}$, then their convolution also belongs to class $\mathcal{C}$ because it is a function defined and continuous in the interval $0 \leqslant t < \infty$.

In Chapter I only functions of class $\mathcal{C}$ will be considered; this assumption will henceforth be taken for granted.

Exercise. Show which of the following functions belong to class $\mathcal{C}$ and which do not:

$$\frac{1}{t+1},\ \frac{1}{t-1},\ \frac{1}{t-i},\ \frac{1}{e^t+e^{-t}},\ \frac{1}{e^t-e^{-t}},\ \frac{1}{\cos t},\ \frac{1}{1+\cos t},\ \frac{1}{2+\cos t},\ \frac{1}{i+\cos t}.$$

§ 3. Commutativity of convolution. Comparing the results of the exercises given in § 1 we see that *the value of a convolution is independent of the successive order of the functions appearing in it.* This is true for any pair of functions $a(t)$ and $b(t)$. In order to prove this in the general case we must show the validity of the formula

$$\int_0^t a(t-\tau)b(\tau)\,d\tau = \int_0^t b(t-\tau)a(\tau)\,d\tau. \tag{3.1}$$

Substituting in the first integral $t - \tau = \sigma$ we obtain

$$-\int_t^0 a(\sigma)b(t-\sigma)\,d\sigma = \int_0^t b(t-\sigma)a(\sigma)\,d\sigma,$$

whence follows the equality (3.1).

The property we have just proved is termed the *commutativity* of convolution. It is analogous to the commutativity of the multiplication of numbers in arithmetics, where the equality $ab = ba$ holds for any pair of numbers a and b.

---

(1) $\operatorname{sh} t = \dfrac{e^t - e^{-t}}{2}$ (the function *sinus hiperbolicus*).

§ 4. Associativity of convolution. Convolution possesses also a property that is analogous to the associativity of the multiplication of numbers:

$$(ab)c = a(bc).$$

For numbers this property can be expressed by the proposition: *If* $ab = g$ *and* $bc = h$, *then* $gc = ah$.

The theorem on the associativity of convolution is most conveniently expressed in a similar form:

If $\int_0^t a(t-\tau)b(\tau)d\tau = g(t)$ *and* $\int_0^t b(t-\tau)c(\tau)d\tau = h(t)$, *then always* $\int_0^t g(t-\tau)c(\tau)d\tau = \int_0^t a(t-\tau)h(\tau)d\tau$.

Proof. Write

$$\int_0^t g(t-\tau)c(\tau)d\tau = \int_0^t \Big[\int_0^t a(t-\tau-\sigma)b(\sigma)d\sigma\Big] c(\tau)d\tau.$$

Substituting $\sigma = \omega - \tau$ we obtain

$$\int_0^t g(t-\tau)c(\tau)d\tau = \int_0^t \Big[\int_0^t a(t-\omega)b(\omega-\tau)d\omega\Big] c(\tau)d\tau$$

$$= \iint_T a(t-\omega)b(\omega-\tau)c(\tau)d\omega\, d\tau,$$

where the double integral is extended to the triangular region T defined by the inequalities $0 \leqslant \tau \leqslant \omega \leqslant t$. If we change the double integral again into an iterated one altering the order of integration, we obtain

$$\int_0^t g(t-\tau)c(\tau)d\tau = \int_0^t a(t-\omega)\Big[\int_0^\omega b(\omega-\tau)c(\tau)\,d\tau\Big]d\omega = \int_0^t a(t-\omega)h(\omega)d\omega.$$

The associativity of convolution is thus proved.

§ 5. Addition and convolution as fundamental operations in the operational calculus. In arithmetic, owing to the associativity of multiplication, the product of three numbers, a, b and c, can be written in the form abc; for it makes no difference whether we calculate it according to the pattern $(ab)c$ or $a(bc)$. Similarly, in calculating the convolution of three functions, $a(t)$, $b(t)$ and $c(t)$, it is irrelevant how we associate them. It can be seen, however, that with the use of the integral symbols we cannot conveniently write a convolution of three functions as we do the product abc, *i. e.* disregarding the order in which they are associated.

A far-reaching simplification will be obtained if we agree to denote the convolution of two functions, $a(t)$ and $b(t)$, just as we denote the product of two numbers, *i. e.* by means of the symbols ab or $a \cdot b$. On the strength of this agreement we shall consistently denote the convolution of three functions, $a(t)$, $b(t)$ and $c(t)$, by abc. A convolution of more than three functions can be written in a similar way.

Since the convolution has the same properties (of associativity and commutativity) as the product in arithmetic, formal calculations will also be the same. This fact will play an essential role in the operational calculus. The fundamental operations in the operational calculus are *addition* and *convolution*, just as in arithmetic they are addition and multiplication.

Numbers are the elements on which we perform operations in arithmetic: functions of class $\mathcal{C}$ [1] constitute such elements in the operational calculus.

Writing a convolution as an ordinary product we risk of course a certain ambiguity. For instance, the equalities

$$ab = ba \qquad \text{and} \qquad (ab)c = a(bc)$$

will have one meaning in classical algebra and another in the operational calculus. This ambiguity, however, will be no obstacle since the meaning of the above equalities will depend on what we shall substitute for the letters a, b, c. Substituting numbers we shall have an ordinary product to deal with, substituting functions we shall have a convolution.

Besides commutativity and associativity, convolution has one more fundamental property of the product, namely *distributivity with respect to addition*:

$$a(b+c) = ab+ac.$$

Indeed, we have

$$\int_0^t a(t-\tau)[b(\tau)+c(\tau)]d\tau = \int_0^t a(t-\tau)b(\tau)d\tau + \int_0^t a(t-\tau)c(\tau)d\tau.$$

Similarly we can prove the law of distributivity of convolution with respect to subtraction: $a(b-c) = ab-ac$.

The use in the operational calculus of the notation of ordinary algebra facilitates matters considerably, enabling us to follow our established habits and replace complicated transformations of integrals by almost mechanical calculations.

---

(1) Later on we shall introduce into the calculus also discontinuous functions (§ 51) and elements termed *operators* (§ 15).

§ 6. Function and value of a function. A misunderstanding is possible if we want to write in the short manner a convolution of two constant functions, *e. g.* the value of the first being 2 and that of the second 3. In this case the symbol $2 \cdot 3$ would stand for the number 6 in arithmetic and for the function $\int_0^t 2 \cdot 3 d\tau = 6t$ in the operational calculus. The difficulty is due to the fact that the concept of constant function is not, on the whole, strictly distinguished from the concept of number, the same symbols being used for both. We shall not enter here into precise logical definitions, but let us illustrate the difference geometrically. As we know, numbers are represented geometrically by means of the so called *number axis*. Every real number has a certain point on the axis corresponding to it, and *vice versa*: every point on the axis has a corresponding number.

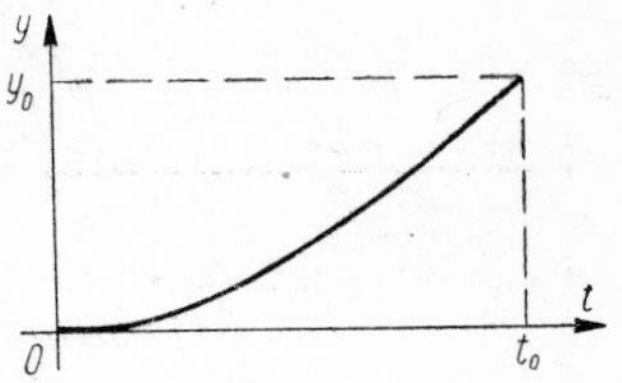

Fig. 1

For the representation of numbers one straight line is sufficient but to represent *functions* (of real values) we need a *plane*. Fig. 1 shows the graph of the function $\frac{1}{6}t^2$. The function is represented not by one point but by an infinite number of points, which form a parabola. Given a point t_0 on the t axis we can find, by means of the construction shown in the figure, a point y_0 lying on the y axis. The number corresponding to the point y_0 is termed the *value of the function at the point* t_0.

This example shows that there is a difference in meaning between the function $f(t)$ and the *value of the function at the point* t. If a function admits complex values, then a plane is not sufficient for its geometrical representation. It is clear, however, that also in that case the function and the value of the function are two distinct concepts. In classical mathematics there has been no need to introduce separate symbols for those concepts. In certain new branches of mathematics, however, for instance in functional analysis and in particular in the operational calculus, this distinction becomes absolutely necessary.

Henceforth we shall agree to use the symbol $f(t)$ *not preceded by the word "function"* for the value of the function at the point t; the function itself will be denoted by the symbol $\{f(t)\}$ (1).

(1) In order to distinguish a function from its value some authors use for the function the symbol $f(\hat{t})$, others use $f(:)$ or $f(\cdot)$, This notation, however, cannot be consistently applied everywhere: it would be difficult for instance to distinguish in this way a function having the value 1953 everywhere from the number 1953 itself.

This agreement can be expressed schematically in the form of the following equality:

$$\{f(t)\} = \text{function } f(t),$$

$$f(t) = \text{value of the function } f(t) \text{ at the point } t.$$

Thus for instance the symbol $\{2\}$ will denote a constant function whose value is 2 at every point t, the figure 2 itself denoting the number. Geometrically the function $\{2\}$ represents a straight line parallel to the t axis, while the number 2 is represented by one point on a fixed number axis. Moreover, it will be observed that the value of the function $\{2\}$ is 2 for every point t and is represented in fig. 2 by the point marked 2 on the y axis.

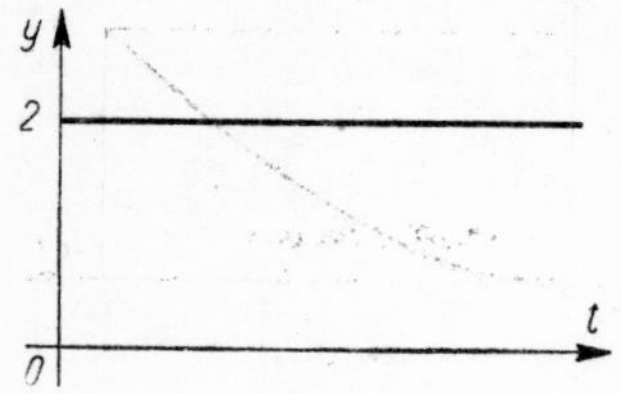

Fig. 2

In view of the agreement made above the meaning of the symbol $2\cdot 3$ is no longer ambiguous: it is the ordinary product of numbers 2 and 3, which is equal to 6. And the symbol $\{2\}\{3\}$ denotes the *convolution of the function* 2 *with the function* 3, *i. e.* the *function* $6t$. We thus have the equalities

$$2\cdot 3 = 6 \quad \text{and} \quad \{2\}\{3\} = \{6t\}.$$

Exercise. Using the notation introduced in this section verify the formulas:

(α) $\{1\}\{e^t\} = \{e^t - 1\}$; (β) $\{1\}\{\cos t\} = \{\sin t\}$;

(γ) $\{1\}\{1\} = \{t\}$; (δ) $\{t^2\}\{t^3\} = \{\frac{1}{60}t^6\}$.

§ 7. Symbolics. We have the general formulas

$$\{a(t)\} + \{b(t)\} = \{a(t) + b(t)\},$$

$$\{a(t)\}\cdot\{b(t)\} = \left\{\int_0^t a(t-\tau)\,b(\tau)\,d\tau\right\}.$$

The first formula means that the addition of functions is simply the addition of their values; the second is a consequence of the agreement made in the preceding section.

Writing a function always in the form $\{f(t)\}$ might prove cumbersome. If a function appears several times in the calculation, it is most convenient to denote it by a single letter, *e. g.*

$$a = \{e^{t^2}\cos t\}, \quad b = \left\{t^3 - \frac{1}{\sqrt{1+t}}\right\}, \quad \text{etc.}$$

If we are dealing with the general symbol $\{f(t)\}$ and not with any particular example of a function, then, for brevity, it is best to use the same letter

$$f = \{f(t)\}.$$

It is also convenient to introduce the notation

$$a^2 = a \cdot a,$$
$$a^3 = a \cdot a \cdot a,$$
$$a^4 = a \cdot a \cdot a \cdot a \quad \text{etc.}$$

If m and n are natural numbers, we have the general formulas

$$a^m a^n = a^{m+n}, \qquad a^n b^n = (ab)^n, \qquad (a^m)^n = a^{mn};$$

these formulas are proved in the same manner as in ordinary algebra.

Exercises.

1. Verify the equalities:

(α) $\{t\}^2 = \{\frac{1}{6}t^3\}$; (β) $\{t\}^3 = \{\frac{1}{120}t^5\}$; (γ) $\{e^t\}^2 = \{te^t\}$;

(δ) $\{e^t\}^3 = \{\frac{1}{2}t^2 e^t\}$; (ε) $\{2\}^3 = \{4t^2\}$; (ζ) $\{2\}^5 = \{\frac{4}{3}t^4\}$.

2. Simplify the expressions:

(α) $\{\cos^2 t\}\{t\} + \{t\}\{\sin^2 t\}$;

(β) $\{1-\sqrt{t}\}\{\sin t\} + \{1+\sqrt{t}\}\{\cos t\} + \{1-\sqrt{t}\}\{\cos t\} + \{1+\sqrt{t}\}\{\sin t\}$.

§ 8. Integral operator. According to the definition of convolution we have

$$\{1\}\{f(t)\} = \left\{\int_0^t f(\tau)\,d\tau\right\};$$

what distinguishes the function $\{1\}$ is that the formation of its convolution with an arbitrary function $\{f(t)\}$ causes the integration of the latter in the interval from 0 to t. Consequently the function $\{1\}$ will be termed the *integral operator* and denoted shortly by the letter l:

$$l = \{1\}.$$

It is easy to calculate the successive powers of the integral operator:

$$l^2 = \left\{\frac{t}{1}\right\}, \qquad l^3 = \left\{\frac{t^2}{1\cdot 2}\right\}, \qquad l^4 = \left\{\frac{t^3}{1\cdot 2\cdot 3}\right\}, \qquad \text{etc.}$$

Using the notation

$$n! = 1\cdot 2\cdot \ldots \cdot n$$

we can write the general formula

$$l^n = \left\{\frac{t^{n-1}}{(n-1)!}\right\}.$$

This formula is valid for any natural number $n \geqslant 2$. If we assume that $0! = 1$, then the formula remains valid also for $n = 1$.

In view of the associativity of convolution it is possible to interpret the expression $l^n\{f(t)\}$ in two ways: 1° as a function obtained by integrating the function $\{f(t)\}$ n times in the interval from 0 to t or 2° as the convolution of the functions $\left\{\frac{t^{n-1}}{(n-1)!}\right\}$ and $\{f(t)\}$. Hence we have the formula

$$\underbrace{\int_0^t dt \ldots \int_0^t}_{n} f(t)\,dt = \int_0^t \frac{(t-\tau)^{n-1}}{(n-1)!} f(\tau)\,d\tau,$$

known as *Cauchy's formula.*

Exercises.

1. Calculate the expressions:

(α) $l^2\{n \sin nt\}$, (β) $l^2\{ne^{-nt}\}$, (γ) $l^3\{n^2 te^{-nt}\}$.

2. Prove the formula

$$l^3\{n^2 \cos nt\} = l^2 - \left\{\frac{1}{n} \sin nt\right\}.$$

CHAPTER II

THEOREM OF TITCHMARSH

§ 9. Formulation of the theorem and general remarks. In sections 3, 4, and 5 we proved the transitivity, associativity and distributivity of convolution with respect to addition. A much more profound property of convolution is expressed by the following theorem:

If functions f and g of class $\mathcal{C}$ (see § 2, p. 8) *are not identically equal to* 0, *then neither is their convolution identically equal to* 0.

This theorem was formulated and proved by E. Titchmarsh ([45] and [46]) in 1924. The proof consisted in investigating the distribution of zeros in certain analytical functions. Simpler proofs, consisting in investigating the rate of growth of analytical or harmonic functions, were given by M. Crum [1] in 1941 and J. Dufresnoy ([1] and [2]) in the years 1947 and 1948. A proof based exclusively on the methods of functions of a real variable was given by C. Ryll-Nardzewski (1) in 1952 — it will be presented in this chapter. First we shall prove a few preparatory propositions, stating them for continuous functions (2).

Those who are interested only in the applications of the operational calculus may leave out this chapter without lessening their understanding of the rest of the book and continue their study with Chapter III.

§ 10. Theorem of Phragmén. In 1904 E. Phragmén [1] proved the following theorem:

If g is a continuous function in the interval $[0, T]$, *then*

$$\lim_{x\to\infty}\sum_{k=1}^{\infty}\frac{(-1)^{k-1}}{k!}\int_0^T e^{kx(t-\tau)}g(\tau)\,d\tau=\int_0^t g(\tau)\,d\tau \tag{10.1}$$

for every t satisfying the inequalities $0\leqslant t<T$.

---

(1) Nardzewski's proof has not been published in any separate paper.

(2) Those theorems, as well as Titchmarsh's theorem, can easily be generalized to arbitrary functions integrable in the sense of Lebesgue.

If we assume that the signs

$$\lim_{x\to\infty}\sum_{k=1}^{\infty} \quad \text{and} \quad \int_0^T \tag{10.2}$$

can change places with each other, then we can easily carry out the proof by writing the left side of formula (10.1) in the form

$$\int_0^T g(\tau)\lim_{x\to\infty}\sum_{k=1}^{\infty}\frac{(-1)^{k-1}}{k!}e^{kx(t-\tau)}d\tau,$$

i. e.

$$\int_0^T g(\tau)\lim_{x\to\infty}[1-\exp(-e^{x(t-\tau)})]d\tau. \tag{10.3}$$

Obviously

$$\lim_{x\to\infty}\exp(-e^{x(t-\tau)}) = \begin{cases} 0 & \text{for} \quad \tau < t, \\ 1 & \text{for} \quad t < \tau. \end{cases}$$

Hence the integrand in (10.3) is equal to $g(\tau)$ in the interval $0<\tau<t$ and equal to 0 in the interval $t<\tau<T$. Therefore the integral (10.3) is simply reduced to the integral $\int_0^t g(\tau)d\tau$, q. e. d.

The permutability of signs (10.2) can be justified for the left side of formula (10.1) by means of certain theorems on the integration of sequences of functions.

If we wish to have a proof that is quite elementary and at the same time exact, we can carry it out by the following calculation method.

Let us fix an arbitrary t in the interval $0 \leqslant t < T$. Then for every natural n and positive x we can write

$$\sum_{k=1}^{n}\frac{(-1)^{k-1}}{k!}\int_0^T e^{kx(t-\tau)}g(\tau)d\tau = I_n(x)+K_n(x), \tag{10.4}$$

where

$$\begin{aligned} I_n(x) &= \sum_{k=1}^{n}\frac{(-1)^{k-1}}{k!}\int_0^t e^{kx(t-\tau)}g(\tau)d\tau, \\ K_n(x) &= \sum_{k=1}^{n}\frac{(-1)^{k-1}}{k!}\int_t^T e^{kx(t-\tau)}g(\tau)d\tau. \end{aligned} \tag{10.5}$$

Changing in the first formula of (10.5) the order of summation and integration (which is always permissible in the case of a finite sum), we easily obtain the equality

$$I_n(x) = \int_0^t g(\tau)\,d\tau - \int_0^t g(\tau) \sum_{k=0}^{n} \frac{(-1)^k}{k!} e^{kx(t-\tau)}\,d\tau$$

$$= \int_0^t g(\tau)\,d\tau - \int_0^t g(\tau)\Big(\exp[-e^{x(t-\tau)}] - \sum_{k=n+1}^{\infty} \frac{(-1)^k}{k!} e^{kx(t-\tau)}\Big),$$

i. e.,

$$I_n(x) = \int_0^t g(\tau)\,d\tau + J(x) + L_n(x), \tag{10.6}$$

where

$$J(x) = -\int_0^t g(\tau)\exp[-e^{x(t-\tau)}]\,d\tau \quad \text{and} \quad L_n(x) = \int_0^t g(\tau) \sum_{k=n+1}^{\infty} \frac{(-1)^k}{k!} e^{kx(t-\tau)}\,d\tau.$$

If M denotes the maximum of the absolute value of g in the interval $[0, T]$, then

$$|L_n(x)| \leqslant \int_0^T M \sum_{k=n+1}^{\infty} \frac{1}{k!} e^{kxT}\,d\tau = MT \sum_{k=n+1}^{\infty} \frac{1}{k!} e^{kxT} = MT\Big(\exp(e^{xT}) - \sum_{k=0}^{n} \frac{1}{k!}(e^{xT})^k\Big);$$

we see hence that $\lim\limits_{n\to\infty} L_n(x) = 0$ since the last sum tends in the limit to $\exp(e^{xT})$.

In view of formula (10.6) we have

$$\lim_{n\to\infty} I_n(x) = \int_0^t g(\tau)\,d\tau + J(x). \tag{10.7}$$

On the other side we have

$$\Big|\int_t^T e^{kx(t-\tau)} g(\tau)\,d\tau\Big| \leqslant M \int_t^T e^{kx(t-\tau)}\,d\tau = \frac{M}{kx}(1 - e^{-kx(T-t)}) \leqslant \frac{M}{x};$$

the series $\sum\limits_{k=1}^{\infty} \frac{1}{k!} \frac{M}{x}$ being convergent, there exists a limit

$$\lim_{n\to\infty} K_n(x) = \sum_{k=1}^{\infty} \frac{(-1)^{k-1}}{k!} \int_t^T e^{kx(t-\tau)} g(\tau)\,d\tau = K(x) \tag{10.8}$$

and the following inequality holds for it:

$$|K(x)| \leqslant \sum_{k=1}^{\infty} \frac{1}{k!} \frac{M}{x} \leqslant \frac{eM}{x}.$$

It follows from this inequality that

$$\lim_{x\to\infty} K(x) = 0. \tag{10.9}$$

It can be seen from (10.7) and (10.8) that as n tends to infinity, formula (10.4) becomes in the limit

$$\sum_{k=1}^{\infty} \frac{(-1)^{k-1}}{k!} \int_0^T e^{kx(t-\tau)} g(\tau)\, d\tau = \int_0^t g(\tau)\, d\tau + J(x) + K(x).$$

In order to obtain hence formula (10.1) it suffices, in view of (10.9), to show that

(10.10) $$\lim_{x\to\infty} J(x) = 0.$$

Indeed, we have

$$|J(x)| \leqslant M \int_0^T \exp[-e^{x(t-\tau)}]\, d\tau \leqslant M \int_0^t e^{x(t-\tau)} \exp[-e^{x(t-\tau)}]\, d\tau$$

since the factor $e^{x(t-\tau)}$ included in the last integral is greater than 1 in the interval of integration. The last integral can easily be evaluated effectively by introducing the variable $u = e^{x(t-\tau)}$; in this way we obtain for the integral the value

$$\frac{1}{x}\left(\frac{1}{e} - \exp(-e^{-xt})\right).$$

It is less than $1/ex$. Consequently we have $|J(x)| < M/ex$, whence follows (10.10). Phragmén's theorem is thus proved.

§ 11. Theorem on moments. Using Phragmén's theorem, we shall now prove the following theorem:

I. *If f is a continuous function in the interval $[0, T]$ and there exists such a number N that*

(11.1) $$\left|\int_0^T e^{nt} f(t)\, dt\right| \leqslant N \quad \textit{for} \quad n = 1, 2, \ldots,$$

then $f(t) = 0$ in the whole interval $[0, T]$.

Proof. Phragmén's formula (10.1) can be written in the form

(11.2) $$\lim_{k\to\infty} \sum_{k=1}^{\infty} \frac{(-1)^{k-1}}{k!} e^{-kx(T-t)} \int_0^T e^{kx(T-\tau)} g(\tau)\, d\tau = \int_0^t g(\tau)\, d\tau$$

for every t satisfying the inequalities $0 \leqslant t < T$.

If k and x are natural numbers and

(11.3) $$g(\tau) = f(T-\tau),$$

then, by the assumption (11.1), we have

$$\left|\int_0^T e^{kx(T-\tau)} g(\tau)\, d\tau\right| = \left|\int_0^T e^{kx(T-\tau)} f(T-\tau)\, d\tau\right| = \left|\int_0^T e^{kxt} f(t)\, dt\right| \leqslant N$$

since in that case the product kx is also a natural number. Consequently the expression preceeded by the sign "lim" in formula (11.2) is not greater than

$$N \sum_{k=1}^{\infty} \frac{1}{k!} e^{-kx(T-t)} = N[1-\exp(e^{-kx(T-t)})]$$

and therefore tends to 0 as x increases infinitely running over natural values. The existence of a limit of this expression for $x \to \infty$ is ensured by Phragmén's theorem for x running over arbitrary positive values; this limit must always be equal to 0, since it is equal to 0 if x runs over natural values. Therefore the right-hand side of formula (11.2) must be equal to 0:

$$\int_0^t g(\tau)d\tau = 0 \qquad (0 \leqslant t < T).$$

Differentiating this equality we obtain $g(t) = 0$ for $0 < t < T$ and by (11.3) also $f(t) = 0$ for $0 < t < T$. The function f being continuous, we must have $f(t) = 0$ in the whole interval $[0, T]$, q. e. d.

From the theorem proved above we draw the following corollary:

II. *If a function g is continuous in the interval $[1, X]$ and there exists a number N such that*

$$\left|\int_1^X x^n g(x)\,dx\right| \leqslant N \quad \textit{for} \quad n = 1, 2, \ldots, \tag{11.4}$$

then $g(x) = 0$ in the whole interval $[1, X]$.

Indeed, by the substitution $x = e^t$, $X = e^T$ and $xg(x) = f(t)$ inequalities (11.4) change into (11.1). It follows hence that $f(t) = 0$ in $[0, T]$, *i. e.*, that $xg(x) = 0$ in $[1, X]$, which proves our theorem.

From theorem II we can easily deduce the classical *theorem of Lerch* (see Lerch [1] and Mikusiński [1]):

III. *If a function f is continuous in the interval $[0, T]$ and*

$$\int_0^T t^n f(t)\,dt = 0 \quad \textit{for} \quad n = 1, 2, \ldots, \tag{11.5}$$

then $f(t) = 0$ in the whole interval $[0, T]$.

Proof. Let Θ be an arbitrary fixed number from the interval $[0, T]$. By the substitution

$$t = \Theta x, \quad T = \Theta X \quad \text{and} \quad f(t) = g(x)$$

equality (11.5) yields

$$\Theta^{n+1}\int_0^x x^n g(x)\,dx = 0 \quad \text{for} \quad n = 1, 2, \ldots,$$

and hence

$$\left|\int_1^x x^n g(x)\,dx\right| = \left|\int_0^1 x^n g(x)\,dx\right| \leqslant \int_0^1 |g(x)|\,dx = N \quad \text{for} \quad n = 1, 2, \ldots$$

Thus, by theorem II, we have $g(x) = 0$ in the interval $[1, X]$, *i. e.* $f(t) = 0$ in the interval $[\Theta, T]$. It follows hence that $f(t) = 0$ for every t from the interval $(0, T]$, since Θ can be fixed arbitrarily small. The function f, being continuous, must be equal to 0 also for $t = 0$, and our proof is complete.

Note. The integral $\int_a^b x^n f(x)\,dx$ is termed the *n-th moment* of the function $f(x)$ in the interval $[a, b]$. That is why the above theorems are termed *theorems on moments.*

§ 12. Proof of Titchmarsh's theorem in the case $f = g$. Suppose that f is a continuous function in the interval $[0, 2T]$ and that

$$\int_0^t f(t-\tau)f(\tau)\,d\tau = 0 \quad \text{for} \quad 0 \leqslant t \leqslant 2T. \tag{12.1}$$

We shall prove that $f(t) = 0$ for $0 \leqslant t \leqslant T$.

It follows from equality (12.1) that

$$I_n = \int_0^{2T} e^{n(2T-t)}dt \int_0^t f(t-\tau)f(\tau)\,d\tau = 0. \tag{12.2}$$

The iterated integral (12.2) can be represented as a double integral,

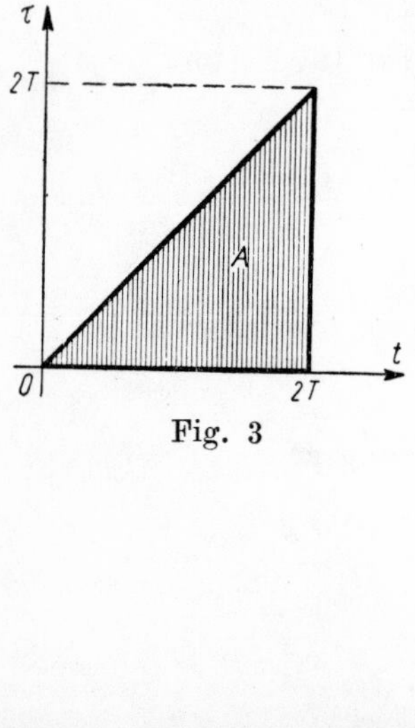

Fig. 3

$$I_n = \iint_A e^{n(2T-t)} f(t-\tau)f(\tau)\,dt\,d\tau,$$

where A is a triangle, defined by the inequalities

$$0 \leqslant \tau \leqslant t \leqslant 2T.$$

After the substitution

$$t = 2T - u - v, \qquad \tau = T - v,$$

this integral assumes the form

$$I_n = \iint\limits_B e^{n(u+v)} f(T-u) f(T-v)\, du\, dv,$$

where B is a triangle defined by the inequalities

$$0 \leqslant u+v, \quad u \leqslant T, \quad v \leqslant T.$$

We can write

$$\iint\limits_{B+C} = \iint\limits_B + \iint\limits_C$$

where C is a triangle, defined by the inequalities

$$-T \leqslant u, \quad -T \leqslant v, \quad u+v \leqslant 0,$$

and the sum $B+C$ is a square, defined by the inequalities

$$-T \leqslant u \leqslant T, \quad -T \leqslant v \leqslant T.$$

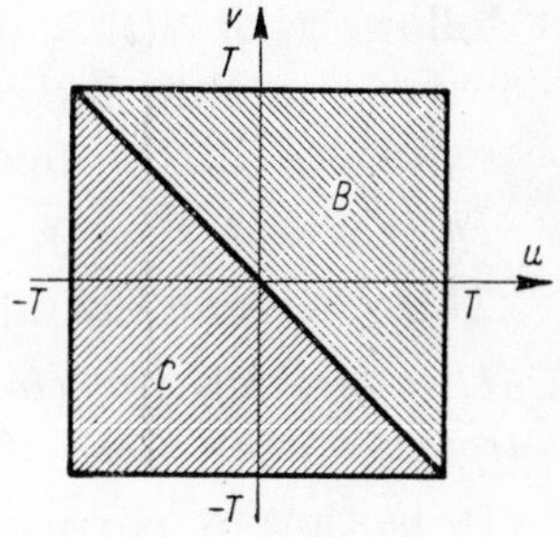

Fig. 4

Since $\iint\limits_B = I_n = 0$, we have

$$\iint\limits_{B+C} e^{nu} f(T-u) \cdot e^{nv} f(T-v)\, du\, dv =$$

$$= \iint\limits_C e^{n(u+v)} f(T-u)\, f(T-v)\, du\, dv.$$

If $n > 0$, then the factor $e^{n(u+v)}$ in the integral on the right-hand side is less than 1. Thus if M denotes the maximum absolute value of f, we have

$$\left| \int\limits_{-T}^{T} e^{nu} f(T-u)\, du \cdot \int\limits_{-T}^{T} e^{nv} f(T-v)\, dv \right| \leqslant \iint\limits_C M^2 du\, dv = 2T^2 M^2,$$

and consequently

$$\left| \int\limits_{-T}^{T} e^{nu} f(T-u)\, du \right| \leqslant \sqrt{2}\, TM.$$

Therefore

$$\left| \int\limits_0^T e^{nu} f(T-u)\, du \right| = \left| \int\limits_{-T}^{T} e^{nu} f(T-u)\, du - \int\limits_{-T}^{0} e^{nu} f(T-u)\, du \right|$$

$$\leqslant \sqrt{2}\, TM + \left| \int\limits_{-T}^{0} e^{nu} f(T-u)\, du \right|.$$

But in the last interval the factor e^{nu} is less than 1, and thus

$$\left|\int_0^T e^{nu} f(T-u)\,du\right| \leqslant \sqrt{2}\,TM + \int_{-T}^{0} M\,du = (\sqrt{2}+1)TM.$$

This inequality being valid for any $n > 0$, we have, by the first theorem on moments, $f(T-u) = 0$ for $0 \leqslant u \leqslant T$, *i. e.* $f(t) = 0$ for $0 \leqslant t \leqslant T$, q. e. d.

Now if the function f is continuous in every infinite interval $0 \leqslant t < \infty$ and the equality

$$\int_0^t f(t-\tau) f(\tau)\,d\tau = 0$$

always holds in that interval, then it holds in every interval $[0, 2T]$. It follows that $f(t) = 0$ in every interval $[0, T]$ and consequently in the whole infinite interval $0 \leqslant t < \infty$. In operational symbols this can be expressed in the form of the following theorem:

If $f \in \mathcal{C}$ *and* $f^2 = 0$, *then* $f = 0$.

This theorem can also be expressed as follows:

If a function f *of class* $\mathcal{C}$ *is not identically equal to* 0, *then neither is its convolution with itself* f^2 *identically equal to* 0.

It is thus a particular case of Titchmarsh's theorem, given at the beginning of this chapter.

§ 13. General proof. C. Ryll-Nardzewski has shown that the above particular case can easily be generalized to arbitrary functions f and g of class $\mathcal{C}$.

Suppose that the convolution of functions f and g (of class $\mathcal{C}$) is identically equal to zero,

$$fg = 0.$$

This means that

$$\int_0^t f(t-\tau) g(\tau)\,d\tau = 0 \quad \text{for} \quad 0 \leqslant t < \infty. \tag{13.1}$$

Thus in the interval $0 \leqslant t < \infty$ we also have

$$\int_0^T (t-\tau) f(t-\tau) g(\tau)\,d\tau + \int_0^t f(t-\tau)\cdot \tau g(\tau)\,d\tau = t\int_0^t f(t-\tau) g(\tau)\,d\tau = 0. \tag{13.2}$$

Introducing the notation

$$f_1(t) = tf(t) \quad \text{and} \quad g_1(t) = tg(t) \quad (0 \leqslant t < \infty),$$

we can express equality (13.2) in operational symbols as

$$f_1 g + f g_1 = 0.$$

Hence we have $fg_1(f_1 g + f g_1) = 0$ and, by the associativity, commutativity and distributivity of convolution,

$$fg \cdot f_1 g_1 + (fg_1)^2 = 0.$$

Since, by hypothesis, $fg = 0$, the last equality can be reduced to the equality $(fg_1)^2 = 0$. Hence, by the theorem proved in the preceding section, we obtain

$$tg = 0,$$

i. e.

$$\int_0^t f(t-\tau)\cdot \tau g(\tau)\,d\tau = 0 \qquad (0 \leqslant t < \infty). \tag{13.3}$$

Since equality (13.3) follows from equality (13.1), we conclude from equality (13.3) that

$$\int_0^t f(t-\tau)\cdot \tau^2 g(\tau)\,d\tau = 0 \qquad (0 \leqslant t < \infty),$$

and generally

$$\int_0^t f(t-\tau)\cdot \tau^n g(\tau)\,d\tau = 0 \qquad (0 \leqslant t < \infty)$$

for every natural n.

Hence, by Lerch's theorem (see § 11), we have

$$f(t-\tau)g(\tau) = 0 \quad \text{for} \quad 0 \leqslant \tau \leqslant t < \infty.$$

If $g(\tau_0) \neq 0$ for a certain $\tau_0 \geqslant 0$, then we read from the equality $f(t-\tau_0)g(\tau_0) = 0$ that $f = 0$ in the whole infinite interval $0 \leqslant t < \infty$. If no such τ_0 exists, then $g = 0$ in the whole of this interval.

In this manner we have proved that *if a convolution fg is identically equal to* 0, *then at least one of the functions f and g is identically equal to* 0.

We can also put it as follows: *If functions f and g are not identically equal to zero, then neither is the convolution fg identically equal to zero.*

And this is how we formulated *Titchmarsh's theorem* at the beginning of the chapter.

CHAPTER III

OPERATORS

§ 14. An operation inverse to convolution. In the operational calculus, just as in algebra, fractions

$$\frac{a}{b}$$

can be introduced; this symbol will often be written for convenience in the form a/b. It will be observed at once that if a and b are functions and ab is understood as their convolution, then a/b should not be regarded as ordinary division but as an operation that is inverse to convolution. The symbol a/b (where b is not identically equal to zero) will then denote such a function c that

$$a = bc. \tag{14.1}$$

For instance, if $a = \{t^3\}$ and $b = \{t\}$, then

$$\frac{a}{b} = \frac{\{t^3\}}{\{t\}} = \{6t\}$$

since

$$\{t\}\{6t\} = \left\{\int_0^t (t-\tau)6\tau\, d\tau\right\} = \{t^3\}.$$

In order that the definition of the symbol a/b be unique for given a and b (b not being identically equal to zero) it is necessary that there exist at most one function c satisfying equality (14.1). This unicity is ensured by Titchmarsh's theorem, which was proved in chapter II:

If functions f and g of class $\mathcal{C}$ (see § 2, p. 2) *are not identically equal to zero, then neither is their convolution fg identically equal to zero.*

If equality (14.1) were satisfied by two different functions c_1 and c_2, *i. e.*, if we had $a = bc_1$ and $a = bc_2$, then we should have

$$b(c_1 - c_2) = 0$$

and the convolution of two functions b and $(c_1 - c_2)$, not vanishing, would be identical, contrary to Titchmarsh's theorem. Therefore, equality (14.1) is satisfied by at most one function c, which proves the unicity of the symbol a/b.

Exercise. Verify the equalities:

$$(\alpha)\quad \frac{\{t^2\}}{\{t\}} = \{2\},\qquad (\beta)\quad \frac{\{t^3-6t\}}{\{t-1\}} = \{6t+6\},\qquad (\gamma)\quad \frac{\{e^t - \sin t - \cos t\}}{\{\sin t\}} = \{2e^t\}.$$

§ 15. Operators. It may occur that for given functions a and $b \neq \{0\}$ of class $\mathcal{C}$ there exists no function c satisfying the equation $a = bc$. Take for istance $a = b = \{1\}$; in this case the equality $\{1\} = \{1\}c$ cannot hold for any function $c = \{c(t)\}$, since that would imply

$$1 = \int_0^t c(\tau)\,d\tau$$

for any $t \geqslant 0$, which is not true even for $t = 0$. A great many similar examples might be given.

It is at a quite elementary stage of the study of mathematics that we come across the phenomenon of an inverse operation not being performable: in the arithmetic of integers, division is not always performable. For instance number 2 is not divisible by 3. But it will be observed that the very non-divisibility is the source of a new kind of numbers, viz. fractions. It is assumed that the quotient 2 by 3 is a new number (no longer an integer), which is written in the form of a fraction $\frac{2}{3}$. Generally, if an integer a cannot be divided without a remainder by another integer, b, it is assumed that their quotient is equal to the fraction a/b.

We also admit fractions a/b in which the numerator a can be divided without a remainder by the denominator b, for instance $\frac{6}{3}$. Consequently, fractions can be regarded as a generalization of the concept of number (integer). Every integer c is a fraction (since it can be represented in the form cb/b $(b \neq 0)$) but not every fraction is an integer.

Similarly, *the non-performability of the operation inverse to convolution leads to a new mathematical concept, that of operators.*

The fraction $\{1\}/\{1\}$ thus represents an *operator* (which is no longer a function). Generally, if for two given functions, a and $b \neq \{0\}$, of class $\mathcal{C}$ there exists no function c satisfying the equation $a = bc$, then the fraction a/b represents an *operator*.

We also admit operators a/b for which there exists such a function c of class $\mathcal{C}$ that $a = bc$. Consequently, operators may be regarded as a generalization of the concept of function. Every function c of class $\mathcal{C}$

is an operator (since it can be represented in the form cb/b, where $b \neq \{0\}$ is a function of class $\mathcal{C}$), but not every operator is a function.

§ 16. Operations on operators. The introduction of operators of the form a/b can be useful only when we define on them certain operations permitting the employment of operators in calculations.

In arithmetic we adopt for fractions the following definitions:

1. We write $\dfrac{a}{b} = \dfrac{c}{d}$ if and only if $ad = bc$;

2. $\dfrac{a}{b}\,\dfrac{c}{d} = \dfrac{ac}{bd}$;

3. $\dfrac{a}{b} + \dfrac{c}{d} = \dfrac{ad+bc}{bd}$.

Moreover, it is assumed throughout, that the denominators b and d are not equal to 0; consequently also the denominator $bd \neq 0$.

For the operators a/b we adopt the same definitions, 1, 2, and 3. We shall not write these formulas again. It is taken for granted that in the case of operators the letters a, b, c and d no longer stand for numbers but denote functions of class $\mathcal{C}$.

Moreover, it is assumed throughout that the denominators b and d are not identically equal to zero; consequently it follows from Titchmarsh's theorem that neither is the denominator bd identically equal to 0.

Owing to the complete analogy between operators and fractions of classical arithmetic, operations on operators are performed in the same way as those on ordinary fractions.

Exercise. Prove the equalities:

(α) $\dfrac{\{t\}\{te^t\}}{\{e^t\}\{1\}} = \{e^t - 1\}$; (β) $\dfrac{\{1\}}{\{\cos t\}} + \dfrac{\{3t^2\}}{\{2\}} = \dfrac{\{2t\}}{\{\sin 2t\}}$.

§ 17. Numerical operators. We shall now deal with operators of the form $\dfrac{\{\alpha\}}{\{1\}}$ where $\{\alpha\}$ is an arbitrary constant function (*i. e.*, a function assuming everywhere the value α); we shall denote them by

$$[\alpha] = \frac{\{\alpha\}}{\{1\}}.$$

It is easy to verify the formulas

(17.1) $$[\alpha]+[\beta] = [\alpha+\beta], \qquad [\alpha][\beta] = [\alpha\beta].$$

Indeed, writing for simplicity $l = \{1\}$, we have

$$[\alpha]+[\beta] = \frac{\{\alpha\}}{l} + \frac{\{\beta\}}{l} = \frac{\{\alpha\}+\{\beta\}}{l} = \frac{\{\alpha+\beta\}}{l} = [\alpha+\beta],$$

$$[\alpha][\beta] = \frac{\{\alpha\}}{l}\frac{\{\beta\}}{l} = \frac{\{\alpha\beta t\}}{l^2} = \frac{l\{\alpha\beta\}}{l^2} = \frac{\{\alpha\beta\}}{l} = [\alpha\beta].$$

Operators of type $[\alpha]$ will be termed *numerical operators.* They must be distinguished from operators $\{\alpha\}$, which are *constant functions* for which, instead of formulas (17.1), the following formulas hold:

$$\{\alpha\}+\{\beta\} = \{\alpha+\beta\}, \quad \{\alpha\}\{\beta\} = \{\alpha\beta t\}.$$

Thus we have, for instance,

$$[2][3] = [6], \quad \{2\}\{3\} = \{6t\}.$$

Owing to formulas (17.1) the brackets [ ] can be omitted in the operational calculus; thus, instead of $[\alpha]$ we shall simply write α. This simplification gives us one more advantage: formulas (17.1) take the form

$$\alpha+\beta = \alpha+\beta, \quad \alpha\beta = \alpha\beta,$$

i. e., they become altogether superfluous.

§ 18. Remarks on terminology. Equalities (17.1) permit us to assume a still more radical attitude. Owing to them numerical operators behave in calculations like ordinary numbers. Therefore it is possible to identify numerical operators with numbers and call them simply *numbers.* In arithmetic, fractions with the denominator 1 are thus identified with integers, and complex numbers with the imaginary part equal to zero are identified with real numbers. The advantage lies in the fact that it is unnecessary to consider each of these kinds of numbers separately since they are all finally covered by the concept of complex number.

In our case complex numbers are covered by the concept of operators. Thus operators not only are a generalization of the concept of function but also generalize complex numbers. The different stages of the generalization of numbers can be represented in the form of the following chain:

$$\text{integers} \subset \text{rational numbers} \subset \text{real numbers} \subset$$
$$\subset \text{complex numbers} \subset \text{operators}.$$

In § 16 we defined the meaning of the expression

$$\frac{a}{b}\cdot\frac{c}{d}. \tag{18.1}$$

If the operators a/b and c/d are reduced to functions, then expression (18.1) denotes their convolution; if they are reduced to numbers, expression (18.1) denotes an ordinary product. Thus expression (18.1) represents an operation which is a generalization of both the convolution and the ordinary product. Having the choice of the term in the general case, we shall adopt, for practical reasons, the term *product*. For then we shall be able to use freely such terms connected with the product as *multiplication*, *factor*, *power*, *division*, *inverse*, etc. This suggests the possibility of replacing the term *convolution of functions* by *product of functions*; in that case the ordinary product should be called the *product of the values of functions*. However, we shall retain the term *convolution*, particularly in situations which might give rise to a misunderstanding.

The term *operator* itself requires some explanation. The concept under consideration comprises not only numbers and functions but also numerous elements corresponding to what has so far been called *operators* in mathematical literature. In the former treatment of operational calculus these operators and the functions upon which they act constituted two distinct classes of elements. In this book the parts played by the two kinds of elements are symmetrical since these elements all enter the same class of fractions a/b, comprising also numbers. Consequently any of the terms *number, function* and *operator* might be *a priori* regarded as equally suitable to cover the whole. However, in view of traditional usage, the term operator seems the most fitting.

§ 19. Product of a number and a function. It is easy to prove that for any number α and any constant function $\{\beta\}$ we have the formula

$$\alpha\{\beta\} = \{\alpha\beta\}.$$

Indeed,

$$\alpha\{\beta\} = \frac{\{\alpha\}\{\beta\}}{l} = \frac{\{\alpha\beta t\}}{l} = \frac{l\{\alpha\beta\}}{l} = \{\alpha\beta\}.$$

For example let us compare the formulas

$$2\cdot 3 = 6, \quad 2\{3\} = \{6\}, \quad \{2\}\{3\} = \{6t\}.$$

The first expresses the fact that the product of numbers 2 and 3 is equal to number 6; the second states that the product of number 2 and the constant function $\{3\}$ is equal to the constant function $\{6\}$; the third states that the product (convolution) of two functions $\{2\}$ and $\{3\}$ is equal to the function $\{6t\}$.

As a particular case of the formula $\alpha\{\beta\} = \{\alpha\beta\}$ we obtain for $\beta = 1$,

$$\alpha l = \{\alpha\}.$$

Thus every constant function $\{a\}$ can be represented as a product of number a and integral operator l.

It will be observed that we have the general formula

$$a\{f(t)\} = \{af(t)\}, \tag{19.1}$$

which expresses the fact that *multiplying a function $f(t)$ by a number means the same as multiplying its value by that number.*

Indeed, we have

$$a\{f(t)\} = \frac{\{a\}\{f(t)\}}{l} = \frac{\{\int_0^t af(\tau)\,d\tau\}}{l} = \frac{l\{af(t)\}}{l} = \{af(t)\}.$$

Formula (19.1) expresses a practical rule which enables us to include the numerical factor within the brackets.

It will be observed that with regard to addition there exists no formula analogical to (19.1). The sum of number a and function $\{f(t)\}$ can be written only in the form $a+\{f(t)\}$; this sum is an operator which can at most be reduced to the fraction form $\dfrac{\{a+\int_0^t f(\tau)\,d\tau\}}{\{1\}}$. It can easily be observed that, in view of commutativity and associativity, the following equality holds for operators of the above type:

$$(a+\{f(t)\})(\beta+\{g(t)\}) = a\beta\Big\{\beta f(t)+ag(t)+\int_0^t f(t-\tau)g(\tau)\,d\tau\Big\}.$$

Exercise. Verify the equalities:

(α) $(1+l)(1-l) = 1-\{t\}$; (β) $(1+2l)^3 = 1+2\{3+6t+2t^2\}$;

(γ) $(1+\{1\})(1-\{e^{-t}\}) = 1$; (δ) $(1+\{t\})(1-\{\sin t\}) = 1$;

(ε) $(1+\{4t\})(1+2\{\cos 2t-\sin 2t\}) = 1+\{2\}$.

§ 20. Numbers 0 and 1. Substituting in formula (19.1) 1 for a, we obtain the equality $1\{f(t)\} = \{f(t)\}$. It is easy to prove in the general case that if c is an arbitrary operator, then the equality

$$1c = c \tag{20.1}$$

always holds.

Indeed, writing $1 = l/l$ and $c = a/b$, where a and b are functions of class $\mathcal{C}$, we have, by the definition of equality and multiplication of operators, $la/lb = a/b$, whence follows equality (20.1).

For number 0 we shall prove the general formulas

$$0c = 0, \quad c+0 = c. \tag{20.2}$$

Indeed, writing $0 = \{0\}/l$ and $c = a/b$, where a and $b \neq \{0\}$ are functions of class $\mathcal{C}$, we have

$$0c = \frac{\{0\}a}{lb} = \frac{\{0\}}{lb} = \frac{\{0\}b}{lb} = \frac{\{0\}}{l} = 0,$$

$$c + 0 = \frac{a}{b} + \frac{\{0\}}{l} = \frac{al + \{0\}b}{b \cdot l} = \frac{al + \{0\}}{b \cdot l} = \frac{al}{b \cdot l} = \frac{a}{b} = c.$$

Observe, moreover, that

$$\{0\} = 0;$$

indeed, this follows from the equality $0l = \{0\}$ and from the first formula of (20.2). Therefore the function $\{0\}$ should be identified with number 0. This is an exception to the principle adopted in § 6, where we stressed the necessity of distingusihing between a function and a number. Namely $\{0\}$ is the only function which possesses the same properties with respect to addition and multiplication as number 0; consequently it can be replaced in every formula by number 0 and *vice versa*. And this is what the identification of symbols $\{0\}$ and 0 means.

§ 21. Differential operator. Operators can be divided by one another. For instance, if $g = a/b$, $h = c/d$, then

$$\frac{g}{h} = \frac{a}{b} : \frac{c}{d} = \frac{ad}{bc}.$$

In this example the numerator and the denominator of the fraction g/h are arbitrary operators, and not necessarily functions.

In particular, $1/h$ is termed the *inverse of the operator h*. It will be observed that if h is a function, then the inverse $1/h$ cannot be a function. Indeed, if h and $1/h$ were functions, then the product $h \cdot 1/h$ would also be a function, whereas actually it is the numerical operator 1.

A fundamental role in the operational calculus is played by the *inverse of the integral operator* $l = \{t\}$, which will be denoted by

$$s = \frac{1}{l}.$$

By this definition we have

$$ls = sl = 1.$$

We shall prove the following important

THEOREM [1]. *If a function* $a = \{a(t)\}$ *has a derivative* $a' = \{a'(t)\}$ *continuous for* $0 \leqslant t < \infty$, *then we have the formula*

$$sa = a' + a(0) \tag{21.1}$$

where $a(0)$ *is the value of the function* a *at the point* $t = 0$.

Indeed, we have

$$\{a(t)\} = \left\{\int_0^t a'(\tau)\,d\tau\right\} + \{a(0)\},$$

i. e.

$$\{a(t)\} = l\{a'(t)\} + la(0).$$

Hence, multiplying both sides by s, we obtain formula (21.1).

If the function a is equal to 0 at the point $t = 0$, then formula (21.1) reduces to the form

$$sa = a';$$

in this case the multiplication of a function by the operator s simply means its differentiation. For this reason s will be termed the *differential operator*.

It should be remembered, however, that in the general case multiplication by s means the differentiation of a function and the addition of its initial value. This results in an operator which is a function if and only if the initial value of the given function is zero.

EXAMPLES.

$$s\{\sin t\} = \{\cos t\}, \quad s\{e^t\} = \{e^t\} + 1,$$

$$s\{t^n\} = \{nt^{n-1}\} \quad \text{for} \quad n \geqslant 1, \quad s\{t+1\} = \{1\} + 1.$$

Not only differentiable functions can be multiplied by the differential operator. The product sa will always be meaningful, whether a is a differentiable function, a non-differentiable one or an arbitrary operator. Thus if we regard multiplying by s as a generalization of differentiation, then in the domain of operators every continuous function (and even every integrable one) is differentiable (the result of the differentiation being an operator but not necessarily a function).

Remark. At first sight it might seem that calculations would be more convenient if the multiplication of a differentiable function by s were exactly equivalent to differentiation, *i. e.*, if we did not have to add the initial value. It can easily be seen, however, that ordinary differen-

[1] This theorem will be generalized in § 60.

tiation is not commutative with integration (in the interval from 0 to t); for instance, if we differentiate the function $\{\cos t\}$ and then integrate it, we shall obtain $\{\cos t - 1\}$; reversing the order of these operations, we shall obtain $\{\cos t\}$. For the simplicity of the operational calculus it is essential that the differential and the integral operators be commutative: $sl = ls$. This commutativity is obtained thanks to the definition given in this section.

§ 22. Powers of operator s. If a function $a = \{a(t)\}$ has the second derivative, $a'' = \{a''(t)\}$, continuous in the interval $0 \leqslant t < \infty$, then multiplying (21.1) by s we obtain

$$s^2 a = sa' + sa(0),$$

whence, applying formula (21.1) once more to the derivative a', we obtain

$$s^2 a = a'' + a'(0) + sa(0).$$

We have the following general theorem:

If a function $a = \{a(t)\}$ has an n-th derivative, $a^{(n)} = \{a^{(n)}(t)\}$, continuous in the interval $0 \leqslant t < \infty$, then

$$s^n a = a^{(n)} + a^{(n-1)}(0) + sa^{(n-2)}(0) + \ldots + s^{n-1}a(0).$$

In view of its application to the solution of differential equations the last formula is most conveniently written in the form

$$a^{(n)} = s^n a - s^{n-1}a(0) - \ldots - sa^{(n-2)}(0) - a^{(n-1)}(0).$$

Exercise. Verify the equalities:

(α) $s^2\{\sin t\} = 1 - \{\sin t\}$; ($\beta$) $s^2\{\cos t\} = s - \{\cos t\}$.

§ 23. Polynomials of operator s. An important role is played by operators in the form of polynomials

(23.1) $$\alpha_n s^n + \alpha_{n-1} s^{n-1} + \ldots + \alpha_1 s + \alpha_0,$$

where $\alpha_n, \ldots, \alpha_0$ are arbitrary numbers. Operations on these polynomials are performed in the same way as in ordinary algebra, *e. g.*:

$$(s-1)(s^{n-1} + s^{n-2} + \ldots + 1) = s^n - 1.$$

If two polynomials of the operator s are equal, then their coefficients are respectively equal, i. e., the equality

(23.2) $$\alpha_n s^n + \alpha_{n-1} s^{n-1} + \ldots + \alpha_1 s + \alpha_0 = \beta_n s^n + \beta_{n-1} s^{n-1} + \ldots + \beta_1 s + \beta_0$$

always implies the equalities

(23.3) $$\alpha_n = \beta_n, \quad \alpha_{n-1} = \beta_{n-1}, \quad \ldots, \quad \alpha_1 = \beta_1, \quad \alpha_0 = \beta_0.$$

Indeed, multiplying equality (23.2) by l^{n+1}, we obtain

$$\alpha_n l + \ldots + \alpha_0 l^{n+1} = \beta_n l + \ldots + \beta_0 l^{n+1};$$

this equality means that

$$\alpha_n + \ldots + \alpha_0 \frac{t^n}{n!} = \beta_n + \ldots + \beta_0 \frac{t^n}{n!} \quad \text{for} \quad 0 \leqslant t < \infty.$$

Hence, by the known theorem on ordinary polynomials, follow equalities (23.3).

Exercises.

1. Prove the formula

$$1 + s + s^2 + \ldots + s^{n-1} = (s^n - 1)\{e^t\}.$$

2. Verify that

$$\gamma^4 s^4 + \delta^4 = \gamma^4 [(s-\alpha)^2 + \alpha^2][(s+\alpha)^2 + \alpha^2] \quad \text{for} \quad \alpha = \frac{1}{\sqrt{2}} \cdot \frac{\delta}{\gamma}.$$

§ 24. Connections of the operator s with the exponential function. Applying formula (21.1) to the function $\{e^{\alpha t}\}$ we obtain the equality

$$s\{e^{\alpha t}\} = 1 + \alpha\{e^{\alpha t}\},$$

from which we easily get

$$(24.1) \qquad \{e^{\alpha t}\} = \frac{1}{s-\alpha}.$$

By the definition of convolution we have

$$\frac{1}{(s-\alpha)^2} = \{e^{\alpha t}\}^2 = \left\{\int_0^t e^{\alpha(t-\tau)} e^{\alpha\tau} d\tau\right\} = \left\{e^{\alpha t}\int_0^t d\tau\right\} = \left\{\frac{t}{1!} e^{\alpha t}\right\},$$

$$\frac{1}{(s-\alpha)^3} = \{e^{\alpha t}\}\left\{\frac{t}{1!} e^{\alpha t}\right\} = \left\{\int_0^t e^{\alpha(t+\tau)} \frac{\tau}{1!} e^{\alpha t} d\tau\right\} = \left\{e^{\alpha t}\int_0^t \frac{\tau}{1!} d\tau\right\} = \left\{\frac{t^2}{2!} e^{\alpha t}\right\}$$

and generally

$$(24.2) \qquad \frac{1}{(s-\alpha)^n} = \left\{\frac{t^{n-1}}{(n-1)!} e^{\alpha t}\right\} \qquad (n = 1, 2, \ldots).$$

This formula is a generalization of the formula $l^n = \left\{\frac{t^{n-1}}{(n-1)!}\right\}$, deduced in § 8 (p. 8), and can be reduced to it by the substitution $\alpha = 0$.

§ 25. Connections of the operator s with trigonometric functions. By the well-known formulas of Euler,

$$\sin x = \frac{e^{ix} - e^{-ix}}{2i}, \qquad \cos x = \frac{e^{ix} + e^{-ix}}{2},$$

we have

$$\{e^{\alpha t} \sin \beta t\} = \frac{1}{2i}\{e^{(\alpha+i\beta)t} - e^{(\alpha-i\beta)t}\}, \qquad \{e^{\alpha t} \cos \beta t\} = \frac{1}{2}\{e^{(\alpha+i\beta)t} + e^{(\alpha-i\beta)t}\}.$$

Using (24.1) we can write

$$\left\{\frac{1}{\beta} e^{\alpha t} \sin \beta t\right\} = \frac{1}{2i\beta}\left(\frac{1}{s-\alpha-i\beta} - \frac{1}{s-\alpha+i\beta}\right) = \frac{1}{(s-\alpha)^2+\beta^2},$$

$$\{e^{\alpha t} \cos \beta t\} = \frac{1}{2}\left(\frac{1}{s-\alpha-i\beta} + \frac{1}{s-\alpha+i\beta}\right) = \frac{s-\alpha}{(s-\alpha)^2+\beta^2}.$$

We have thus deduced the formulas

$$(25.1) \qquad \frac{1}{(s-\alpha^2)+\beta^2} = \left\{\frac{1}{\beta} e^{\alpha t} \sin \beta t\right\} \quad (\beta > 0), \qquad \frac{s-\alpha}{(s-\alpha)^2+\beta^2} = \{e^{\alpha t} \cos \beta t\}.$$

Powers of the operator $1/[(s-\alpha)^2+\beta^2]$ can be calculated by the successive performance of the convolution

$$\frac{1}{[(s-\alpha)^2+\beta^2]^2} = \left\{\frac{1}{\beta^2}\int_0^t e^{\alpha(t-\tau)} \sin \beta (t-\tau)^2 e^{\alpha\tau} \sin \beta\tau \, d\tau\right\}$$

$$= \left\{\frac{e^{\alpha t}}{2\beta^2}\left[\frac{1}{\beta} \sin \beta t - t \cos \beta t\right]\right\},$$

$$\frac{1}{[(s-\alpha)^2+\beta^2]^3} = \left\{\frac{1}{2\beta^3}\int_0^t e^{\alpha(t-\tau)} \sin \beta (t-\tau)\left[\frac{1}{\beta} e^{\alpha\tau} \sin \beta\tau - \tau e^{\alpha\tau} \cos \beta\tau\right] d\tau\right\}$$

$$= \left\{\frac{e^{\alpha t}}{4\beta^4}\left[\left(\frac{3}{2} - \frac{\beta^2 t^2}{2}\right) \cdot \frac{1}{\beta} \sin \beta t - \frac{3}{2} t \cos \beta t\right]\right\}.$$

The general formula is rather complicated. It will be given in § 63 of Part III.

The particular case of formulas (25.1) obtained by the substitution $\alpha = 0$ is of importance:

$$\frac{1}{s^2+\beta^2} = \left\{\frac{1}{\beta} \sin \beta t\right\}, \qquad \frac{s}{s^2+\beta^2} = \{\cos \beta t\}.$$

Exercise. Prove the formulas

$$(\alpha)\quad \frac{1}{(s-a)^2-\beta^2}=\left\{\frac{1}{\beta}e^{at}\operatorname{sh}\beta t\right\}\quad(\beta>0);\qquad(\beta)\quad \frac{s-a}{(s-a)^2-\beta^2}=\{e^{at}\operatorname{ch}\beta t\}.$$

§ 26. Rational operators. By a *rational operator* we understand a fraction

$$\text{(26.1)}\qquad \frac{\gamma_m s^m+\ldots+\gamma_1 s+\gamma_0}{\delta_n s^n+\ldots+\delta_1 s+\delta_0}\qquad(m<n)$$

where $\gamma_m,\ldots,\gamma_0,\delta_n,\ldots,\delta_0$ are complex numbers and $\delta_n\neq 0$.

It is known from algebra that if $m<n$ and numbers γ_ν, δ_ν are real, then expression (26.1) can be decomposed into simple fractions of the following types:

$$\frac{1}{(s-a)^p},\qquad \frac{1}{[(s-a)^2+\beta^2]^p},\qquad \frac{s}{[(s-a)^2+\beta^2]^p}$$

where a and β are also real numbers and p is a natural number. By the use of the method given in the preceding section, fractions of the first two types can always be represented by means of an exponential function and trigonometric functions. In fractions of the third type the factor s comes into play; therefore they can also be reduced to an exponential function and trigonometric functions by means of formula (21.1). For example

$$\frac{s}{[(s-a)^2+\beta^2]^2}=s\left\{\frac{e^{at}}{2\beta^2}\left[\frac{1}{\beta}\sin\beta t-t\cos\beta t\right]\right\};$$

since the expression in $\{\ \}$ is equal to 0 for $t=0$ and the derivative of that expression has the form

$$\frac{e^{at}}{2\beta^2}\left[(a+\beta^2t)\frac{1}{\beta}\sin\beta t-at\cos\beta t\right],$$

we have

$$\frac{s}{[(s-a)^2+\beta^2]^2}=\left\{\frac{e^{at}}{2\beta^2}\left[(a+\beta^2t)\frac{1}{\beta}\sin\beta t-at\cos\beta t\right]\right\}.$$

Finally, every rational expression (16.1) can be reduced by decomposition into simple fractions to an exponential function and trigonometric functions. In decomposing into simple fractions it is best to use, according to the practice observed in the integral calculus, the method of indetermined coefficients.

EXAMPLE 1. Calculate $\dfrac{s+1}{s^2+2s}$.

The denominator can be decomposed into two different linear factors, s and $s+2$. It is thus possible to find two numbers, A and B, such that

$$\frac{s+1}{s(s+2)}=\frac{A}{s}+\frac{B}{s+2}.$$

Multiplying both sides of this equality by $s(s+2)$, we have

$$s+1=(A+B)s+2A.$$

This equality will be satisfied if $A+B=1$ and $2A=1$, *i. e.*, if $A=B=\frac{1}{2}$. Hence

$$\frac{s+1}{s^2+2s}=\frac{1}{2}\cdot\frac{1}{s}+\frac{1}{2}\cdot\frac{1}{s+2},$$

and finally

$$\frac{s+1}{s^2+2s}=\left\{\frac{1}{2}+\frac{1}{2}e^{-2t}\right\}.$$

EXAMPLE 2. Calculate $\dfrac{5s+3}{(s-1)(s^2+2s+5)}$.

We seek such constants A, B and C, that

$$\frac{5s+3}{(s-1)(s^2+2s+5)}=\frac{A}{s-1}+\frac{B(s+1)+C}{(s+1)^2+4}.$$

Multiplying both sides of this equality by $(s-1)(s^2+2s+5)$ and comparing the coefficients of equal powers, we find that

$$A=1,\qquad B=-1\quad\text{and}\quad C=3.$$

Thus

$$\frac{5s+3}{(s-1)(s^2+2s+5)}=\frac{1}{s-1}-\frac{s+1}{(s+1)^2+4}+\frac{3}{(s+1)^2+4}$$

$$=\left\{e^t-e^{-t}\cos 2t+\frac{3}{2}e^{-t}\sin 2t\right\}.$$

EXAMPLE 3. Calculate $\dfrac{1}{s(2s+1)^3}$.

We decompose this expression into simple fractions:

$$\frac{1}{s(2s+1)^3}=\frac{A}{s}+\frac{B}{s+\frac{1}{2}}+\frac{C}{(s+\frac{1}{2})^2}+\frac{D}{(s+\frac{1}{2})^3}$$

$$=\frac{8\left[A(s+\frac{1}{2})^3+Bs(s+\frac{1}{2})^2+Cs(s+\frac{1}{2})+Ds\right]}{s(2s+1)^3}.$$

Comparing, in the numerators, the coefficients of equal powers of s we obtain the equalities

$$0 = 8A+8B, \qquad 0 = 6A+2B+4C+8D,$$
$$0 = 12A+8B+8C, \qquad 1 = a.$$

Solving this system of equations we obtain

$$A = 1, \quad B = -1, \quad C = -\tfrac{1}{2}, \quad D = -\tfrac{1}{4}.$$

Consequently

$$\frac{1}{s(2s+1)^3} = \frac{1}{s} - \frac{1}{s+\frac{1}{2}} - \frac{1}{2(s+\frac{1}{2})^2} - \frac{1}{4(s+\frac{1}{2})^3}$$

$$= \left\{1-e^{-t/2} - \frac{1}{2}te^{-t/2} - \frac{1}{8}t^2e^{-t/2}\right\}$$

$$= \left\{1-\frac{1}{8}(8+4t+t^2)e^{-t/2}\right\}.$$

EXAMPLE 4. Calculate $\dfrac{2s^6+6s^4+3s^2+5}{s^8+2s^6-2s^2-1}$.

We write

$$\frac{2s^6+6s^4+3s^2+5}{s^8+2s^6-2s^2-1} = \frac{2s^6+6s^4+3s^2+5}{(s-1)(s+1)(s^2+1)^3}$$

$$= \frac{A}{s-1} + \frac{B}{s+1} + \frac{Cs+D}{s^2+1} + \frac{Es+F}{(s^2+1)^2} + \frac{Gs+H}{(s^2+1)^3}$$

$$= \frac{[A(s+1)+B(s-1)](s^2+1)^3}{(s-1)(s+1)(s^2+1)^3} +$$

$$+ \frac{[(Cs+D)(s^2+1)^2+(Es+F)(s^2+1)+Gs+H](s^2-1)}{(s-1)(s+1)(s^2+1)^3}.$$

Comparing the coefficients in the numerators we obtain the equalities

$$0 = A+B+C, \qquad 0 = 3A+3B-C+6,$$
$$2 = A-B+D, \qquad 3 = 3A-3B-D+H,$$
$$0 = 3A+3B+C+E, \qquad 0 = A+B-C-E-G,$$
$$6 = 3A-3B+D+F, \qquad 5 = A-B-D-F-H.$$

Hence

$$A = 1, \quad B = -1, \quad H = -3, \quad C = D = E = F = G = 0,$$

and

$$\frac{2s^6 + 6s^4 + 3s^2 + 5}{s^8 + 2s^6 - 2s^2 - 1} = \frac{1}{s-1} - \frac{1}{s+1} - \frac{3}{(s^2+1)^3}$$

$$= \left\{e^t - e^{-t} - \frac{3}{8}(3-t^2)\sin t + \frac{9}{8}t\cos t\right\}.$$

If $m \geqslant n$, then expression (26.1) is represented as the sum of a polynomial of the operator s and a fraction in which the degree of the numerator is less than the degree of the denominator. After this transformation we can use the method of decomposition into simple fractions.

EXAMPLE 5.

$$\frac{s^3}{s-1} = s^2 + s + 1 + \frac{1}{s-1} = s^2 + s + 1 + \{e^t\}.$$

Exercises.

1. Reduce the following expressions to exponential and trigonometric functions:

(α) $\dfrac{1}{2s^2 - 2s + 5}$; (β) $\dfrac{3s-4}{s^2 - s - 6}$; (γ) $\dfrac{s^3 + 2s - 6}{s^2 - s - 2}$; (δ) $\dfrac{6s^3 + 4s + 1}{s^4 + s^2}$;

(ε) $\dfrac{1}{s^3 + s^2 + s}$; (ζ) $\dfrac{s^4}{s^2 + 1}$; (η) $\dfrac{5s^3 + 3s^2 + 12s - 12}{s^4 - 16}$; (ϑ) $\dfrac{1}{(s^2 + s + 1)^2}$.

2. Show that

(α) $\dfrac{\alpha - \beta}{(s-\alpha)(s-\beta)} = \{e^{\alpha t} - e^{\beta t}\}$;

(β) $\dfrac{s}{(s^2+\alpha^2)(s^2+\beta^2)} = \left\{\dfrac{1}{\alpha^2 - \beta^2}(\cos\beta t - \cos\alpha t)\right\}$ $\quad (\alpha^2 \neq \beta^2)$;

(γ) $\dfrac{\beta^2 - \alpha^2}{(s^2+\alpha^2)(s^2+\beta^2)} = \left\{\dfrac{1}{\alpha}\sin\alpha t - \dfrac{1}{\beta}\sin\beta t\right\}$ $\quad (\alpha \neq 0, \ \beta \neq 0)$;

(δ) $\dfrac{1}{s^4 - \alpha^4} = \left\{\dfrac{1}{2\alpha^3}(\operatorname{sh}\alpha t - \sin\alpha t)\right\}$ $\quad (\alpha \neq 0)$;

(ε) $\dfrac{1}{s^4 - \alpha^4} = \left\{\dfrac{1}{\sqrt{2}\alpha^3}\left(\operatorname{ch}\dfrac{\alpha t}{\sqrt{2}}\sin\dfrac{\alpha t}{\sqrt{2}} - \operatorname{sh}\dfrac{\alpha t}{\sqrt{2}}\cos\dfrac{\alpha t}{\sqrt{2}}\right)\right\}$ $\quad (\alpha \neq 0)$;

(ζ) $\dfrac{s}{s^4 + \alpha^4} = \left\{\dfrac{1}{\alpha^2}\sin\dfrac{\alpha t}{\sqrt{2}}\operatorname{sh}\dfrac{\alpha t}{\sqrt{2}}\right\}$ $\quad (\alpha \neq 0)$;

(η) $\dfrac{s(s^2+7)}{(s^2+1)(s^2+9)} = \{\cos^3 t\}$;

(ϑ) $\dfrac{3s^2 - 1}{(s^2+1)^3} = \left\{\dfrac{1}{2}t^2\sin t\right\}$.

§ 27. Some properties of operators. As we know, admitting complex numbers a we can decompose every expression (26.1) into simple fractions of the type

$$\frac{1}{(s-a)^p};$$

the same can be done with complex coefficients $\gamma_m, \ldots, \gamma_0, \delta_n, \ldots, \delta_0$.

It follows hence that in the complex domain every operator (26.1) where $m < n$ is a linear combination of functions $\{t^{p-1}e^{at}\}$. Thus it is always a function different from zero in a certain right-hand neighbourhood of the point $t = 0$ and indefinitely differentiable in the interval $0 \leqslant t < \infty$.

If $n \leqslant m$, then, as can be seen from the example at the end of the preceding section, the operator (26.1) is not necessarily a function.

There exist functions $\{q(t)\}$ whose product by any operator (26.1) *different from zero is a function of class $\mathcal{C}$, different from zero in a certain right-hand neighbourhood of the point $t = 0$.*

Such for instance is the function defined by the formulas

$$q(t) = \begin{cases} e^{-1/t} & \text{for} \quad 0 < t < \infty, \\ 0 & \text{for} \quad t = 0. \end{cases}$$

This is obvious in the case of $m < n$. In order to prove it for $n \leqslant m$ as well, we must first verify that for $0 < t < \infty$ we have the equalities

$$q'(t) = \frac{1}{t^2}e^{-1/t}, \qquad q''(t) = -\frac{1-2t}{t^4}e^{-1/t}, \qquad q(t) = \frac{1-6t+6t^2}{t}e^{-1/t},$$

and generally

$$q^{(\nu)}(t) = \frac{w_\nu(t)}{t^{2\nu}}e^{-1/t},$$

where $w_\nu(t)$ is a polynomial. We see hence that $\lim\limits_{t\to 0} q^{(\nu)}(t) = 0$ for every $\nu = 0, 1, 2, \ldots$ Since, by the mean value theorem,

$$\frac{q(0+\varepsilon)-q(0)}{\varepsilon} = q'(\xi)$$

where $0 < \xi < \varepsilon$, we have $q'(0) = \lim\limits_{\xi\to 0} q'(\xi) = 0$. Similarly we have $q''(0) = 0$, and generally $q^{(\nu)}(0) = 0$, for every natural ν.

We have thus proved that every derivative of the function q is continuous and equal to 0 at $t = 0$. It follows hence that, for every natural ν, the product $s^\nu q$ is a function of class $\mathcal{C}$ different from zero in a right-hand neighbourhood of the point $t = 0$.

If $n \leqslant m$, then the product P of multiplying fraction (26.1) by $1/s^{n-m+1}$ has a numerator of less degree than that of its denominator; hence it is a function of class $\mathcal{C}$, different from 0 in the right-hand neighbourhood of the point $t = 0$. Consequently the operator $P \cdot s^{n-m+1}q$ is also a function of class $\mathcal{C}$, different from zero in a right-hand neighbourhood of $t = 0$, which proves the theorem.

This theorem immediately implies that *if operator* (26.1) *represents a function that is identically equal to zero in a right-hand neighbourhood of the point* $t = 0$, *then that operator is null.*

Moreover, we shall prove the following theorem:

If

$$\frac{\alpha_m s^m + \ldots + \alpha_0}{\beta_n s^n + \ldots + \beta_0} = \frac{\gamma_p s^p + \ldots + \gamma_0}{\delta_q s^q + \ldots + \delta_0}, \tag{27.1}$$

then for every (real or complex) number ξ *such that*

$$\beta_n \xi^n + \ldots + \beta_0 \neq 0 \quad \text{and} \quad \delta_q \xi^q + \ldots + \delta_0 \neq 0 \tag{27.2}$$

we have the equality

$$\frac{\alpha_m \xi^m + \ldots + \alpha_0}{\beta_n \xi^n + \ldots + \beta_0} = \frac{\gamma_p \xi^p + \ldots + \gamma_0}{\delta_q \xi^q + \ldots + \delta_0}.$$

Proof. Equality (27.1) implies that

$$(\alpha_m s^m + \ldots + \alpha_0)(\delta_q s^q + \ldots + \delta_0) = (\gamma_p s^p + \ldots + \gamma_0)(\beta_n s^n + \ldots + \beta_0).$$

On performing the multiplication we shall obtain, on both sides, polynomials of the operator s. Those polynomials will have equal coefficients on account of the theorem given in § 23. It follows hence that we also have

$$(\alpha_m \xi^m + \ldots + \alpha_0)(\delta_q \xi^q + \ldots + \delta_0) = (\gamma_p \xi^p + \ldots + \gamma_0)(\beta_n \xi^n + \ldots + \beta_0).$$

By (27.2) this equality immediately implies (27.1).

CHAPTER IV

ORDINARY DIFFERENTIAL EQUATIONS WITH CONSTANT COEFFICIENTS

§ 28. General method and examples. The operational calculus provides us with convenient methods of solving linear differential equations. Partial equations open a rich field of applications, but also in case of ordinary equations the use of operators presents certain advantages over the classical methods. It requires no separate theory for those equations, reducing them automaticaly, both homogeneous and non--homogeneous ones, to ordinary algebraic equations.

Consider the differential equation of the n-th degree

$$a_n x^{(n)} + a_{n-1} x^{(n-1)} + \ldots + a_0 x = f, \tag{28.1}$$

in which the coefficients $a_n, \ldots, a_0$ $(a_n \neq 0)$ are constant and f is an arbitrary function continuous for $t \geqslant 0$. We seek a solution $x(t)$ satisfying the initial conditions

$$x(0) = \gamma_0, \quad x'(0) = \gamma_1, \quad \ldots, \quad x^{(n-1)}(0) = \gamma_{n-1}.$$

In virtue of the general formula

$$x^{(n)} = s^n x - s^{n-1} x(0) - \ldots - x^{(n-1)}(0)$$

worked out in § 22 (p. 29), equation (28.1) may be written in the form

$$a_n s^n x + a_{n-1} s^{n-1} + \ldots + a_0 x = \beta_{n-1} s^{n-1} + \beta_{n-2} s^{n-2} + \ldots + \beta_0 + f$$

where

$$\beta_\nu = a_{\nu+1}\gamma_0 + a_{\nu+1}\gamma_1 + \ldots + a_n \gamma_{n-\nu-1} \quad (\nu = 0, 1, \ldots, n-1).$$

Hence we immediately find

$$x = \frac{\beta_{n-1} s^{n-1} + \ldots + \beta_0 + f}{a_n s^n + \ldots + a_0}.$$

In order to obtain the solution in the usual form we can work it out according to the pattern

$$x = \frac{\beta_{n-1}s^{n-1}+\ldots+\beta_0}{a_n s^n+\ldots+a_0} + \frac{f}{a_n s^n+\ldots+a_0}$$

and apply decomposition into simple fractions.

Similar methods of solution can be used for systems of differential equations with constant coefficients,

$$x_1'+a_{11}x_1+\ldots+a_{1n}x_n = f_1,$$
$$\ldots\ldots\ldots\ldots\ldots\ldots$$
$$x_n'+a_{n1}x_1+\ldots+a_{nn}x_n = f_n.$$

Assuming that

$$x_1(0) = \gamma_1, \quad \ldots, \quad x_n(0) = \gamma_n,$$

we can give to this system, on the grounds of the general relation $x' = sx - x(0)$, the form

$$(a_{11}+s)x_1+\ldots+a_{1n}x_n = \gamma_1+f_1,$$
$$\ldots\ldots\ldots\ldots\ldots\ldots$$
$$a_{1n}x_1+\ldots+(a_{nn}+s)x_n = \gamma_n+f_n.$$

Determinants or any other classical method of solving systems of algebraic equations may be used to solve this system.

EXAMPLE 1. Find the solution $x(t)$ of the differential equation

$$x' = x(2t-1)e^{t^2} \text{ (}^1\text{)}$$

such that $x(0) = 2$.

Solution. By the initial condition we have $x' = sx-2$; therefore

$$sx - x = 2+f,$$

where

$$f = \{(2t-1)e^{t^2}\}.$$

---

(1) If we wished to apply consistently the notation adopted in § 7, we should rather write

$$x' - x = \{(2t-1)e^{t^2}\},$$

since the right side of the equation, as well as the left, is a function. However, in order to get some practice in applying correctly the operational calculus in domains where problems are presented in the old, non-operational notation, we use that notation in formulating our problems and pass to the operational form only in the course of solving them.

Hence

$$x = \frac{2+f}{s-1} = \frac{2}{s-1} + \frac{1}{s-1} f = \{2e^t\} + \{e^t\}\{(2t-1)e^{t^2}\}$$

$$= \left\{2e^t + \int_0^t e^{t-\tau}(2\tau-1)e^{\tau^2}d\tau\right\} = \{e^t + e^{t^2}\}.$$

EXAMPLE 2. Find the solution $x(t)$ of the differential equation

$$x'' + \lambda^2 x = 0 \qquad (\lambda \neq 0)$$

satisfying the initial conditions

$$x(0) = \alpha, \quad x'(0) = \beta.$$

Solution. We have $x'' = s^2x - \alpha s - \beta$ and consequently

$$s^2x + \lambda^2 x = \alpha s + \beta;$$

hence

$$x = \frac{\alpha s}{s^2+\lambda^2} + \frac{\beta}{s^2+\lambda^2} = \left\{\alpha \cos \lambda t + \frac{\beta}{\lambda} \sin \lambda t\right\}.$$

EXAMPLE 3. Find the solution $x(t)$ of the equation

$$x'' - x' - 6x = 2,$$

satisfying the initial conditions

$$x(0) = 1, \quad x'(0) = 0.$$

Solution. Since the function 2, appearing on the right-hand side, may give rise to a misunderstanding, let us rewrite this equation in the form

$$\{x''(t)\} - \{x'(t)\} - 6\{x(t)\} = \{2\};$$

since $\{2\} = 2l = 2\frac{1}{s}$, on taking into account the initial conditions we have

$$s^2x - sx - 6x = s - 1 + 2\frac{1}{s},$$

whence

$$x = \frac{s^2 - s + 2}{s(s-3)(s+2)} = -\frac{1}{3} \cdot \frac{1}{s} + \frac{8}{15} \cdot \frac{1}{s-3} + \frac{4}{5} \cdot \frac{1}{s+2}$$

$$= \left\{-\frac{1}{3} + \frac{8}{15} e^{3t} + \frac{4}{5} e^{-2t}\right\}.$$

EXAMPLE 4. Find the solution of the equation

$$x^{(8)}+2x^{(6)}-2x''-x=0$$

satisfying the initial conditions

$$x(0)=x''(0)=x^{(4)}(0)=x^{(6)}(0)=0,$$

$$x'(0)=2,\quad x^{(3)}(0)=2,\quad x^{(5)}(0)=-1,\quad x^{(7)}(0)=11.$$

Solution. From the operational form of the equation,

$$s^8x+2s^6x-2s^2x-x=2s^6+6s^4+3s^2+5,$$

we find, considering the solution of example 4 in § 26 (p. 37), that

$$x=\frac{2s^6+6s^4+3s^2+5}{s^8+2s^6-2s^2-1}=\left\{e^t-e^{-t}-\frac{3}{8}(3-t)^2\sin t+\frac{9}{8}t\cos t\right\}.$$

EXAMPLE 5. Solve the system of differential equations

$$x'-ax-\beta y=\beta e^{at},\qquad y'+\beta x-ay=0$$

assuming that

$$x(0)=0,\qquad y(0)=1,.$$

Solution.

$$sx-ax-\beta y=\frac{\beta}{s-a},$$

$$sy+\beta x-ay=1.$$

Applying henceforth the usual methods of solving systems of algebraic equations, we obtain

$$x=\frac{2\beta}{(s-a)^2+\beta^2},\qquad y=\frac{(s-a)^2-\beta^2}{(s-a)[(s-a)^2+\beta^2]}$$

and further

$$x=\{2e^{at}\sin\beta t\},$$

$$y=\frac{2(s-a)}{(s-a)^2+\beta^2}-\frac{1}{s-a}=\{2e^{at}\cos\beta t-e^{at}\}=\{e^{at}(2\cos\beta t-1)\}.$$

EXAMPLE 6. Solve the system of differential equations

$$x'+z'-z=0,$$

$$-x'-2z'+x+y=\operatorname{th}t,$$

$$2x''+y''+z''=-2\frac{\operatorname{sh}t}{\operatorname{ch}^3t}\ (^1)$$

---

(1) $\operatorname{th}t=\dfrac{e^t-e^{-t}}{e^t+e^{-t}}$ (*tangens hiperbolicus*),

$\operatorname{sh}t=\frac{1}{2}(e^t-e^{-t})$ (*sinus hiperbolicus*),

$\operatorname{ch}t=\frac{1}{2}(e^t+e^{-t})$ (*cosinus hiperbolicus*).

assuming that

$$x(0) = x'(0) = y(0) = y'(0) = z(0) = z'(0) = 0 .$$

Solution. Introduce the notation $f = \{\operatorname{th} t\}$; then $\left\{-2\,\frac{\operatorname{sh} t}{\operatorname{ch}^3 t}\right\} = s^2 f - 1$ and the equations can be written in the form

$$sx + sz - z = 0,$$
$$-sx - 2sz + x + y = f,$$
$$2s^2x + s^2y + s^2z + z = s^2f - 1.$$

Denoting by D the determinant of this system, we have

$$D = \begin{vmatrix} s & 0 & s-1 \\ -s+1 & 1 & -2s \\ 2s^2 & s^2 & s^2+1 \end{vmatrix} = s(s+1)(s^2+1),$$

$$x = \frac{1}{D}\begin{vmatrix} 0 & 0 & s-1 \\ f & 1 & -2s \\ s^2f-1 & s^2 & s^2+1 \end{vmatrix} = \frac{s-1}{s(s+1)(s^2+1)} = -\frac{1}{s} + \frac{1}{s+1} + \frac{1}{s^2+1},$$

$$y = \frac{1}{D}\begin{vmatrix} s & 0 & s-1 \\ -s+1 & f & -2s \\ 2s^2 & s^2f-1 & s^2+1 \end{vmatrix} = \frac{-s^2-2s+1}{s(s+1)(s^2+1)} + f = \frac{1}{s} - \frac{1}{s+1} - 2\frac{1}{s^2+1} + f,$$

$$z = \frac{1}{D}\begin{vmatrix} s & 0 & 0 \\ -s+1 & 1 & f \\ 2s^2 & s^2 & s^2f-1 \end{vmatrix} = \frac{-1}{(s+1)(s^2+1)} = -\frac{1}{2}\cdot\frac{1}{s+1} - \frac{1}{2}\cdot\frac{1}{s^2+1} + \frac{1}{2}\cdot\frac{s}{s^2+1},$$

and finally

$$x = \{-1 + e^{-t} + \sin t\},$$
$$y = \{1 - e^{-t} - 2\sin t + \operatorname{th} t\},$$
$$z = \tfrac{1}{2}\{-e^{-t} - \sin t + \cos t\}.$$

Exercises.

1. Solve the following equations with the given initial conditions:

(α) $x'' - 2\alpha x' + (\alpha^2 + \beta^2)x = 0, \quad x(0) = 0, \quad x'(0) = 1;$
(β) $x'' + 4x = \sin t, \quad x(0) = x'(0) = 0;$
(γ) $x''' + x' = e^{2t}, \quad x(0) = x'(0) = x''(0) = 0;$
(δ) $x'' + x' = t^2 + 2t, \quad x(0) = 4, \quad x'(0) = -2;$
(ε) $x^{(4)} + x''' = \cos t, \quad x(0) = x'(0) = x''(0) = 0, \quad x'''(0) = \gamma;$
(ζ) $4x''' - 8x'' - x' - 3x = -8e^t, \quad x(0) = x'(0) = x''(0) = 1;$

(η) $x^{(4)} + 4x = t^2, \quad x(0) = x'(0) = x''(0) = x'''(0) = 0;$

(ϑ) $x^{(4)} + 2a^2x'' + a^4x = \operatorname{ch} at, \quad x(0) = x'(0) = 1, \quad x''(0) = 1 - 2a^2,$
$x'''(0) = -2a^2;$

(ι) $x^{(5)} + 2x''' + x' = \alpha t + \beta \sin t + \gamma \cos t,$
$x(0) = x'(0) = x''(0) = x'''(0) = x^{(4)}(0) = 0;$

($\varkappa$) $x'' - 4x = \sin\frac{3}{2}t \cdot \sin\frac{1}{2}t, \quad x(0) = 1, \quad x'(0) = 0.$

(Hint. Change the product of sines into the difference of cosines).

2. Solve the following systems of equations with the given initial conditions:

(α) $x' - y' - 2x + 2y = 1 - 2t,$
$x'' + 2y' + x = 0,$
$x(0) = y(0) = x'(0) = 0;$

(β) $x' = -y,$
$y' = 2x + 2y,$
$x(0) = y(0) = 1;$

(γ) $x' + 2y = 3t,$
$y' - 2x = 4,$
$x(0) = 2, \ y(0) = 3;$

(δ) $x' + y' - y = e^t,$
$2x' + y' + 2y = \cos t,$
$x(0) = y(0) = 0;$

(ε) $2x' + y' - 3x = 0,$
$x'' + y' - 2y = e^{2t},$
$x(0) = -1, \ x'(0) = 1, \ y(0) = 0;$

(ζ) $x' - x + 2y = 0,$
$x'' - 2y' = 2t - \cos 2t,$
$x(0) = 0, \ x'(0) = -1;$

(η) $x' = y - z,$
$y' = x + y,$
$z' = x + z,$
$x(0) = 1, \ y(0) = 2, \ z(0) = 3;$

(ϑ) $x' = 6x - 72y + 44z,$
$y' = -4x + 40y - 22z,$
$z' = -6x + 57y - 31z,$
$x(0) = 9, \ y(0) = 5, \ z(0) = 7.$

CHAPTER V

THEORY OF ELECTRIC CIRCUIT

§ 29. Remarks on the application of the operational calculus to physical and technical problems. Applying the operational calculus to problems in physics and technology, where the use of certain symbols is a long-established tradition, we may have some difficulty in the correct conversion of the data of the equation into operational notation. In order to clarify any doubts that might arise in this connection let us discuss as an example the differential equation of electric current,

(29.1) $$LI'+RI=E$$

where L, R, E and I denote self-induction, resistance, electromotive force and current intensity respectively, L and R being assumed to be constant.

Suppose that we want to determine the current I being given L, R and E and knowing that at the instant $t=0$ current intensity is equal to zero:

$$I(0)=0.$$

We then simply have

(29.2) $$LsI+RI=E,$$

whence

$$I=\frac{E}{Ls+R}=E\frac{1}{L}\cdot\frac{1}{s+R/L}=\{E(t)\}\left\{\frac{1}{L}\cdot\exp\left(-\frac{R}{L}t\right)\right\},$$

and finally

(29.3) $$I=\left\{\frac{1}{L}\int_0^t E(t-\tau)\exp\left(-\frac{R}{L}\tau\right)d\tau\right\}$$

If in particular the electromotive force is constant, then formula (29.3) is simplified and the integration can be effectively performed:

(29.4) $$I=\left\{\frac{E}{L}\int_0^t\exp\left(-\frac{R}{L}\tau\right)d\tau\right\}=\left\{\frac{E}{R}\left[1-\exp\left(-\frac{R}{L}t\right)\right]\right\}.$$

In this case the letter E may be regarded from the start as a number, just as the letters L and R; if we wish to perform the calculation correctly we must modify the operational equation (29.2). Indeed, if we regard L, R and E as numbers, then in order to put the original equation (29.1) more precisely we should write

$$\{LI'(t)+RI(t)\} = \{E\};$$

then, in view of $I(0) = 0$, we shall have in the shortened operational notation

$$LsI+RI = E\frac{1}{s}. \tag{29.5}$$

Hence

$$I = \frac{E}{s(Ls+R)} = \frac{E}{R}\left(\frac{1}{s}-\frac{1}{s+R/L}\right) = \left\{\frac{E}{R}\left[1-\exp\left(-\frac{R}{L}t\right)\right]\right\}.$$

We have obtained on different lines the same result as in (29.4), having avoided integration.

It will be observed that according to whether we regard E as a function or as a number we obtain different operational equations, (29.2) or (29.5). It can be seen from the above example that a correct introduction of operational symbols necessitates very careful use of the letters. In doubtful cases we can always avoid difficulties if, from the very start, we make it clear where the variable t occurs in the original equation. For instance, it we want to take into consideration the variability of the electromotive force, we shall first write equation (29.1) in the form

$$\{LI'(t)+RI(t)\} = \{E(t)\};$$

and if we assume the electromotive force to be constant, we may write

$$\{LI'(t)+RI(t)\} = \{E\}.$$

Introducing in the first case symbols $I = \{I(t)\}$, $I' = \{I'(t)\}$ and $E = \{E(t)\}$, we have

$$LI'+RI = E; \tag{29.6}$$

in the second case we have $\{E\} = E\frac{1}{s}$ and consequently

$$LI'+RI = E\frac{1}{s}. \tag{29.7}$$

Finally, using the equality $I' = sI-I(0) = sI$, we obtain equation (29.2) or (29.5). With a little practice we can at once write the equations in the operational form, provided we make it clear which letters are regarded as functions and which as numbers.

It is worth noticing that the operational equation (29.6) is formally identical with the original equation (29.1), while equation (29.7) is different from those two. This is of course explained by the fact that the symbol E is regarded as a function in equation (29.6) and as a number in equation (29.7).

It will also be observed that if, for instance, it is the resistance R that is variable in equation (29.1), the equation cannot be reduced to the operational form. This will be obvious if we write

$$\{LI'(t)+R(t)I(t)\} = \{E\}.$$

The expression $\{R(t)I(t)\}$ cannot be written in the form RI since in the operational calculus that would denote the convolution $\{\int_0^t R(t-\tau)I(\tau)d\tau\}$. It can be proved generally that if the coefficients of a differential equation are variable, then that equation, unlike equations with constant coefficients, cannot be reduced to an algebraical equation by means of operational notation.

§ 30. The electric circuit. We shall now solve a more general problem. To an electric circuit with self-induction L, resistance R and capacity C an electromotive force E is applied. If I denotes the current, and Q the charge on the electrodes of the condenser, then the following differential equations are satisfied:

$$LJ'+RI+\frac{Q}{C} = E, \quad Q' = I,$$

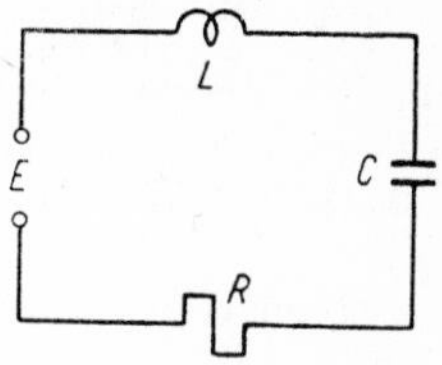

Fig. 5. The electric circuit

where the sign $'$ denotes differentiation with respect to time.

Writing these equations in the operational form we have

$$LsI+RI+\frac{Q}{C} = E+LI(0), \quad sQ = I+Q(0),$$

where $I(0)$ and $Q(0)$ denote the current and the charge at the instant $t = 0$ respectively.

Hence by eliminating Q we obtain the equation

$$\left(Ls+R+\frac{1}{Cs}\right)I = E+LI(0)+\frac{V(0)}{s}, \tag{30.1}$$

where $V(0) = -Q(0)/C$ is the voltage on the condenser.

Now assume that the original current intensity and the original charge are equal to zero. Then equation (30.1) is reduced to the form

$$\left(Ls+R+\frac{1}{Cs}\right)I = E. \tag{30.2}$$

Suppose that at the instant $t = 0$ we apply to the circuit a constant electromotive force E_0. We then have $E = E_0/s$ and

$$\left(Ls+R+\frac{1}{Cs}\right)I = \frac{E_0}{s},$$

whence

$$I = \frac{E_0}{L\left(s^2+\frac{R}{L}s+\frac{1}{LC}\right)} = \frac{E_0}{L[(s+a)^2+\mu]},$$

where

$$a = \frac{R}{2L}, \qquad \mu = \frac{1}{LC}-\frac{R^2}{4L^2}. \tag{30.3}$$

It is easy to find that

$$\frac{1}{(s+a)^2+\mu} = \begin{cases} \dfrac{1}{\sqrt{\mu}}\, e^{-at}\sin\sqrt{\mu t} & \text{for} \quad \mu > 0, \\ te^{-at} & \text{for} \quad \mu = 0, \\ \dfrac{1}{\sqrt{-\mu}}\, e^{-at}\,\mathrm{sh}\,\sqrt{-\mu t} & \text{for} \quad \mu < 0. \end{cases}$$

Hence we easily obtain the formulas

(I) for $\mu > 0$:

$$I(t) = \frac{E_0}{\sqrt{\mu}L}\, e^{-at}\sin\sqrt{\mu t};$$

(II) for $\mu = 0$:

$$I(t) = \frac{E_0}{L}\, te^{-at};$$

(III) for $\mu < 0$:

$$I(t) = \frac{E_0}{\sqrt{-\mu}L}\, e^{-at}\,\mathrm{sh}\,\sqrt{-\mu t}.$$

Let us now consider the general case. Suppose that at the instant $t = 0$ we apply an arbitrary electromotive force $E = \{E(t)\}$.

From equation (30.2) we find

$$I = E\frac{s}{L\left(s^2+\frac{R}{L}s+\frac{1}{LC}\right)} = E\frac{s}{L[(s+a)^2+\mu]}$$

$$= E\left(\frac{s+a}{L[(s+a)^2+\mu]} - \frac{a}{L[(s+a)^2+\mu]}\right).$$

Since

$$\frac{s+a}{(s+a)^2+\mu} = \begin{cases} e^{-at}\cos\sqrt{\mu t} & \text{for} \quad \mu = 0, \\ e^{-at} & \text{for} \quad \mu < 0, \\ e^{-at}\,\mathrm{ch}\sqrt{-\mu t} & \text{for} \quad \mu > 0, \end{cases}$$

we have the formulas

(I) for $\mu > 0$:

$$I(t) = \frac{1}{L}\int_0^t E(t-\tau)e^{-a\sigma}\left[\cos\sqrt{\mu\tau} - \frac{a}{\sqrt{\mu}}\sin\sqrt{\mu\tau}\right]d\tau;$$

(II) for $\mu = 0$:

$$I(t) = \frac{1}{L}\int_0^t E(t-\tau)(1-a\tau)e^{-a\tau}\,d\tau;$$

(III) for $\mu < 0$

$$I(t) = \frac{1}{L}\int_0^t E(t-\tau)e^{-a\tau}\left[\mathrm{ch}\sqrt{-\mu\tau} - \frac{a}{\sqrt{-\mu}}\,\mathrm{sh}\sqrt{-\mu\tau}\right]d\tau.$$

§ 31. The short-circuit current. In the preceding section we constantly assumed that $I(0) = 0$ and $Q(0) = 0$. Now we shall assume $I(0)$ and $Q(0)$ to be arbitrary and $E = 0$. This corresponds to the assumption that the terminals of the circuit are short-circuited at the instant $t = 0$ without any electromotive force being applied. Let us term the current which then flows through the circuit the *short-circuit current* and denote it by $\bar{I}$.

The short-circuit current satisfies the equation

$$\left(Ls+R+\frac{1}{Cs}\right)\bar{I} = LI(0)+\frac{V(0)}{s} \tag{31.1}$$

where $V(0) = -Q(0)/C$ is the potential difference on the condenser. Hence

$$\bar{I} = \frac{LI(0)+\frac{V(0)}{s}}{Ls+R+\frac{1}{Cs}}. \tag{31.2}$$

We may also write

$$\bar{I} = \frac{LsI(0)+V(0)}{L\left(s^2+\frac{R}{L}s+\frac{1}{C}\right)} = I(0)\frac{s+a}{(s+a)^2+\mu} - \frac{\delta}{(s+a)^2+\mu},$$

where

$$\delta = \frac{R}{2L}I(0) - \frac{1}{L}V(0),$$

a and μ being defined by (30.3).

In view of the formulas given in the preceding section we find at once the shape of the short-circuit current:

(I) for $\mu > 0$:

$$\bar{I}(t) = I(0)\cdot e^{-at}\cos\sqrt{\mu}t - \frac{\delta}{\sqrt{\mu}}e^{-at}\sin\sqrt{\mu}t;$$

(II) for $\mu = 0$:

$$\bar{I}(t) = \left(I(0)-\delta t\right)e^{-at};$$

(III) for $\mu < 0$:

$$\bar{I}(t) = I(0)e^{-at}\operatorname{ch}\sqrt{-\mu}t - \frac{\delta}{\sqrt{-\mu}}e^{-at}\operatorname{sh}\sqrt{-\mu}t.$$

The above calculation is valid on the assumption that $L > 0$.

If $L = 0$, $R > 0$ and $C > 0$, then

$$\bar{I} = -\frac{CV(0)}{CRs+1},$$

whence

$$\bar{I}(t) = \frac{V(0)}{R}\exp\left(-\frac{t}{CR}\right). \tag{31.3}$$

If the circuit is without a condenser, then instead of (31.1) we have the equation

$$(Ls+R)\bar{I} = L\cdot I(0);$$

this corresponds to the assumption that $C = \infty$. In this case we have

$$\bar{I} = \frac{LI(0)}{Ls+R}$$

and

$$I(t) = I(0)\exp\left(-\frac{R}{L}t\right).$$

It can easily be seen that with the assumption of $R > 0$ the short--circuit current decreases to zero, like an exponential function, in all the cases discussed above. A doubt may arise only in case (III); but it will suffice to verify that for $\mu < 0$ we have

$$e^{-at}\operatorname{ch}\sqrt{-\mu}t = \tfrac{1}{2}(e^{-(a-\sqrt{-\mu})t}+e^{-(a+\sqrt{-\mu})t}),$$

$$e^{-at}\operatorname{sh}\sqrt{-\mu}t = \tfrac{1}{2}(e^{-(a-\sqrt{-\mu})t}-e^{-(a+\sqrt{-\mu})t}),$$

and that

$$a-\sqrt{-\mu} = \frac{R}{2L}-\sqrt{\frac{R^2}{4L^2}-\frac{1}{LC}} > 0.$$

The reduction of the short-circuit current to zero is understandable since there is no electromotive force within the circuit in question and the existing current is being constantly used up to overcome the resistance.

In certain calculations, when the resistance of the circuit is small, it is assumed that $R = 0$. This approximation is justified only if we observe the shape of the current during a short period. If $R = 0$, $L > 0$ and the circuit has a condenser, then by formula (31.1) we have

$$\bar{I} = \frac{sI(0)+\dfrac{V(0)}{L}}{s^2+\dfrac{1}{LC}} \tag{31.4}$$

and

$$\bar{I}(t) = I(0)\cos\frac{t}{\sqrt{LC}}+\sqrt{\frac{C}{L}}\,V(0)\sin\frac{t}{\sqrt{LC}}$$

i. e.,

$$\bar{I}(t) = \beta\sin\left(\gamma+\frac{t}{\sqrt{LC}}\right),$$

where

$$\beta = \sqrt{I^2(0)+\frac{CV^2(0)}{L}}, \qquad \operatorname{tg}\gamma = \sqrt{\frac{L}{C}}\,\frac{I(0)}{V(0)}.$$

In this case the short-circuit current is sinusoidal.

If $R = 0$, $L > 0$ and the circuit has no condenser, then instead of (31.1) we have the equation

$$Ls\bar{I} = LI(0),$$

whence

$$\bar{I} = \frac{I(0)}{s},$$

i. e.,

$$\bar{I}(t) = I(0)$$

for every $t \geqslant 0$. In this case the short-circuit current is constant.

Let us now consider the case of a circuit with a condenser but without resistance and self-induction. Equation (31.1) is then reduced to the form

$$\frac{1}{Cs}\bar{I} = \frac{V(0)}{s}.$$

We have hence

$$\bar{I} = CV(0). \tag{31.5}$$

The operator $\bar{I}$ is a number in this case. But now we can also associate a certain intuitive meaning with the short-circuit current. For this purpose we consider first a circuit with a condenser and resistance; the phenomenon is then described by equation (31.3). Fig. 6 represents

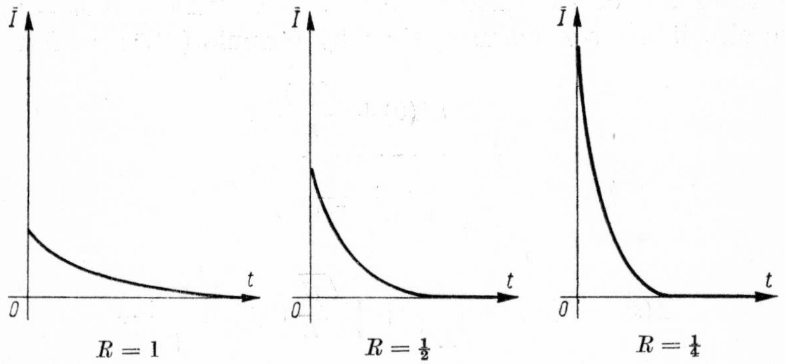

Fig. 6

the shapes of the short-circuit current for different resistances, with constant capacity and initial charge. Obviously the smaller the resistance the greater the current at the initial instant but the faster it vanishes. This is explained by the fact that with a smaller resistance the condenser is discharged more quickly. If $R = 0$, we have a short-circuit and the condenser is discharged at once, giving momentarily an infinitely great current intensity, which at once drops to zero.

In practice such conditions can be realized only approximately since every circuit has a certain (however small) resistance. Nevertheless, the generalization of the concept of short-circuit current to the case in which the active resistance R is equal to zero gives great calculatory advantages and permits a uniform treatment of all cases in calculations.

In applications, the case of $I(0)=0$ and $V(0)=0$ is important; at the instant $t=0$ no current flows and all the condensers are discharged. Then it follows from formula (31.1) that the short-circuit current is equal to zero from the beginning.

Remark. Equation (31.1) loses all meaning if $C=0$. But that case never occurs since in a circuit with a condenser we always have $C>0$, and to a circuit without a condenser corresponds the value $C=\infty$. The parts played by the constants of an electric circuit would be more symmetrical, if, instead of the capacity of the condenser, we introduced its inverse, $1/C$. However, conforming to accepted usage, we retain the traditional notation.

§ 32. Impendance. Making use of the concept of short-circuit current $\bar{I}$, we can write equation (32.1) in the form

$$\left(Ls+R+\frac{1}{Cs}\right)(I-\bar{I})=E. \tag{32.1}$$

Introducing the notation

$$Z=Ls+R+\frac{1}{Cs},$$

we can write this equation still more simply:

$$Z(I-\bar{I})=E. \tag{32.2}$$

This is the fundamental equation of the electric circuit. In the case of the short-circuit current being equal to zero, this equation is reduced to the form

$$ZI=E. \tag{32.3}$$

The operator Z will be termed the *impedance* of a given system of self-induction, resistance and capacity. The impedance Z completely characterizes the dynamic properties of the system; the short-circuit current $\bar{I}$ characterizes its initial state.

The impedance Z is in a certain sense a generalization of the impedance of the theory of sinusoidal currents, which will be discussed in the next section.

§ 33. Sine wave currents. Of great importance in applications is the case where the voltage is given by the function

$$E(t)=E_1\cos\omega t-E_2\sin\omega t,$$

or in the operational notation

$$E = \frac{E_1 s - E_2 \omega}{s^2 + \omega^2}.$$

Number ω is termed the *voltage pulsation*.

If we assume that the short-circuit current is equal to zero, we shall have the equation

$$\left(Ls + R + \frac{1}{Cs}\right) I = \frac{E_1 s - E_2 \omega}{s^2 + \omega^2}.$$

Consequently

$$(33.1) \qquad I = \frac{E_1 s - E_2 \omega}{s^2 + \omega^2} \cdot \frac{1}{Ls + R + \dfrac{1}{Cs}} = \frac{I_1 s - I_2 \omega}{s^2 + \omega^2} + \frac{As + B}{Ls^2 + Rs + \dfrac{1}{C}},$$

where the constants I_1, I_2, A and B can be determined by the usual method.

Introducing the notation

$$(33.2) \qquad I_u = \frac{I_1 s - I_2 \omega}{s^2 + \omega^2}, \qquad I_p = \frac{As + B}{Ls^2 + Rs + \dfrac{1}{C}},$$

we can write

$$I = I_u - I_p.$$

The current I_p has an analogical form to that of the short-circuit current (31.2), whence it follows that it decreases fast to zero (under the assumption that $R > 0$). Presently a sine wave current I_u will establish itself: it will be termed the *stationary current*; this current does not vanish, which is obvious at once if we write it in the ordinary form

$$I_u(t) = I_1 \cos \omega t - I_2 \sin \omega t.$$

To distinguish it, we shall term the current I_p the *transient current*.

In practice we mostly seek the stationary current only; the calculation of coefficients A and B in formula (33.1) becomes then superfluous. In order to determine I_1 and I_2 we write

$$(33.3) \qquad I_1 s - I_2 \omega + I_p (s^2 + \omega^2) = \frac{E_1 s - E_2 \omega}{Ls + R + \dfrac{1}{Cs}}.$$

This equality, which is a consequence of formulas (33.1) and (33.2), will remain valid if we replace s by any number for which the denominator in (33.3) is different from zero (see § 26). In particular, if we replace s by ωi for instance, then the coefficient of I_p will be equal to zero; dividing the whole equality by ωi we shall finally obtain

$$I_1+iI_2=\frac{E_1+iE_2}{L\omega i+R+\dfrac{1}{C\omega i}}. \tag{33.4}$$

Hence by comparing the real and the imaginary parts on both sides of the equation we can easily calculate I_1 and I_2:

$$I_1=\frac{1}{Z_0^2}\left[E_1R-E_2\left(L\omega-\frac{1}{C\omega}\right)\right],\qquad I_2=\frac{1}{Z_0^2}\left[E_1\left(L\omega-\frac{1}{C\omega}\right)+E_2R\right],$$

where

$$Z_0^2=R^2+\left(L\omega-\frac{1}{C\omega}\right)^2.$$

In applications it is more important to determine other constants, which will be discussed below.

The voltage $E(t)$ can be represented in the form

$$E(t)=E_0\cos(\omega r+\varphi),$$

where

$$E_0=\sqrt{E_1^2+E_2^2},\qquad \operatorname{tg}\varphi=\frac{E_2}{E_1};$$

the number E_0 is termed the *voltage amplitude* and φ the *voltage phase.*

Similarly we can represent the intensity $I(t)$ as

$$Iu(t)=I_0\cos(\omega t+\psi),\qquad\text{where}\qquad I_0=\sqrt{I_1^2+I_2^2},\qquad \operatorname{tg}\psi=\frac{I_2}{I_1};$$

the quantity I_0 is the *current intensity amplitude* and ψ the *current intensity phase.*

The voltage E and the current I_u are, with a given frequency, completely characterized by their amplitudes and phases.

With the above notation we have

$$E_1+iE_2=E_0e^{i\varphi},\qquad I_1=iI_2=I_0e^{i\psi};$$

we can also write

$$L\omega i+R+\frac{1}{C\omega i}=Z_0e^{i\theta},$$

where

$$Z_0=\sqrt{R^2+\left(L\omega-\frac{1}{C\omega}\right)^2},\qquad \operatorname{tg}\theta=\frac{L\omega-\dfrac{1}{C\omega}}{R}.$$

Equation (33.4) assumes the form

$$Z_0 e^{i\theta} I_0 e^{i\psi} = E_0 e^{i\varphi},$$

whence we have

$$(33.5) \qquad Z_0 I_0 = E_0, \qquad \theta + \psi = \varphi.$$

The quantity Z_0 is usually termed the *impedance* or the *apparent resistance* of the circuit in question. Since we have previously introduced the term impedance in a different sense, we shall use for Z_0 the term apparent resistance [1]. Quantity θ is termed the *phase translation.*

In order to find the amplitude of a continuous current it is sufficient to divide the amplitude by the apparent resistance. The phase of a stationary current is found by subtracting the phase translation from the voltage phase.

The application of complex numbers to the calculation of a stationary current is well known to electricians. As has been seen, this method can be deduced in an easy and natural manner from the operational calculus.

Let us observe that it would be equally useful to replace in equation (33.3) s by $-\omega i$ (instead of ωi); in that case, however, the formal calculations would differ in certain small details from the traditional calculations.

In calculating the whole current I we must also determine the transitory current I_p. From formula (33.3) we have

$$(33.6) \quad I_p = \frac{1}{(s^2+\omega^2)\left(Ls+R+\dfrac{1}{Cs}\right)} \left[E_1 s - E_2 \omega - (I_1 s - I_2 \omega)\left(Ls+R+\frac{1}{Cs}\right)\right].$$

But formula (33.4) can be written in the form

$$E_1 + iE_2 = \left(L\omega i + R + \frac{1}{C\omega i}\right)(I_1 + iI_2),$$

whence by comparing the real and the imaginary parts we obtain

$$E_1 = I_1 R - I_2\left(L\omega - \frac{1}{C\omega}\right), \qquad E_2 = I_1\left(I\omega - \frac{1}{C\omega}\right) + I_2 R.$$

---

(1) Operator Z in equation (32.3) and number Z_0 in equation (33.5) play similar roles. While, however, operator Z characterizes all the dynamic properties of a system and is applicable to currents of all kinds, number Z_0 makes it possible only to calculate the amplitude of a current with constant frequency (if we know the amplitude of the electromotive force) and neglects phase translation for instance. For these reasons impedance Z may be regarded as a generalization of the concept of apparent resistance Z_0 (Carslaw-Jaeger [1], p. 29).

Substituting in formula (33.6) we obtain after some simplifications

$$I_p = \frac{-LI_1 + \dfrac{I_2}{\omega Cs}}{Ls + R + \dfrac{1}{Cs}}.$$

The transitory current is thus identical with a short-circuit current in which the initial intensity is $-I_1$, and the initial charge on the condenser is equal to $-I_2/\omega$.

Moreover, if there exist at the instant $t = 0$ a certain initial current $I(0)$ and a charge $Q(0)$ on the condenser, then the whole current I will consist of three parts,

$$I = I_u + I_p + \bar{I},$$

the current $\bar{I}$ being given by formula (33.2).

Since the currents I_p and $\bar{I}$ are of the same nature, it suffices to calculate the stationary current I and add to it the short-circuit current corresponding to the initial intensity $I(0) - I_1$ and the charge $Q(0) - I_2/\omega$.

§ 34. Kirchhoff's laws. In forming equations for currents in electric networks we base ourselves on Kirchhoff's laws.

The first law of Kirchhoff. *At every point of a network the algebraic sum of the currents meeting at that point is equal to zero.*

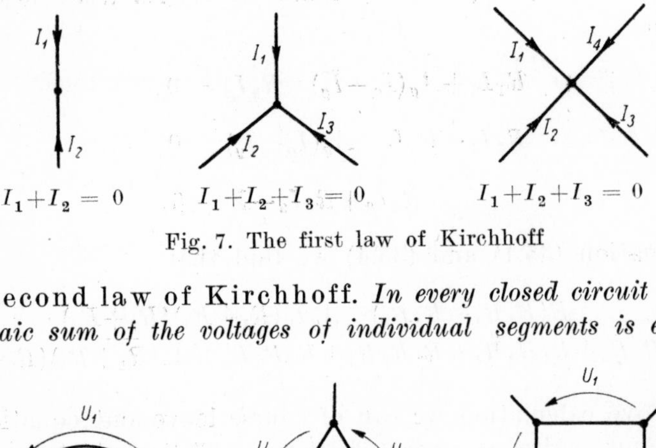

Fig. 7. The first law of Kirchhoff

The second law of Kirchhoff. *In every closed circuit of a network the algebraic sum of the voltages of individual segments is equal to zero.*

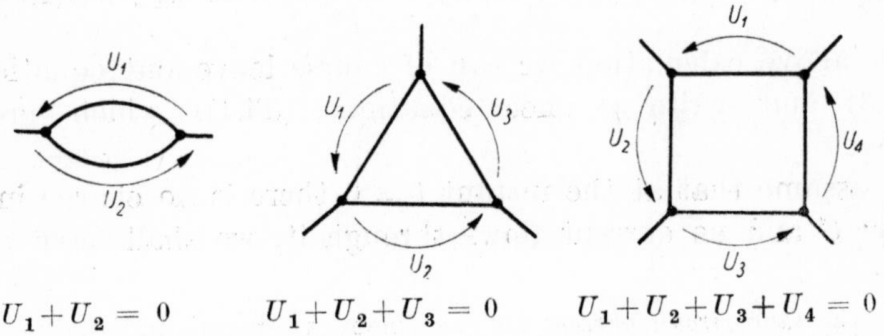

Fig. 8. The second law of Kirchhoff

§ 35. Wheatstone bridge. A simple example of the application of Kirchhoff's laws is offered by the *Wheatstone bridge*, shown in fig. 9.

On the basis of the first law of Kirchhoff we have the following equations for the nodes B, D and F:

$$I-I_1-I_2=0,\quad I_1-I_4-I_g=0,\quad I_3+I_4-I=0. \tag{35.1}$$

On the basis of the second law of Kirchhoff we have the following equations for the circuits BDH, DFH and $BHFK$:

$$U_1+U_g-U_2=0,\quad U_4-U_3-U_g=0,\quad U_2+U_3-E=0. \tag{35.2}$$

The short-circuit currents for all the segments [1] except DH, which contains a galvanometer, are equal to zero.

Thus we have the equalities

$$\begin{aligned} R_1I_1&=U_1 \qquad R_2I_2=U_2,\\ R_3I_3&=U_3, \qquad R_4I_4=U_4,\\ A_g(I_g&-\bar{I}_g)=U_g \end{aligned} \tag{35.3}$$

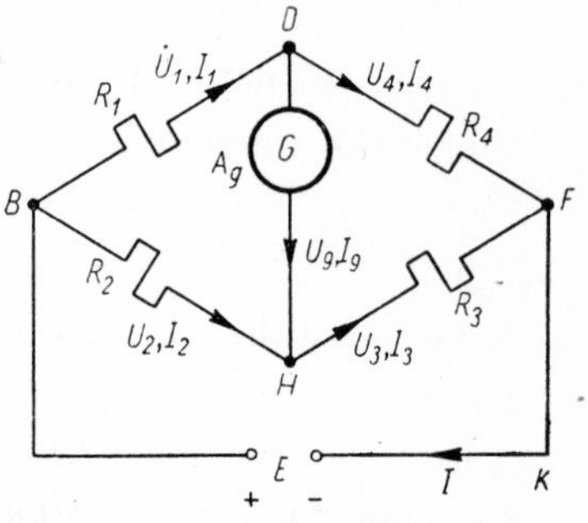

Fig. 9. Wheatstone bridge

where A_g denotes the impedance of the galvanometer G.

Substituting (35.3) in (35.2) we obtain the equations

$$\begin{aligned} R_1I_1+A_g(I_g-\bar{I}_g)-R_2I_2&=0,\\ R_4I_4-R_3I_3-A_g(I_g-\bar{I}_g)&=0,\\ R_2I_2+R_3I_3-E&=0. \end{aligned} \tag{35.4}$$

From equation (35.1) and (35.4) we find that

$$I_g=\frac{E(R_2R_4-R_1R_3)+A_g\bar{I}_g(R_1+R_4)(R_2+R_3)}{R_1R_2R_3+R_1R_2R_4+R_1R_3R_4+R_2R_3R_4+A_g(R_1+R_4)(R_2+R_3)}.$$

In the above calculation we can of course leave out equations (35.2) and (35.3) and write at once equations (35.4), which present no difficulties.

If we assume that at the instant $t=0$ there is no charge in the galvanometer G and no current flows through it, we shall have $\bar{I}_g=0$. If

(1) By the *short-circuit current* for a segment we understand the current which would flow through it on short-circuiting its terminals.

we further demand that $I_g = 0$, we shall obtain the known condition of balance

$$R_1 R_3 - R_2 R_4 = 0. \tag{35.5}$$

If we are concerned only with finding the condition of balance, we can make the calculation much shorter by assuming at once that $I_g = 0$ and $\bar{I}_g = 0$.

Then we have

$$I_1 = I_4 \quad \text{and} \quad I_2 = I_3,$$

and for the circuits BDH and DFH we have the equations

$$R_1 I_1 - R_2 I_2 = 0, \quad R_4 I_1 - R_3 I_2 = 0,$$

which, by the elimination of I_1 and I_2, immediately imply equality (35.5).

§ 36. Anderson bridge. As a further example of the application of Kirchhoff's laws we shall consider the *Anderson bridge*. It is an instrument used to measure self-induction by means of known resistances and capacities.

The diagram of the connections is given in fig. 10. The coil whose self-induction is to be measured is connected to the terminals B and D. A battery with constant voltage is connected to the terminals B and F, and the resistances R_1, R_2 and R_4 are regulated (according to the resistance R of the coil) so that the galvanometer G shows no flow of current.

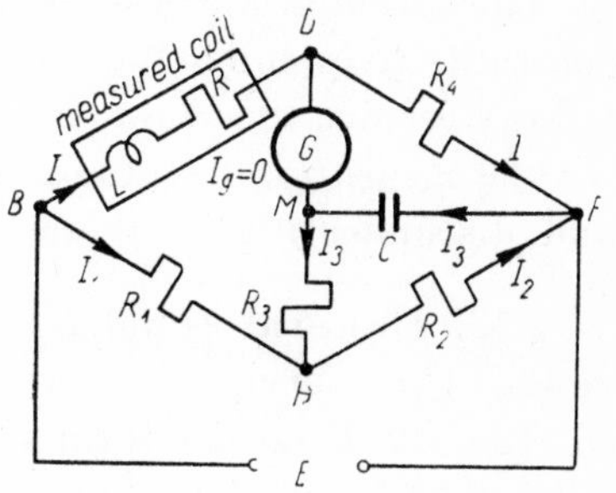

Fig. 10. Anderson bridge

Since under a constant voltage no current flows through the segment FM, the system acts as a Wheatstone bridge and we have the following equality:

$$R_1 R_4 = R R_2 = 0. \tag{36.1}$$

Let us now apply to the terminals BF an arbitrary variable electromotive force and tune the condenser so that the galvanometer shows no current. Assuming that at the instant of connection $t = 0$ there were no currents and no charges in the system (which can be attained for instance by momentarily short-circuiting the nodes B and F before applying the variable electromotive force), we have, on the basis of Kirchhoff's laws, the following equations for the node H and the circuits $BDMH$, DFM and FMH:

$$I_1 - I_2 + I_3 = 0,$$

$$(Ls+R)I + R_3 I_3 - R_1 I_1 = 0,$$

$$R_4 I + \frac{1}{Cs} I_3 = 0,$$

$$\frac{1}{Cs} I_3 + R_3 I_3 + R_2 I_2 = 0.$$

Eliminating I, I_1, I_2 and I_3 from these equations and taking into account relation (36.1) we easily obtain the equality

$$L = C\frac{R_4}{R_2}(R_1 R_2 + R_1 R_3 + R_2 R_3).$$

The calculation has been performed not only for currents with constant frequency but for arbitrary alternating currents. Hence it follows for instance that, having no source of alternating current at hand, we can measure self-induction with the aid of direct current by connecting and disconnecting it at short time intervals.

§ 37. General remarks on forming equations for network currents. The network represented in fig. 11 (corresponding for instance to the Wheatstone bridge) is composed of six segments, which are marked with the numbers 1, 2, 3, 4, 5 and 6. In order to determine the currents I_1, I_2, I_3, I_4, I_5, and I_6, flowing in the individual segments, we must form six equations.

The network has four nodes, B, D, F and H; we can form four equations for them (on the basis of the first law of Kirchoff),

$$B:\quad -I_1 - I_2 + I_6 = 0,$$

$$D:\quad I_1 - I_4 - I_5 = 0,$$

$$F:\quad -I_3 + I_4 - I_6 = 0,$$

$$H:\quad I_2 + I_3 + I_5 = 0.$$

Adding up the four equations we obtain $0 = 0$. This is understandable from the physical point of view, since the sum of the currents flowing up to the nodes must be equal to zero if no currents flow out of the system.

It follows hence that each of the four equations can be deduced from the remaining three. Consequently one of them (no matter which one) may be rejected, so that only three equations will remain.

Moreover, seven circuits can be distinguished in the network, *BDH*, *DFH*, *BHF*, *BDF*, *BDFH*, *BDHF* and *BHDF*, for which we again have seven equations (on the basis of the second law of Kirchoff). Four of them can be rejected on similar grounds as before.

Thus there remain six equations, exactly as many as there are unknowns.

Let us now consider a more complicated system (corresponding to the Anderson bridge) shown in fig. 12. We have here eight segments and consequently eight, generally different, currents.

For the five nodes, *B*, *D*, *F*, *H* and *M*, we have 5 equations, one of which can be rejected. There remain four equations. Since we have

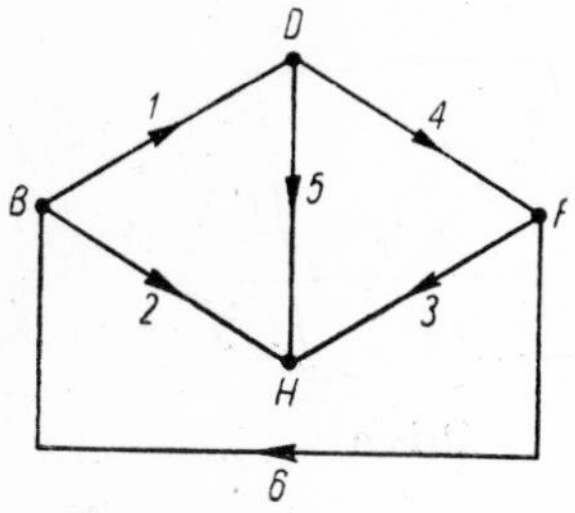

Fig. 11

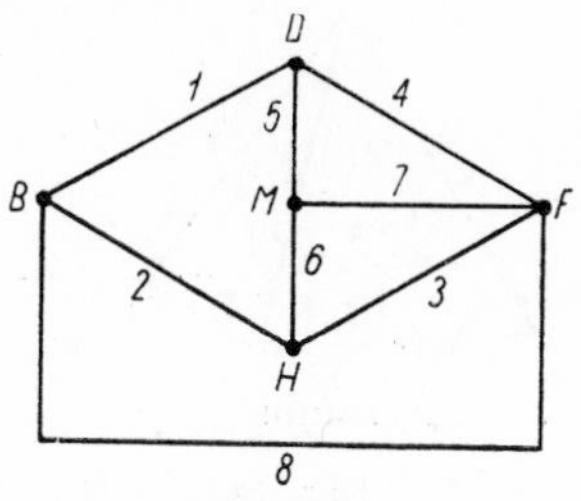

Fig. 12

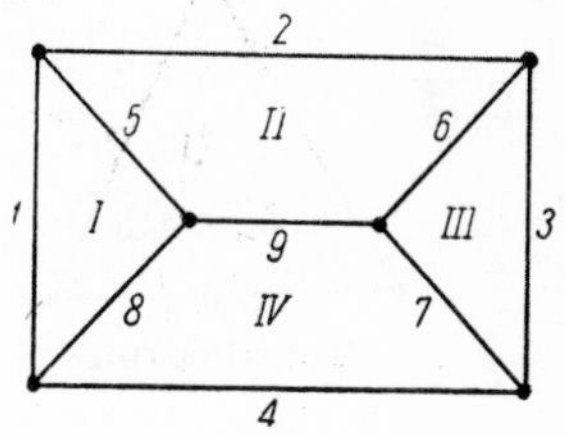

Fig. 13

eight currents to determine, four more equations are needed. Now in the system in question there are no fewer than thirteen circuits,

$$DFHM, \quad DFM, \quad FHM, \quad BHF, \quad BDF,$$
$$BDMH, \quad BDFH, \quad BDMFH, \quad BDFMH,$$
$$BHMF, \quad BDMF, \quad BDMHF, \quad BHMDF.$$

We must choose four of these circuits, but the question is which four.

For plane systems, *i. e.* those in which the wires do not cross one another, a simple hint can be given: it is sufficient to take those circuits inside which there are no wires. In our case there are four such circuits.

$$DFM, \quad FHM, \quad BDMH, \quad BHF,$$

i. e., exactly as many as are needed. This is not the only solution but in any case one of the most convenient.

Similarly as regards the system represented in fig. 13 and having six nodes we can write the equations for any five of them and four equations for the circuits I, II, III and IV. The total number of equations is then $5+4 = 9$ and is exactly equal to the number of segments.

The method described here is connected with *Euler's theorem* stating that in every polyhedron the number of vertices added to the number of sides gives the number of edges increased by 2. Indeed, any plane network (*i. e.*, a network having no intersecting wires) can be imagined as a polyhedron whose vertices are the nodes, faces the circuits and edges the segments of the network. Only those circuits that have no segments inside them should be counted as faces plus one more circuit, which has not been taken into account so far, containing all the segments of the network. To the circuits shown in figs. 11, 12 and 13 correspond the following polyhedrons: a tetrahedron, a pyramid and a prism shown in fig. 14.

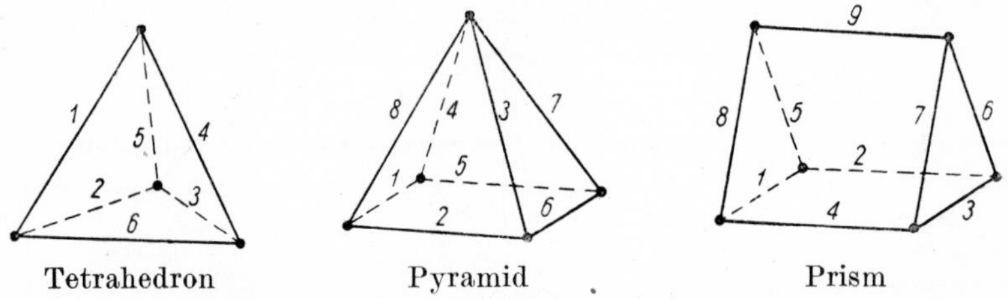

Fig. 14

There exist networks that cannot be drawn on a plane without crossing the wires. The simplest network of this kind, having nine segments, is shown in fig. 15; no polyhedron corresponds to it. In this case it is sufficient to write the equations for five of the six existing nodes and four equations for the circuits

$$ACD, \quad BCD, \quad AFDE, \quad BFDE.$$

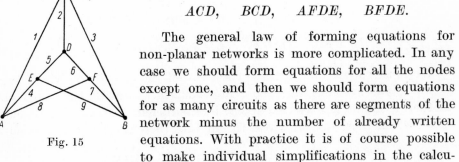

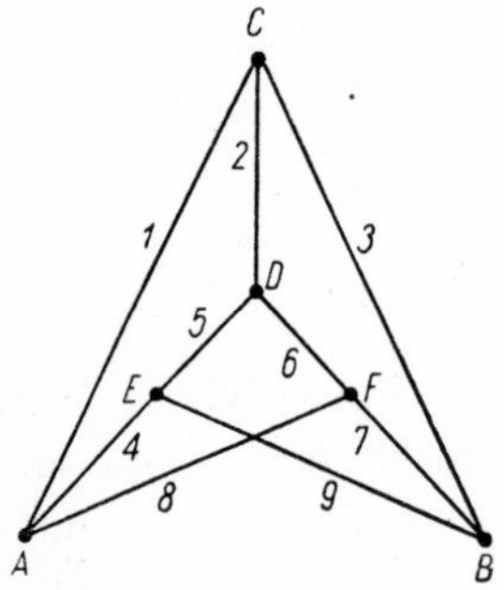

Fig. 15

The general law of forming equations for non-planar networks is more complicated. In any case we should form equations for all the nodes except one, and then we should form equations for as many circuits as there are segments of the network minus the number of already written equations. With practice it is of course possible to make individual simplifications in the calculation. It is also possible to apply any other calculation method used by electricians, for instance the method of circuit currents (Huygens' method).

Exercises.

1. Determine the current I in the systems given in figs. 16 and 17.

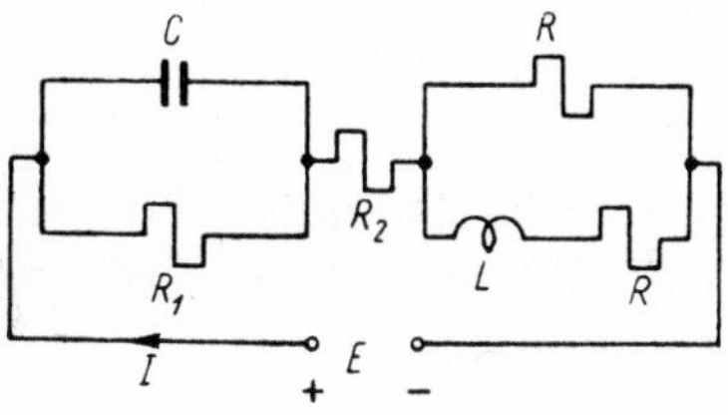

Fig. 16

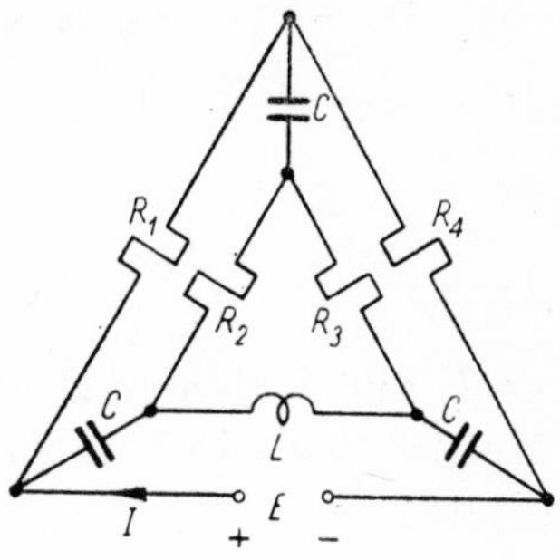

Fig. 17

2. Find the condition under which, for any alternating voltage E, the galvanometer G in the system given in fig. 18 shows no current.

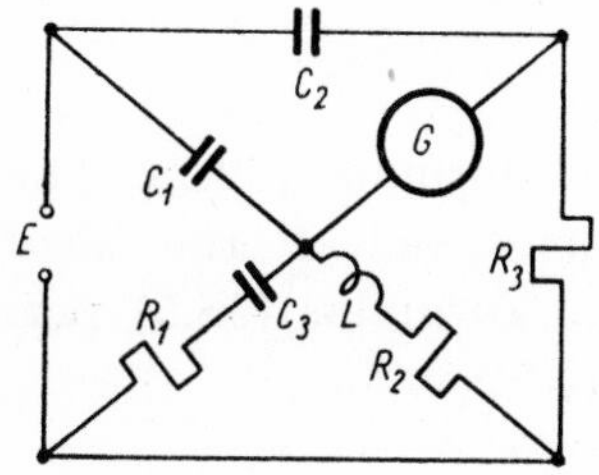

Fig. 18

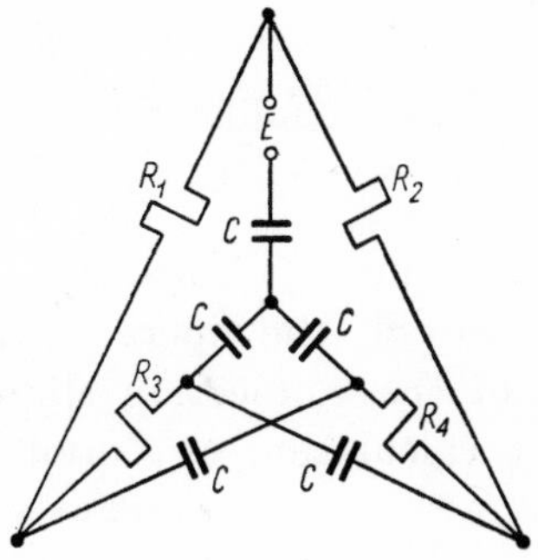

Fig. 19

3. Form the equations for the currents in the network shown in fig. 19.

§ 38. Impedance and the short-circuit current of compound two--terminal networks.

Let us term the simplest system consisting of self-induction L, resistance R and capacity C connected in series (fig. 20), an *elementary two-terminal network*; such a system has an impedance $Z = Ls+R+1/Cs$.

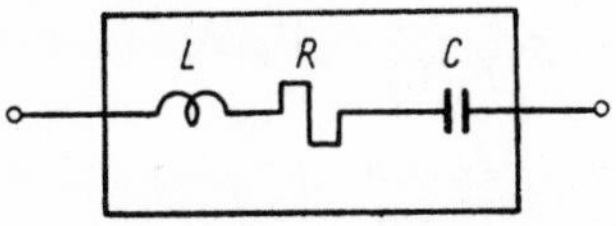

Fig. 20. An elementary two-terminal network

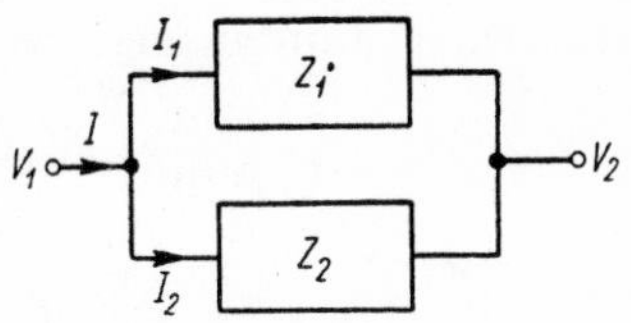

Fig. 21. A parallel connection

Let us connect in parallel two elementary two-terminal networks with impedances Z_1 and Z_2 (fig. 21). If we apply to the terminals V_1 and V_2 of the compound two-terminal network an electromotive force E, we shall have the equations

$$I = I_1 + I_2, \tag{38.1}$$

$$Z_1(I_1 - \bar{I}_1) = E, \tag{38.2}$$

$$Z_2(I_2 - \bar{I}_2) = E, \tag{38.3}$$

where $\bar{I}_1$ and $\bar{I}_2$ denote the short-circuit current in the individual systems.

Multiplying equation (38.2) by $1/Z_1$ and adding to it equation (38.3) multiplied by $1/Z_2$, we obtain by (38.1) the equality

$$I - (\bar{I}_1 + \bar{I}_2) = \left(\frac{1}{Z_1} + \frac{1}{Z_2}\right) E. \tag{38.4}$$

Introducing operators Z and $\bar{I}$, defined by the formulas

$$\frac{1}{Z} = \frac{1}{Z_1} + \frac{1}{Z_2}, \qquad \bar{I} = \bar{I}_1 + \bar{I}_2, \tag{38.5}$$

we can write equality (33.4) in the form

$$Z(I - \bar{I}) = E.$$

This formula is formally identical with formula (32.2). Thus it is natural to call the operator Z the *impedance* and $\bar{I}$ the *short-circuit current* of the connection shown in fig. 21. Formulas (38.5) permit the effective calculation of Z and $\bar{I}$; namely if we write

$$Z_1 = L_1 s + R_1 + \frac{1}{C_1 s}, \qquad Z_2 = L_2 s + R_2 + \frac{1}{C_2 s},$$

we shall have

$$Z = \frac{Z_1 Z_2}{Z_1 + Z_2} = \frac{\left(L_1 s^2 + R_1 s + \frac{1}{C_1}\right)\left(L_2 s^2 + R_2 s + \frac{1}{C_2}\right)}{s\left[\left(L_1 s^2 + R_1 s + \frac{1}{C_1}\right) + \left(L_2 s^2 + R_2 \cdot s + \frac{1}{C_2}\right)\right]}. \tag{38.6}$$

Knowing the initial current intensities $I_1(0)$ and $I_2(0)$ in the individual elementary two-terminal networks and the initial voltages $V_1(0)$ and $V_2(0)$ on their condensers, we have

$$\bar{I}_1 = \frac{L_1 I_1(0) - \frac{V_1(0)}{vs}}{L_1 s + R_1 + \frac{1}{C_1 s}}, \qquad \bar{I}_2 = \frac{L_2 I_2(0) - \frac{V_2(0)}{vs}}{L_2 s + R_2 + \frac{1}{C_2 s}},$$

and consequently

$$\bar{I} = \frac{L_1 I_1(0)s + V_1(0)}{L_1 s^2 + R_1 s + \dfrac{1}{C_1}} + \frac{L_2 I_2(0)s + V_2(0)}{L_2 s^2 + R_2 s + \dfrac{1}{C_2}}.$$

It follows from formula (38.6) that the system shown in fig. 21 can be replaced by an equivalent elementary two-terminal network only if the product of the trinomials

$$(38.7) \qquad L_1 s^2 + R_1 s + \frac{1}{C_1} \quad \text{and} \quad L_2 s^2 + R_2 s + \frac{1}{C_2}$$

is divisible by their sum.

Example. If we denote by Z the impedance of the network shown in fig. 22, we shall have

$$\frac{1}{Z} = \frac{1}{Ls+R} + \frac{1}{R_1 + \dfrac{1}{Cs}},$$

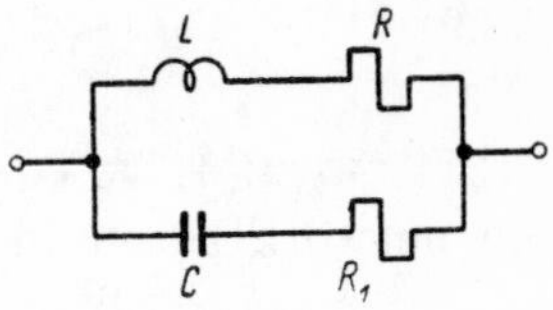

Fig. 22

whence

$$Z = \frac{LR_1 s^2 + \left(\dfrac{L}{C} + RR_1\right)s + \dfrac{R}{C}}{Ls^2 + (R+R_1)s + \dfrac{1}{C}}.$$

The numerator will be divisible by the denominator if and only if their coefficients are proportional:

$$\frac{LR_1}{L} = \frac{\dfrac{L}{C} + RR_1}{R+R_1} = \frac{R}{1}.$$

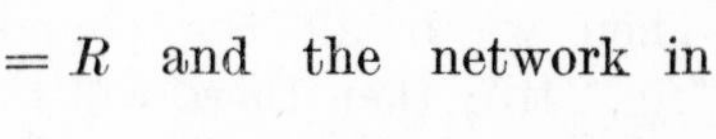

Fig. 23. Connection in series

From this condition we easily obtain

$$R_1 = R, \qquad L = CR^2.$$

When these relations hold, we have $Z = R$ and the network in question acts as a pure Ohm resistance.

Let us now connect in series two elementary two-terminal networks (fig. 23) and apply an electromotive force E to the terminals V_1 and V_2. If $\bar{I}_1$ and $\bar{I}_2$ are the short-circuit currents of the two elementary two-terminal networks, we shall have the following equation for the whole:

$$Z_1(I - \bar{I}_1) + Z_2(I - \bar{I}_2) = E,$$

i. e.,

$$(38.8)\qquad (Z_1+Z_2)\left(I-\frac{Z_1\bar{I}_1+Z_2\bar{I}_2}{Z_1+Z_2}\right)=E.$$

Introducing the notation

$$Z=Z_1+Z_2,\qquad \bar{I}=\frac{Z_1\bar{I}_1+Z_2\bar{I}_2}{Z_1+Z_2}$$

we can write

$$Z(I-\bar{I})=E.$$

In this case the impedance of the compound network is the sum of the impedances of the component elementary two-terminal networks.

If the initial currents in those networks have the values $I_1(0)$ and $I_2(0)$ and the initial voltages $V_1(0)$ and $V_2(0)$, then the formula of the short-circuit current can be written in the form

$$(38.9)\qquad \bar{I}=\frac{L_1I_1(0)+L_2I_2(0)-\frac{1}{s}\big(V_1(0)+V_2(0)\big)}{Z}.$$

EXAMPLE 1. A constant electromotive force $E=E_0/s$ is applied to the network given in fig. 24a. After a certain time interval the cur-

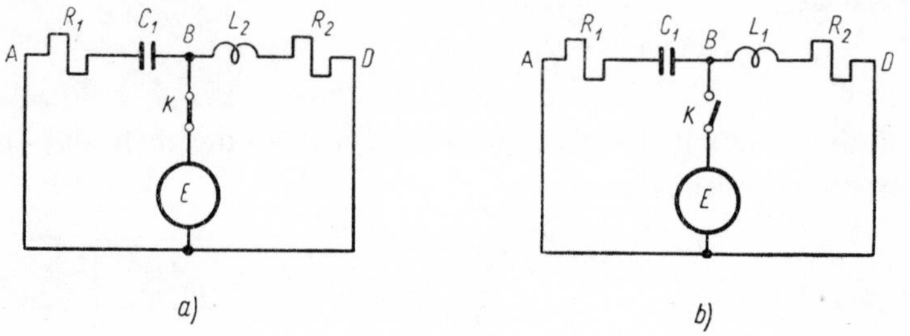

Fig. 24

rents $I_1(0)=0$ and $I_2(0)=E_0/R_2$ will be established in the segments AB and BD respectively, and a voltage E_0 will appear on the condenser. Then we break the connection at the instant $t=0$ at the point K (fig. 24b); then there will flow in the circuit a current which, in accordance with formula (38.9), has the form

$$\bar{I}=\frac{\dfrac{E_0L_2}{R_1}+\dfrac{E_0}{s}}{L_2s+(R_1+R_2)+\dfrac{1}{C_1s}}=\frac{E_0}{R_2}\cdot\frac{L_2s+R_2}{L_2s^2+(R_1+R_2)s+\dfrac{1}{C_1}}.$$

In general, a given two-terminal network is said to have *impedance* Z and *short-circuit current* $\bar{I}$ if on applying the electromotive force E (fig. 25) a current I satisfying the equation

$$Z(I-\bar{I}) = E \tag{38.10}$$

flows in it.

If the network is very complicated, then also its impedance and short-circuit current may be very complicated operators. If at the instant $t = 0$ no current flows in any segment of the network and none of its condensers is charged, then of course the short-circuit current is equal to zero and instead of equation (38.10) we shall have

$$ZI = E.$$

If we know the impedance and the short-circuit current, then we know in full all the dynamic properties of the network in question, as well as its initial state, and we can always foresee how it will behave as a whole, even if we do not know the details of its internal structure.

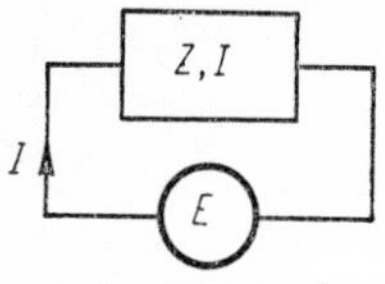

Fig. 25

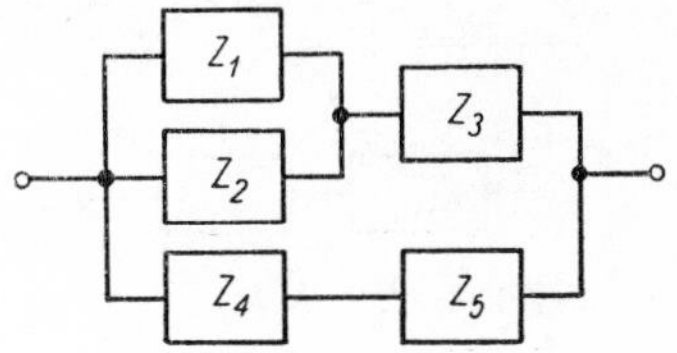

Fig. 26

Example 2. Find the impedance of the network represented in fig. 26, knowing the impedances of its individual segments.

Connecting networks 1 and 2 in parallel we have the impedance

$$\frac{Z_1 Z_2}{Z_1+Z_2},$$

the connection in series with network 3 gives the impedance

$$\frac{Z_1 Z_2}{Z_1+Z_2}+Z_3.$$

Networks 1, 2 and 3 taken as a whole are connected in parallel with networks 4 and 5, which jointly give the impedance Z_4+Z_5. It follows hence that the impedance of the whole network will have the form

$$Z = \frac{\left(\dfrac{Z_1 Z_2}{Z_1+Z_2}\right)(Z_4+Z_5)}{\dfrac{Z_1 Z_2}{Z_2+Z_1}+Z_3+Z_4+Z_5} = \frac{[Z_1 Z_2+(Z_1+Z_2)Z_3](Z_4+Z_5)}{Z_1 Z_2+(Z_1+Z_2)(Z_3+Z_4+Z_5)}.$$

Fig. 27 represents a network which is not a combination of connections in series and in parallel. To find the impedance and the short-circuit current for such a network we must start directly from Kirchhoff's laws.

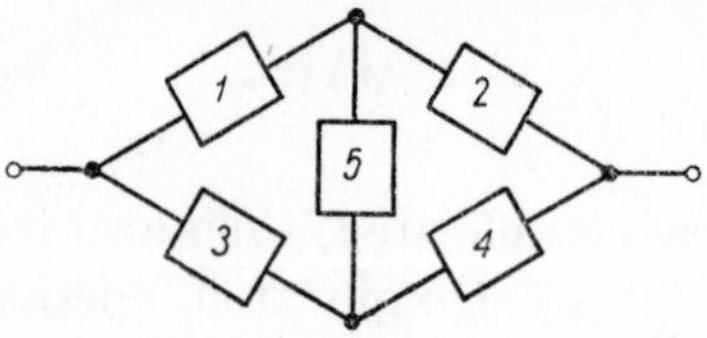

Fig. 27

Since, however, parallel connections and connections in series are particularly important, we list them in a table (fig. 28). It will be observed that the formulas given in the table are valid for any impedance, not only in elementary two-terminal networks.

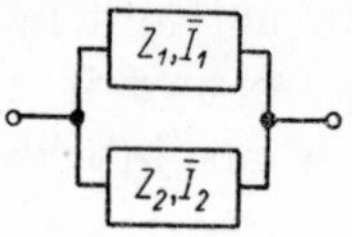	$\frac{1}{Z}=\frac{1}{Z_1}+\frac{1}{Z_2}$	$\bar{I}=\bar{I}_1+\bar{I}_2$
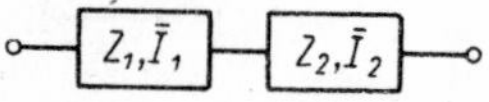	$Z=Z_1+Z_2$	$Z\bar{I}=Z_1\bar{I}_1+Z_2\bar{I}_2$

Fig. 28

Exercises.

1. Find the impedances and the short-circuit currents for the connections given in figs. 29 and 30, knowing the impedances and the short-circuit currents of the individual elements.

Fig. 29

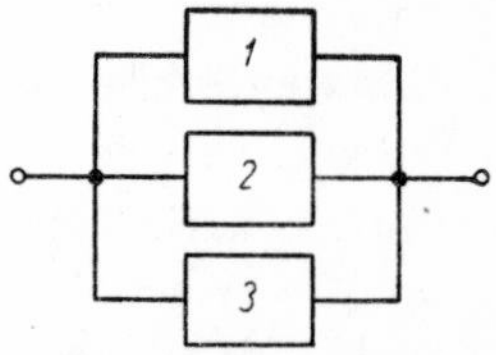

Fig. 30

2. Find the impedances of the networks given in figs. 31, 32 and 33 knowing the impedances of the individual elements.

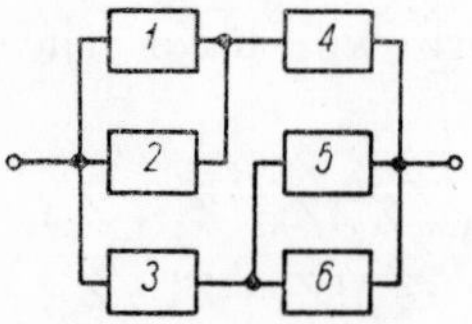

Fig. 31

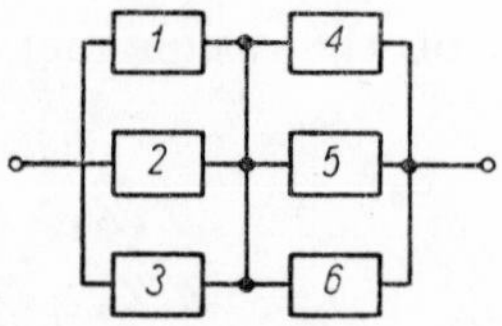

Fig. 32

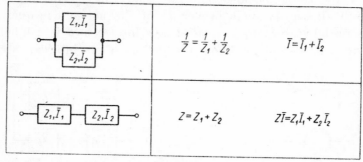

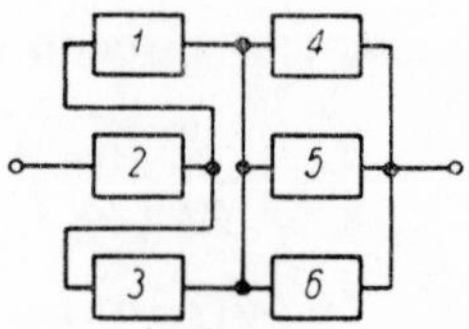

Fig. 33

3. Find the impedance of the network given in fig. 27.
4. Give a diagram having the impedance

$$Z = \frac{(s+1)(s+2)(s+3)}{s(2s+5)}.$$

Is the solution unique?

§ 39. The case of a sinusoidal electromotive force. If the electromotive force is sinusoidal,

$$E = \frac{E_1 s - E_2 \omega}{s^2+\omega^2},$$

then equation (38.10) has the form

$$Z(s)(I-\bar{I}) = \frac{E_1 s - E_2 \omega}{s^2+\omega^2}.$$

The impedance $Z = Z(s)$ is a rational expression of the operator s; the appearence of that operator in the equation will be necessary in further calculations. Namely, we have

$$I = \frac{E_1 s - E_2 \omega}{(s^2+\omega^2)Z(s)} + \bar{I}, \tag{39.1}$$

whence

$$I = I_u + I_p + \bar{I}, \tag{39.2}$$

where $I_u = \dfrac{I_1 s - I_2 \omega}{s^2+\omega^2}$, and I_p is a certain rational expression of the operator s which is assumed to have no factors of the form $s^2+\omega^2$ in the denominator.

To find the stationary current I_u we shall apply the same method as the one used in § 33. From formulas (39.1) and (39.2) we have

$$I_1 s + I_2 \omega + (I_p + \bar{I})(s^2+\omega^2) = \frac{E_1 s + E_2 \omega}{Z(s)}.$$

If we substitute in this equality the number ωi for the operator s, we shall have (on dividing by $-\omega i$)

$$I_1 + iI_2 = \frac{E_1 + iE_2}{Z(\omega i)}.$$

Introducing the notation

$$E_1 + iE_2 = E_0 e^{i\varphi}, \quad I_1 + iI_2 = I_0 e^{i\psi}, \quad Z(\omega i) = Z_0 e^{i\theta},$$

we have the relation

$$Z_0 e^{i\theta} \cdot I_0 e^{i\psi} = E_0 e^{i\varphi}.$$

This is a generalization of the calculation performed in § 33. The resistance Z_0 remains equal to the module of the complex number obtained from the impedance by replacing the operator s by the number ωi:

$$Z_0 = |Z(\omega i)|;$$

the phase translation is equal to the argument of this number:

$$\theta = \arg Z(\omega i).$$

Remark. In the above reasoning we have assumed that there are no factors $s^2+\omega^2$ in the denominator of the rational expression corresponding to the current I_p. This hypothesis is justified if we assume that there exists some, however small, resistance in each circuit of the network in question.

EXAMPLE. Find the stationary current obtained from a sine wave electromotive force with amplitude E_0 and phase φ, applied to the networks given in fig. 34.

The impedance Z of this network satisfies the relation

$$\frac{1}{Z} = \frac{1}{R_1} + \frac{1}{R_2 + \frac{1}{Cs}};$$

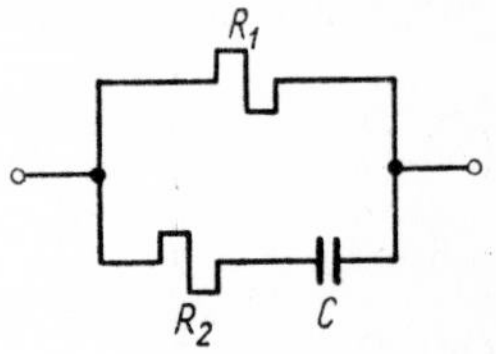

Fig. 34

consequently

$$Z = \frac{R_1(R_2Cs+1)}{(R_1+R_2)Cs+1}.$$

Hence we have the apparent resistance

$$Z_0 = \left|\frac{R_1(R_2C\omega i+1)}{(R_1+R_2)C\omega i+1}\right| = R_1\sqrt{\frac{R_2^2C^2\omega^2+1}{(R_1+R_2)^2C^2\omega^2+1}}$$

and the phase translation

$$\theta = \arg\frac{R_1(R_2C\omega i+1)}{(R_1+R_2)C\omega i+1} = -\operatorname{arctg}\frac{R_1C\omega}{R_2(R_1+R_2)C^2\omega^2+1}.$$

The current sought has the current amplitude $I_0 = E_0/Z_0$ and the phase $\psi = \varphi - \theta$.

Exercise. Find the stationary currents obtained from a sinusoidal voltage with amplitude E_0 and phase φ applied to the networks shown in figs. 35, 36 and 37.

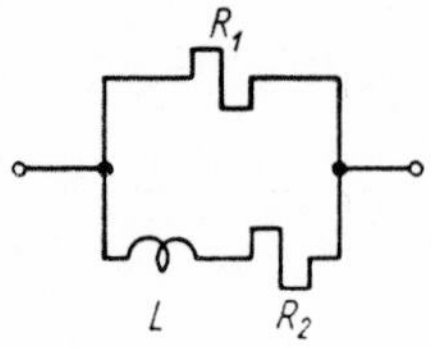

Fig. 35

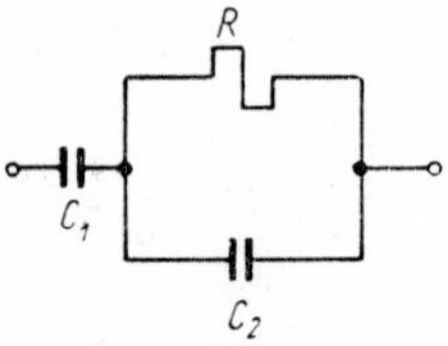

Fig. 36

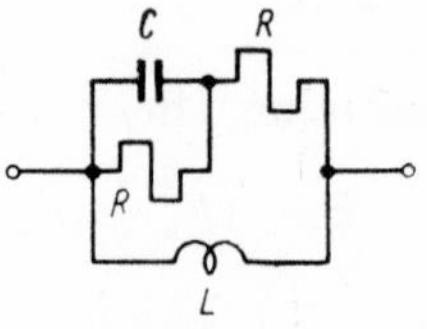

Fig. 37

§ 40. The electromotive impulse and its application to the measurement of impedance. The *electromotive impulse* is the term we shall give to the voltage $E = \{E(t)\}$ with a constant sign, lasting for a brief instant and vanishing completely. If the interval $0 < t < \varepsilon$ is the period of duration of the impulse, then $E(t) = 0$ for $t > \varepsilon$ (¹), the integral

$$\acute{E} = \int_0^\varepsilon E(t)\,dt$$

will be termed the *magnitude* of the impulse.

If $J = \{J(t)\}$ is an arbitrary function with a continuous derivative, then for $t > \varepsilon$, in virtue of the theorems on the mean value, we have

$$\int_0^\varepsilon J(t-\tau)E(\tau)\,d\tau = \int_0^\varepsilon J(t-\tau)E(\tau)\,d\tau = \acute{E}J(\xi_1) = \acute{E}J(t) - \varepsilon\acute{E}J'(\xi),$$

where $t - \varepsilon < \xi_1 < \xi < t$.

Hence it is obvious that if ε decreases to 0 and the magnitude $\acute{E}$ of the impulse is always the same, then the convolution $\int_0^t J(t-\tau)E(\tau)\,d\tau$ tends in the limit to the product $\acute{E}J(t)$. Consequently in approximate calculations EJ can always be replaced by $\acute{E}J$, the value $\acute{E}$ being regarded as a number; the absolute value of the error involved is less than $\varepsilon\acute{E}M$, where M denotes the maximum absolute value of the derivative $J'(t)$. The shorter the time ε, the smaller the error.

Number $\acute{E}$ itself may be intuitively regarded as the ideal impulse with the initial voltage $\acute{E}\cdot\infty$ which in the next instant immediately drops to zero. The concept of ideal impulse is not suited to the calculations of ordinary analysis, but can be adequately treated in the operational calculus, where to the ideal impulse corresponds a numerical operator, *i. e.*, simply a number (equal to the magnitude of the impulse). Such treatment gives considerable calculation advantages since it permits us to neglect quantities that are inessential in certain problems, such as for instance the period of duration of the impulse and its shape in the interval $0 < t < \varepsilon$.

The inverse of impedance is, with the exclusion of certain exceptional cases, a function of the variable t; *e. g.*, for an impedance $Z = Ls + R$ we have

$$\frac{1}{Z} = \frac{1}{Ls+R} = \left\{\frac{1}{L}\exp\left(-\frac{R}{L}t\right)\right\}.$$

(¹) In § 65 we shall also discuss impulses arbitrarily translated in time.

If we connect with a two-terminal network with impedance Z and short-circuit current $\bar{I} = 0$ an electromotive impulse with value $\acute{E}$, we shall obtain the current

$$I = \frac{\acute{E}}{Z};$$

from this equality we have

$$Z = \frac{\acute{E}}{I}.$$

It follows hence that the impedance of a two-terminal network can be found experimentally, without going into the details of its structure, by the measurement of the current created by the impulse $\acute{E}$. The short-circuit current $\bar{I}$ can always be reduced to zero by short-circuiting the terminals of the given network.

The *unit current* of a given two-terminal network is the term we shall apply to the current J corresponding to the impulse with the value 1. Thus

$$J = \frac{1}{Z};$$

the unit current is the inverse of the impedance.

Knowing the unit current we can foresee the shape of the current with any given voltage E. It is sufficient to form the convolution of the unit current with the given voltage

$$I = JE;$$

this is self-evident in view of the fact that the unit current is the inverse of the impedance.

Instead of measuring the unit current we can also apply to the network any constant electromotive force $E = E_0/s$. Then we have $I = E_0/sZ$ and consequently

$$J = \frac{1}{Z} = \frac{sI}{E_0}.$$

Remark. The unit current corresponds to the ideal impulse and therefore its practical measurement will always involve a certain error. The limits of that error cannot be determined theoretically: we should have to know the derivative of the unit current which is just being measured. This vicious circle can be avoided if we gradually shorten the period of duration of the impulse (retaining its value) until the current we are measuring ceases to change. Then the theoretical error will be within the limits of the measurement error.

§ 41. Inductive couplings. Equation (32.2) is valid only if no outside induction influences act upon the given two-terminal network. If, however, we consider two circuits coupled inductively with each other (fig. 38), then in the corresponding equations we must add the expressions MI_2' and MI_1', M being the natural induction coefficient of the circuits, to the electromotive forces E_1 and E_2. Since $I_2' = sI_2 - I_2(0)$ and $I_1' = sI_1 - I_1(0)$, we shall have the equations

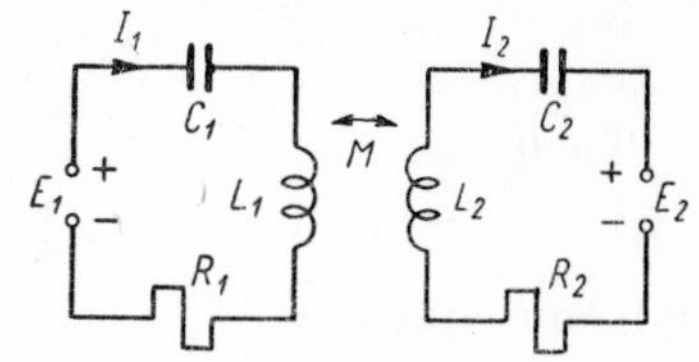

Fig. 38. Inductively coupled circuits

(41.1)
$$Z_1(I_1 - \bar{I}_1) - MsI_2 = E_1 - MI_2(0),$$
$$-MsI_1 + Z_2(I_2 - \bar{I}_2) = -E_2 - MI_1(0),$$

where

(41.2)
$$Z_1 = L_1 s + R_1 + \frac{1}{C_1 s}, \qquad Z_2 = L_2 s + R_2 + \frac{1}{C_2 s},$$
$$Z_1 \bar{I}_1 = L_1 I_1(0) - \frac{V_1(0)}{vs}, \qquad Z_2 \bar{I}_2 = L_2 I_2(0) - \frac{V_2(0)}{vs}.$$

In the case of $I_1(0) = I_2(0) = 0$ and $V_1(0) = V_2(0) = 0$, equations (41.1) are reduced to the form

(41.3)
$$Z_1 I_1 - MsI_2 = E_1,$$
$$-MsI_1 + Z_2 I_2 = -E_2.$$

Solving system (41.3) we shall have

$$I_1 = \frac{E_1 Z_2 - E_2 Ms}{Z_1 Z_2 - M^2 s^2}, \qquad I_2 = \frac{E_1 Ms - E_2 Z_1}{Z_1 Z_2 - M^2 s^2}.$$

If we substitute the values (41.1) and multiply the numerators and the denominators by s^2, the currents I_1 and I_2 will be expressed as quotients of the polynomials of the operator s. Theoretically there are no difficulties in passing to the ordinary, non-operational form, but in order to decompose the denominators into factors we must solve an algebraical equation of the fourth degree.

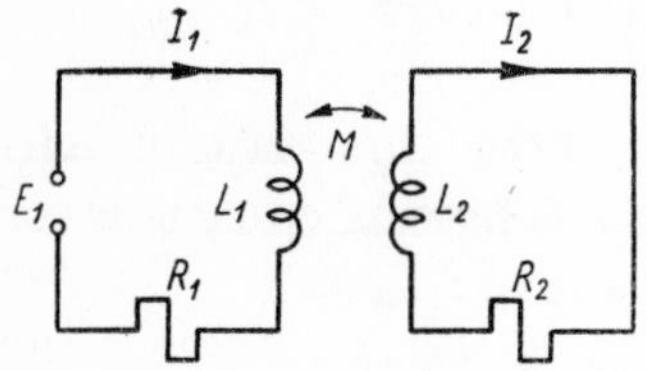

Fig. 39

The problem is simplified in the particular case where both circuits under consideration are without condensers. For example, let us calculate the current I_2 on the assumption that the electromotive force E_1

is constant and the circuit is closed without an electromotive force (fig. 39):

$$E_1 = \frac{E_0}{s}, \qquad E_2 = 0.$$

Then

$$Z_1 = L_1 s + R_1, \qquad Z_2 = L_2 s + R_2,$$

and consequently

$$I_2 = \frac{E_0 M}{(L_1 s + R_1)(L_2 s + R_2) - M^2 s^2} = \frac{E_0 M}{(L_1 L_2 - M^2)(\lambda_1 - \lambda_2)} \left(\frac{1}{s - \lambda_1} - \frac{1}{s - \lambda_2} \right),$$

where λ_1 and λ_2 are the roots of the equation

$$(L_1 \lambda + R_1)(L_2 \lambda + R_2) - M^2 \lambda^2 = 0.$$

Writing this equation in the form

$$(L_1 L_2 - M^2)\lambda^2 + (L_1 R_2 + L_2 R_1)\lambda + R_1 R_2 = 0$$

we see that both roots are real and negative because the discriminant is positive (on the assumption that $M > 0$, $R_1 > 0$ and $R_2 > 0$):

$$(L_1 R_2 + L_2 R_1)^2 - 4(L_1 L_2 - M^2) R_1 R_2 = (L_1 R_2 - L_2 R_1)^2 + 4 M^2 R_1 R_2 > 0.$$

Thus finally

$$I_2(t) = \frac{-E_0 M}{(L_1 L_2 - M^2)(\lambda_1 - \lambda_2)} (e^{\lambda_1 t} - e^{\lambda_2 t}).$$

In an electric network individual parts may be related in various ways by inductive couplings. For example, let us consider the network shown in fig. 40. We have here three inductive couplings, whose coefficients are denoted by the letters M_1, M_2 and M_3.

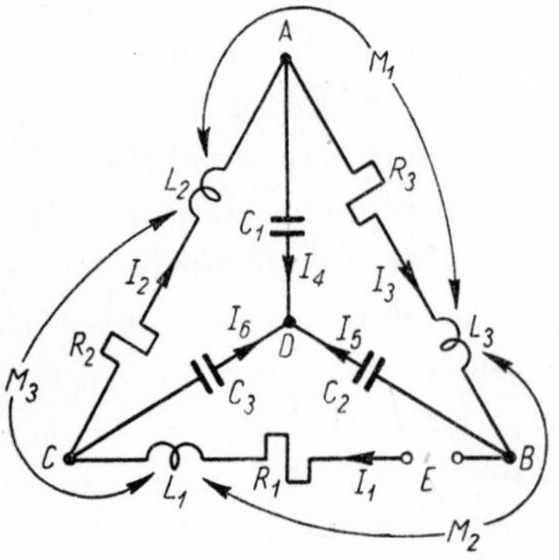

Fig. 40

On the basis of the first law of Kirchhoff we have the following equations for the nodes A, B and C:

$$I_2 - I_3 - I_4 = 0,$$

$$I_3 - I_1 - I_5 = 0,$$

$$I_1 - I_2 - I_6 = 0.$$

By the second law of Kirchhoff, taking into account the inductive couplings we have the following equations for the circuits *BCD*, *DAC* and *ABD*:

$$(L_1s+R_1)(I_1-\bar{I}_1)+M_3sI_2+M_2sI_3+\frac{1}{C_3s}(I_6-\bar{I}_6)-\frac{1}{C_2s}(I_5-\bar{I}_5)$$
$$=E+M_3I_2(0)+M_2I_3(0),$$

$$(L_2s+R_2)(I_2-\bar{I}_2)+M_1sI_3+M_3sI_1+\frac{1}{C_1s}(I_4-\bar{I}_4)-\frac{1}{C_3s}(I_6-\bar{I}_6)$$
$$=M_1I_3(0)+M_3I_1(0),$$

$$(L_3s+R_3)(I_3-\bar{I}_3)+M_2sI_1+M_1sI_2+\frac{1}{C_2s}(I_5-\bar{I}_5)-\frac{1}{C_1s}(I_4-\bar{I}_4)$$
$$=M_2I_1(0)+M_1I_2(0).$$

The solution of these six equations would of course be troublesome and uninteresting; the example has been given only to illustrate the method of forming equations in the case where several inductive couplings exist.

Exercise. Find the currents in the diagrams given in figs 41 and 42 assuming that the initial conditions are zero.

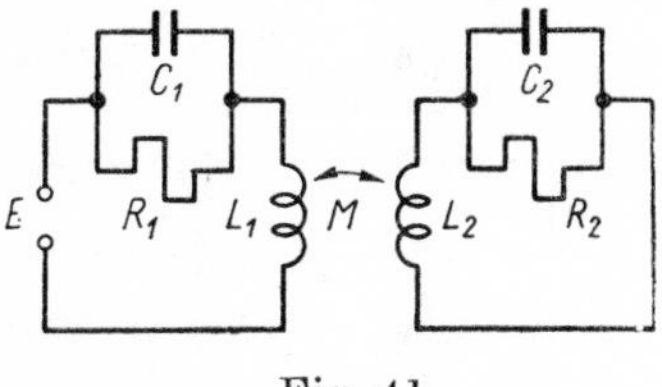

Fig. 41

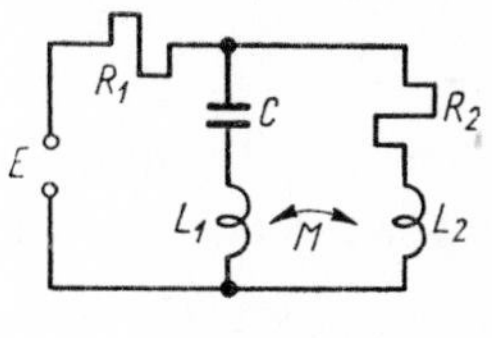

Fig. 42

§ 42. Four-terminal networks. The diagram given in fig. 38 (p. 75) is an example of a *four-terminal* network. We have here two input wires, to which an electromotive force E_1 is applied, and two output wires, to which an electromotive force E_2 is applied. If we assume the initial conditions to be zero, the properties of this network are characterized by equations (41.3). Solving those equations with respect to E_1 and I_1 we have

$$E_1=\left(\frac{Z_1}{Ms}E_2+\frac{Z_1Z_2}{Ms}-Ms\right)I_2,\qquad I_1=\frac{1}{Ms}E_2+\frac{Z_2}{Ms}I_2.$$

Generally, a *four-terminal network* is the term given to every electric system provided with two input and two output wires (fig. 43) which transforms E_1, I_1 into E_2, I_2 according to the formulas

$$E_1 = A_{11}E_2 + A_{12}I_2, \qquad (42.1)$$
$$I_1 = A_{21}E_2 + A_{22}I_2,$$

where A_{11}, A_{12}, A_{21} and A_{22} are certain operators.

Every four-terminal network is characterized by a matrix

$$\begin{bmatrix} A_{11} & A_{12} \\ A_{21} & A_{22} \end{bmatrix}.$$

The simplest four-terminal network is a *direct connection* of the wires (fig. 44). In this case

$$E_1 = E_2 + 0\cdot I_2, \qquad I_1 = 0\cdot E_1 + I_2,$$

consequently to this four-terminal network corresponds the matrix

$$\begin{bmatrix} 1 & 0 \\ 0 & 1 \end{bmatrix}.$$

This matrix is termed a *unit matrix*; it characterized a four-terminal network which causes no change of either voltage or intensity.

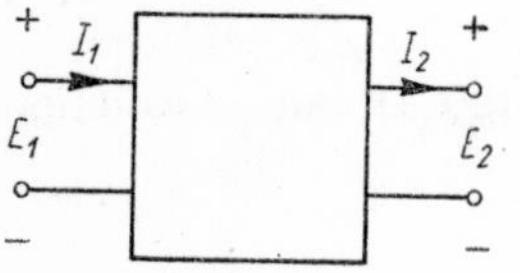

Fig. 43

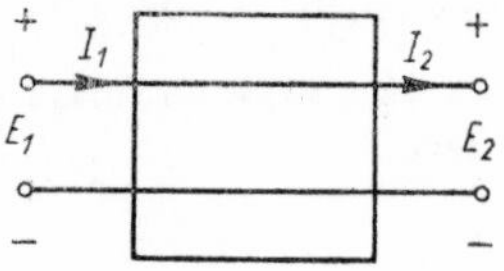

Fig. 44

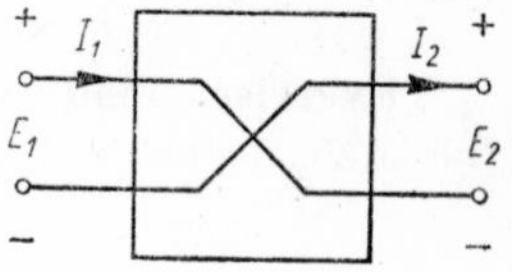

Fig. 45

Another four-terminal network is an intersection of the wires (fig. 45), for which we have the equations

$$E_1 = -E_2 + 0\cdot I_2, \qquad I_1 = 0\cdot E_2 - I_2.$$

The matrix of this network has the form

$$\begin{bmatrix} -1 & 0 \\ 0 & -1 \end{bmatrix}.$$

An important type of a four-terminal network is shown in figs 46 and 47. With one of their wires a system with an arbitrary impedance Z is connected.

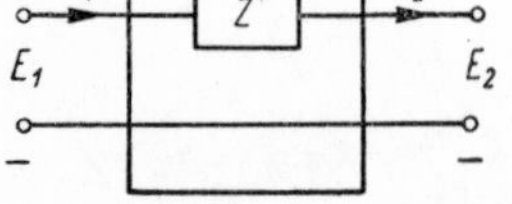

Fig. 46

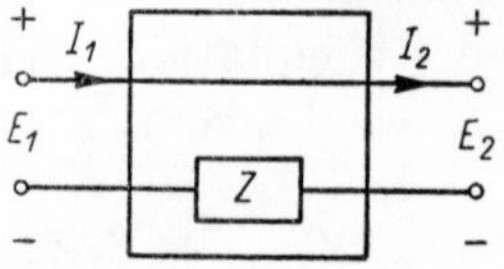

Fig. 47

In both cases (the initial conditions being zero) we have the equations

$$E_1 = E_2 + ZI_2,$$
$$I_1 = 0 \cdot E_2 + I_2;$$

consequently these networks have the matrix

$$\begin{bmatrix} 1 & Z \\ 0 & 1 \end{bmatrix}.$$

Another important type of a four-terminal network is shown in fig. 48. A system with impedance Z has been connected between two parallel conductors. In this case (the initial conditions being zero) we have the equations

$$E_1 = E_2, \qquad (I_1 - I_2)Z = E_1.$$

Hence we have the relations

$$E_1 = E_2 + 0 \cdot I_2, \qquad I = \frac{E_2}{Z} + I_2,$$

and the matrix of the network is

$$\begin{bmatrix} 1 & 0 \\ 1/Z & 1 \end{bmatrix}.$$

For a four-terminal network which is a simple inductive coupling (fig. 49) we have the equations

$$L_1 s I_1 - M s I_2 = E_1,$$
$$-M s I_1 + L_2 s I_2 = -E_2,$$

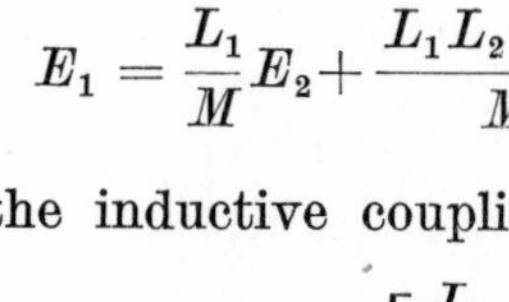

Fig. 48

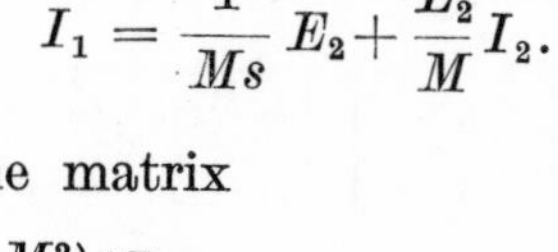

Fig. 49

whence

$$E_1 = \frac{L_1}{M} E_2 + \frac{L_1 L_2 - M^2}{M} s I_2, \quad I_1 = \frac{1}{Ms} E_2 + \frac{L_2}{M} I_2.$$

Thus the inductive coupling has the matrix

$$\begin{bmatrix} \dfrac{L_1}{M} & \dfrac{(L_1 L_2 - M^2)s}{M} \\ \dfrac{1}{Ms} & \dfrac{L_2}{M} \end{bmatrix}.$$

The most important simple four-terminal networks are given in a table at the end of the book.

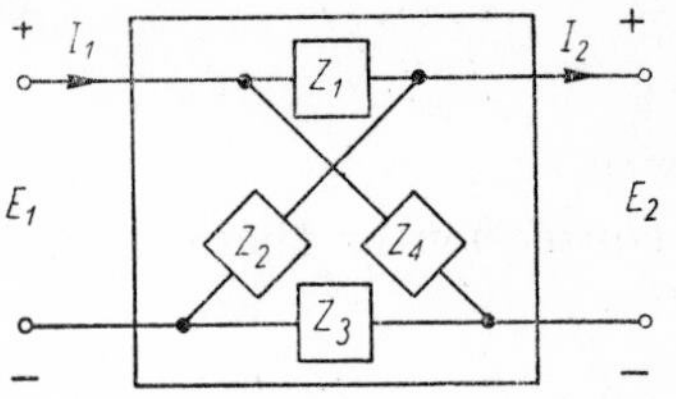

Fig. 50

Exercises.

1. The determinant $\begin{vmatrix} A_{11} & A_{12} \\ A_{21} & A_{22} \end{vmatrix}$ is termed the *determinant of the matrix* $\begin{pmatrix} A_{11} & A_{12} \\ A_{21} & A_{22} \end{pmatrix}$. Verify that the determinants of all the matrices discussed above are equal to 1.

2. Show that to the network shown in fig. 50 corresponds the matrix

$$\begin{bmatrix} \dfrac{(Z_1+Z_2)(Z_3+Z_4)}{Z_2Z_4-Z_1Z_3} & \dfrac{(Z_1+Z_2)Z_3Z_4+Z_1Z_2(Z_3+Z_4)}{Z_3Z_4-Z_1Z_3} \\ \dfrac{Z_1+Z_2+Z_3+Z_4}{Z_2Z_4-Z_1Z_3} & \dfrac{(Z_1+Z_4)(Z_2+Z_3)}{Z_2Z_4-Z_1Z_3} \end{bmatrix}.$$

Verify that the determinant of this matrix is equal to 1.

§ 43. Connecting four-terminal networks. Two four-terminal networks are connected as in fig. 51.

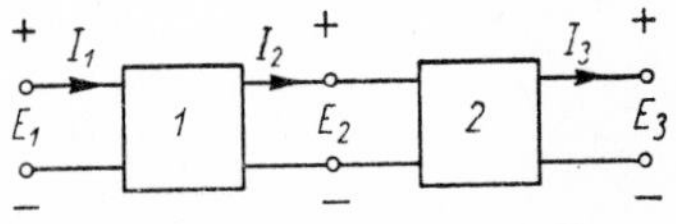

Fig. 51. Connection of two four-terminal networks

If

$$\begin{bmatrix} A_{11} & A_{12} \\ A_{21} & A_{22} \end{bmatrix} \quad \text{and} \quad \begin{bmatrix} B_{11} & B_{12} \\ B_{21} & B_{22} \end{bmatrix} \tag{43.1}$$

are the matrices of those networks, we have the relations

$$E_1 = A_{11}E_2+A_{12}I_2, \qquad E_2 = B_{11}E_3+B_{12}I_3,$$
$$I_1 = A_{21}E_2+A_{22}I_2, \qquad I_2 = B_{21}E_3+B_{22}I_3.$$

Eliminating E_2 and I_2 from these equations we obtain the relations

$$E_1 = (A_{11}B_{11}+A_{12}B_{21})E_3+(A_{11}B_{12}+A_{12}B_{22})I_3,$$
$$I_2 = (A_{21}B_{11}+A_{22}B_{21})E_3+(A_{21}B_{12}+A_{22}B_{22})I_3.$$

Obviously the system of the two networks can be regarded as a new four-terminal network with the matrix

$$\begin{bmatrix} A_{11}B_{11}+A_{12}B_{21} & A_{11}B_{12}+A_{12}B_{22} \\ A_{21}B_{11}+A_{22}B_{21} & A_{21}B_{12}+A_{22}B_{22} \end{bmatrix}. \tag{43.2}$$

Matrix (43.2) is termed the *product of matrices* (43.1), and we write

$$\begin{bmatrix} A_{11} & A_{12} \\ A_{21} & A_{22} \end{bmatrix} \begin{bmatrix} B_{11} & B_{12} \\ B_{21} & B_{22} \end{bmatrix} = \begin{bmatrix} A_{11}B_{11}+A_{12}B_{21} & A_{11}B_{12}+A_{12}B_{22} \\ A_{21}B_{11}+A_{22}B_{21} & A_{21}B_{12}+A_{22}B_{22} \end{bmatrix}.$$

According to this formula a multiplication of two matrices is performed as follows:

I. The elements of the first line of the first matrix are multiplied by the elements of the first column of the second matrix and the sum is written in the top left-hand corner of the product matrix;

II. The elements of the first line of the first matrix are multiplied by the elements of the second column of the second matrix and the sum is written in the top right-hand corner of the product matrix;

III. The elements of the second line of the first matrix are multiplied by the elements of the first column of the second matrix and the sum is written in the bottom left-hand corner of the product matrix;

IV. The elements of the second line of the first matrix are multiplied by the elements of the second column of the second matrix and the sum is written in the bottom right-hand corner of the product matrix.

To be brief, although not very exact, we can say that *in multiplying matrices we multiply lines by columns.*

EXAMPLES.

1. 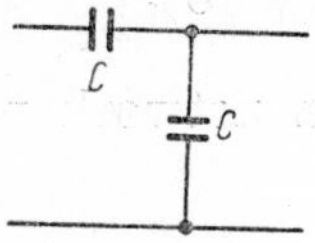

$$\begin{bmatrix}1 & \frac{1}{Cs}\\ 0 & 1\end{bmatrix}\begin{bmatrix}1 & 0\\ Cs & 1\end{bmatrix}=\begin{bmatrix}2 & \frac{1}{Cs}\\ Cs & 1\end{bmatrix};$$

2. 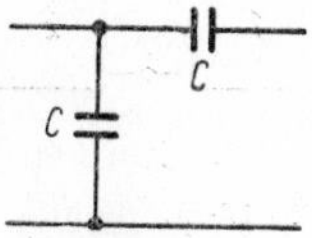

$$\begin{bmatrix}1 & 0\\ Cs & 1\end{bmatrix}\begin{bmatrix}1 & \frac{1}{Cs}\\ 0 & 1\end{bmatrix}=\begin{bmatrix}1 & \frac{1}{Cs}\\ Cs & 2\end{bmatrix};$$

3. 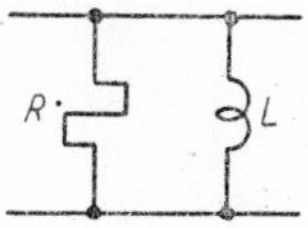

$$\begin{bmatrix}1 & 0\\ \frac{1}{R} & 1\end{bmatrix}\begin{bmatrix}1 & 0\\ \frac{1}{Ls} & 1\end{bmatrix}=\begin{bmatrix}1 & 0\\ \frac{1}{Ls}+\frac{1}{R} & 1\end{bmatrix};$$

4. 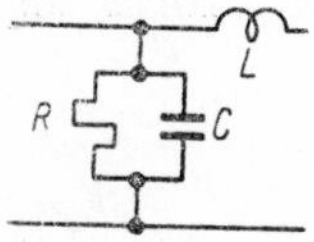

$$\begin{bmatrix}1 & 0\\ \frac{1}{Z} & 1\end{bmatrix}\begin{bmatrix}1 & Ls\\ 0 & 1\end{bmatrix}=\begin{bmatrix}1 & Ls\\ \frac{1}{Z} & \frac{Ls}{Z}+1\end{bmatrix};$$

the operator Z denotes impedance for a system of resistance and condenser. On the basis of the first formula of (38.5) we have

$$\frac{1}{Z}=\frac{1}{R}+Cs.$$

Consequently the matrix of the whole network given in example 4 can be written in the form

$$\begin{bmatrix} 1 & Ls \\ \dfrac{1}{R}+Cs & LCs^2+\dfrac{L}{R}s+1 \end{bmatrix}.$$

Exercise. Find the following four-terminal networks by the method of multiplying matrices:

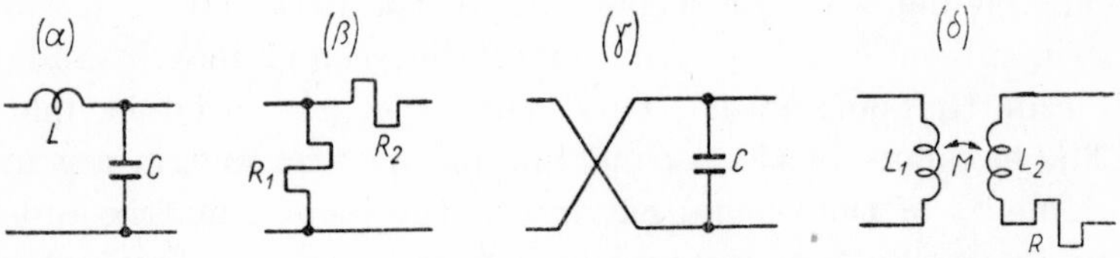

§ 44. Connections of three four-terminal networks. Suppose that we connect three four-terminal networks (fig. 52) with matrices

$$\begin{bmatrix} A_{11} & A_{12} \\ A_{21} & A_{22} \end{bmatrix}, \quad \begin{bmatrix} B_{11} & B_{12} \\ B_{21} & B_{22} \end{bmatrix}, \quad \begin{bmatrix} C_{11} & C_{12} \\ C_{21} & C_{22} \end{bmatrix}.$$

Networks *1* and *2* taken together form of a network whose matrix is the product

$$\begin{bmatrix} A_{11} & A_{12} \\ A_{21} & A_{22} \end{bmatrix} \begin{bmatrix} B_{11} & B_{12} \\ B_{21} & B_{22} \end{bmatrix};$$

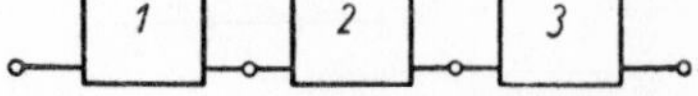

Fig. 52. Connection of three four-terminal networks

this network is connected with network *3*, whence the matrix of the whole arrangement will be the product

$$\begin{bmatrix} A_{11} & A_{12} \\ A_{21} & A_{22} \end{bmatrix} \begin{bmatrix} B_{11} & B_{12} \\ B_{21} & B_{22} \end{bmatrix} \begin{bmatrix} C_{11} & C_{12} \\ C_{21} & C_{22} \end{bmatrix}. \tag{44.1}$$

But we can reason differently. Networks *2* and *3* form together a four-terminal network with the matrix

$$\begin{bmatrix} B_{11} & B_{12} \\ B_{21} & B_{22} \end{bmatrix} \begin{bmatrix} C_{11} & C_{12} \\ C_{21} & C_{22} \end{bmatrix}.$$

This network is preceded by network *1*, whence the matrix of the whole arrangement can be written in the form

$$\begin{bmatrix} A_{11} & A_{12} \\ A_{21} & A_{22} \end{bmatrix} \left(\begin{bmatrix} B_{11} & B_{12} \\ B_{21} & B_{22} \end{bmatrix} \begin{bmatrix} C_{11} & C_{12} \\ C_{21} & C_{22} \end{bmatrix} \right). \tag{44.2}$$

The products (44.1) and (44.2) represent the matrix of the same network, consisting of elements *1*, *2* and *3*, *i. e.*, they must be equal:

$$\left(\begin{bmatrix} A_{11} & A_{12} \\ A_{21} & A_{22} \end{bmatrix}\begin{bmatrix} B_{11} & B_{12} \\ B_{21} & B_{22} \end{bmatrix}\right)\begin{bmatrix} C_{11} & C_{12} \\ C_{21} & C_{22} \end{bmatrix} = \begin{bmatrix} A_{11} & A_{12} \\ A_{21} & A_{22} \end{bmatrix}\left(\begin{bmatrix} B_{11} & B_{12} \\ B_{21} & B_{22} \end{bmatrix}\begin{bmatrix} C_{11} & C_{12} \\ C_{21} & C_{22} \end{bmatrix}\right).$$

This equality expresses the associativity of a product of matrices. It can also be proved directly by performing the multiplications according to the rule given in the preceding section. Owing to associativity we can write a product of three matrices without indicating the successive order of the operations:

$$\begin{bmatrix} A_{11} & A_{12} \\ A_{21} & A_{22} \end{bmatrix}\begin{bmatrix} B_{11} & B_{12} \\ B_{21} & B_{22} \end{bmatrix}\begin{bmatrix} C_{11} & C_{12} \\ C_{21} & C_{22} \end{bmatrix}.$$

It will be observed that *the matrix product does not satisfy the law of commutativity*, *i. e.*, that on the whole we cannot change the order of the matrices appearing in the product without affecting the result of the operation. This follows from examples 1 and 2, discussed in the preceding section.

EXAMPLES.

1. 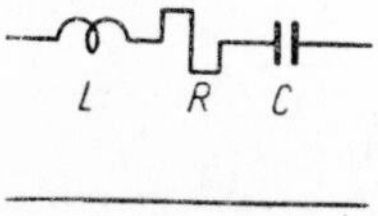

$$\begin{bmatrix} 1 & Ls \\ 0 & 1 \end{bmatrix}\begin{bmatrix} 1 & R \\ 0 & 1 \end{bmatrix}\begin{bmatrix} 1 & \frac{1}{Cs} \\ 0 & 1 \end{bmatrix} = \begin{bmatrix} 1 & Ls+R+\frac{1}{Cs} \\ 0 & 1 \end{bmatrix};$$

2. 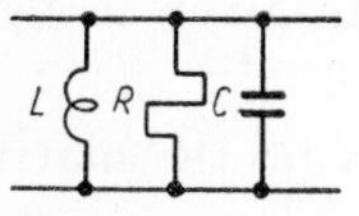

$$\begin{bmatrix} 1 & 0 \\ \frac{1}{Ls} & 1 \end{bmatrix}\begin{bmatrix} 1 & 0 \\ \frac{1}{R} & 1 \end{bmatrix}\begin{bmatrix} 1 & 0 \\ Cs & 1 \end{bmatrix} = \begin{bmatrix} 1 & 0 \\ \frac{1}{Ls}+\frac{1}{R}+Cs & 1 \end{bmatrix};$$

3. 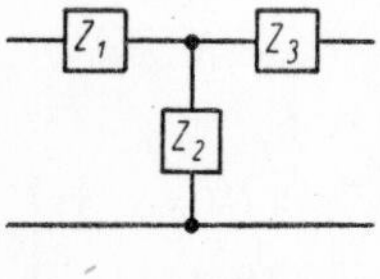

$$\begin{bmatrix} 1 & Z_1 \\ 0 & 1 \end{bmatrix}\begin{bmatrix} 1 & 0 \\ \frac{1}{Z_2} & 1 \end{bmatrix}\begin{bmatrix} 1 & Z_3 \\ 0 & 1 \end{bmatrix} = \begin{bmatrix} 1+\frac{Z_1}{Z_2} & Z_1+Z_3+\frac{Z_1Z_3}{Z_2} \\ \frac{1}{Z_1} & 1+\frac{Z_3}{Z_2} \end{bmatrix};$$

4. 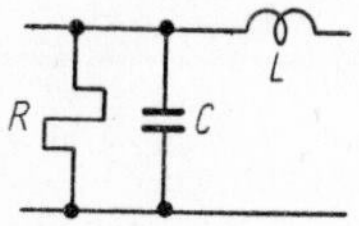

$$\begin{bmatrix} 1 & 0 \\ \frac{1}{R} & 1 \end{bmatrix}\begin{bmatrix} 1 & 0 \\ Cs & 1 \end{bmatrix}\begin{bmatrix} 1 & Ls \\ 0 & 1 \end{bmatrix} = \begin{bmatrix} 1 & Ls \\ \frac{1}{R}+Cs & LCs^2+\frac{L}{R}s+1 \end{bmatrix}.$$

The network given in example 4 is in fact identical with the network in example 4 of the preceding section. In both cases we have obtained the same result, although the calculation has followed different lines.

Exercise. Calculate the following four-terminal networks by the method of multiplying matrices:

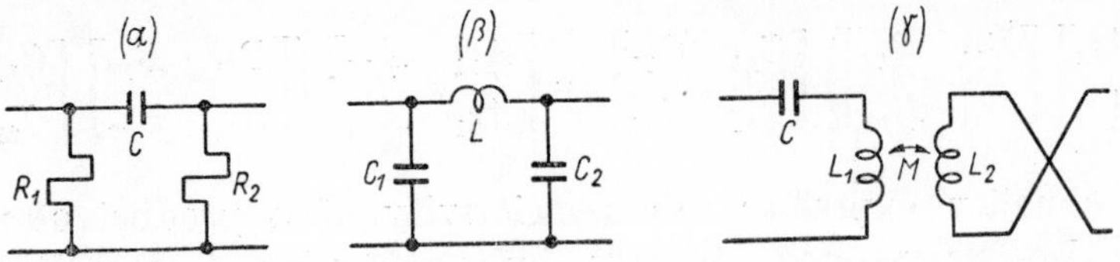

§ 45. Four-terminal networks with short-circuited terminals. If the terminals of a four-terminal network are short-circuited (fig. 55), we have $E = 0$ and from equations (42.1) we obtain

$$\frac{A_{12}}{A_{22}} I_1 = E_1.$$

Thus a four-terminal network with short-circuited terminals may be regarded as a two-terminal network.

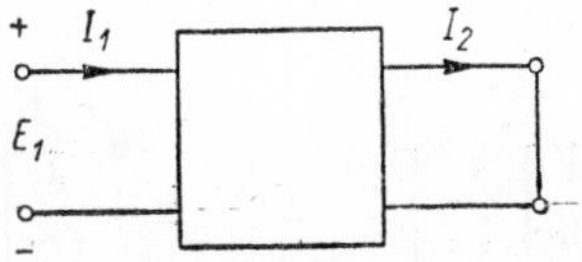

Fig. 53

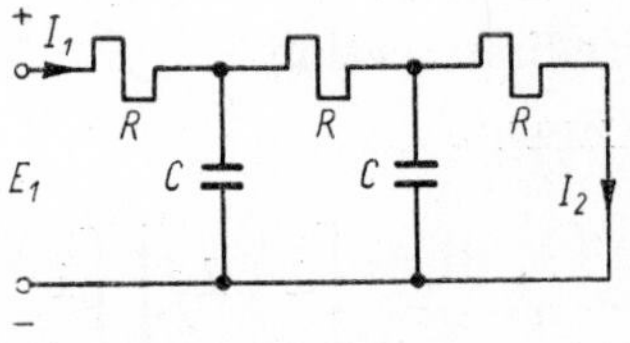

Fig. 54

Example. Find the currents I_1 and I_2 in the system given in fig. 54 (on the assumption that the initial conditions are zero).

We calculate the matrix of the network by multiplying the matrices:

$$\begin{bmatrix} 1 & R \\ 0 & 1 \end{bmatrix} \begin{bmatrix} 1 & 0 \\ Cs & 1 \end{bmatrix} \begin{bmatrix} 1 & R \\ 0 & 1 \end{bmatrix} \begin{bmatrix} 1 & 0 \\ Cs & 1 \end{bmatrix} \begin{bmatrix} 1 & R \\ 0 & 1 \end{bmatrix} \tag{45.1}$$

$$= \begin{bmatrix} R^2C^2s^2+3RCs+1 & R(R^2C^2s^2+4RCs+3) \\ Cs(RCs+2) & R^2C^2s^2+3RCs+1 \end{bmatrix};$$

whence

$$I_1 = \frac{R^2C^2s^2+3RCs+1}{R(R^2C^2s^2+4RCs+3)} E_1, \tag{45.2}$$

$$I_2 = \frac{1}{R(R^2C^2s^2+4RCs+3)} E_1. \tag{45.3}$$

In particular if the electromotive force applied is constant, $E_1 = E_0/s$, we have

$$I_1 = \frac{E_0}{R} \cdot \frac{R^2C^2s^2+3RCs+1}{s(R^2C^2s^2+4RCs+3)} = E_0\left(\frac{1}{3Rs} + \frac{C}{2(RCs+1)} + \frac{C}{6(RCs+3)}\right),$$

$$I_2 = \frac{E_0}{R} \cdot \frac{1}{s(R^2C^2s^2+4RCs+3)} = E_0\left(\frac{1}{3Rs} - \frac{C}{2(RCs+1)} + \frac{C}{6(RCs+3)}\right),$$

i. e.,

$$I_1(t) = \frac{E_0}{R}\left(\frac{1}{3} + \frac{1}{2}\exp\frac{-t}{RC} + \frac{1}{6}\exp\frac{-3t}{RC}\right),$$

$$I_2(t) = \frac{E_0}{R}\left(\frac{1}{3} - \frac{1}{2}\exp\frac{-t}{RC} + \frac{1}{6}\exp\frac{-3t}{RC}\right).$$

If the electromotive force is sinusoidal, $E_0e^{i\varphi}$ (see § 39), then the stationary current at the input of the network can be determined from formula (45.2) by replacing E_1 by $E_0e^{i\varphi}$, I_1 by $I_0e^{i\psi}$ and finally s by ωi:

$$I_0e^{i\psi} = \frac{-R^2C^2\omega^2-3RC\omega i+1}{R(-R^2C^2\omega^2-4RC\omega i+3)}E_0e^{i\varphi},$$

whence

$$I_0 = \frac{E_0}{R}\sqrt{\frac{R^4C^4\omega^4+7R^2C^2\omega^2+1}{R^4C^4\omega^4+10R^2C^2\omega^2+9}},$$

$$\psi = \varphi - \operatorname{arctg}\frac{3RC\omega}{R^2C^2\omega^2-1} + \operatorname{arctg}\frac{4RC\omega}{R^2C^2\omega^2-3}.$$

Similarly we can determine from formula (45.3) the amplitude and the phase of the current at the output of the network:

$$\frac{E_0}{R\sqrt{R^4C^4\omega^4+10R^2C^2\omega^2+g}}, \qquad \varphi + \operatorname{arctg}\frac{4RC\omega}{R^2C^2\omega^2-3}.$$

The validity of this calculation method is proved in the same way as in §§ 33 and 39.

§ 46. Four-terminal networks with free terminals. If the terminals of a four-terminal network are free (fig. 55), we have $I = 0$ and from equations (37.1) we obtain

$$\frac{A_{11}}{A_{21}}I_1 = E_1.$$

Thus a four-terminal network with free terminals may be regarded as a two-terminal network with the impedance A_{11}/A_{21}.

EXAMPLE. Find the input current and the end voltage in the network given in fig. 56. It is the same network that we dealt with in the preceding section except that its terminals are free. Thus we can at once avail ourselves of the shape of matrix (45.1), on the grounds of which we have

$$(46.1)\quad I_1 = \frac{Cs(RCs+2)}{R^2C^2s^2+3RCs+1}E_1, \qquad E_2 = \frac{1}{R^2C^2s^2+3RCs+1}E_1.$$

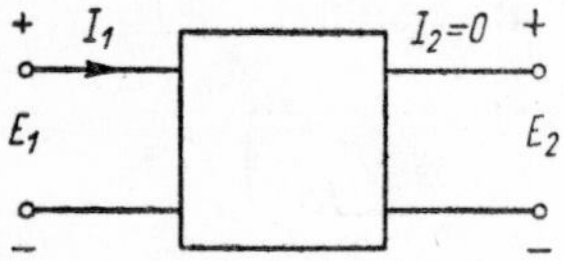

Fig. 55

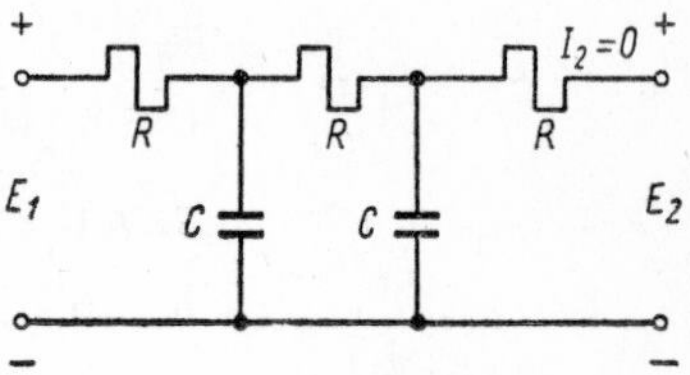

Fig. 56

If the applied electromotive force is constant, $E_1 = E_0/s$, we have

$$I_1 = E_0\frac{C(RCs+2)}{R^2C^2s^2+3RCs+1} = E_0C\left(\frac{5-\sqrt{5}}{10}\,\frac{1}{RCs+\alpha}+\frac{5+\sqrt{5}}{10}\,\frac{1}{RCs+\beta}\right),$$

$$E_2 = E_0\frac{1}{s(R^2C^2s^2+3RCs+1)}$$

$$= E_0\left(\frac{1}{s}+\frac{3\sqrt{5}-5}{10}\,\frac{RC}{RCs+\alpha}-\frac{3\sqrt{5}+5}{10}\,\frac{RC}{RCs+\beta}\right)$$

where $\alpha = \frac{1}{2}(3+\sqrt{5})$ and $\beta = \frac{1}{2}(3-\sqrt{5})$. Hence

$$I_1(t) = \frac{E_0}{R}\left(\frac{5-\sqrt{5}}{10}\exp\frac{-\alpha t}{RC}+\frac{5+\sqrt{5}}{10}\exp\frac{-\beta t}{RC}\right),$$

$$E_2(t) = E_0\left(1+\frac{3\sqrt{5}-5}{10}\exp\frac{-\alpha t}{RC}-\frac{3\sqrt{5}+5}{10}\exp\frac{-\beta t}{RC}\right).$$

If the electromotive force is sinusoidal, $E_0e^{i\varphi}$, we can apply a similar calculation to that used in the preceding section. Thus for instance we find from formula (46.1) the amplitude and the phase of the terminal voltage

$$\frac{E_0}{\sqrt{R^4C^4\omega^4+7R^2C^2\omega^2+1}}, \qquad \varphi+\operatorname{arctg}\frac{3RC\omega}{R^2C^2\omega^2-1}.$$

Exercise. Find the input current I_1 and the output current I_2 of the four-terminal networks given in the exercise on p. 83 when their terminals are free and when they are short-circuited.

§ 47. Four-terminal network with terminals short-circuited by a two-terminal network. If we connect the terminals of a four-terminal network with a two-terminal network with impedance Z, then through the latter network a current I_2 will flow, related to the voltage E_2 by the equality $E_2 = ZI_2$. Substituting this value in equations (42.1) we shall obtain the equalities

$$E_1 = (A_{11}Z+A_{12})I_2,$$

$$I_1 = (A_{21}Z+A_{22})I_2,$$

whence by eliminating I_2

$$E_1 = \frac{A_{11}Z+A_{12}}{A_{21}Z+A_{22}} I_1.$$

It can be seen from this equality that a four-terminal network short-circuited by a two-terminal one may be regarded as a new two-terminal network with the impedance

$$Z_1 = \frac{A_{11}Z+A_{12}}{A_{21}Z+A_{22}}.$$

If the terminals of the four-terminal network are short-circuited, then $E_2 = 0$ and we can assume that $Z = 0$. Then $Z_1 = A_{12}/A_{22}$, according to § 45.

If the terminals of the four-terminal network are free, then $I_2 = 0$ and we can assume that $Z = \infty$. Then $Z_1 = A_{11}/A_{22}$, according to § 46.

For any four-terminal network we can find a two-terminal one with impedance Z, which, connected with the terminal wires of the four-terminal network, gives a two-terminal network with the same impedance Z. The impedance Z must then satisfy the equation

$$Z = \frac{A_{11}Z+A_{12}}{A_{21}Z+A_{22}},$$

i. e.,

$$A_{21}Z^2-(A_{11}-A_{22})Z-A_{12} = 0.$$

The formal solution of this equation has the form

$$Z = (A_{11}-A_{22}\pm\Delta)/2A_{21},$$

where $\Delta = \sqrt{(A_{11}-A_{22})^2+4A_{12}A_{21}}$ is an operator whose square is equal to the expression under the radical sign. This solution will have an actual meaning if $A_{21} \neq 0$ and if we are able to find an operator Δ whose square is equal to $(A_{11}-A_{12})^2+4A_{12}A_{21}$. On the whole it is difficult to find such an operator but in certain cases it can easily be done.

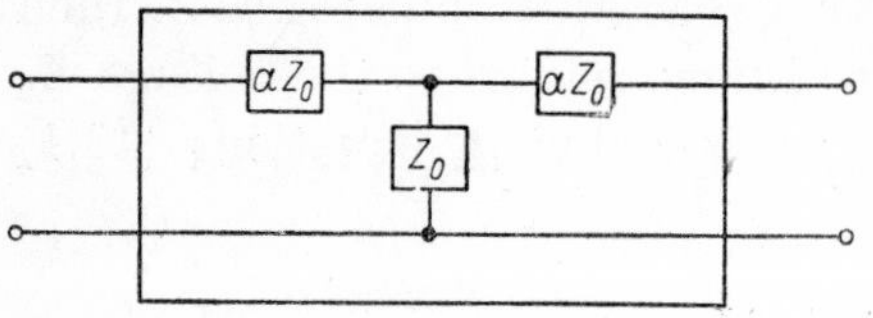

Fig. 57

Let us take for instance the four-terminal network shown in fig. 57; Z_0 is an arbitrary impedance, a a numerical coefficient. The matrix of this network is

$$\begin{bmatrix} 1 & aZ_0 \\ 0 & 1 \end{bmatrix} \begin{bmatrix} 1 & 0 \\ 1/Z_0 & 1 \end{bmatrix} \begin{bmatrix} 1 & aZ_0 \\ 0 & 1 \end{bmatrix} = \begin{bmatrix} 1+a & (2a+a^2)Z_0 \\ 1/Z_0 & 1+a \end{bmatrix}.$$

In this case we have $\Delta = 2\sqrt{2a+a^2}$ and consequently

$$Z = \sqrt{2a+a^2}\,Z_0. \tag{47.1}$$

§ 48. Chains of four-terminal networks. If we connect n four-terminal networks with the matrix

$$\begin{bmatrix} A_{11} & A_{12} \\ A_{21} & A_{22} \end{bmatrix}$$

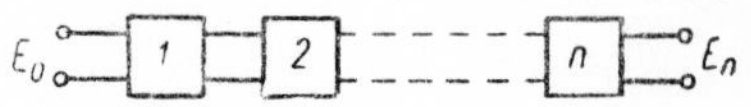

Fig. 58

we shall obtain a four-terminal network (fig. 58) whose matrix is equal to the product of n matrices

$$\begin{bmatrix} A_{11} & A_{12} \\ A_{21} & A_{22} \end{bmatrix}^n.$$

The calculation of this product, *i. e.*, its reduction to one matrix, as a rule involves complicated computations.

Suppose that each network of the chain has the form shown in fig. 59. Introducing the notation

$$1+a = \operatorname{ch}\beta, \qquad \operatorname{sh}\beta \cdot Z_0 = Z_1$$

and availing ourselves of the relation

$$2a+a^2 = (1+a)^2-1 = \operatorname{ch}^2\beta-1 = \operatorname{sh}^2\beta,$$

we can write the matrix of the four-terminal network in the form

$$\begin{bmatrix} \operatorname{ch}\beta & \operatorname{sh}\beta \cdot Z_1 \\ \operatorname{sh}\beta/Z_1 & \operatorname{ch}\beta \end{bmatrix}.$$

By the general formulas

$$\operatorname{ch}(\alpha+\beta) = \operatorname{ch}\alpha\operatorname{ch}\beta+\operatorname{sh}\alpha\operatorname{sh}\beta,$$
$$\operatorname{sh}(\alpha+\beta) = \operatorname{sh}\alpha\operatorname{ch}\beta+\operatorname{ch}\alpha\operatorname{sh}\beta,$$

we obtain the relations

$$\begin{bmatrix} \operatorname{ch}\beta & \operatorname{sh}\beta\cdot Z_1 \\ \operatorname{sh}\beta/Z_1 & \operatorname{ch}\beta \end{bmatrix}^2 = \begin{bmatrix} \operatorname{ch}2\beta & \operatorname{sh}2\beta\cdot Z_1 \\ \operatorname{sh}2\beta/Z_1 & \operatorname{ch}2\beta \end{bmatrix},$$

$$\begin{bmatrix} \operatorname{ch}\beta & \operatorname{sh}\beta\cdot Z_1 \\ \operatorname{sh}\beta/Z_1 & \operatorname{ch}\beta \end{bmatrix}^3 = \begin{bmatrix} \operatorname{ch}2\beta & \operatorname{sh}2\beta\cdot Z_1 \\ \operatorname{sh}2\beta/Z_1 & \operatorname{ch}2\beta \end{bmatrix}\begin{bmatrix} \operatorname{ch}\beta & \operatorname{sh}\beta\cdot Z_1 \\ \operatorname{sh}\beta/Z_1 & \operatorname{ch}\beta \end{bmatrix}$$

$$= \begin{bmatrix} \operatorname{ch}3\beta & \operatorname{sh}3\beta\cdot Z_1 \\ \operatorname{sh}3\beta/Z_1 & \operatorname{ch}3\beta \end{bmatrix},$$

and generally

$$\begin{bmatrix} \operatorname{ch}\beta & \operatorname{sh}\beta\cdot Z_1 \\ \operatorname{sh}\beta/Z_1 & \operatorname{ch}\beta \end{bmatrix}^n = \begin{bmatrix} \operatorname{ch}n\beta & \operatorname{sh}n\beta\cdot Z_1 \\ \operatorname{sh}n\beta/Z_1 & \operatorname{ch}\cdot n\cdot\beta \end{bmatrix}.$$

This is the desired matrix of the chain network. Its shape implies the relations between the voltage E_0 and the current I_0 at the input of the chain network on one hand and the voltage E_n and the current I_n at its output on the other:

$$E_0 = \operatorname{ch}n\beta\cdot E_n + \operatorname{sh}n\beta\operatorname{sh}\beta\cdot Z_0\cdot I_n,$$

$$I_0 = \frac{\operatorname{sh}n\beta}{\operatorname{sh}\beta\cdot Z_0}E_n + \operatorname{ch}n\beta\cdot I_n.$$

When the terminals of the four-terminal network are short-circuited, we have by § 45

$$I_0 = \frac{\operatorname{ch}n\beta}{\operatorname{sh}n\beta\operatorname{sh}\beta Z_0}E_0 = \frac{\operatorname{cth}n\beta}{\operatorname{sh}\beta}\cdot\frac{E_0}{Z_0}.$$

When the terminals are free, we have by § 46

$$I_0 = \frac{\operatorname{sh}n\beta}{\operatorname{ch}n\beta\cdot\operatorname{sh}\beta\cdot Z_0}E_0 = \frac{\operatorname{th}n\beta}{\operatorname{sh}\beta}\cdot\frac{E_0}{Z_0}.$$

When the chain is sufficiently long, we can assume that $\operatorname{cth}n\beta = 1$ and $\operatorname{th}n\beta = 1$. Then, in accordance with physics intuition, the two formulas given above are reduced to the same form,

$$I_0 \approx \frac{1}{\operatorname{sh}\beta}\cdot\frac{E_0}{Z_0} = \frac{1}{\sqrt{2a+a^2}}\cdot\frac{E_0}{Z_0}.$$

§ 49. Transformers. A *transformer* can be pictured as a four-terminal network shown in fig. 59. Actually the resistances R_1 and R_2 are bound with the self-induction inside the coils, but their separate presentation in the diagram is convenient for calculation purposes. Indeed, it permits us to calculate the matrix of the network by multiplying three matrices of simple four-terminal networks:

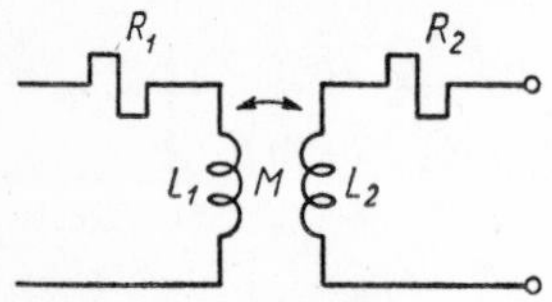

Fig. 59

$$\begin{bmatrix} 1 & R_1 \\ 0 & 1 \end{bmatrix} \begin{bmatrix} \dfrac{L_1}{M} & \dfrac{(L_1 L_2 - M^2)s}{M} \\ \dfrac{1}{Ms} & \dfrac{L_2}{M} \end{bmatrix} \begin{bmatrix} 1 & R_2 \\ 0 & 1 \end{bmatrix}.$$

Having performed the calculations we have

$$\begin{bmatrix} \dfrac{L_1 s + R_1}{Ms} & \dfrac{(L_1 s + R_1)(L_2 s + R_2) - M^2 s^2}{Ms} \\ \dfrac{1}{Ms} & \dfrac{L_2 s + R_2}{Ms} \end{bmatrix}. \tag{49.1}$$

This is the matrix of a transformer in the general case.

In *power transformers*, aiming at the least possible loss of energy, we try to reduce the resistances to the minimum. Moreover, by inserting a core of soft iron we try to increase as much as possible the mutual induction coefficient M; thus the difference $L_1 L_2 - M^2$ approaches zero. In such transformers it can be assumed that, approximately,

$$R_1 = R_2 = 0 \quad \text{and} \quad L_1 L_2 - M^2 = 0.$$

Matrix (49.1) assumes the form

$$\begin{bmatrix} \sqrt{\dfrac{L_1}{L_2}} & 0 \\ \dfrac{1}{\sqrt{L_1 L_2}\, s} & \sqrt{\dfrac{L_2}{L_1}} \end{bmatrix}. \tag{49.2}$$

This is the simplified matrix of a transformer.

Suppose that at the input of a transformer we have a sinusoidal voltage $E_{10} e^{i\varphi}$. Then on the output wires we shall have a voltage $E_{20} e^{i\varphi}$, such that

$$E_{10} e^{i\varphi} = \sqrt{\frac{L_1}{L_2}}\, E_{20} e^{i\varphi}, \tag{49.3}$$

which follows from the first line of matrix (49.2). To find relations for stationary currents, denote by $I_{10} e^{i\varphi_1}$ the stationary current at the input and by $I_{20}e^{i\varphi_2}$ the stationary current at the output of the transformer. Using the method given in §§ 33 and 39 we shall have, in view of the shape of the second line of matrix (49.2),

$$I_{10}e^{i\varphi_1} = \frac{1}{-\sqrt{L_1L_2}\omega i} - \sqrt{\frac{L_2}{L_1}}E_{10}e^{i\varphi} + \sqrt{\frac{L_2}{L_1}}I_{20}e^{i\varphi_2},$$

whence

$$(49.4)\qquad I_{10}e^{i\varphi_1} - \frac{i}{L_1\omega}E_{10}e^{i\varphi} = \sqrt{\frac{L_2}{L_1}}I_{20}e^{i\varphi_2}.$$

In power transformers the product $L_1\omega$ is usually large and the term

$$(49.5)\qquad \frac{i}{L_1\omega}E_{10}e^{i\varphi},$$

in equation (49.4) can be omitted. Thus we have approximately

$$(49.6)\qquad I_{10}e^{i\varphi_1} = \sqrt{\frac{L_2}{L_1}}I_{20}e^{i\varphi_2}.$$

Equations (49.3) and (49.6) have the matrix

$$(49.7)\qquad \begin{bmatrix} \sqrt{\frac{L_1}{L_2}} & 0 \\ 0 & \sqrt{\frac{L_2}{L_1}} \end{bmatrix};$$

this is the matrix of the ideal transformer. This matrix is convenient in calculations and sufficiently accurate for power transformers. If, however, the pulsation ω is very low and the self-induction L_1 so small that the term (49.5) must be taken into account, matrix (49.2) should be used. Also if the voltage is not sinusoidal of if we want to consider the transient currents arising as the transformer is being connected, we should always use matrix (49.2) or (49.1).

Denote by m the number of loops in the primary winding of the transformer and by n the number of loops in the secondary winding. If L denotes the self-induction of a single loop, we shall have

$$L_1 = m^2L \quad \text{and} \quad L_2 = n^2L.$$

Substituting these values in matrix (49.7), we have

$$\begin{bmatrix} m/n & 0 \\ 0 & n/m \end{bmatrix}.$$

§ 50. Cathode-ray tube as a four-terminal network. A cathode-ray tube (a triode) may be regarded as a four-terminal network if the relation between the grid voltage E_1, the anode voltage increment E_2 and the anode current I_2 (fig. 60) is

$$E_1 = \frac{1}{\mu}(E_2 + RI_2), \tag{50.1}$$

where μ is the amplification coefficient and R the internal resistance of the tube. Since the current intensity I_1 in the grid circuit may be assumed to be equal to zero, we have

$$I_2 = 0 \cdot E_2 + 0 \cdot I_2. \tag{50.2}$$

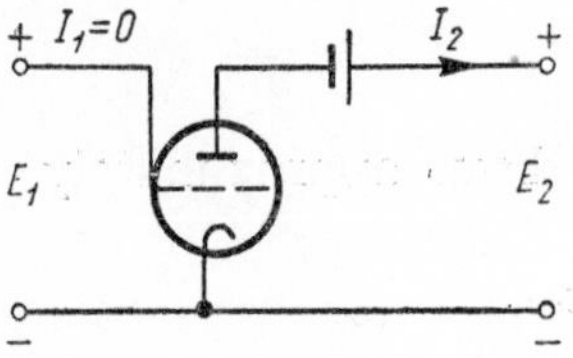

Fig. 60

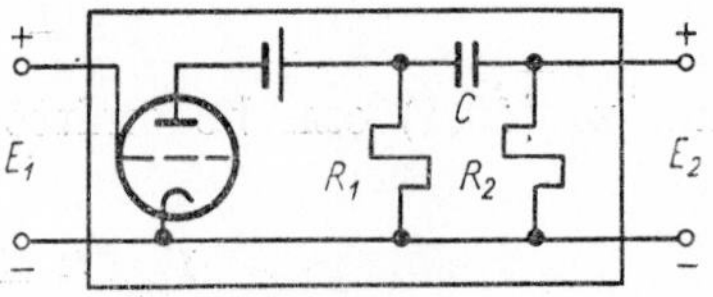

Fig. 61

By equalities (50.1) and (50.2) we have the following matrix for a tube regarded as a four-terminal network:

$$\begin{bmatrix} 1/\mu & R/\mu \\ 0 & 0 \end{bmatrix}. \tag{50.3}$$

It should be remembered that the tube may be regarded as a four-terminal network only if it works in suitable conditions, *i. e.*, if the heights of the grid voltage and the anode voltage vary within permissible limits. If these conditions are not satisfied, then an inadvertent use of matrix (50.3) may lead to entirely false results.

Availing ourselves of our knowledge of matrix (50.3) we can easily find the matrix for the network shown in fig. 61; namely it is equal to the product of the matrices

$$\begin{bmatrix} 1/\mu & R/\mu \\ 0 & 0 \end{bmatrix} \begin{bmatrix} 1 & 0 \\ 1/R_1 & 1 \end{bmatrix} \begin{bmatrix} 1 & 1/Cs \\ 0 & 1 \end{bmatrix} \begin{bmatrix} 1 & 0 \\ 1/R_2 & 1 \end{bmatrix}.$$

Performing the multiplication, we obtain the matrix

$$\begin{bmatrix} \dfrac{s+\lambda}{\alpha s} & \dfrac{s+v}{\beta s} \\ 0 & 0 \end{bmatrix},$$

where

$$\alpha = \frac{\mu R_1 R_2}{R_1R_2 + R_1R + R_2R}, \qquad \beta = \frac{\mu}{R},$$

$$\lambda = \frac{R+R_1}{C(R_1R_2+R_1R+R_2R)}, \qquad \nu = \frac{1}{C}\left(\frac{1}{R}+\frac{1}{R_1}\right).$$

If we connect n four-terminal networks of the type considered here, we shall obtain a four-terminal network (fig. 58) whose matrix is equal to

$$\begin{bmatrix} \dfrac{s+\lambda}{\alpha s} & \dfrac{s+\nu}{\beta s} \\ 0 & 0 \end{bmatrix}^n,$$

i. e., if we perform the calculation,

$$\begin{bmatrix} \left(\dfrac{s+\lambda}{\alpha s}\right)^n & \left(\dfrac{s+\lambda}{\alpha s}\right)^{n-1} \dfrac{s+\nu}{\beta s} \\ 0 & 0 \end{bmatrix}.$$

It follows hence that if we denote by E_n the input voltage and by E_m and I_n the output voltage and the output current intensity respectively, we have the relation

$$E = \left(\frac{s+\lambda}{\alpha s}\right)^n E_n + \left(\frac{s+\lambda}{\alpha s}\right)^{n-1} \frac{s+\nu}{\beta s} I_n. \tag{50.4}$$

In particular let us calculate the output voltage E_n if the input voltage is constant, $E = E_0/s$, and the terminals of the network are free. Then $I_n = 0$ and from formula (50.2) we have

$$E_n = E_0 \alpha^n \frac{s^{n-1}}{(s+\lambda)^n}.$$

Since

$$s^{n-1} = [(s+\lambda)-\lambda]^{n-1} = \sum_{\varkappa=0}^{n-1} (-1)^\varkappa \binom{n-1}{\varkappa} \lambda^\varkappa (s+\lambda)^{n-\varkappa-1},$$

we can write

$$E_n = E_0 \alpha^n \sum_{\varkappa=0}^{n-1} (-1)^\varkappa \binom{n-1}{\varkappa} \frac{\lambda^\varkappa}{(s+\lambda)^{\varkappa+1}}$$

or by formula (24.2)

$$E_n(t) = E_0 \alpha^n e^{-\lambda t} \sum_{\varkappa=0}^{n-1} (-1)^\varkappa \binom{n-1}{\varkappa} \frac{(\lambda t)^\varkappa}{\varkappa!}.$$

The function obtained is closely related to the so-called *Laguerre polynomials*,

$$L_n(t) = \sum_{\varkappa=0}^{n} (-1)^{\varkappa} \binom{n}{\varkappa} \frac{t^{\varkappa}}{\varkappa!}.$$

Using this notation we can write

$$E_n(t) = E_0 \alpha^n e^{-\lambda t} L_{n-1}(\lambda t).$$

It is easy to find certain differential relations for the Laguerre polynomials. Namely we have

$$\{e^{-t} L_n(t)\} = \frac{s^n}{(s+1)^{n+1}} = s^n \left\{\frac{t^n}{n!} e^{-t}\right\} = \left\{\frac{d^n}{dt^n} \frac{t^n}{n!} e^{-t}\right\},$$

since function $\frac{t^n}{n!} e^{-t}$ and its derivatives up to the order $n-1$ are equal to zero for $t = 0$. Hence

$$\mathrm{L}_n(t) = e^t \frac{d^n}{dt^n} \left(\frac{t^n}{n!} e^{-t}\right).$$

Here is a table of the Laguerre polynomials for the initial values of n:

$$\mathrm{L}_0(t) = 1, \qquad \mathrm{L}_3(t) = 1-3t+\tfrac{3}{2}t^2-\tfrac{1}{6}t^3,$$

$$\mathrm{L}_1(t) = 1-t, \qquad \mathrm{L}_4(t) = 1-4t+3t^2-\tfrac{2}{3}t^3+\tfrac{1}{24}t^4,$$

$$\mathrm{L}_2(t) = 1-2t+\tfrac{1}{2}t^2, \qquad \mathrm{L}_5(t) = 1-5t+5t^2-\tfrac{5}{3}t^3+\tfrac{5}{24}t^4-\tfrac{1}{120}t^5.$$

§ 51. Four-terminal network with determinant 1. The *determinant of a four-terminal network* with the matrix $\begin{bmatrix} A_{11} & A_{12} \\ A_{21} & A_{22} \end{bmatrix}$ is the expression

$$\begin{vmatrix} A_{11} & A_{12} \\ A_{21} & A_{22} \end{vmatrix}, \quad \textit{i. e.,} \quad A_{11}A_{22}-A_{12}A_{21}.$$

All the four-terminal networks so far discussed, with the exception of the last example (that of the electronic tube), have the determinant equal to 1. It can be proved that every four-terminal network composed of a finite number of two-terminal networks with the impedance $Ls+R+1/Cs$, connected with one another in an arbitrary manner, have the determinant 1 no matter whether the quantities L, R and C are positive or negative (negative self-induction, as well as negative resistance or capacity, being realizable by means of electronic tubes).

By connecting two four-terminal networks with the determinant 1 *we always obtain a four-terminal network with the determinant* 1. This follows from the equality

$$\begin{vmatrix} A_{11} & A_{12} \\ A_{21} & A_{22} \end{vmatrix} \begin{vmatrix} B_{11} & B_{12} \\ B_{21} & B_{22} \end{vmatrix} = \begin{vmatrix} A_{11}B_{11}+A_{12}B_{21} & A_{11}B_{12}+A_{12}B_{22} \\ A_{21}B_{11}+A_{22}B_{21} & A_{21}B_{12}+A_{22}B_{22} \end{vmatrix},$$

i. e., from the equality

$$(A_{11}A_{22}-A_{12}A_{21})(B_{11}B_{22}-B_{12}B_{21})$$
$$=(A_{11}B_{11}+A_{12}B_{21})(A_{21}B_{12}+A_{22}B_{22})-(A_{11}B_{12}+A_{12}B_{22})(A_{21}B_{11}+A_{22}B_{21}).$$

The above property of the four-terminal network, namely its determinant being equal to 1, is the mathematical expression of the physical *principle of reciprocity*. We have this theorem:

If $A_{12} = 0$, *then the four-terminal network has the determinant* 1 *if and only if it satisfies the following principle of reciprocity*:

The electromotive force E *applied to the input wires of a four-terminal network causes in the short-circuited output wires the same current as that which would flow between the short-circuited input wires under the influence of the electromotive force* E *applied to the output wires.*

Indeed, from the equations

$$E_1 = A_{11}E_2+A_{12}I_2, \qquad I_1 = A_{21}E_2+A_{22}I_2 \tag{51.1}$$

it follows that

$$I_1 = \frac{A_{22}}{A_{12}} E_1 - \frac{\Delta}{A_{12}} E_2, \qquad I_2 = \frac{1}{A_{12}} E_1 - \frac{A_{11}}{A_{12}} E_2 \qquad \left(\Delta = \begin{vmatrix} A_{11} & A_{12} \\ A_{21} & A_{22} \end{vmatrix}\right).$$

If we short-circuit the end wires of a four-terminal network, we shall have $E_2 = 0$ and

$$I_2 = \frac{1}{A_{12}} E_1;$$

and if we short-circuit the input wires of a four-terminal network, then $E_1 = 0$ and

$$I_1 = -\frac{\Delta}{A_{12}} E_2.$$

Since according to accepted usage the direction of the voltage in the output wires of a four-terminal network is established inversely to the direction of the current, when using the principle of reciprocity we must first change the sign $-$ to $+$ in the last formula. Then it is obvious that with equal voltages E_1 and E_2 the currents I_1 and I_2 are equal if and only if $\Delta = 1$. The theorem is thus proved.

If $A_{21} \neq 0$, then the four-terminal network has a determinant 1 *if and only if it satisfies the following principle of reciprocity*:

The current I flowing through the input wires of the four-terminal network causes on the open output wires the same voltage as that which would arise on free input wires if the current I flowed through the output wires.

Indeed, it follows from (51.1) that

$$E_1 = \frac{A_{11}}{A_{21}} I_1 - \frac{\Delta}{A_{21}} I_2, \qquad E_2 = \frac{1}{A_{21}} I_1 - \frac{A_{22}}{A_{21}} I_2.$$

If the output wires of the four-terminal network are free, then $I_2 = 0$ and consequently

$$E_1 = \frac{1}{A_{21}} I_2;$$

and if the input wires are free, then $I_1 = 0$ and

$$E_1 = -\frac{\Delta}{A_{21}} I_2.$$

As previously, these equalities imply the theorem on the grounds of the observation concerning the sign of the output voltage.

If $A_{12} \neq 0$ and $A_{21} \neq 0$, then of course both forms of the principle of reciprocity are applicable.

Finally, if $A_{12} = A_{21} = 0$, then

$$E_1 = A_{11} E_2 \quad \text{and} \quad I_1 = A_{22} I_2.$$

Examples of such four-terminal networks are given by the *direct connection*, the *crossing* and the *ideal transformer*. The following matrices correspond to them:

$$\begin{bmatrix} 1 & 0 \\ 0 & 1 \end{bmatrix}, \quad \begin{bmatrix} -1 & 0 \\ 0 & -1 \end{bmatrix}, \quad \text{and} \quad \begin{bmatrix} m/n & 0 \\ 0 & m/n \end{bmatrix}.$$

In all these cases the operators A_{11} and A_{22} are numbers with the product equal to 1. Thus we can write

$$E_1(t) = A_{11} E_2(t) \quad \text{and} \quad I_1(t) = A_{22} I_2(t).$$

Multiplying these equalities in the ordinary (non-operational) sense, we have

$$E_1(t) I_1(t) = E_2(t) I_2(t),$$

which means that the power of the current at the input at any instant is equal to the power at the output of the four-terminal network.

The ideal transformer is realizable by means of inductive couplings only in a largely approximate way. A better approximation can be obtained by means of electronic tubes by introducing resistances and negative self-induction. The use of similar means would also make it possible to realize four-terminal networks with determinant 1 in which $A_{12} = A_{21} = 0$ and the operators A_{11} and A_{22} are not numbers.

§ 52. Inverted four-terminal networks and symmetrical four-terminal networks. In the case of a four-terminal network with determinant 1 it can be found from equations (51.1) that

$$\begin{aligned} E_2 &= A_{22}E_1 - A_{12}I_1, \\ I_2 &= -A_{21}E_1 + A_{11}I_1. \end{aligned} \tag{52.1}$$

Hence we can easily establish the equations of an *inverted four-terminal network*, *i. e.*, a network in which the parts played by the input and the output wires have been interchanged. For this purpose we must replace in equations (52.1) E_1 by E_2, E_2 by E_1 and, the currents being now measured in the opposite directions, I_1 by $-I_2$ and I_2 by I_1. We shall thus obtain the equations

$$\begin{aligned} E_1 &= A_{22}E_2 + A_{12}I_2, \\ I_1 &= A_{21}E_2 + A_{11}I_2. \end{aligned}$$

Therefore the inverted four-terminal network has the matrix

$$\begin{bmatrix} A_{22} & A_{12} \\ A_{21} & A_{11} \end{bmatrix}.$$

The matrix of an inverted four-terminal network with determinant 1 is obtained by replacing in the matrix of the given network the terms on the main diagonal.

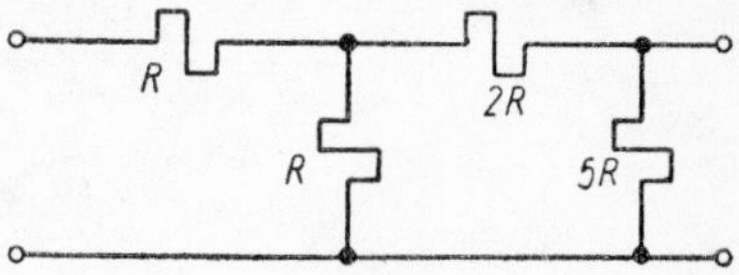

Fig. 62

If those terms are equal, $A_{11} = A_{22}$, the matrix does not change on inverting the network. Such a network is termed *symmetric* whether its internal structure is symmetric or not.

A symmetric four-terminal network has a matrix symmetric with respect to the transverse axis.

For example the networks shown in figs. 44-48 and 57 are symmetric. Fig. 62 shows the simplest symmetric four-terminal network with an asymmetric internal structure; its matrix has the form

$$\begin{bmatrix} 3 & \frac{8}{5}R \\ 5/R & 3 \end{bmatrix}.$$

If we take any (symmetric or asymmetric) four-terminal network with the matrix

$$\begin{bmatrix} A_{11} & A_{12} \\ A_{21} & A_{22} \end{bmatrix}$$

and connect it with the same network inverted, we shall obtain a symmetric four-terminal network with the matrix

$$\begin{bmatrix} A_{11} & A_{12} \\ A_{21} & A_{22} \end{bmatrix} \begin{bmatrix} A_{22} & A_{12} \\ A_{21} & A_{11} \end{bmatrix} = \begin{bmatrix} A_{11}A_{22}+A_{12}A_{21} & 2A_{11}A_{12} \\ 2A_{21}A_{22} & A_{11}A_{22}+A_{12}A_{21} \end{bmatrix}.$$

CHAPTER VI

GENERAL SOLUTIONS OF DIFFERENTIAL EQUATIONS AND BOUNDARY PROBLEMS

§ 53. General solution. So far we have been solving differential equations with given initial conditions at the point $t = 0$; the operational calculus is particularly suited to those cases. However, it can also be used to advantage in other problems, for instance in finding the general solution, in solving boundary problems, etc.

To begin with, we shall deal with the problem of *general solution.* In § 28 we have seen that the solution of the equation

$$a_n x^{(n)} + a_{n-1} x^{(n-1)} + \ldots + a_0 x = f$$

can be written in the form

$$x = \frac{\beta_{n-1} \cdot s^{n-1} + \ldots + \beta_0}{a_n s^n + \ldots + a_0} + \frac{1}{a_n s^n + \ldots + a_0} \cdot f \tag{53.1}$$

where the constants $\beta_0, \ldots, \beta_{n-1}$ depend on the initial conditions at the point $t = 0$. If these conditions are not imposed beforehand, then $\beta_0, \ldots, \beta_{n-1}$ are arbitrary constants and formula (53.1) gives the general solution of the differential equation. The ordinary, non-operational form can be most conveniently reached by decomposition into simple fractions. It will be observed, however, that in finding the general solution it is unnecessary to calculate the coefficients $A, B, C, \ldots$ in the simple fractions

$$\frac{A}{(s-\lambda)^j}, \quad \frac{B+Cs}{[(s-a)^2+\beta^2]^k}$$

which arise in the decomposition of the expression

$$\frac{\beta_{n-1} s^{n-1} + \ldots + \beta_0}{a_n s^n + \ldots + a_0};$$

it is sufficient to take these coefficients as arbitrary constants instead of $\beta_{n-1}, \ldots, \beta_0$. In this way the calculation may be considerably shortened.

Example. Find the general solution of the differential equation

$$x^{(4)}-2x'''+2x''-2x'+x = f.$$

Solution. The initial conditions being arbitrary, the equation will have the operational form

$$s^4x-2s^3x+2s^2x-2sx+x = W+f,$$

where $W = \beta_3 s^3+\beta_2 s^2+\beta_1 s+\beta_0$ is an arbitrary polynomial of the third degree. Hence we have

$$x = \frac{W}{(s-1)^2(s^2+1)}+\frac{1}{(s-1)^2(s^2+1)}f.$$

We decompose the first of the above equations into simple fractions

$$\frac{A}{s-1}+\frac{B}{(s-1)^2}+\frac{C+Ds}{s^2+1}$$

considering A, B, C and D as arbitrary constants and disregarding their connection with polynomial W. In the decomposition of the second fraction, however, the coefficients are uniquely determined and we find them in the usual way:

$$\frac{1}{(s-1)^2(s^2+1)} = -\frac{1}{2(s-1)}+\frac{1}{2(s-1)^2}+\frac{s}{2(s^2+1)}.$$

Finally, as the general solution we obtain the function

$$x(t) = Ae^t+Bte^t+C\sin t+D\cos t+\tfrac{1}{2}\int_0^t f(t-\tau)(-e^\tau+\tau e^\tau+\cos\tau)\,d\tau.$$

If the form of the function f is known, the calculation may sometimes be modified so that all integration is left out. Suppose for instance that $f = \{\cos 2t\}$. Then

$$x = \frac{W}{(s-1)^2(s^2+1)}+\frac{1}{(s-1)^2(s^2+1)}\cdot\frac{s}{s^2+4}$$

$$= \frac{A}{s-1}+\frac{B}{(s-1)^2}+\frac{C+Ds}{s^2+1}+\frac{E+Fs}{s^2+4}.$$

The constants A, B, C and D remain arbitrary and only the values E and F must be determined. Since these values are completely independent of the polynomial W, in order to determine them we can temporarily assume that $W = 0$; we obtain the equality

$$[A(s-1)+B](s^2+1)(s^2+4)+$$
$$+[(C+Ds)(s-1)^2(s^2+4)+(E+Fs)(s^2+1)](s-1)^2 = s.$$

The simplest way to calculate the coefficients E and F is by substituting number $2i$ for s; we then have

$$-3(E+2Fi)(1-2i)^2 = 2i;$$

comparing the real and the imaginary parts we obtain the equations

$$3(3E-8F) = 0,$$

$$6(2E+3F) = 2,$$

and hence the values

$$E = \tfrac{8}{75}, \quad F = \tfrac{1}{25}.$$

Thus the general solution has the form

$$x = \frac{A}{s-1} + \frac{B}{(s-1)^2} + \frac{C+Ds}{s^2+1} + \frac{8+3s}{75(s^2+4)},$$

i.e.,

$$x(t) = Ae^t + Bte^t + C\sin t + D\cos t + \tfrac{4}{75}\sin 2t + \tfrac{1}{25}\cos 2t.$$

As we see, determining a general solution is, as regards calculation, somewhat simpler than determining a particular solution with given initial conditions; for it is unnecessary to find all the coefficients of decomposition into simple fractions. In the case of a system of equations, however, this simplification cannot be introduced, since then certain relations between the coefficients of decomposition must be taken into account. For instance the system of equations

$$x' = x-2y,$$

$$y' = x-y+f$$

will always have its solution in the form

$$x = \frac{A+Bs}{s^2+1} - \frac{2}{s^2+1}f, \quad y = \frac{C+Ds}{s^2+1} + \frac{-1+s}{s^2+1}f$$

but of the constants A, B, C, and D only two can be fixed arbitrarily, while the remaining ones depend on those two.

In order to find a general solution containing only two (independent) parameters it is most convenient to introduce first the initial conditions

$$x(0) = \alpha, \quad y(0) = \beta.$$

Now solving a suitable system of operational equations,

$$sx = x-2y+\alpha,$$

$$sy = x-y+\beta+f,$$

we shall find

$$x = \frac{(\alpha-2\beta)+\alpha\cdot s}{s^2+1} - \frac{s}{s^2+1}\cdot f, \quad y = \frac{(\alpha-\beta)+\beta s}{s^2+1} + \frac{-1+s}{s^2+1}\cdot f,$$

whence

$$x(t) = (\alpha-2\beta)\sin t + \alpha\cos t - 2\int_0^t f(t-\tau)\sin\tau\, d\tau,$$

$$y(t) = (\alpha-\beta)\sin t + \beta\cos t + \int_0^t f(t-\tau)(-\sin\tau+\cos\tau)\, d\tau.$$

This of course is the desired general solution, since the constants α and β appearing in it are arbitrary.

This method of finding general solutions is profitable only in the case of systems of equations; for a single equation it is more convenient to use the previously given method, in which the introduction of arbitrary constants is postponed till the decomposition into simple fractions.

Exercises.

1. Find the general solutions of the following equations:

(α) $x''' - 3ax'' + 3a^2x' - a^3x = e^{at}$; (β) $x''' - 2x'' - 3x' + 10x = 0$;

(γ) $x^{(4)} - 12x'' + 12x = 16t^4e^{t^2}$; (δ) $4x^{(4)} - 12x''' + 11x'' - 3x' = 4\cos t$.

2. Find the general solutions of the following systems of equations:

(α) $x' + y = t^2 + 6t + 1, \quad y' - x = -3t^2 + 3t + 1$;

(β) $4x' + 9y' + 2x + 31y = e^t, \quad 3x' + 7y' + x + 24y = 3$;

(γ) $x' = -3x + 18y - 8z, \quad y' = 4x - y + 2z, \quad z' = 6x - 36y - 10z$.

§ 54. Boundary problems. We speak of a *boundary problem* if we are given, instead of initial conditions, the values of the required functions and possibly also of their derivatives at the two ends of a fixed interval. For instance, we shall have a boundary problem to deal with if we demand, for a function satisfying the equation

(54.1) $$x^{(4)} - 2x''' + 2x'' - 2x' + x = \cos 2t,$$

that

$$x(0) = \tfrac{1}{25}, \quad x(\pi) = \tfrac{1}{25}, \quad x'(0) = \tfrac{2}{15}, \quad x'(\pi) = \tfrac{2}{25};$$

we find the required function from the general solution

(54.2) $$x(t) = Ae^t + Bte^t + C\sin t + D\cos t + \tfrac{4}{75}\sin 2t + \tfrac{1}{25}\cos 2t$$

choosing the coefficients A, B, C, and D so that the conditions are satisfied.

For this purpose we solve the system of equations

$$x(0) = A+D+\tfrac{1}{25} = \tfrac{1}{25},$$

$$x(\pi) = Ae^{\pi}+B\pi e^{\pi}-D+\tfrac{1}{25} = \tfrac{1}{25},$$

$$x'(0) = A+B+C+\tfrac{8}{75} = \tfrac{2}{15},$$

$$x'(\pi) = Ae^{\pi}+B(\pi e^{\pi}+e^{\pi})-C+\tfrac{8}{75} = \tfrac{2}{25},$$

and obtain

$$A = 0, \quad B = 0, \quad C = \tfrac{2}{75}, \quad D = 0.$$

Substituting these values in (54.2) we find the required solution

$$x(t) = \tfrac{2}{75}\sin t+\tfrac{4}{75}\sin 2t+\tfrac{1}{25}\cos 2t.$$

In a similar manner we can solve more general problems, *e. g.* determine the solutions given the values of functions or of their derivatives at more than two points. Suppose that we want to find a function satisfying equation (54.1) and such that

$$x(0) = 0, \quad x(\tfrac{\pi}{2}) = 0, \quad x(\pi) = \tfrac{2}{25}, \quad x(\tfrac{3\pi}{2}) = -\tfrac{2}{25};$$

it is then sufficient to solve the system of equations

$$x(0) = A+D+\tfrac{1}{25} = 0,$$

$$x(\tfrac{1}{2}\pi) = A\exp\tfrac{1}{2}\pi\exp\tfrac{1}{2}\pi+B\tfrac{1}{2}\pi+C-\tfrac{1}{25} = 0,$$

$$x(\pi) = A\exp\pi+B\pi\exp\pi-D+\tfrac{1}{25} = \tfrac{2}{25},$$

$$x(\tfrac{3}{2}\pi) = A\exp\tfrac{3}{2}\pi+B\tfrac{3}{2}\exp\tfrac{3}{2}\pi-C-\tfrac{1}{25} = -\tfrac{2}{25}.$$

In this way we find that

$$A = 0, \quad B = 0, \quad C = \tfrac{1}{25}, \quad D = -\tfrac{1}{25}$$

and consequently

$$x(t) = \tfrac{1}{25}\sin t-\tfrac{1}{25}\cos t+\tfrac{4}{75}\sin 2t+\tfrac{1}{25}\cos 2t.$$

In some cases the algebraic system of equations obtained for A, B, ... may happen to be insolvable; then a solution of the differential equation under the given conditions is also a non-existent. Generally, the discussion of the existence of a solution under given conditions is reduced to the discussion of the solvability of the system of algebraic equations with respect to the constants $A, B, \ldots$

Exercises.

1. Show which of the following boundary problems is solvable:

(α) $x'' - x = 0, \quad x(0) = 0, \quad x(2\pi) = 1,$

(β) $x'' + x = 0, \quad x(0) = 0, \quad x(2\pi) = 1.$

2. Find the function satisfying the equation

$$x^{(4)} + 4x = 0$$

and the conditions

$$x\left(-\tfrac{\pi}{2}\right) = -e^{-\pi}, \quad x(0) = 0, \quad x\left(\tfrac{\pi}{2}\right) = 1, \quad x(\pi) = 0.$$

§ 55. Solution of differential equations under given initial conditions at the point $t_0 \neq 0$. The method discussed in the preceding section can of course be successfully applied also if the values of a fraction and its derivatives are given at one point only. In that case, instead of seeking the general solution, it is more convenient to apply direct calculation. If the point t_0, at which the conditions are imposed, is different from 0, we solve the problem in the same way as if the initial conditions were given at the point $t = 0$, but we must take into account a suitable translation of the system of coordinates.

EXAMPLE. Find the solution of the differential equation

$$x^{(4)} - 2x''' + 2x'' - 2x' + x = f(t) \tag{55.1}$$

satisfying at a given point $t_0 \neq 0$ the initial conditions

$$x(t_0) = x'(t_0) = x''(t_0) = x'''(t_0) = 0.$$

Solution. We first seek the solution of the equation

$$x^{(4)} - 2x''' + 2x'' - 2x + x = f(t + t_0)$$

satisfying the same initial conditions at the point $t = 0$:

$$x(0) = x'(0) = x''(0) = x'''(0) = 0.$$

We then have the operational equation

$$s^4 x - 2s^3 x + 2s^2 x - 2sx + x = \{f(t + t_0)\},$$

whence

$$x = \left(-\frac{1}{2(s-1)} + \frac{1}{2(s-1)^2} + \frac{s}{2(s''+1)}\right)\{f(t+t_0)\} =$$

$$= \left\{\tfrac{1}{2}\int_0^t f(t + t_0 - \tau)(-e^\tau + \tau e^\tau + \cos\tau)\, d\tau\right\}.$$

Now in order to obtain the desired solution of equation (55.1) it suffices to write everywhere $t-t_0$ instead of t; thus we finally have

$$x(t) = \tfrac{1}{2}\int_0^{t-t_0} f(t+\tau_0-\tau)(-e^\tau+\tau e^\tau+\cos\tau)\,d\tau.$$

Exercise. Solve the following differential equations with given initial conditions:

(α) $x''' - 4x' = e^{4t}\sin^2 t,\quad x(1) = x'(1) = x''(1) = 1;$

(β) $x' = -5x - 2y;\quad y' = x - 7y,\quad x(2) = y(2) = 2.$

CHAPTER VII

DISCONTINUOUS FUNCTIONS

§ 56. Functions of class $\mathcal{K}$. Now we want to introduce into the operational calculus certain discontinuous functions. From the theoretical point of view it would be most natural to introduce the class of *L*-integrable functions, but that would require the knowledge of Lebesgue's integral. Therefore we shall limit ourselves to a narrower class of functions, which can be treated in an elementary manner and yet are sufficient for most applications.

An important example of a discontinous function is provided by the function $\{E(t)\}$, defined in such a way that its value at the point t is equal to the greatest integer that is less than or equal to t, e. g.:

$$E(5{,}71) = 5, \quad E(\tfrac{1}{2}) = 0, \quad E(\pi) = 3, \quad E(10) = 10 \quad \text{etc.}$$

The function $\{E(t)\}$ is often termed the *integral part of* t; in the study of logarithms the term *characteristic* is used. The graph of this function is given in fig. 63.

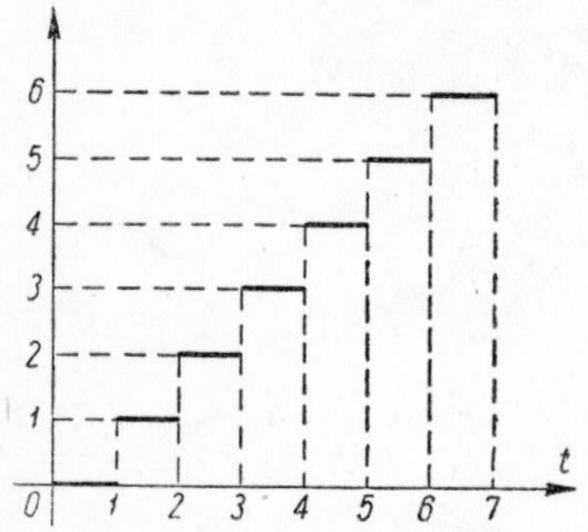

Fig. 63

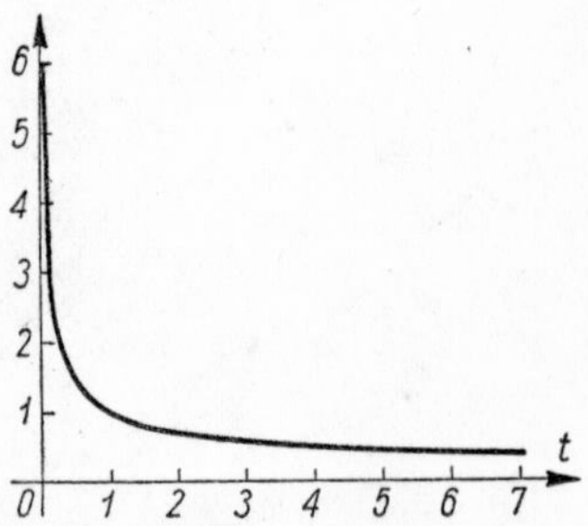

Fig. 64

The function $\{1/\sqrt{t}\}$, whose graph is shown in fig. 64, presents another type of a discontinuous function. It is discontinuous at the point $t = 0$ and unbounded in the neighbourhood of this point.

The functions $\{E(t)\}$ and $\{1/\sqrt{t}\}$ represent two types of discontinuous functions that are important in applications. In order to define class $\mathcal{K}$ comprising both continuous and discontinuous functions of the two types we shall adopt the following definition.

A function $\{f(t)\}$ (of real or complex values) considered in the interval $0 \leqslant t < \infty$ *belongs to class* $\mathcal{K}$ if

(I) it has at most a finite number of points of continuity in every finite interval;

(II) the integral $\int_0^t |f(\tau)|\,d\tau$ has a finite value for every $t > 0$.

If $f = \{f(t)\}$ is a function of class $\mathcal{K}$, then by the definition of convolution, we have

$$lf = \{1\}\{f(t)\} = \Big\{\int_0^t f(\tau)\,d\tau\Big\}.$$

The integral on the right side always represents a continuous function; denoting it by a we shall have $lf = a$, whence

$$f = a/l.$$

Consequently every function of class $\mathcal{K}$ can be formally regarded as an operator, since it is a quotient (in the sense of an inverse operation to convolution) of two functions of class $\mathcal{C}$.

Exercise. Verify that the following functions belong to class $\mathcal{K}$:

(α) $\left\{\dfrac{1}{t^\lambda}\right\}$ $(\lambda < 1)$; (β) $\left\{\dfrac{1}{\sqrt{|\sin t|}}\right\}$; (γ) $\left\{\dfrac{1}{\sqrt[3]{t-1}}\right\}$; (δ) $\left\{\dfrac{d}{dt}\,|t-1|\right\}$.

§ 57. Operations on functions of class $\mathcal{K}$. Once we have agreed to regard functions of class $\mathcal{K}$ as operators, all the operations which we have defined for operators are also defined for those functions.

To begin with, let us consider when two functions, f and g, of class $\mathcal{K}$ are to be regarded as equal. Writing

$$a = \Big\{\int_0^t f(\tau)\,d\tau\Big\} \quad \text{and} \quad b = \Big\{\int_0^t g(\tau)\,d\tau\Big\},$$

i. e., $a = f$ and $b = g$, we have

$$f = \frac{a}{l} \quad \text{and} \quad g = \frac{b}{l}.$$

The equality $a/l = b/l$ is equivalent to the equality $a = b$, *i. e.*, to the equality

$$\int_0^t f(\tau)\,d\tau = \int_0^t g(\tau)\,d\tau \quad \text{for every} \quad t \geqslant 0.$$

The last equality will hold if (and only if) the functions f and g have the same values at every point where both are continuous. In that case the functions f and g should be regarded as equal: $f = g$. With such a definition the values of the functions at points of discontinuity are completely unimportant and at those points the functions may be undefined.

For instance, all the functions presented in figs 65 a, b, c will be regarded as equal although the first two have different values at the points *1* and *2* and the last is undefined at these points.

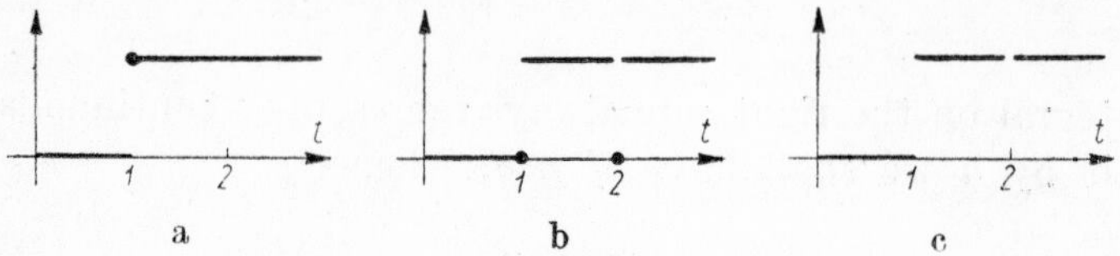

Fig. 65

In the operational calculus, a different conception of the equality of discontinuous functions might lead to a contradiction.

By the sum of functions f and g of class $\mathcal{K}$ we must consistently understand the sum

$$f+g = \frac{a}{l}+\frac{b}{l} = \frac{1}{l}\Big[\Big\{\int_0^t f(\tau)\,d\tau\Big\}+\Big\{\int_0^t g(\tau)\,d\tau\Big\}\Big] \tag{57.1}$$

$$= \frac{1}{l}\Big\{\int_0^t [f(\tau)+g(\tau)]\,d\tau\Big\}.$$

If

$$h(t) = f(t)+g(t)$$

for every value of t at which f and g are defined, then

$$lh = \Big\{\int_0^t [f(\tau)+g(\tau)]\,d\tau\Big\}$$

and, by (57.1), we have $f+g = h$, *i. e.*

$$\{f(t)\}+\{g(t)\} = \{f(t)+g(t)\}.$$

This equality means that we add functions of class $\mathcal{K}$ by adding their values (at points where they are defined). In this way the definition of the sum $f+g$ as a sum of operators has brought us to the natural definition of a sum of two functions.

We similarly prove the formulas

$$\{f(t)\}-\{g(t)\} = \{f(t)-g(t)\},$$

$$a\{f(t)\} = \{af(t)\} \qquad (a \text{ is a number}).$$

The first formula means that we subtract functions of class $\mathcal{K}$ by subtracting their values (at points where they are defined). The second formula means that we multiply a function of class $\mathcal{K}$ by a number multiplying its values by that number (at points where it is defined).

It is obvious that a sum and a difference of functions of class $\mathcal{K}$ and a product of functions of class $\mathcal{K}$ by a number are again functions of class $\mathcal{K}$. It can be proved that a convolution of functions of class $\mathcal{K}$ is also a function of class $\mathcal{K}$ (see Mikusiński and Ryll-Nardzewski [1], p. 54, Corollaire 2(α)). On this basis it is easy to deduce (in the same way as has been done for continuous functions) the associativity, commutativity and distributivity of convolution in the domain of all the functions of class $\mathcal{K}$. Hence it follows in particular that

$$l^2 \cdot fg = lf \cdot lg = ab$$

and

$$fg = \frac{a}{l} \cdot \frac{b}{l}.$$

Thus the product — in the operational sense — of two functions of class $\mathcal{K}$ is equal to their convolution, as is the case with continuous functions.

It can be seen that all operations are performed on functions of class $\mathcal{K}$ in the same way as on continuous functions.

Remark. The starting point of the concept of operator have been the functions of class $\mathcal{C}$, of which we have formed fractions a/b ($a, b \in \mathcal{C}$). If we start from class $\mathcal{K}$ and formed fractions f/g ($f, g \in \mathcal{K}$), it would give us nothing new, since every fraction of that kind could be represented in the form lf/lg, where the numerator and the denominator already are continuous functions.

Exercise. Let f_λ ($\lambda > 0$) denote a function which has the value 0 in the interval $0 < t < \lambda$ and the value 1 in the interval $\lambda < t < \infty$; prove that

$$f_\lambda \cdot f_\mu = l \cdot f_{\lambda+\mu} \qquad (\lambda, \mu > 0).$$

§ 58. Euler's gamma integral. In § 8 we deduced the formula

$$l^n = \left\{ \frac{t^{n-1}}{(n-1)!} \right\} \tag{58.1}$$

for natural values of n. In the operational calculus it is also useful to introduce non-integer powers of the operator l. We can do this by introducing Euler's gamma integral,

$$\Gamma(\lambda) = \int_0^\infty t^{\lambda-1} e^{-t} dt,$$

which has the property of being equal to $(\lambda-1)!$ for natural values of λ. This integral, considered as a function of the variable λ, is represented in fig. 66.

For our purposes it is sufficient to discuss the integral $\Gamma(\lambda)$ in the case of positive real values of λ. Here is a list of a few essential properties which will be made use of in the sequel:

(I) $\Gamma(\lambda+1) = \lambda\Gamma(\lambda)$;

(II) $\Gamma(n) = (n-1)!$;

(III) $\dfrac{\Gamma(\lambda)\Gamma(\mu)}{\Gamma(\lambda+\mu)} = \int_0^1 t^{\lambda-1}(1-t)^{\mu-1} dt$;

(IV) $\Gamma(\frac{1}{2}) = \sqrt{\pi}$.

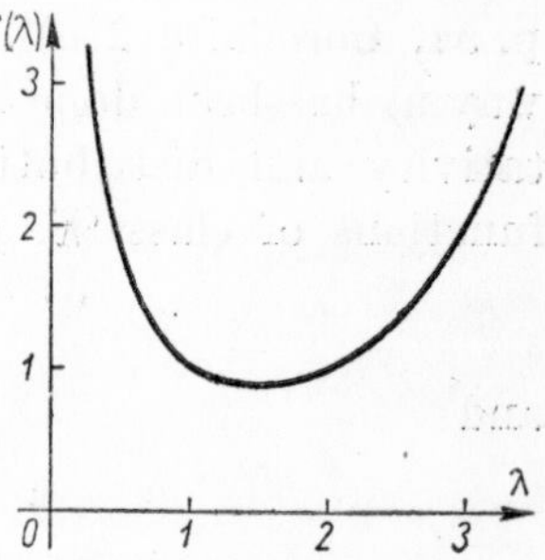

Fig. 66

And here are the proofs of these properties:

Ad (I). Integrating by parts we have

$$\Gamma(\lambda) = \frac{1}{\lambda}\int_0^\infty t^\lambda e^{-t} dt = \frac{1}{\lambda}\Gamma(\lambda+1).$$

Ad (II). For $\lambda = 1$ we have $\Gamma(1) = \int_0^\infty e^{-t} dt = 1$. Hence by formula (I) we have, successively,

$$\Gamma(2) = 1 \cdot \Gamma(1) = 1!, \quad \Gamma(3) = 2\Gamma(2) = 2!, \quad \Gamma(4) = 3\Gamma(3) = 3!$$

and, by induction, generally $\Gamma(n) = (n-1)!$

Ad (III). The product $\Gamma(\lambda)\Gamma(\mu)$ can be represented in the form of the double integral

$$\Gamma(\lambda)\Gamma(\mu) = \iint_D x^{\lambda-1} e^{-x} y^{\mu-1} e^{-y} dx\, dy$$

extended to the domain $D: x, y > 0$. On substituting $x = tu$, $y = (1-t)u$, we shall have

$$\Gamma(\lambda)\Gamma(\mu) = \iint_{D'} t^{\lambda-1}(1-t)^{\mu-1} u^{\lambda+\mu-1} e^{-u} dt\, du$$

where the domain of integration D' is defined by the inequalities: $0 < t < 1$, $u > 0$. Hence

$$\Gamma(\lambda)\Gamma(\mu) = \int_0^1 t^{\lambda-1}(1-t)^{\mu-1}dt \cdot \int_0^\infty u^{\lambda+u-1} e^u du$$

and consequently equality (III).

Ad (IV). By formulas (II) and (III) we have

$$\Gamma(\tfrac{1}{2})\Gamma(\tfrac{1}{2}) = \frac{\Gamma(\frac{1}{2})\Gamma(\frac{1}{2})}{\Gamma(\frac{1}{2}+\frac{1}{2})} = \int_0^1 \frac{dt}{\sqrt{t(1-t)}} = \pi,$$

whence $\Gamma(\frac{1}{2}) = \pm\sqrt{\pi}$. Since the integrand is positive, the plus sign should be adopted.

Owing to formula (I) we can find the value of $\Gamma(\lambda)$ for every λ provided we know its values in any interval of the length 1. The table of approximate values for $1 \leqslant \lambda < 2$ is supplied at the end of the book.

Property (IV) permits an easy deduction of an important formula,

$$\int_0^\infty e^{-\sigma^2} d\sigma = \frac{\sqrt{\pi}}{2}. \tag{58.2}$$

Indeed, we have

$$\Gamma(\tfrac{1}{2}) = \int_0^\infty t^{-\frac{1}{2}} e^{-t} dt$$

and on substituting $t = \sigma^2$

$$\Gamma(\tfrac{1}{2}) = 2\int_0^\infty e^{-\sigma^2} d\sigma,$$

whence, by (IV), formula (58.2) follows.

Exercise. Prove that

$$\binom{-\beta}{\nu} = (-1)^\nu \frac{\Gamma(\beta+\nu)}{\Gamma(\beta)\cdot\nu!}$$

for $\beta > 0$ and natural ν.

§ 59. Non-integer powers of the operators l and $s-\alpha$. Formula (58.1) can be generalized by writing

$$l^\lambda = \left\{\frac{t^{\lambda-1}}{\Gamma(\lambda)}\right\} \tag{59.1}$$

for all positive values of λ; strictly speaking, equality (59.1) should be regarded as a definition of the operator l^λ, which in the case of a natural

λ is identical with the definition given in § 8. We find that with this definition the fundamental property of power is retained:

$$l^\lambda \cdot l^\mu = l^{\lambda+\mu} \qquad (\lambda, \mu > 0). \tag{59.2}$$

Let us work out the proof at once for a more general operator, defined by the formula

$$(s-\alpha)^{-\lambda} = \left\{\frac{t^{\lambda-1}}{\Gamma(\lambda)} e^{\alpha t}\right\} \tag{59.3}$$

where λ is a positive number and α an arbitrary real or complex number. In the case of $\alpha = 0$ formula (59.3) is reduced to the form (59.1) and in the case of a natural λ it is identical with formula (24.2), which has already been deduced (p. 33).

By the definition of convolution we have

$$(s-\alpha)^{-\lambda}(s-\alpha)^{-\mu} = \frac{1}{\Gamma(\lambda)\Gamma(\mu)}\left\{\int_0^t (t-\tau)^{\lambda-1} e^{\alpha(t-\tau)} \tau^{\mu-1} e^{\alpha\tau}\, d\tau\right\}$$

$$= \frac{1}{\Gamma(\lambda)\Gamma(\mu)}\left\{e^{\alpha t}\int_0^t (t-\tau)^{\lambda-1} \tau^{\mu-1}\, d\tau\right\}$$

and on substituting $t-\tau = t\sigma$:

$$(s-\alpha)^{-\lambda}(s-\alpha)^{-\mu} = \frac{1}{\Gamma(\lambda)\Gamma(\mu)}\int_0^1 \sigma^{\lambda-1}(1-\sigma)^{\mu-1} d\sigma \cdot \{t^{\lambda+\mu-1} e^{\alpha t}\}$$

$$= \frac{1}{\Gamma(\lambda+\mu)}\{t^{\lambda+\mu-1} e^{\alpha t}\}.$$

By (59.3) we finally have the formula

$$(s-\alpha)^{-\lambda}(s-\alpha)^{-\mu} = (s-\alpha)^{-\lambda-\mu} \qquad (\lambda, \mu > 0) \tag{59.4}$$

which in the particular case of $\alpha = 0$ becomes formula (59.2).

Having defined the operator $(s-\alpha)^{-\lambda}$ for $\lambda > 0$ we can easily extend its definition to all real values of λ, writing

$$(s-\alpha)^0 = 1 \quad \text{and} \quad (s-\alpha)^\lambda = \frac{1}{(s-\alpha)^{-\lambda}} \qquad (\lambda > 0). \tag{59.5}$$

It is not difficult to verify that with this definition formula (59.4) is valid for any real λ and μ.

For $\alpha = 0$ formulas (59.5) take the form

$$l^0 = 1 \quad \text{and} \quad l^{-\lambda} = \frac{1}{l^\lambda} \qquad (\lambda > 0).$$

Owing to formulas (59.2) and (59.4) operations can be performed on the operators in question in the same way as on ordinary powers.

It will also be observed that if $\lambda \geqslant 1$ then the operator $(s-a)^{-\lambda}$ represents a function of class $\mathcal{C}$, and if $0<\lambda<1$, then it represents a function discontinuous at the point $t=0$ and belonging to class $\mathcal{K}$; finally if $\lambda \leqslant 0$, then the operator $(s-a)^{-\lambda}$ is not a function.

From formula (59.3) we have in particular

$$\frac{1}{\sqrt{s+a}}=\left\{\frac{1}{\sqrt{\pi t}}\, e^{-at}\right\},$$

whence

$$\frac{1}{s\sqrt{s+a}}=\left\{\frac{1}{\sqrt{\pi}}\int_0^t \frac{1}{\sqrt{\tau}}\, e^{-a\tau}\, d\tau\right\}=\left\{\frac{2}{a\sqrt{\pi}}\int_0^{\sqrt{at}} e^{-\tau^2}\, d\tau\right\} \qquad (a>0).$$

Introducing the symbol

$$\text{(59.6)} \qquad \operatorname{erf} t=\frac{2}{\sqrt{\pi}}\int_0^t e^{-\tau^2}\, d\tau$$

we can write

$$\frac{1}{s\sqrt{s+a}}=\left\{\frac{1}{a}\operatorname{erf}\sqrt{at}\right\}.$$

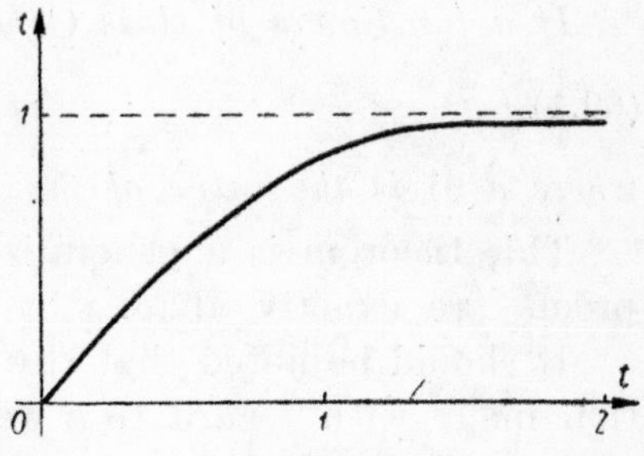

Fig. 67

It can be seen from formula (59.6) that erf is a continuous function which increases in the interval $0 \leqslant t<\infty$ from 0 to 1 according to formula (58.2).

The function $\operatorname{erf} t$ occurs in the theory of probability and is termed the error function, whence the symbol "erf". In German textbooks it is often denoted by the letter φ.

Exercises.

1. Prove the formula

$$l\,\frac{1-a^\lambda l^\lambda}{1-al}=\frac{a}{\Gamma(\lambda)}\left\{\int_t^\infty \tau^{\lambda-1} e^{-a(\tau-t)}\, d\tau\right\} \qquad (a,\lambda>0).$$

2. Prove the formula

$$\binom{-\beta}{\nu}\frac{1}{s^{\nu+\beta}}=\left\{\frac{t^{\beta-1}(-t)^\nu}{\Gamma(\beta)\cdot\nu!}\right\} \qquad (\beta>0,\ \nu \text{ natural}).$$

§ 60. Functions having a derivative of class $\mathcal{K}$. A function a will be said *to have a derivative of class* $\mathcal{K}$ if it is differentiable in the interval $0<t<\infty$ with the exception of points whose number is finite in every finite interval. For example, the function whose graph is given in fig. 68 is differentiable at all points except $t = 1, 2, \ldots$; in every finite interval the number of those points is of course finite. The derivative of the function a is shown in fig. 69.

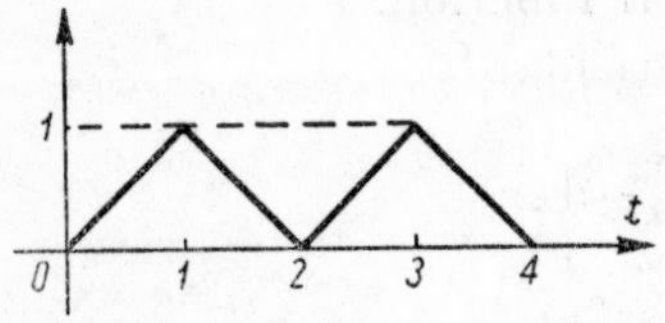

Fig. 68

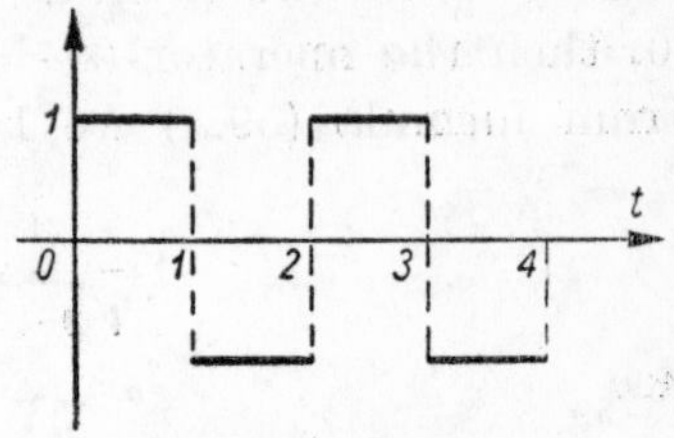

Fig. 69

We have the following theorem:

If a function a of class $\mathcal{C}$ has a derivative a' of class $\mathcal{K}$, then

(60.1) $$sa' = a' + a(0)$$

where $a(0)$ is the value of the function a at the point $t = 0$.

This theorem is a generalization of the theorem given in § 21; their proofs are exactly alike.

It should be noted that the theorem would be false if the only assumption made with regard to a were its being a function of class $\mathcal{K}$. Indeed, suppose that a is a function of class $\mathcal{K}$ defined by the equalities

(60.2) $$a = \left\{\begin{matrix} 0 & \text{for} & 0 \leqslant t < 1 \\ 1 & \text{for} & 1 < t < \infty \end{matrix}\right\};$$

this function is differentiable at all points except $t = 1$ and we have

$$a' = \{0 \quad \text{for} \quad t \neq 1\}.$$

The derivative a' is undefined at the point $t = 1$, being elsewhere equal to 0. According to the definition of equality for functions of class $\mathcal{K}$ we thus have $a' = \{0\} = 0$. Function (60.2) obviously cannot satisfy equality (60.1) since in view of $a(0) = 0$ it would follow that $sa = 0$, and consequently $a = 0$, which is not true.

It will also be observed that every function f of class $\mathcal{K}$ may be represented in the form sa where a is a function of class $\mathcal{C}$: $f = sa$; indeed, it suffices to write $a = lf$. The function a satisfying this relation is of course unique.

Exercise. Give the graphs of the functions represented by the expressions:
(α) $s\{t - 1 + |t - 1|\}$; (β) $s\{|t-1| + |t-2| - |t-3|\}$.

§ 61. Differential equations with a discontinuous right side.

Let us consider the differential equation

$$a_n x^{(n)} + a_{n-1} x^{(n-1)} + \ldots + a_0 x = f,$$

where f is an arbitrary function of class $\mathcal{K}$ and thus not necessarily continuous. The function x will be called the *solution* of this equation if

1° it has $n-1$ continuous derivatives,

2° it has the n-th derivative $x^{(n)}$ at all points where f is continuous,

3° the equation is satisfied at all points where f is continuous.

If we impose initial or boundary conditions at the points where the function f is continuous, then the whole theory is applicable, just as in the case of equations with a continuous right side. It should be observed that without assumption 1° the theorem on the unicity of solutions would be false.

EXAMPLE. Given the differential equation

$$x' + x = f, \tag{61.1}$$

where the function f is defined by the formula

$$f(t) = (-1)^n (t-2n) \quad \text{for} \quad 2n < t < 2n+2 \quad (n = 0, 1, 2, \ldots),$$

we seek a continuous function satisfying the equation everywhere except the points $2, 4, \ldots$ where the function f is discontinuous (fig. 70); as an initial condition we take $x(0) = -1$.

From equation (61.1) we have

$$sx + x = -1 + f,$$

whence

$$x = -\frac{1}{s+1} + \frac{1}{s+1} f$$

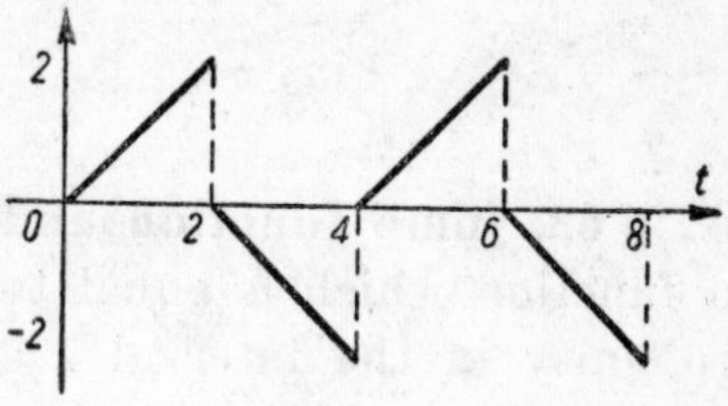

Fig. 70

and

$$x = \left\{-e^{-t} + \int_0^t e^{-t+\tau} f(\tau)\, d\tau\right\} = \left\{e^{-t}\left[-1 + \int_0^t e^{\tau} f(\tau)\, d\tau\right]\right\}.$$

In order to find the above integral observe that

$$\int_{4n}^{4n+2} e^{\tau} f(\tau)\, d\tau = \int_{4n}^{4n+2} e^{\tau}(\tau - 4n)\, d\tau = e^{4n} + e^{4n+2},$$

$$\int_{4n+2}^{4n+4} e^{\tau} f(\tau)\, d\tau = -\int_{4n+2}^{4n+4} e^{\tau}(\tau - 4n - 2)\, d\tau = -e^{4n+2} - e^{4n+4};$$

thus if $4n \leqslant t \leqslant 4n+2$, then

$$x(t) = e^{-t}\Big[-e^{4n} + \int_{4n}^{t} e^{\tau}(\tau-4n)\,d\tau\Big] = t-4n-1,$$

and if $4n+2 \leqslant t \leqslant 4n+4$, then

$$x(t) = e^{-t}\Big[e^{4n+2} + \int_{4n+2}^{t} e^{\tau}(\tau-4n-2)\,d\tau\Big] = -t+4n+3.$$

The last two formulas can be comprised in one,

$$x(t) = (-1)^n(t-2n-1)$$

for $2n \leqslant t \leqslant 2n+2$ $(n = 0, 1, 2, \ldots)$; this function is represented in fig. 71. Differential equations with discontinuous right sides are important in applications to the theory of electric currents, since they permit calculations with a completely arbitrary electromotive force E without the restriction to a continuous electromotive force only.

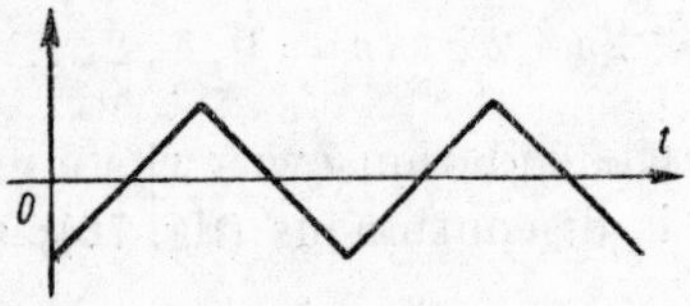

Fig. 71

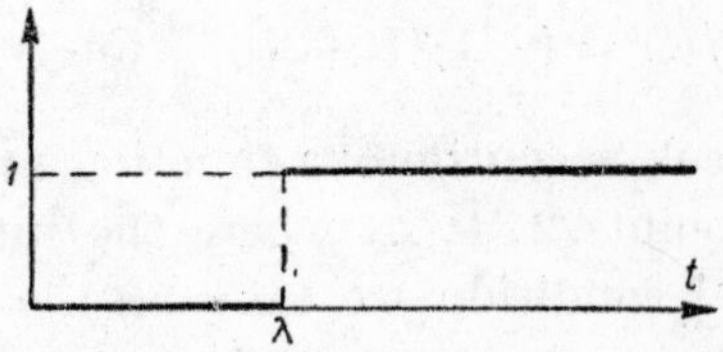

Fig. 72. Jump function

§ 62. Jump function and translation operator. Denote by $\{H_\lambda(t)\}$ a function which is equal to zero in the interval $0 \leqslant t \leqslant \lambda$ and equal to unity in the interval $\lambda \leqslant t < \infty$. This function has only one jump at the point λ, being elsewhere continuous. It is termed the *jump function* or *Heaviside's function.*

It is not so much the jump function as the operator

$$h^\lambda = s\{H_\lambda(t)\} \qquad (\lambda > 0) \tag{62.1}$$

connected with it and termed the *translation operator* that plays an important role in the operational calculus. The term "translation operator" is justified by the following theorem:

If $f(t)$ is an arbitrary function (of class $\mathcal{K}$), then

$$h^\lambda\{f(t)\} = \left\{\begin{matrix} 0 & \textit{for} & 0 \leqslant t < \lambda \\ f(t-\lambda) & \textit{for} & 0 \leqslant \lambda < t \end{matrix}\right\}.$$

This theorem has a very simple geometrical interpretation, as can be seen from figs. 73 and 74. The multiplication of a given function $\{f(t)\}$ by h^λ causes a translation of its graph by the length λ in the positive direction of axis t.

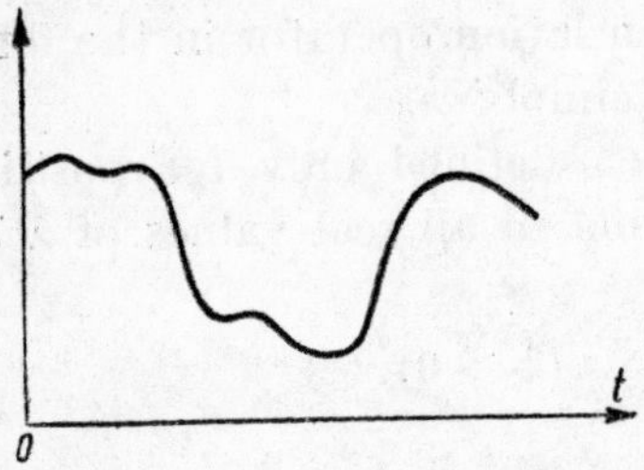

Fig. 73. The graph of $\{f(t)\}$

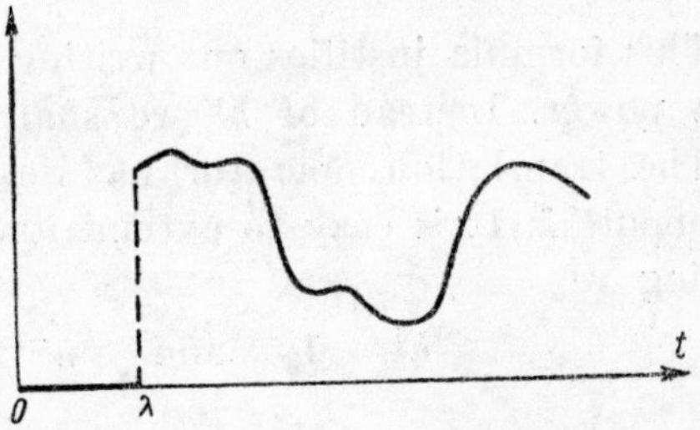

Fig. 74. The graph of $h^\lambda\{f(t)\}$

The theorem can be proved directly by verification. Indeed we have the equality

$$h^\lambda\{f(t)\} = s\{F_\lambda(t)\}$$

where

$$F_\lambda(t) = \int_0^t H_\lambda(t-\tau)f(\tau)\,d\tau.$$

But obviously

$$F_\lambda(t) = \begin{cases} 0 & \text{for} \quad 0 \leqslant t < \lambda, \\ \int_0^{t-\lambda} f(\tau)\,d\tau & \text{for} \quad 0 \leqslant \lambda < t, \end{cases}$$

whence

$$F'_\lambda(t) = \begin{cases} 0 & \text{for} \quad 0 \leqslant t < \lambda, \\ f(t-\lambda) & \text{for} \quad 0 \leqslant \lambda < t. \end{cases}$$

Since $F_\lambda(0) = 0$,

$$h^\lambda\{f(t)\} = s\{F_\lambda(t)\} = \{F'_\lambda(t)\} = \left\{\begin{matrix} 0 & \text{for} & 0 \leqslant t < \lambda \\ f(t-\lambda) & \text{for} & 0 \leqslant \lambda < t \end{matrix}\right\}.$$

This theorem implies that

$$h^\lambda h^\mu f = h^{\lambda+\mu} f \qquad (\lambda > 0,\ \mu > 0). \tag{62.2}$$

This equality is obvious, particularly from the geometrical interpretation, for it makes no difference whether the graph of the function is translated first by the length μ and then again by the length λ or at once by the length $\mu + \lambda$. Since formula (62.2) holds for every function f

of class $\mathcal{K}$, under the assumption that f is not identical with 0 we can multiply it by the operator $1/f$, which gives an important formula,

$$h^\lambda h^\mu = h^{\lambda+\mu}. \tag{62.3}$$

This formula justifies our writing the translation operator in the form of a power. Instead of h^1 we shall write simply h.

The translation operator has so far been defined only for positive exponents λ. It is easy to extend its definition to all real values of λ by writing

$$h^0 = 1 \quad \text{and} \quad h^{-\lambda} = 1/h^\lambda \quad (\lambda > 0).$$

We can easily verify that with this definition formula (62.3) holds for any real λ and μ.

If the function $\{f(t)\}$ is equal to zero in the interval $0 \leqslant t < a$, then we can also translate its graph to the left multiplying that function by the operator $h^{-\lambda}$ provided only that $0 \leqslant \lambda \leqslant a$.

In order to familiarize ourselves with the properties of the translation operator let us discuss a few examples.

EXAMPLE 1. The operator $\dfrac{h^\lambda}{s}$ represents (for fixed λ) the jump function shown in fig. 74. This follows immediately from formula (62.1).

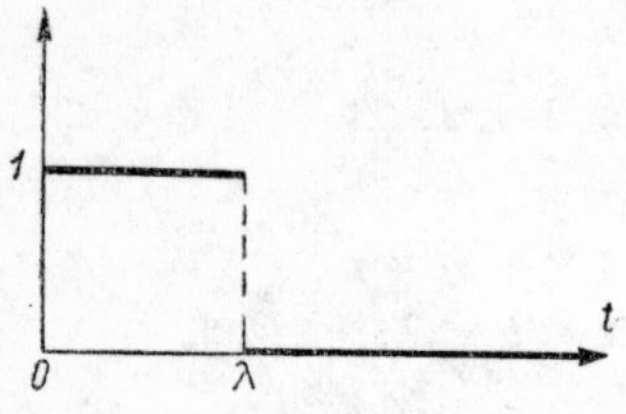

Fig. 75

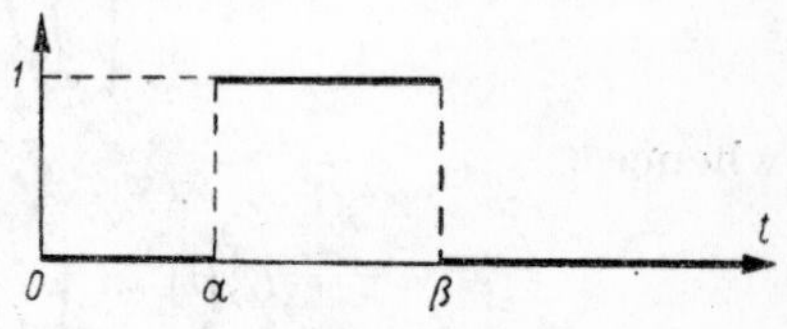

Fig. 76

EXAMPLE 2. The operator $\dfrac{1-h^\lambda}{s}$ is equal to the function $\{1-H_\lambda(t)\}$ whose graph is that given in fig. 75.

EXAMPLE 3. The operator $\dfrac{h^\alpha - h^\beta}{s}$ is equal to the function $\{H_\alpha(t) - H_\beta(t)\}$ whose graph is shown in fig. 76.

EXAMPLE 4. The operator $\dfrac{h^\lambda}{s^2}$ is a function whose graph is obtained from the graph of $1/s^2 = \{t\}$ through a translation by the length λ (fig. 77).

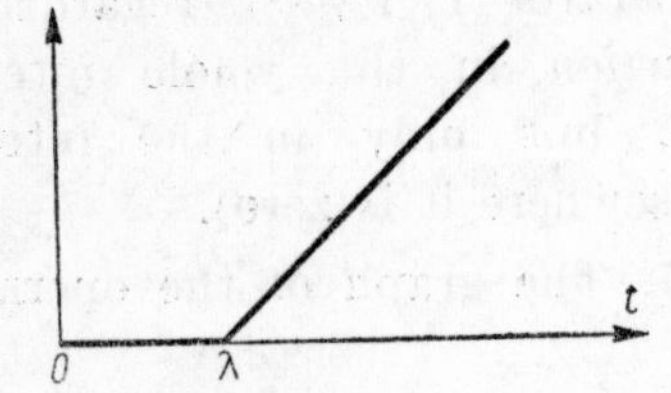

Fig. 77

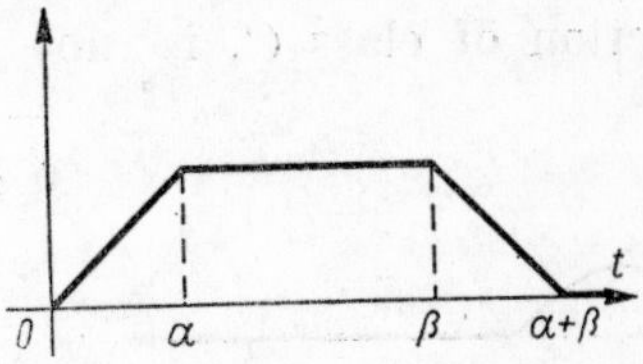

Fig. 78

By combining these functions we can obtain various polygonals, for example $(1-h^{\alpha}-h^{\beta}+h^{\alpha+\beta})/s^2$ (fig. 78) or $(1-7h+7h^{4/3}-h^{7/3})/s^2$ (fig. 79).

EXAMPLE 5. The "tooth" shown in fig. 80 can be obtained by subtracting from the function $\{t\}$ the function $\{\beta+t\}$ translated to the right

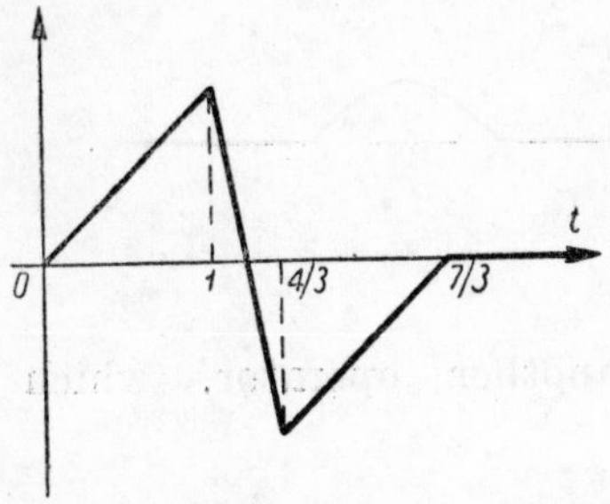

Fig. 79

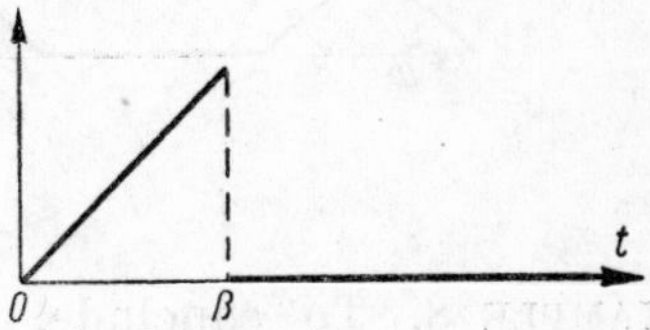

Fig. 80

by the length β. The function obtained in this way will be expressed by the formula

$$\frac{1}{s^2}-\left(\frac{\beta}{s}+\frac{1}{s^2}\right)h^{\beta}.$$

EXAMPLE 6. The geometrical meaning of the operator

$$\frac{1}{1+s^2}(1+h^{\pi})$$

will be found by a translation of the graph of the function $1/(1+s^2) = \{\sin t\}$ (fig. 81) by the length π and a graphical addition of the trans-

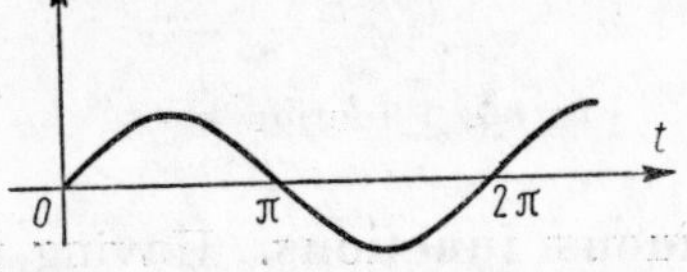

Fig. 81. The graph of $\{\sin t\}$

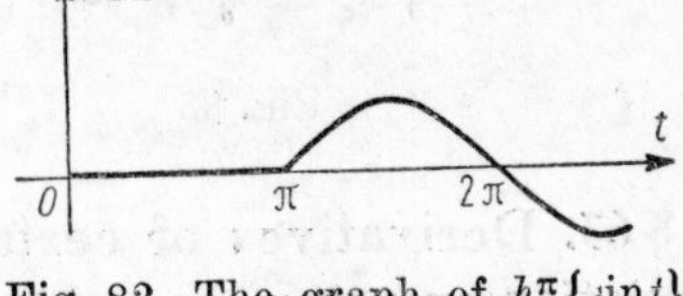

Fig. 82. The graph of $h^{\pi}\{\sin t\}$

lated graph to the original one (fig. 82). We shall thus obtain a half of one wave (fig. 83).

(It will be observed here that the operator $1/(1+s^2)$, regarded as a function of class $\mathcal{C}$, is not a *sine function* in the whole interval $-\infty < t < \infty$, but only in the interval $0 \leqslant t < \infty$; elsewhere it is zero).

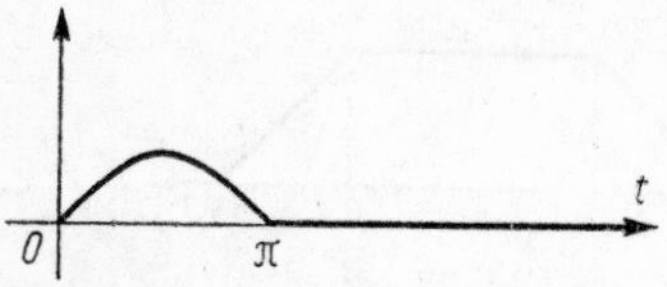

Fig. 83. Sum of these functions

EXAMPLE 7. The graph of the operator

$$\frac{1}{1+s^2}(1+h^{\pi})(1+h^{2\pi}+h^{4\pi})$$

can easily be obtained from the preceeding graph by translating it first by 2π and then by 4π and plotting the three graphs upon one another (fig. 84).

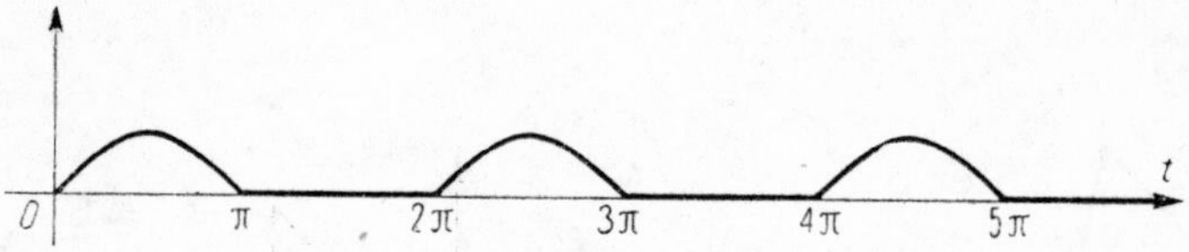

Fig. 84

EXAMPLE 8. To conclude, we give another operator, which is a little more complicated:

$$\frac{3}{5}-\frac{3}{s^2}+\frac{6}{s^2}(h-h^{3/2}+h^2)+\left(\frac{5}{s^3}-\frac{8}{s^2}-\frac{1}{2s}\right)h^3-$$

$$-\frac{1}{3}\left(\frac{7}{s^3}+\frac{16}{s^2}+\frac{13}{2s}\right)h^5-\left(\frac{8}{3s^3}+\frac{5}{s^2}+\frac{13}{3s}\right)h^7.$$

We leave it to the reader to verify that it is a function having the graph shown in fig. 85.

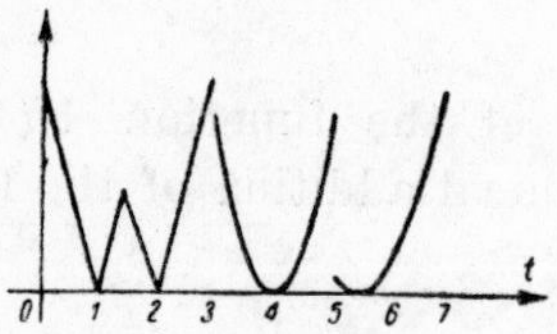

Fig. 85

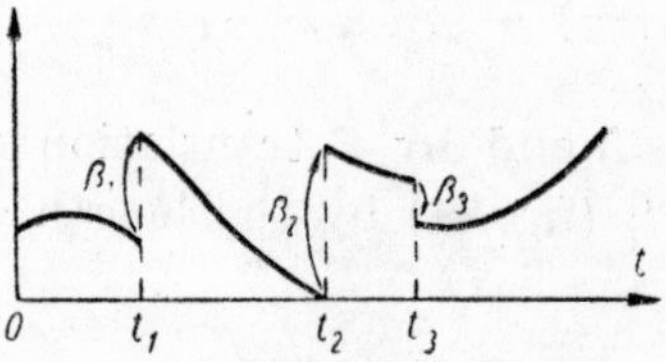

Fig. 86. Function a

§ 63. Derivatives of certain discontinuous functions. Having the translation operator, we can generalize the theorem of § 60.

If a function a has jumps $\beta_1, \ldots, \beta_n$ at the points $t_1, \ldots, t_n$, is elsewhere continuous and has a derivative of class $\mathcal{K}$, then

$$sa = a' + a(0) + \sum_{\nu=1}^{n} \beta_\nu h^{t_\nu} \tag{63.1}$$

where $a(0)$ is the value of the function a at the point $t = 0$.

In the case of all jumps $\beta_1, \ldots, \beta_n$ being equal to zero the function a is continuous and the theorem is reduced to the one discussed in § 60.

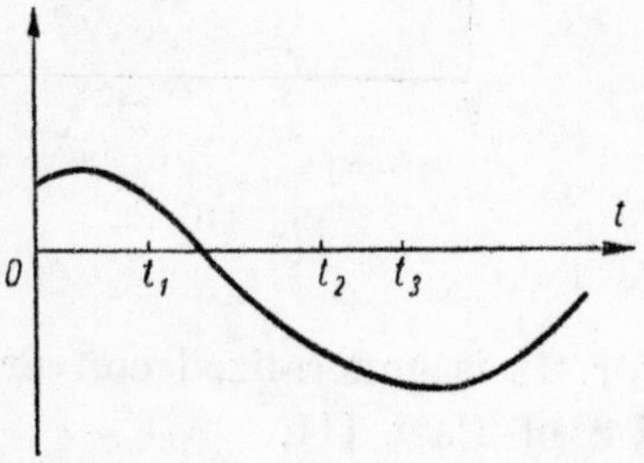

Fig. 87.
The continuous part of function a

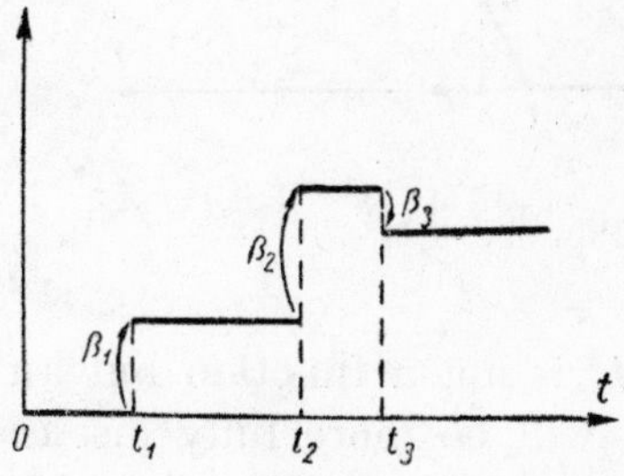

Fig. 88.
The jump-forming part of function a

In order to prove the theorem we represent the function a in the form

$$a = b + \frac{1}{s} \sum_{\nu=1}^{n} \beta_\nu h^{t_\nu}, \tag{63.2}$$

where b constitutes the *continuous part* of the function a, shown in fig. 87, and the remaining sum is the *jump-forming part* of this function, shown in fig. 88.

Since the function b is continuous, we have, by the theorem of § 60,

$$sb = b' + b(0).$$

Multiplying (63.2) by s and considering that $a' = b$, $a(0) = b(0)$, we obtain formula (63.1).

§ 64. Approximation of the translation operator by functions. It is easy to prove the formula

$$\frac{1}{s^2} \frac{h^{\lambda-\varepsilon} - h^{\lambda+\varepsilon}}{2\varepsilon} \to \frac{h^\lambda}{s} \quad (\varepsilon \to 0); \tag{64.1}$$

the proof follows for example from the graph of the functions appearing in this formula (figs 89 and 90).

It is natural to assume, formula (64.1) being multiplied by s, that

(64.2) $$\frac{1}{s}\,\frac{h^{\lambda-\varepsilon}-h^{\lambda+\varepsilon}}{2\varepsilon}\to h^{\lambda}\qquad(\varepsilon\to 0)$$

but this is not convergence in the usual sense, if only because the

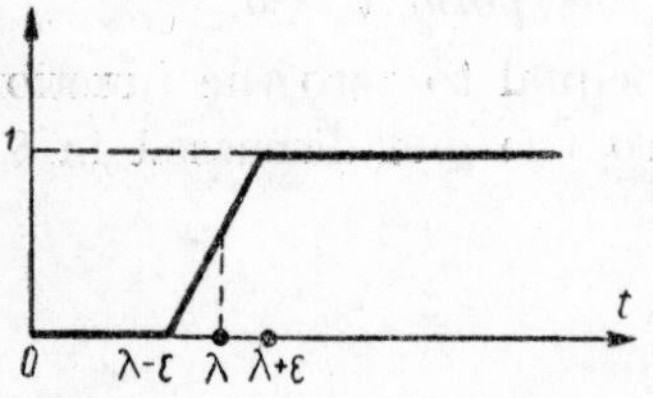

Fig. 89. $\frac{1}{s^2}\cdot\frac{h^{\lambda-\varepsilon}-h^{\lambda+\varepsilon}}{2\varepsilon}$

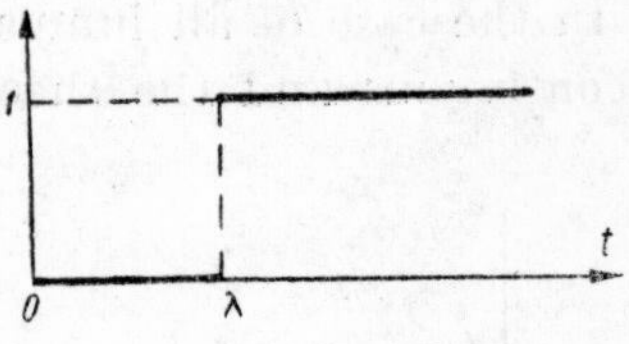

Fig. 90. $\frac{h^{\lambda}}{s}$

limit h^{λ} is not a function but an operator. It is generalized convergence, which will be more fully discussed in § 2 of Part III.

The function on the left side of formula (64.2) has the graph shown in fig. 91; the shaded area is equal to 1. The translation operator h^{λ} can be interpreted as the limit of the function as $\varepsilon\to 0$. As ε decreases, the shaded rectangle becomes more and more elongated retaining the area 1.

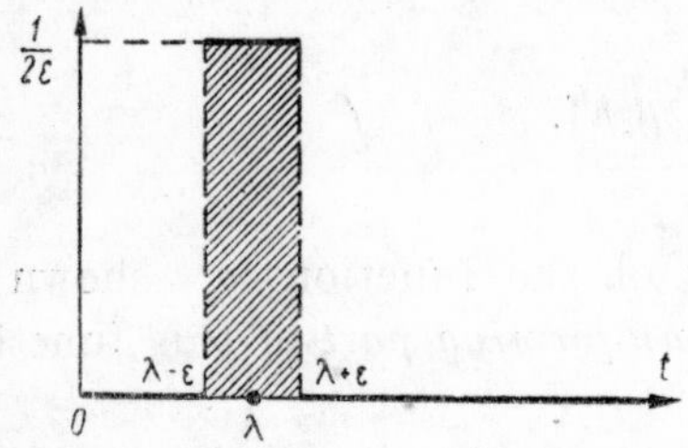

Fig. 91. $\frac{1}{s}\cdot\frac{h^{\lambda-\varepsilon}-h^{\lambda+\varepsilon}}{2\varepsilon}$

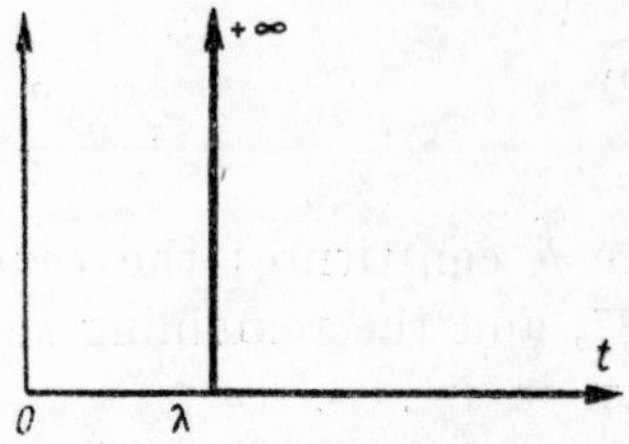

Fig. 92. h^{λ}

Obviously the values of the function tend to zero everywhere except the point $t=\lambda$ at which the value tends to $+\infty$. This is why it is sometimes intuitively assumed that the operator h^{λ} is a function whose value is zero everywhere except the point $t=\lambda$, at which its value is infinity (fig. 92).

This interpretation is widespread among physicists, who give to the translation operator the term *Dirac delta function* and denote it by the symbol $\delta(t-\lambda)$. This interpretation, however, cannot be regarded as an exact definition of the Dirac function, or translation operator, since it does not imply the fundamental properties, *e. g.* the fact that h_{λ}/s is a jump function.

The Dirac function has been introduced in physics in order to simplify calculations. In this case practice has preceded mathematical theory. Actually the Dirac delta function is no function at all in the classical sense and cannot be strictly defined on the grounds of ordinary analysis. In the operational calculus on the other hand this "function" appears in a natural way as the translation operator with a precise meaning.

It is worth mentioning that the Dirac function can also be correctly defined within the theory of distributions (see Schwartz [1]), whose aims, however, are different from those of the operational calculus.

§ 65. Various interpretations of the translation operator. Instead of the function represented in fig. 93, we can take another, more general function h_ε and obtain the same effect.

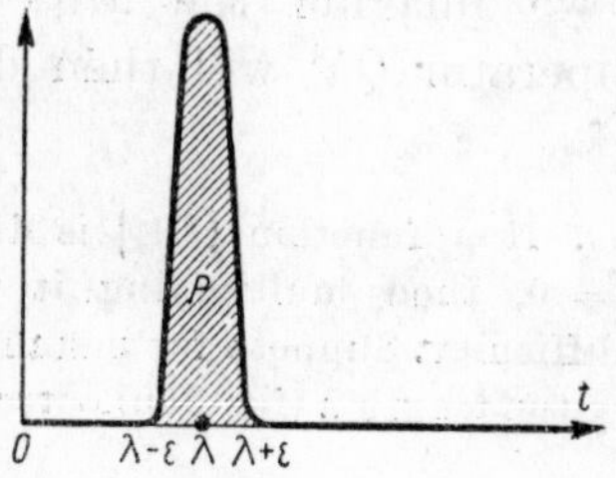

Fig. 93

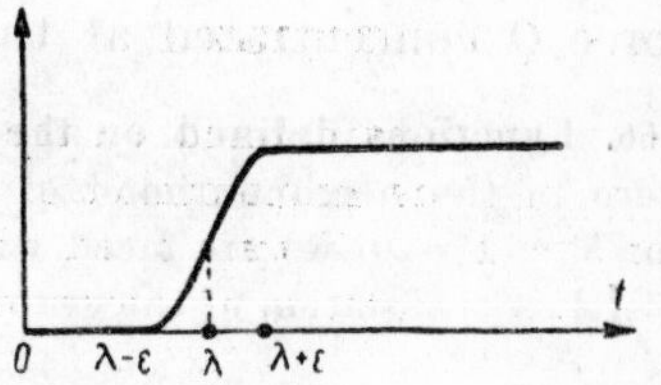

Fig. 94.

Let us assume that the values of $h(t)$ are non-negative everywhere and equal to 0 outside the interval $\lambda-\varepsilon<t<\lambda+\varepsilon$, and that

$$\int_{\lambda-\varepsilon}^{\lambda+\varepsilon} h_\varepsilon(\tau)\,d\tau = 1. \tag{65.1}$$

The geometrical meaning of this equality is that the area P contained between the curve h_ε and the axis t is equal to 1 (fig. 93).

The function h_ε/s has the graph shown in fig. 94; just as is the case with the function shown in fig. 88, it is obvious that

$$\frac{h_\varepsilon}{s} \to \frac{h^\lambda}{s} \quad (\varepsilon \to 0). \tag{65.2}$$

Multiplying this equality by s we can assume that

$$h_\varepsilon \to h^\lambda \quad (\varepsilon \to 0)$$

as we have done in formula (64.2).

The translation operator can thus be interpreted as the limit of the function represented in fig. 95. The shape of that function in the interval $\lambda-\varepsilon<t<\lambda+\varepsilon$ is irrelevant provided the area P has the value 1.

If the area P has constantly the value μ, the operator obtained in the limit will not be h^λ but μh^λ.

The operator h^λ has several important physical interpretations. We shall confine ourselves to a few examples.

The area P may be interpreted as a *mass* μ distributed on the segment $(\lambda-\varepsilon, \lambda+\varepsilon)$. At the limit this mass is concentrated at the point λ. Thus we can assume that the operator μh^λ denotes mass μ concentrated at the point λ.

The function μh_ε may also be regarded as *electromotive force* of short duration, *i. e.*, as an *electromotive impulse*. Taking the duration time of the impulse to be very short and supposing the conditions to be ideal, we can assume that μh^λ in the limit is the impulse acting at the instant $t = \lambda$. In particular, if $\lambda = 0$, we deal with the impulse at the instant $t = 0$ (see § 40).

Another interpretation is obtained if we imagine the area P as a *force* Q distributed on a segment. The operator Qh^λ will then denote the force Q concentrated at the point λ.

§ 66. Functions defined on the whole axis t. If a function $\{f(t)\}$ is different from zero in the neighbourhood of the point $t = 0$, then multiplying it by the operator $h^{-\lambda}$ $(\lambda > 0)$ we are faced with a certain difficulty. Suppose for instance that $\{f(t)\} = \{t\}$. A translation of the graph to the left by the length λ (fig. 95b) corresponds

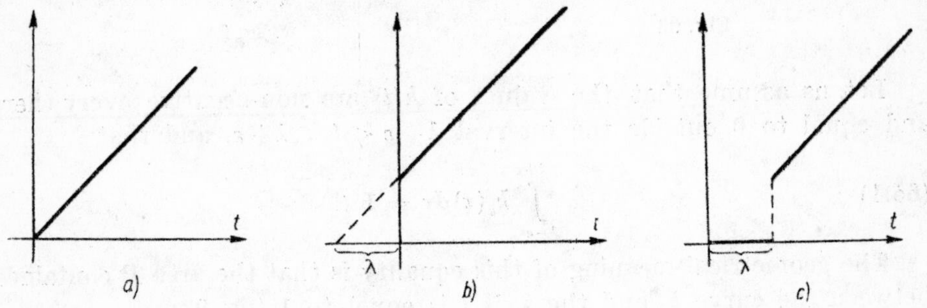

Fig. 95

to the multiplication by $h^{-\lambda}$. But then the graph will shift partly beyond the point $t = 0$ upon the negative part of the axis t. Now in the operational calculus we have so far considered only functions defined in the interval $0 \leqslant t < \infty$. If we simply rejected, after the translation, that part of the graph which corresponds to the negative values of t, then, multiplying the function thus formed by h^λ, we should not obtain the initial function but a different one, represented in fig. 95c, contrary to the equality

$$h^\lambda \cdot h^{-\lambda}\{t\} = 1\cdot\{t\} = \{t\}.$$

Such a rejection is thus inadmissible.

This difficulty can be avoided if we regard an operator of the form $h^{-\lambda} f$ as a function defined in the extended interval $-\lambda \leqslant t < \infty$. We can do so in spite of the fact that the starting point of the theory have been functions of class $\mathcal{C}$, since the very aim of introducing the concept of operators is to include in the calculus new elements, not belonging to $\mathcal{C}$. This is how certain discontinuous functions, the differential operator, the translation operator and other elements have been included in the calculus.

In this book we shall confine ourselves to the discussion of functions which can be represented in the form $h^{-\lambda}f$ where f is a function of class $\mathcal{C}$ or $\mathcal{K}$.

If we apply the operational calculus to describe and investigate a certain physical phenomenon which begins at the instant $t = 0$, then functions of type $h^{-\lambda}f$ can make only a transient appearance in the calculations and always vanish in the final result. Under these circumstances we need not concern ourselves more closely with the direct interpretation of those functions, for it is sufficient to perform the calculations mechanically in accordance with the general operations on operators.

If, however, we are particularly anxious to interpret directly the operations on functions $h^{-\lambda}f$, then, for simplicity, it is best to suppose them to be defined on the whole axis t and their values to be equal to 0 for $t < \lambda$. Number λ may of course vary for different functions. Let us denote the class of those functions by $\mathcal{U}$. According to this interpretation functions of classes $\mathcal{C}$ and $\mathcal{K}$ may be regarded as functions of class $\mathcal{U}$ with values 0 for $t < 0$.

Class $\mathcal{U}$ is wider than class $\mathcal{K}$, just as class $\mathcal{K}$ is wider than class $\mathcal{C}$. Symbolically this may be written as

$$\mathcal{C} < \mathcal{K} < \mathcal{U}.$$

The investigation of functions in the interval $-\infty < t < \infty$ makes it possible to write the fundamental property of the operator of translation in a simpler form,

$$h^{\lambda}\{f(t)\} = \{f(t-\lambda)\},$$

for all values of λ.

If f and g are arbitrary functions of class $\mathcal{U}$, then their product in the operational sense can be written in the form

$$fg = \left\{ \int_{-\infty}^{+\infty} f(t-\tau)g(\tau)\,d\tau \right\}. \tag{66.1}$$

This is obvious in the particular case where f and g belong to class $\mathcal{C}$ or $\mathcal{K}$ since then the integral in (66.1) is reduced to an ordinary convolution, $\int_0^t f(t-\tau)g(\tau)\,d\tau$. In order to prove formula (66.1) in the general case we write the functions f and g in the form

$$f = h^{-\lambda}f_1 = \{f_1(t+\lambda)\} \quad \text{and} \quad g = h^{-\mu}g_2 = \{g_2(t+\mu)\},$$

where f_1 and g_1 belong to class $\mathcal{K}$. Then

$$fg = h^{-(\lambda+\mu)}f_1g_1 = h^{-(\lambda+\mu)}\left\{ \int_{-\infty}^{+\infty} f_1(t-\tau)g_1(\tau)\,d\tau \right\}.$$

The function represented by the last integral has the value 0 for $t < 0$. In view of the properties of the translation operator we can further write

$$fg = \left\{ \int_{-\infty}^{+\infty} f_1(t+\lambda+\mu-\tau)g_1(\tau)\,d\tau \right\},$$

which integral is obviously equal to zero for $t < -(\lambda+\mu)$. By a simple substitution we obtain hence

$$fg = \left\{ \int\limits_{-\infty}^{+\infty} (t+\lambda-\tau)\, g_1(\tau-\mu)\, d\tau \right\}$$

which leads to formula (66.1).

Remark. An operational calculus can be formed by starting from functions of class $\mathcal{U}$; then of course the convolution would have to be defined at once by means of formula (66.1). That, however, would give us nothing essentially new since the fraction f/g $(f, g \in \mathcal{U})$ may, for a suitable λ, be represented in the form $lh^\lambda f/lh^\lambda g$, where the numerator and the denominator are functions of class $\mathcal{C}$.

Another suggestion is to form an operational calculus starting from the class of functions defined in the interval $-\infty < t < \infty$ but not necessarily equal to 0 to the left of a certain point. That of course would give greater generality. But then a convolution of functions not identically equal to zero might be equal to zero, for example

$$\{1\}\left\{\frac{t}{1+t^2}\right\} = \left\{ \int\limits_{-\infty}^{\infty} \frac{\tau}{1+\tau^2}\, d\tau \right\} = 0.$$

In such a calculus the convolution would not have its fundamental property, corresponding to Titchmarsh's theorem, which would make the introduction of fractions impossible (see § 14) and thus overthrow the whole theory so far evolved.

CHAPTER VIII

APPLICATIONS TO THE STATICS OF BEAMS [1]

§ 67. Kinds of load. In the statics of beams we consider *continuous loads*, expressed by functions, and *concentrated forces* and *concentrated moments*, which cannot be expressed by functions. All these kinds of loads are expressed in a simple manner by operators. The term "continuous moment" is often used, but this concept gives us nothing new and can be reduced to the former concepts, as will be seen in § 68.

A *continuous load* is a load distribution expressed by a function q that is continuous (fig. 96) or sectionally continuous (fig. 97).

The function

$$\frac{p}{s}\,\frac{h^{\lambda-\varepsilon}-h^{\lambda+\varepsilon}}{2\varepsilon} \tag{67.1}$$

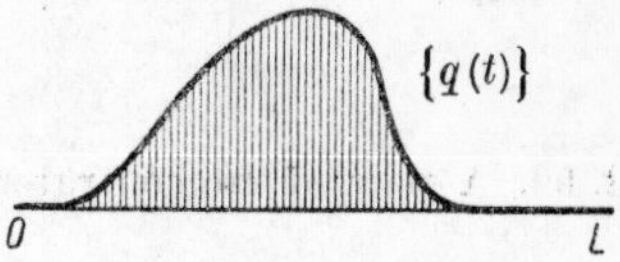

Fig. 96. $\{q(t)\}$ — continuous load

shown in fig. 97 corresponds to a uniform load on the segment $(\lambda-\varepsilon, \lambda+\varepsilon)$; it is continuous except at the points $\lambda-\varepsilon$ and $\lambda+\varepsilon$ (see § 62, example 3). The shaded area P represents the total load of the beam.

We usually conceive a *concentrated force* as the limit load when the total load P remains unchanged and the length 2ε of the loaded part of the beam decreases to zero (fig. 98). Technologists grasp this physical

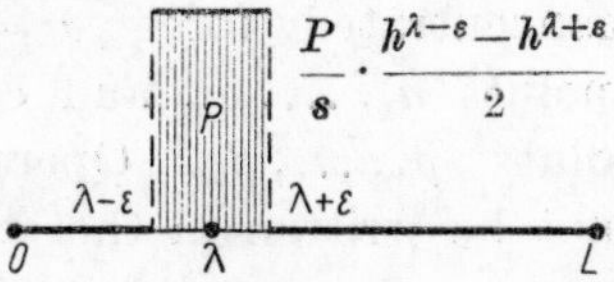

$\frac{P}{s}\cdot\frac{h^{\lambda-\varepsilon}-h^{\lambda+\varepsilon}}{2}$

Fig. 97. Uniform load of a part of beam

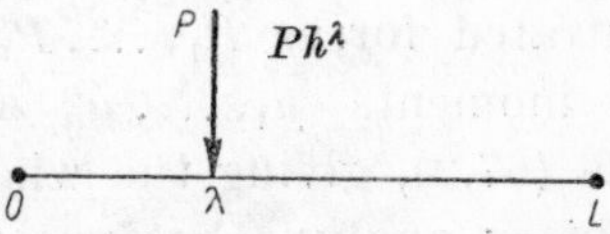

Fig. 98. Concentrated force

concept intuitively. It has no equivalent in classical analysis. In the operational calculus, according to § 65, it is the product Ph^{λ}, constituting the limit of expression (67.1) as $\varepsilon \to 0$, that corresponds to this concept.

---

[1] This chapter has been written in collaboration with S. Drobot.

Thus *the concentrated force P acting at the point Ph^{λ} is represented by the operator Ph^{λ}*. P is positive if the force acts downwards and negative if it acts upwards.

A pair of concentrated loads P acting at the points $\lambda-\varepsilon$ and $\lambda+\varepsilon$ (fig. 99) is represented by the operator $P(h^{\lambda-\varepsilon}-h^{\lambda+\varepsilon})$. This pair gives the moment of force μ equal to the product of the force P by the arm 2ε.

A *concentrated moment* is conceived as the limit load of a pair of concentrated forces when μ remains unchanged and the length of the arm 2ε decreases to zero (fig. 100). This intuitive concept has no counterpart in classical analysis but there is an operator corresponding to it. Namely a pair of concentrated forces with the moment μ is expressed by the operator

$$\frac{\mu}{2\varepsilon}(\lambda^{\lambda-\varepsilon}-h^{\lambda+\varepsilon}) = s\frac{\mu}{s}\,\frac{h^{\lambda-\varepsilon}-h^{\lambda+\varepsilon}}{2\varepsilon};$$

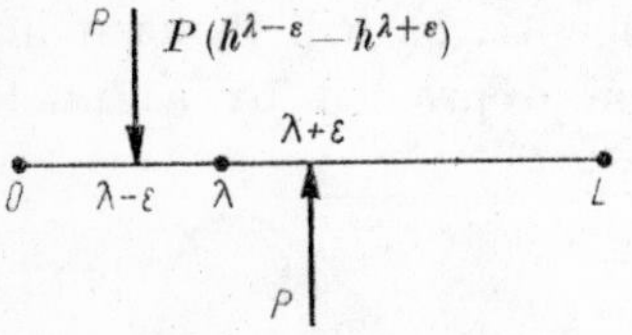

Fig. 99. A pair of concentrated forces

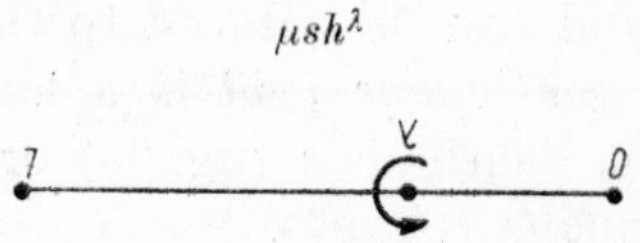

Fig. 100. A concentrated moment

as $\varepsilon \to 0$ we obtain hence in the limit the operator $s \cdot \mu h^{\lambda}$. Thus *a concentrated moment μ acting at a point λ is represented by the operator $\mu s h^{\lambda}$*. Number μ is positive if the moment acts in the opposite direction to that of the hands of a clock, and negative if it acts clockwise.

Loads occurring in practice are often mixed. The operator

$$F = q + \sum_{i=1}^{m} P_i h^{\alpha_i} + \sum_{i=1}^{n} \mu_i s h^{\beta_i} \tag{67.2}$$

represents a load consisting of a non-concentrated force $q = \{q(t)\}$ concentrated forces $P_1, \ldots, P_m$ acting at points $\alpha_1, \ldots, \alpha_m$ and concentrated moments $\mu_1, \ldots, \mu_n$ acting at points $\beta_1, \ldots, \beta_n$. Operational formula (67.2), giving the whole load, cannot be written in the symbols of ordinary analysis because translation operators appear in it side by side with functions.

EXAMPLE.

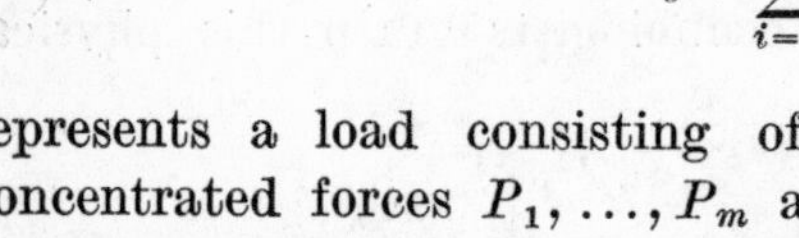

$$F = -20 + \frac{30}{s}(1-h) - 15sh^2 - 10h^3.$$

Exercise. Write operationally the following loads:

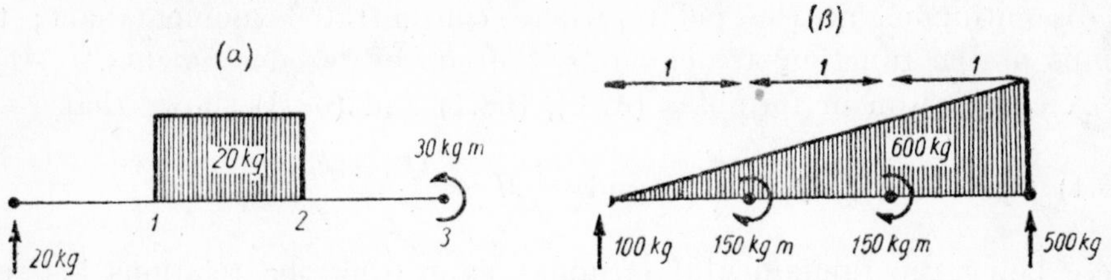

§ 68. Transverse force and bending moment. In statics the *transverse force* at a point t is the term given to the sum of forces acting to the left of the point t together with the reactions in the supports; concentrated forces are added algebraically and non-concentrated forces are integrated. If there are no concentrated moments, the transverse force is expressed by the formula

$$Q = \frac{q}{s} + \sum_{i=1}^{m} \frac{P_i}{s} h^{a_i},$$

i. e., it is an ordinary function. This function is discontinuous at the points where concentrated forces act; the jumps of the function are equal to the magnitudes of the concentrated forces. Graphs of such transverse forces are often given in manuals of statics. Now, concentrated moments are usually neglected in calculating transverse forces because the sum $\sum_{i=1}^{n} \mu_i h^{\beta_i}$ is not a function. In the operational calculus we can define the transverse force taking also the concentrated moments into consideration

$$Q = \frac{q}{s} + \sum_{i=1}^{m} \frac{P_i}{s} h^{a_i} + \sum_{i=1}^{n} \mu_i h^{\beta_i}. \tag{68.1}$$

The *bending moment* at a point t is what we call the sum of the moments of all forces to the left of that point together with the reactions in the supports (the moments in question being taken with respect to the point t)

$$M(t) = \int_0^t (t-\tau) q(\tau) d\tau + \sum_{i=1}^{m(t)} P_i (t - a_i) + \sum_{i=1}^{n(t)} \mu_i; \tag{68.2}$$

the sum comprises only the terms referring to the points on the left of t. Operationally the bending moment will be written as follows

$$M = \frac{q}{s^2} + \sum_{i=1}^{m} \frac{P_i}{s^2} h^{a_i} + \sum_{i=1}^{n} \frac{\mu_i}{s} h^{\beta_i}. \tag{68.3}$$

The bending moment is always an ordinary function. This function is discontinuous at the points where concentrated moments act; the jumps of the function are equal to the concentrated moments.

A comparison of formulas (67.2), (68.1) and (68.3) shows that

$$Q = \frac{F}{s} \quad \text{and} \quad M = \frac{Q}{s} = \frac{F}{s}, \tag{68.4}$$

these being the fundamental formulas expressing the relations between the load, the transverse force and the bending moment. Owing to the operational treatment these formulas have considerable generality, being at the same time very simple in form.

EXAMPLE.

a.

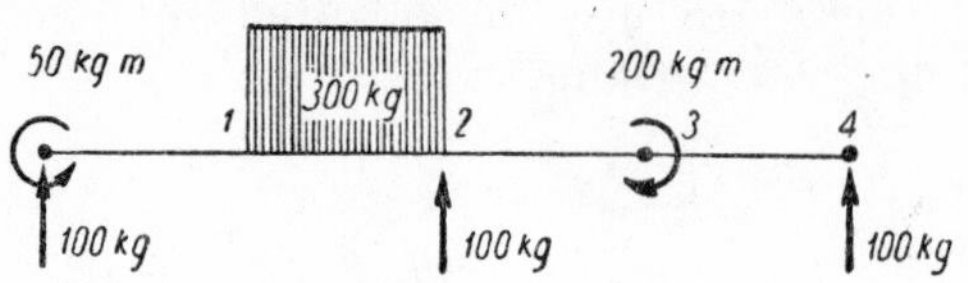

Load:

$$F = 50s - 100 + \frac{300}{s}(h - h^2) - 100h^2 - 200sh^3 - 100h^4.$$

b.

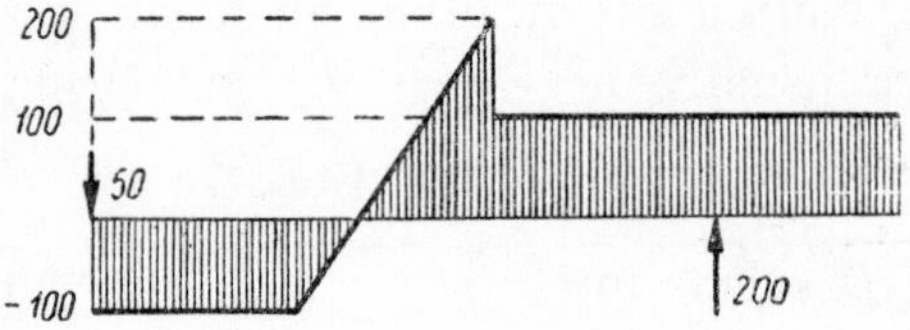

Transverse force:

$$Q = 50 - \frac{100}{s} + \frac{300}{s^2}(h - h^2) - \frac{100h^2}{s} - 200h^3 - \frac{100h^4}{s}.$$

c.

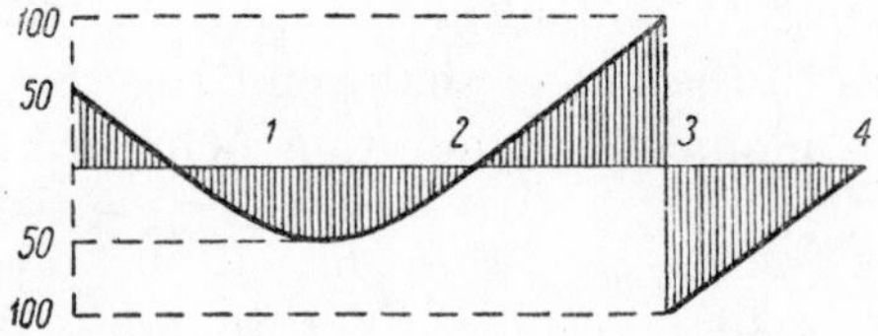

Bending moment:

$$M = \frac{50}{s} - \frac{100}{s^2} + \frac{300}{s^3}(h - h^2) - \frac{100h^2}{s^2} - \frac{200h^3}{s} - \frac{100h^4}{s^2}.$$

The continuous moment is often mentioned as a new kind of load. For instance, if the bending moment increases linearly in the interval

$[\alpha_1, \alpha_2]$ (fig. 101), the continuous moment is considered to be uniformly distributed in $[\alpha_1, \alpha_2]$. The bending moment being then expressed by the operator $M = \frac{P}{s^2}(h^{\alpha_1} - h^{\alpha_2})$, formulas (68.4) imply that

(68.5) $$F = P(h^{\alpha_1} - h^{\alpha_2}),$$

i. e., that we simply have a pair of forces to deal with.

This pair of forces can of course be represented by fig. 102, and it is not necessary to introduce a new graphical representation, as in fig. 103.

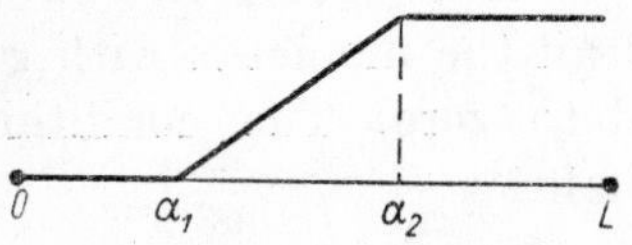

Fig. 101

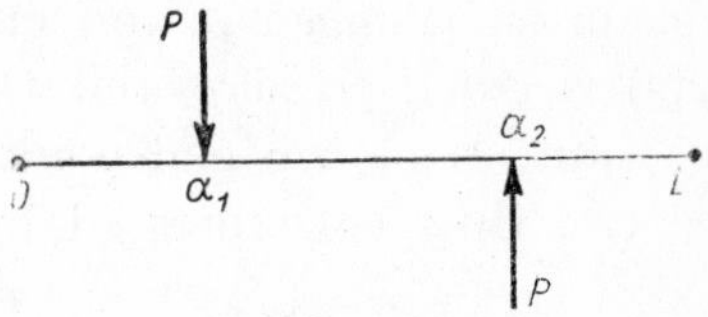

Fig. 102

The same conclusion may be reached intuitively. Let us imagine that an interval $[\alpha_1, \alpha_2]$ has been divided into n partial intervals and that in each of those intervals a pair of concentrated forces $P(h^{t_{i-1}} - h^{t_i})$ act. Intuition tells us that as $n \to \infty$ we shall obtain a moment uniformly distributed over the whole segment. But, as can be seen from fig. 104, the concentrated forces acting inside the interval reduce one another and only the concentrated forces acting at the initial point and at the end point of the segment remain. Together they form a pair of forces (68.5), which does not change as $n \to \infty$.

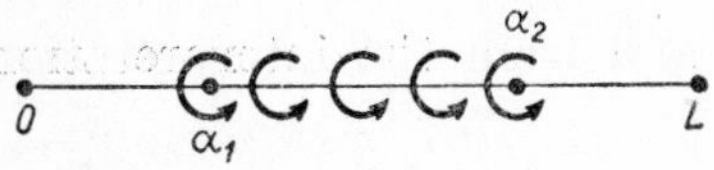

Fig. 103

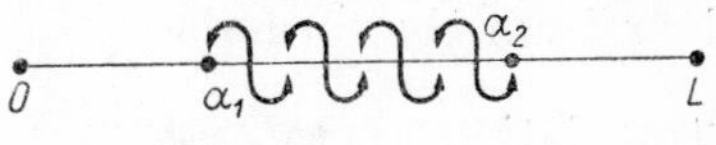

Fig. 104

Also in a more general case the concept of continuous moment gives us nothing new. Suppose the distribution of the moment to be given by a function $\{Q(t)\}$ having jumps $P_1, \ldots, P_m$ at points $\alpha_1, \ldots, \alpha_2$. Then, by formula (63.2), we have (¹)

$$F = sQ = Q' + Q(0) + \sum_{i-1}^{m} P_i h^{\alpha_i}.$$

(¹) Formula (63.2) is true under the assumption that the function Q is sectionally continuous and has a derivative of class $\mathcal{K}$, but in statics no other functions are considered.

Hence it is obvious that the load simply consists of the continuous load Q' and the concentrated forces $Q(0)$, $P_1, \ldots, P_m$ acting at the points $0, a_1, \ldots, a_m$.

Exercise. Express operationally the transverse load and the bending moment for the loads given in the figures on p. 129.

§ 69. Conditions of balance. Anyone with a knowledge of statics can easily establish the conditions of balance. But it is also worth knowing how to establish them from the shape of the operators occurring in the calculation.

A beam is balanced if and only if the total load (together with the supports) is equal to zero and the sum of all the moments with respect to one point, *e. g.*, the end-point, is equal to zero. The conditions of balance can thus be expressed by the equalities

(69.1) $$Q(L) = 0 \quad \text{and} \quad M(L) = 0$$

where L is the length of the beam.

The whole difficulty is reduced to the finding of the value at the point L of a function expressed operationally. It is comparatively easy to do so for functions occurring in the statics of beams. Namely it suffices to know that

(69.2) $$\left[\frac{1}{s^k} h^a\right]_L = \frac{(L-a)^{k-1}}{(k-1)!} \qquad (k \text{ natural, } 0 \leqslant a \leqslant L),$$

i. e., that the function $\frac{1}{s^k} h^a$ has at L the value $\frac{(L-a)^{k-1}}{(k-1)!}$, which is obvious from the formula $\frac{1}{s^k} = \left\{\frac{t^{k-1}}{(k-1)!}\right\}$ and from the interpretation of the translation operator h^a.

Formula (69.2) implies, as particular cases, the following practical formulas:

$$\left[\frac{\gamma}{s} h^a\right] = \gamma \qquad (0 \leqslant a \leqslant L),$$

$$\left[\frac{\gamma}{s^2}(h^a - h^\beta)\right]_L = \gamma(\beta - a) \qquad (0 \leqslant a < \beta \leqslant L).$$

Owing to these formulas we easily find that for instance the value of the function

$$M = \frac{1}{s}(50 - 200h^3) - \frac{100}{s^2}(1 + h^2 + h^4) + \frac{300}{s^3}(h - h^2)$$

at the point $L = 4$ is equal to

$$50-200-100(4+2+0)+300\frac{3^2-2^2}{2} = 0.$$

If the operator beside terms of type $\frac{1}{s^k}h^a$ has terms of type

$$\gamma h^a \quad \text{or} \quad \gamma s h^a \quad (0 \leqslant a \leqslant L),$$

the last terms are omitted in calculation of the value of the operator. This interpretation of the value of an operator at a point corresponds to the obvious assumption that, for instance, in finding the total transverse force we neglect the concentrated moments.

For instance the value of the operator

$$Q = 50-200h^3-\frac{100}{s}(1+h^2+h^4)+\frac{300}{s^2}(h-h^2)$$

at the point 1 is equal to

$$-100(1+1+1)+300(2-1) = 0.$$

Applying this method of calculation and using formulas (69.1) we can easily determine the reactions if the load of a beam is given by an operator.

EXAMPLE 1. The load of a beam whose length is 4 is equal to

$$\frac{100}{s}(1-h)+50h^2-50sh^3.$$

The beam is supported at both ends. We are determine the reactions on the supports.

On the supports we have concentrated forces $-A$ and $-Bh^4$, which together with the given load make up the total load

$$F = \frac{100}{s}(1-h)+(-A+50h^2-8h^4)-50sh^3.$$

Hence we find the operators for the transverse force and the bending moment,

$$Q = \frac{100}{s^2}(1-h)+\frac{1}{s}(-A+50h^2-Bh^4)-50h^3,$$

$$M = \frac{100}{s^3}(1-h)+\frac{1}{s^2}(-A+50h^2-Bh^4)-\frac{50h^3}{s},$$

and, by formulas (69.1), the conditions of balance

$$100(1-0)+(-A+50-B) = 0,$$

$$50(4^2-3^2)+(-4A+2\cdot 50)-50 = 0.$$

From the second of the above formulas we obtain $A = 100$ and then from the first $B = 50$. These are the desired reactions on the supports.

EXAMPLE 2. Calculate the reactions for a beam of length 4 fixed at point 0 under the same load as that given in the preceding example.

We have here a concentrated force $-A$ and a concentrated moment μs acting at the point 0; consequently the total load is

$$F = \frac{100}{s^2}(1-h)+(-A+50h^2)+\mu s-50sh^3,$$

the transverse force and the bending moment being

$$Q = \frac{100}{s^2}(1-h)+\frac{1}{s^2}(-A+50h^2)+\mu-50h^3,$$

$$M = \frac{100}{s^3}(1-h)+\frac{1}{s^2}(-A+50h^2)+\frac{1}{s}(\mu-50h^3).$$

From formulas (69.1) we obtain the conditions of balance

$$\begin{aligned} &100(1-0)+(-A+50) = 0, \\ &50(4^2-3^2)+(-4A+250)+(\mu-50) = 0, \end{aligned} \tag{69.3}$$

whence $A = 150$ and $\mu = 200$. These are the required reactions at the point of fixing the beam.

Instead of equation (69.3) we can take another one, considering that beyond point 3 there is no load on the beam. Assuming the length of the beam to be 3, instead of (69.3) we obtain the equality

$$50(3^2-2^2)+(-3A+50)+(\mu-50) = 0,$$

which in effect gives the same value, $\mu = 200$.

Exercise. Verify by calculation that the conditions of balance are observed in the examples given in figs on p. 129 and 130.

§ 70. Deflection of beams. If the function $y(t)$ represents the deflection of the beam, then with regard to the insignificant deformations occurring in practice the curvature of deflection is assumed to be equal to the second derivative $y''(t)$. Moreover, it is usually assumed that the curvature is proportional at each point to the bending moment $M(t)$. Hence we have the equation

$$y''(t) = \varkappa M(t).$$

The coefficient $\varkappa$ is calculated from the formula $\varkappa = 1/EI$ where E is the Young modulus and I the moment of inertia of the beam section.

The operational equation of deflection of the beam has the form

$$s^2 y = \varkappa M + C + Ds,$$

where the constants C and D are the values of the function y and its derivative at the point 0. In particular these constants are equal to zero when the beam is rigidly (horizontally) fixed at that point.

From the above equation we determine the deflection of the beam

$$y = \frac{\varkappa M}{s^2} + \frac{C}{s^2} + \frac{D}{s}. \tag{70.1}$$

E. g., the shape of the beam in example 1 of the preceding section is given by the operator

$$y = \varkappa\left[\frac{100}{s^5}(1-h) + \frac{1}{s^4}(-100+50h^2-50h^4) - \frac{50h^3}{s^3}\right] + \frac{C}{s^2} + \frac{D}{s}. \tag{70.2}$$

Since the beam is supported at the points 0 and L, we have $y(0) = 0$ and $y(L) = 0$. The first condition gives $D = 0$ and the second

$$\varkappa\left[\tfrac{100}{24}(4^4-3^4) + \tfrac{1}{6}(-100\cdot 4^3 + 50\cdot 2^3 - 50) - \tfrac{1}{2}\cdot 50\right] + 4C + D = 0, \tag{70.3}$$

whence $C = 76\frac{1}{24}\varkappa$.

It is easier to find the shape of the deflection curve when the beam is rigidly fixed at the point 0, as in example 2, because then we can write at once $C = D = 0$.

Exercise. Find the deflection of the beams

(α) represented in figs on p. 128 in the example and in exercise (β) under the assumption that their ends rest freely on supports;

(β) represented in figs on p. 129 in exercise (α) and on p. 130 in the example under the assumption that their left-hand ends are rigidly fixed.

§ 71. Support beams.

§ 71. Support beams. Beams supported at interior points are called *support beams*. In this section we shall confine ourselves to beams supported (freely) at two points, γ_1 and γ_2. Then the constants C and D appearing in equation (70.1) are determined from the conditions

$$y(\gamma_1) = 0 \quad \text{and} \quad y(\gamma_2) = 0.$$

The only new difficulty lies in the fact that we must be able to calculate the value of a function at any point γ from the operational form. For this purpose we can use formula (69.2) replacing in it L by γ; however, all terms in which $a > \gamma$ should be omitted, the function $\frac{1}{s^k} h^a$ being equal to zero for $t = \gamma < a$.

As an example let us take a beam whose length is 4, supported at the points *2* and *3*, with the load

$$\frac{180}{s^2}(1-h^4)\frac{720h^4}{s}.$$

Denoting by A and B the reactions on the supports we shall have the total load

$$F = -Ah^2 + \frac{180}{s^2}(1-h^4) - \frac{720h^4}{s} - Bh^3.$$

From the equations of balance $Q(4) = 0$ and $M(4) = 0$ we calculate $A = 480$ and $B = 960$. Consequently the deflection curve of the beam has the form

$$y = \varkappa\left[-\frac{480h^2}{s^4} + \frac{180}{s^6}(1-h^4) - \frac{720h^4}{s^5} - \frac{960h^3}{s^4}\right] + \frac{C}{s^2} + \frac{D}{s}.$$

The constants C and D are determined from the conditions

$$y(2) = \varkappa\,\tfrac{180}{120}\cdot 2^5 + 2C + D = 0, \quad y(3) = \varkappa\left[-\tfrac{480}{6}1^2 + \tfrac{180}{120}\cdot 3^5\right] + 3C + D = 0,$$

and in this way the values $C = -386\frac{1}{2}\varkappa$ and $D = 425\varkappa$ are obtained.

Exercise. Find the deflection curve of a beam of length 4, supported at the points 1 and 4, on which concentrated loads $300(1+h^2+h^4)$ act.

§ 72. Statically indeterminate cases. In the examples considered so far finding the deflection has necessitated taking into account four conditions in all: two statical conditions (conditions of balance) and two geometrical ones, depending on the manner of fixing the beam. Statical conditions have been sufficient for finding the reactions on the supports but insufficient for finding the deflection curve.

If the number of geometrical conditions is $n > 2$, then the statical conditions are no longer sufficient for the finding of n unknown reactions on the supports. This case is termed *statically indeterminate.* It is then impossible to find the reactions without considering the geometrical conditions. Indeed, those conditions taken together with the statical conditions give $n+2$ equations, and such is the number of all the unknowns, since besides the unknown reactions we have two unknown constants, C and D, occurring in the equation of the deflection (70.1).

Example 1. Find the reactions on the supports for a beam of length 4, rigidly fixed at one end, supported at the other end (fig. 105) and having the load

$$R = \frac{300}{s}(h - h^2) - 100h^2 - 200sh^3.$$

The load together with the reactions totals

$$F = \frac{300}{s}(h - h^2) - A - 100h^2 - Bh^4 + \mu s - 200sh^3,$$

where the concentrated force A and the concentrated moment μs are the reactions at the point 0, and the concentrated force $-Bh^4$ is the reaction at the point *4*. Hence we find Q, M and y from formulas (68.4) and (70.1). The expression for y contains, besides the unknowns A, B, μ, two more unknowns, C and D. All these unknowns are determined from the system of equations

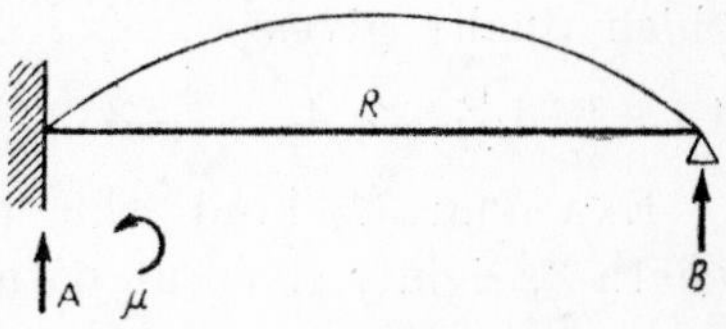

Fig. 105

$$Q(4) = M(4) = y(0) = y'(0) = y(4) = 0,$$

i. e.,

$$Q(4) = 300\cdot(2-1) - A - 100 - B = 0,$$

$$M(4) = 150(3^2 - 2^2) - 4A - 200 + \mu - 200 = 0,$$

$$y(0) = D = 0,$$

$$y'(0) = C = 0,$$

$$y(4) = \varkappa\left[\frac{300}{24}(3^4 - 2^4) - \frac{A}{6}4^3 - \frac{100}{6}2^3 + \frac{\mu}{2}4^2 - \frac{200}{2}\cdot 1\right] = 0;$$

we obtain hence

$$A = 104\frac{15}{128}, \quad B = 95\frac{115}{128}, \quad C = D = 0, \quad \mu = 66\frac{13}{32}.$$

Example 2. Find the reactions on the supports for a beam of length 4, freely supported at points *0*, *2*, *4* and having the load

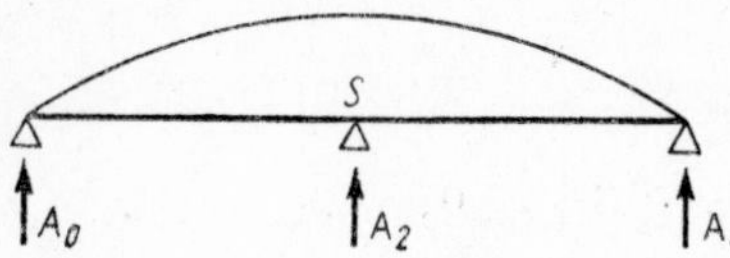

Fig. 106

$$s = \frac{300}{s}(h - h^2) + 50s - 200sh^3.$$

The load together with the reactions on the supports totals

$$F = \frac{300}{s}(h - h^2) - A_0 - A_2h^2 - A_4h^4 + 50s - 200sh^3,$$

where $-A_0$, $-A_2h^2$ and $-A_4h^4$ are concentrated forces exerted by the supports. We find hence the form of Q, M and y and solve with respect to the unknowns A_0, A_2, A_4, C and D the system of equations

$$Q(4) = M(4) = y(0) = y(2) = y(4) = 0,$$

i. e.,

$$Q(4) = 300(2-1)-A_0-A_2-A_4 = 0,$$

$$M(4) = 150(3^2-2^2)-4A_0-2A_2+50-200 = 0,$$

$$y(0) = D = 0,$$

$$y(2) = \varkappa\left[\tfrac{300}{24}1^4-\tfrac{A}{6}2^3+\tfrac{50}{2}2^2\right]+2C = 0,$$

$$y(4) = \varkappa\left[\tfrac{300}{24}(3^4-2^4)-\tfrac{1}{6}(A_0 4^3+A_2 2^3)+\tfrac{50}{2}4^3-\tfrac{200}{2}\cdot 1^3\right]+4C = 0,$$

which finally gives

$$A_0 = 316\tfrac{13}{32}, \quad A_2 = -332\tfrac{13}{16}, \quad A_4 = 316\tfrac{13}{32}, \quad C = 154\tfrac{11}{16}\varkappa, \quad D = 0.$$

EXAMPLE 3. Find the reactions on the supports for a beam of length 3, rigidly fixed at both ends, if a force P acts at point *1* (fig. 107).

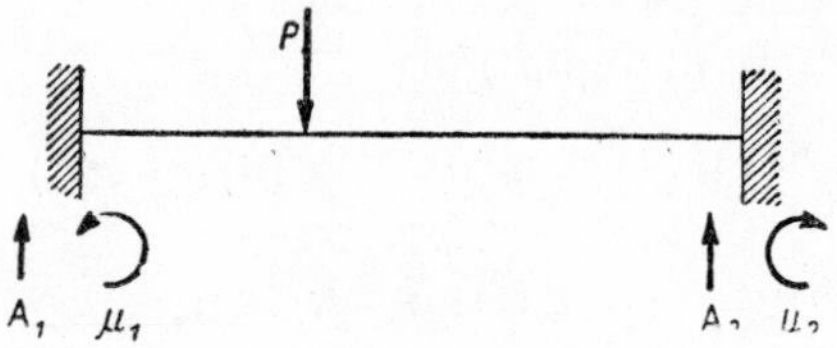

Fig. 107

Together with the reactions the total load is

$$F = -A_1+Ph+A_2h^3+\mu_1 s-\mu_2 sh^3.$$

The constants $A_1, A_2, \mu_1, \mu_2, C$, and D are determined from the equations

$$Q(3) = M(3) = y(0) = y'(0) = y(3) = y'(3) = 0,$$

i. e.,

$$Q(3) = -A_1+P-A_2 = 0,$$

$$M(3) = -3A_1+2P+\mu_1-\mu_2 = 0,$$

$$y(0) = D = 0,$$

$$y'(0) = C = 0,$$

$$y(3) = \varkappa\left[\tfrac{1}{6}(-A_1 3^3+P\cdot 2^3)+\tfrac{\mu}{2}3^2\right] = 0,$$

$$y'(3) = \varkappa\left[\tfrac{1}{2}(-A_1 3^2+P\cdot 2^2)+3\mu_1\right] = 0,$$

whence

$$A_1 = \tfrac{20}{27}P, \quad A_2 = \tfrac{7}{27}P, \quad \mu_1 = \tfrac{4}{9}P, \quad \mu_2 = \tfrac{2}{9}P.$$

In all these examples the magnitude of the reactions does not depend at all on the coefficient $\varkappa$. Only the constants C and D appearing in the equation of deflection depend upon it. It is easy to prove that it will always be so if the geometrical conditions imposed upon the deflection curve are homogeneous, *i. e.*, if the value of the function y or of its derivative is made equal to zero at given points. Indeed, by (70.1) we have

$$y(t) = \varkappa\Big[\int_0^t (t-\tau)M(t)\,d\tau + C_1 t + D_1\Big],$$

$$y'(t) = \varkappa\Big[\int_0^t M(t)\,d\tau + C_1\Big],$$

where $\varkappa C_1 = C$ and $\varkappa D_1 = D$. Every condition $y(a) = 0$ or $y'(a) = 0$ may at once be divided by $\varkappa$. Consequently, after the introduction of new unknowns, C_1 and D_1, the equations derived from the geometrical conditions do not contain the parameter $\varkappa$. Since the statical equations do not contain this parameter either, in the solution we shall always obtain as reactions quantities independent of $\varkappa$. Hence the conclusion that in calculating reactions we can simplify the calculations by assuming that $\varkappa = 1$. Then the constants C and D appearing in the expression for the deflection curve must, in the final result, be multiplied by $\varkappa$.

To conclude this section, let us calculate a more complicated example.

EXAMPLE 4. A grate is made of four beams of length 3 in such a manner that the beams cross one another at points *1* and *2* (fig. 108).

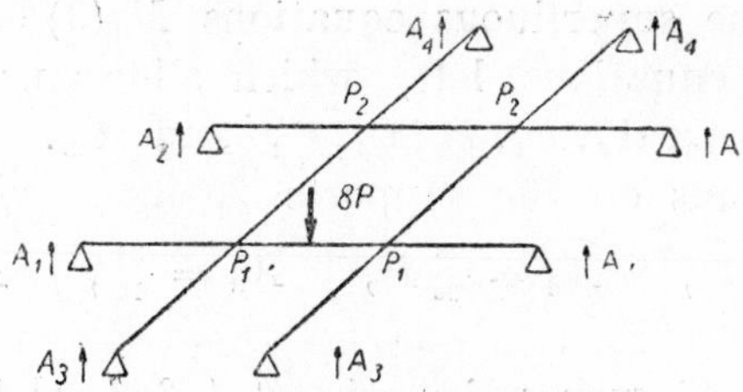

Fig. 108

The beams are freely supported at the ends. In the centre of one of the beams a concentrated force SP acts. Find the reactions on the supports.

Since the beams that are perpendicular to the loaded beam act symmetrically, it is sufficient in the calculation to take only one of them into account. If we denote by P_1 and P_2 the forces binding the beams at the joints, we can, owing to the symmetry, write the total load of the beams as

$$F_1 = -A_1 - P_1 h + 8P h^{3/2} - P_1 h^2 - A_1 h^3,$$

$$F_2 = -A_2 + P_2 h + P_2 h^2 - A_2 h^3,$$

$$F_3 = -A_3 + P_1 h - P_2 h^2 - A_4 h^3.$$

The equations of balance have the form

$$Q_1(3) = Q_2(3) = Q_3(3) = M_1(3) = M_2(3) = M_3(3) = 0.$$

Thus we have six equations and six unknowns, A_1, A_2, A_3, A_4, P_1 and P_2. In spite of this the system has no unique solution, since the first and the fourth equations

$$Q_1(3) = -2A_1 - 2P_1 + 8P = 0, \qquad M_1(3) = -3A_1 - 3P_1 + 6P = 0$$

are equivalent, and so are the first and the fifth equations. The problem is thus statically indeterminate.

We introduce deflection functions $y_i = M_i/s + C_i/s$ $(i = 1, 2, 3)$, where the terms D/s, being equal to zero, vanish, and we add five more equations

$$y_1(3) = y_2(3) = y_3(3) = 0,$$

$$y_1(1) = y_3(1), \qquad y_2(1) = y_3(2).$$

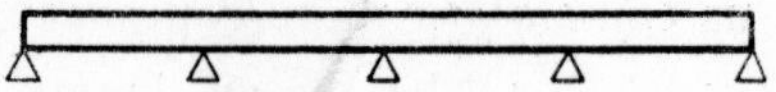

Fig. 109

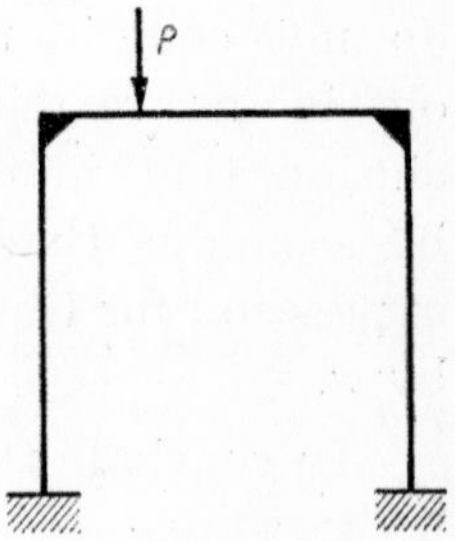

Fig. 110

On cancelling the superfluous equations $M_1(3) = 0$ and $M_2(3) = 0$, we still have nine equations left, which allows us to determine nine unknowns $A_1, A_2, A_3, A_4, P_1, P_2, C_1, C_2$ and C_3. In particular we calculate the reactions on the supports

$$A_1 = \tfrac{29}{36}P, \qquad A_2 = \tfrac{23}{36}P, \qquad A_3 = \tfrac{23}{12}, \qquad A_4 = \tfrac{23}{36}.$$

Exercises.

1. A beam of length 4 is supported at points *0*, *1*, *2*, *3* and *4* and uniformly loaded. Find the reactions on the supports and the deflection curve.

2. A square frame consisting of 3 beams rigidly joined to one another stands rigidly fixed. At one third of its length the horizontal beam is loaded with a force P. Find the reactions on the supports and the deflection curves of the beams.

PART TWO

SEQUENCES AND SERIES OF OPERATORS

CHAPTER I

SEQUENCES OF OPERATORS

§ 1. Uniform convergence. A sequence of functions $\{f_n(t)\}$ bounded in a certain interval I is said to be *uniformly convergent* to the limit $\{f(t)\}$ in that interval if there exists a sequence of numbers ε_n tending to 0 such that

$$|f_n(t)-f(t)| \leqslant \varepsilon_n \quad (n=1,2,\ldots) \tag{1.1}$$

for all t belonging to the interval I.

For instance the sequence $\left\{\frac{\sin nt}{n}\right\}$ tends to 0 uniformly in every interval since the sequence of numbers $1/n$ tends to 0 and moreover

$$\left|\frac{\sin nt}{n}-0\right| \leqslant \frac{1}{n}$$

for all real t.

The sequence $\left\{\frac{nt-\sin nt}{n}\right\}$ tends to the function $\{t\}$ uniformly in every interval because

$$\left|\frac{nt-\sin nt}{n}-t\right| \leqslant \frac{1}{n}.$$

If a sequence of numbers a_n tends to a, then the sequence of constant functions $\{a_n\}$ tends to $\{a\}$ uniformly in every interval. Indeed, the sequence $\varepsilon_n = |a_n-a|$ tends to 0 and we can write

$$|a_n-a| \leqslant \varepsilon_n.$$

The sequence $\{e^{-t/n}\}$ tends to $\{1\}$ uniformly in every finite interval $\alpha \leqslant t \leqslant \beta$. Indeed, in this interval we have the inequalities

$$e^{-\beta/n}-1 \leqslant e^{-t/n}-1 \leqslant e^{-\alpha/n}-1;$$

if we take as ε_n the larger of the numbers

$$|e^{-\beta/n}-1| \quad \text{and} \quad |e^{-\alpha/n}-1|,$$

then in any case the sequence ε_n will tend to 0 and we shall have

$$|e^{-t/n}-1| \leqslant \varepsilon_n,$$

which proves uniform convergence in the interval $\alpha \leqslant t \leqslant \beta$.

On the other hand, it can be proved that the sequence $\{e^{-t/n}\}$ is not uniformly convergent in any infinite interval.

If all the terms of a sequence $\{f_n(t)\}$ are equal to a function $\{f(t)\}$

$$\{f_n(t)\} = \{f(t)\},$$

then the sequence uniformly tends to the function $\{f(t)\}$ in a given interval, since we can write

$$|f_n(t)-f(t)| \leqslant \varepsilon_n$$

where $\varepsilon_n = 0$ for all values of n.

It is known from analysis that if functions $\{f_n(t)\}$ are continuous and their sequence converges uniformly in a certain interval I, then the limit $\{f(t)\}$ is also a function continuous in I.

If functions $\{f_n(t)\}$ are of class $\mathcal{C}$, i. e., if they are defined and continuous in the interval $0 \leqslant t < \infty$, and if the sequence $\{f_n(t)\}$ converges uniformly in every finite interval, then the limit $\{f(t)\}$ is also a function of class $\mathcal{C}$.

Indeed, the function $\{f(t)\}$ is continuous in every finite interval, and thus also in the infinite interval $0 \leqslant t < \infty$.

If a sequence of continuous functions $\{f_n(t)\}$ converges uniformly to the function $\{f(t)\}$ in a certain interval $\alpha \leqslant t \leqslant \beta$, then there exists a number M such that

$$|f_n(t)| \leqslant M \quad \text{and} \quad |f(t)| \leqslant M$$

in that interval.

Indeed, the function $\{f(t)\}$, being continuous, is bounded in the interval $\alpha \leqslant t \leqslant \beta$:

$$|f(t)| \leqslant N. \tag{1.2}$$

It follows from inequality (1.1) that

$$|f_n(t)| \leqslant N+\varepsilon = M,$$

where ε is the greatest of the numbers ε_n. By (1.2) we also have $|f(t)| \leqslant M$.

If the sequences of continuous functions $\{f_n(t)\}$ and $\{g_n(t)\}$ tend to $\{f(t)\}$ and $\{g(t)\}$ uniformly in the interval $0 \leqslant t \leqslant t_0$, then the sequence

$$\left\{\int_0^t f_n(t-\tau)g_n(\tau)\,d\tau\right\}$$

tends to

$$\left\{\int_0^t f(t-\tau)g(\tau)\,d\tau\right\}$$

uniformly in that interval.

Proof. From the assumption we have

$$|f_n(t)-f(t)| \leqslant \varepsilon_n \quad \text{and} \quad |g_n(t)-g(t)| < \eta_n \quad (0 \leqslant t \leqslant t_0)$$

where $\varepsilon_n \to 0$ and $\eta_n \to 0$. Consequently

$$\left|\int_0^t f_n(t-\tau)g_n(\tau)\,d\tau - \int_0^t f(t-\tau)g(\tau)\,d\tau\right|$$

$$\leqslant \int_0^t |f_n(t-\tau)g_n(\tau)-f(t-\tau)g(\tau)|\,d\tau$$

$$= \int_0^t |[f_n(t-\tau)g_n(\tau)-f(t-\tau)g_n(\tau)]+[f(t-\tau)g_n(\tau)-f(t-\tau)g(\tau)]|\,d\tau$$

$$\leqslant \int_0^t |g_n(\tau)|\cdot|f_n(t-\tau)-f(t-\tau)|\,d\tau + \int_0^t |f(t-\tau)|\cdot|g_n(\tau)-g(\tau)|\,d\tau$$

$$\leqslant \int_0^{t_0} M\varepsilon_n\,d\tau + \int_0^{t_0} N\eta_n\,d\tau = Mt_0\varepsilon_n + Mt_0\eta_n,$$

where M and N satisfy the inequalities $|g_n(t)| \leqslant M$ and $|f(t)| < N$.

The sequence of numbers $Mt_0\varepsilon_n + Mt_0\eta_n$ tending to 0, the theorem is proved.

The following particular cases of this theorem will be of importance.

If the sequence of continuous functions $\{g_n(t)\}$ tends to $\{g(t)\}$ uniformly in the interval $0 \leqslant t \leqslant t_0$ and if $\{f(t)\}$ is a function continuous in that interval, then the sequence

$$\left\{\int_0^t f(t-\tau)g_n(\tau)\,d\tau\right\}$$

tends to

$$\left\{\int_0^t f(t-\tau)g(\tau)\,d\tau\right\}$$

uniformly in that interval.

If the sequence of continuous functions $\{g_n(t)\}$ tends to $\{g(t)\}$ uniformly in the interval $0 \leqslant t \leqslant t_0$, then the sequence

$$\left\{\int_0^t g_n(\tau)\,d\tau\right\}$$

tends to

$$\left\{\int_0^t g(\tau)\,d\tau\right\}$$

in that interval.

Exercises.

1. Prove that the sequence $\left\{\frac{\cos nt}{n}\right\}$ tends to 0 uniformly in every interval.

2. Prove that the sequence $\{H_n(t)\}$ where H_n is a jump function (see p. 16) tends to 0 uniformly in every finite interval $0 \leqslant t \leqslant t_0$.

§ 2. Limit of a sequence of operators. A sequence of operators a_n is termed *convergent* if, divided by a suitably chosen operator $q \neq 0$, it becomes a sequence of functions of class $\mathcal{C}$ almost uniformly convergent. By almost uniform convergence we understand uniform convergence in every finite interval.

For example the sequence of operators

$$a_n = \frac{s^2 n^2}{s^2 + n^2}$$

is convergent since on being divided by operator s^4 it becomes a sequence of functions of class $\mathcal{C}$,

$$\frac{a_n}{s^4} = \frac{n^2}{s^2(s^2+n^2)} = \frac{1}{s^2} - \frac{1}{s^2+n^2} = \left\{t - \frac{1}{n}\sin nt\right\},$$

which is almost uniformly convergent.

The limit of the last sequence is the function $\{t\}$. What limit shall we ascribe to the sequence of operators a_n? It is natural to assume that limit to be equal to $s^4\{t\}$, *i. e.*, to s^2. Therefore

$$\lim_{n\to\infty} \frac{s^2 n^2}{s^2+n^2} = s^2.$$

Generally, *a sequence of operators a_n is said to have the limit a if there exists such an operator q that a_n/q is a sequence of functions of class $\mathcal{C}$ tending almost uniformly to a/q.*

Then we can write

$$\lim_{n\to\infty} a_n = q \lim_{n\to\infty} a_n/q,$$

remembering of course that on the left side we deal with convergence in the operational sense while on the right we have the almost uniform convergence of a sequence of functions.

In order to verify the correctness of the adopted definition of limit it should be proved that *at most one limit can exist for any sequence of operators.* Suppose that a and b are limits of a sequence a_n. Then there exist such operators q and r that the sequences

$$f_n = a_n/q \quad \text{and} \quad q_n = a_n/r$$

are sequences of functions of class $\mathcal{C}$ tending almost uniformly to $f = a/q$ and $g = b/r$ respectively.

Let q_1, r_1 and $c \neq 0$ be functions of class $\mathcal{C}$ such that $q = q_1/c$ and $r = r_1/c$. Then

$$q_1 f_n = r_1 g_n,$$

i. e.,

$$\int_0^t q_1(t-\tau) f_n(\tau)\, d\tau = \int_0^t r_1(t-\tau) g_n(\tau)\, d\tau \qquad (0 \leqslant t < \infty),$$

sequences f_n and g_n being uniformly convergent in every interval whence for $n \to \infty$ we have

$$\int_0^t q_1(t-\tau) f(\tau)\, d\tau = \int_0^t r_1(t-\tau) g(\tau)\, d\tau \qquad (0 \leqslant t < \infty)$$

i. e.,

$$q_1 f = r_1 g.$$

Dividing this equality by c, we have $qf = rg$, *i. e.*, $a = b$, which proves that there can be only one limit.

In particular cases operators a may be functions of class $\mathcal{C}$. *If those functions form an almost uniformly convergent sequence, then that sequence tends to the same limit also in the operational sense,* since number 1 can then be taken for q.

However, it is not every sequence of functions of class $\mathcal{C}$ convergent in the operational sense that is almost uniformly convergent. Indeed, operational convergence gives

$$(2.1) \qquad \lim_{n\to\infty}\{\cos nt\} = 0, \qquad \lim_{n\to\infty}\{n \sin nt\} = 1, \qquad \lim_{n\to\infty}\{n^2 \cos nt\} = s,$$

while in every classical sense these sequences are divergent. Their operational limits, 0, 1 and s, can easily be found on the basis of the definition, s, s^2 and s^3 respectively being taken for q. These examples show that for sequences of functions operational convergence is considerably more general than almost uniform convergence.

Another particular case of operational sequences are numerical sequences. For them operational convergence is equivalent to ordinary convergence. In other words a sequence consisting of numbers only is operationally convergent if and only if it is convergent in the ordinary sense, the limit being the same for both kinds of convergence.

Indeed, we can then write $a_n/s = \{a_n\}$, where the sequence of functions $\{a_n\}$ constant in the interval $0 \leqslant t < \infty$ is convergent if and only if the numerical sequence a_n is convergent in the ordinary sense. If $\{a\}$ is the limit of the sequence $\{a_n\}$, then the operational limit is $\{a\}/s = a$, *i. e.*, the ordinary limit.

Exercises.

1. Give a detailed proof of equalities (2.1).

2. Prove that $\lim h^n = 0$ (h being the translation operator).

3. Prove that each of the following sequences tends to number 1:

$$(\alpha)\ \{ne^{-nt}\}, \quad (\beta)\ \{n^2 te^{-nt}\}, \quad (\gamma)\ \{n - n^2 t + |n - n^2 t|\}, \quad (\delta)\ \left\{\frac{1}{n} t^{1/n-1}\right\}.$$

4. Prove that the sequence $\{n^3 \sin nt + n^4 t \cos nt\}$ tends to the limit $2s^2$.

5. Prove that if a and b are arbitrary operators, then the sequence $a + bh^n$ tends to the limit a.

§ 3. Properties of the limit of a sequence of operators. A limit of a sequence of operators has similar properties to those of an ordinary limit of a numerical sequence. If $a_n = a$ where a is an arbitrary fixed operator, then $\lim a_n = a$. If a sequence a_n tends to a certain limit, then every sequence selected from it tends to the same limit. The theorems on adding, subtracting and multiplying sequences are also valid. Namely if there exist limits $\lim a_n = a$ and $\lim b_n = b$, then the sequences $a_n + b_n$, $a_n - b_n$ and $a_n b_n$ also have limits and the following equalities hold:

$$\lim (a_n + b_n) = a + b, \qquad \lim (a_n - b_n) = a - b, \qquad \lim a_n b_n = ab.$$

Indeed, the assumption of the convergence of sequences a_n and b_n implies the existence of such operators q and r that we have the equalities

$$a_n = q\{f_n(t)\}, \qquad a = q\{f(t)\}, \tag{3.1}$$

$$b_n = r\{g_n(t)\}, \qquad b = r\{g(t)\}, \tag{3.2}$$

where $\{f_n(t)\}$ and $\{g_n(t)\}$ are sequences of functions of class $\mathcal{C}$ uniformly tending to $\{f(t)\}$ and $\{g(t)\}$ in every finite interval $0 \leqslant t \leqslant t_0$.

We can write $q = q_1/c$ and $r = r_1/c$ where q_1, r_1 and $c \neq 0$ are functions of class $\mathcal{C}$. We have the equalities

$$a_n + b_n = \frac{1}{c}\left\{\int_0^t q_1(t-\tau) f_n(\tau)\, d\tau + \int_0^t r_1(t-\tau) g_n(\tau)\, d\tau\right\}$$

and, in view of the assumption of the uniform convergence of the sequences $\{f_n(t)\}$ and $\{g_n(t)\}$,

$$\lim(a_n+b_n) = \frac{1}{c}\left\{\int_0^t q_1(t-\tau)f(\tau)\,d\tau + \int_0^t r_1(t-\tau)g(\tau)\,d\tau\right\}$$

$$= \frac{q_1}{c}\{f(t)\} + \frac{r_1}{c}\{g(t)\} = a+b.$$

The proof of the theorem on the difference of sequences is quite similar.

In order to prove the theorem on the product of sequences we write

$$a_n b_n = qr\left\{\int_0^t f_n(t-\tau)g_n(\tau)\,d\tau\right\},$$

whence, again by the assumption of the uniform convergence of the sequences $\{f_n(t)\}$ and $\{g_n(t)\}$, it follows that

$$\lim a_n b_n = qr\left\{\int_0^t f(t-\tau)g(\tau)\,d\tau\right\} = qr\{f(t)\}\{g(t)\} = ab.$$

A particular case of multiplying sequences occurs when one of the sequences is constant, for instance $a_n = a$. Then it follows from the assumption of $\lim b_n = b$ that

$$\lim ab_n = ab.$$

It follows form the theorem on the multiplication of sequences that if $\lim a_n = a$ and $\lim b_n = b$ ($b \neq 0$ and $b_n \neq 0$ for $n = 1, 2, \ldots$) and if the sequence of quotients a_n/b_n has a limit, then

$$\lim \frac{a_n}{b_n} = \frac{a}{b}.$$

The assumption of the convergence of the sequence a_n/b_n cannot be omitted here (contrary to the classical theory of sequences), as can be seen from the following example (1):

Let

$$a_n = 1 \quad \text{and} \quad b_n = s/n - 1;$$

then $\lim a_n = 1$ and $\lim b_n = -1$. But the sequence

$$\frac{a_n}{b_n} = \frac{n}{s-n} = \{ne^{nt}\}$$

is not convergent.

---

(1) Given by C. Ryll-Nardzewski.

Indeed, if it were convergent, there would exist a function

$$f \in \mathcal{C} \quad (f \neq 0) \tag{3.3}$$

such that the sequence

$$\frac{a_n}{b_n} f = \left\{ n \int_0^t e^{n\tau} f(t-\tau)\, d\tau \right\}$$

would be uniformly convergent in every interval $0 \leqslant t \leqslant t_0$, which easily follows from the definition of convergence. Then the sequence

$$\int_0^{t_0} e^{n\tau} f(t_0 - \tau)\, d\tau$$

would be bounded. Hence it would follow by the theorem on moments (see Part I, § 11) that $f(t_0 - \tau) = 0$ for $0 \leqslant \tau \leqslant t_0$, *i. e.*, that $f(t) = 0$ for $0 \leqslant t \leqslant t_0$. Since t_0 can be fixed arbitrarily, $f(t) = 0$ for all $t \geqslant 0$, which contradicts (3.3).

CHAPTER II

SERIES OF TRANSLATION OPERATORS

§ 4. Series with numerical coefficients. We write

$$\sum_{n=0}^{\infty} a_n = a_0 + a_1 + \ldots = A,$$

if the sequence of partial sums

$$A_n = a_0 + \ldots + a_n$$

converges to A. The series under consideration is then said *to have the sum A*.

For example

$$1 + l + l^2 + \ldots = \frac{1}{1-l},$$

since the sequence of partial sums

$$1 + \ldots + l^n = s\left\{1 + \frac{t}{1!} + \ldots + \frac{t^{n-1}}{(n+1)!}\right\}$$

converges to an operator of the form

$$s\{e^t\} = \frac{s}{s-1} = \frac{1}{1-l}.$$

Series of translation operators constitute an important class.

The series

(4.1) $$\alpha_0 h^{\beta_0} + \alpha_1 h^{\beta_1} + \ldots,$$

where the coefficients $\alpha_0, \alpha_1, \ldots$ are arbitrary complex numbers and the exponents $\beta_0, \beta_1, \ldots$ real numbers increasing to ∞, is always convergent.

In order to prove this, let us first consider the sequence of functions $\{f(t)\}$ defined by the equalities

$$\begin{aligned}
\{f_0(t)\} &= l\alpha_0, \\
\{f_1(t)\} &= l(\alpha_0 + \alpha_1 h^{(\beta_1-\beta_0)}), \\
\{f_2(t)\} &= l(\alpha_0 + \alpha_1 h^{(\beta_1-\beta_0)} + \alpha_2 h^{(\beta_2-\beta_0)}), \\
\{f_3(t)\} &= l(\alpha_0 + \alpha_1 h^{(\beta_1-\beta_0)} + \alpha_2 h^{(\beta_2-\beta_0)} + \alpha_3 h^{(\beta_2-\beta_0)}), \\
&\ldots\ldots\ldots\ldots\ldots\ldots
\end{aligned}$$

If $\alpha_1, \alpha_2, \ldots$ are positive, the following graphs correspond to these functions:

$\{f_0(t)\}$

$\{f_1(t)\}$

$\{f^2(t)\}$

$\{f_3(t)\}$

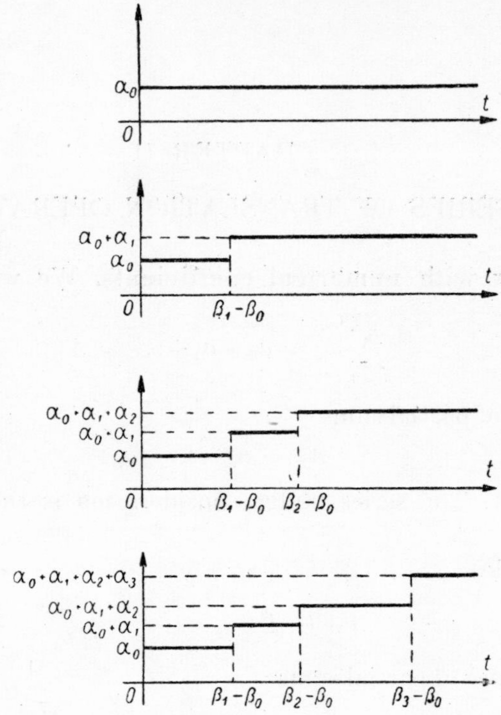

Fig. 111

It will easily be observed that for the subsequent functions

$$\{f_4(t)\},\ \{f_5(t)\},\ \ldots$$

the graph will remain the same in the interval $0 \leqslant t \leqslant \beta_3 - \beta_0$ as for the function $\{f_3(t)\}$. Generally speaking, in every given finite interval $0 \leqslant t \leqslant t_0$, starting from a certain n, functions $\{f_n(t)\}$ will be identical. This will be so whether the coefficients $\alpha_1, \alpha_2, \ldots$ are real or complex, although in the latter case a graph on a plane cannot be made. It follows hence that the sequence of functions $\{f_n(t)\}$ is uniformly convergent in every finite interval.

Further, it follows that the sequence of partial sums

$$\alpha_0 h^{\beta_0} + \ldots + \alpha_n h^{\beta_n} = sh^{\beta_0} \cdot l(\alpha_0 + \ldots + \alpha_n h^{\beta_n - \beta_0})$$

is convergent, and thus series (4.1) is convergent.

The sum of this series can be interpreted as masses $\alpha_0, \alpha_1, \ldots$ (positive, negative or even complex) distributed at points $\beta_0, \beta_1, \ldots$ or as impulses or strokes with values $\alpha_0, \alpha_1, \ldots$ appearing at instants $t = \beta_0, \beta_1, \ldots$

The series

$$l(a_0 h^{\beta_0} + a_1 h^{\beta_1} + \ldots)$$

represents a function whose value is

$$\begin{array}{lll} 0 & \text{for} & -\infty < t < \beta_0, \\ a_0 & \text{for} & \beta_0 \leqslant t < \beta_1, \\ a_0 + a_1 & \text{for} & \beta_1 \leqslant t < \beta_2, \\ \ldots & \ldots & \ldots \end{array}$$

It follows hence that if $a_0 h^{\beta_0} + a_1 h^{\beta_1} + \ldots = 0$, then $a_0 = 0$, $a_2 = 0, \ldots$

On this basis it is easy to prove the following theorem:

If a sequence of numbers $\beta_0, \beta_1, \beta_2, \ldots$ increases to infinity, then the equality

(4.2) $\quad a_0 h^{\beta_0} + a_1 h^{\beta_1} + \ldots = \gamma_0 h^{\beta_0} + \gamma_1 h^{\beta_1} + \ldots$ *(a_n, γ_n complex numbers)*

implies the equalities

(4.3) $$a_0 = \gamma_0, \quad a_1 = \gamma_1, \quad \ldots$$

Indeed, equality (4.2) implies $(a_0 - \gamma_0) h^{\beta_0} + (a_1 - \gamma_1) h^{\beta_1} + \ldots = 0$, whence $a_0 - \gamma_0 = 0$, $a_1 - \gamma_1 = 0, \ldots$

Conversely, of course, equality (4.3) implies equality (4.2). Thus we can say that *series of translation operators with numerical coefficients and identical exponents are equal if and only if their coefficients are equal.*

§ 5. More general series of translation operators. The theorems of the preceding section can easily be generalized to series

(5.1) $$a_0 h^{\beta_0} + a_1 h^{\beta_1} + a_2 h^{\beta_2} + \ldots,$$

with coefficients of the form $a_\nu = p_\nu / q$ where p_ν and q are functions of class $\mathcal{C}$, not identically equal to zero in any right-hand neighbourhood of the point $t = 0$.

If the exponents $\beta_0, \beta_1, \ldots,$ form an increasing sequence, then series (5.1) *is convergent.*

Two series of this kind with identical exponents are equal if and only if their coefficients are equal.

The proof is similar to that in the case of numerical coefficients, operator l being replaced by q.

In particular, these theorems are true if the coefficients a_ν are arbitrary operators rational with respect to s (see p. 35). Indeed, in that case we can take as q a function with the values $e^{-1/t}$ for $0 < t < \infty$ and equal to zero at the point $t = 0$, the product $p_\nu = a_\nu q$ being always a function of class $\mathcal{C}$ different from zero in the right-hand neighbourhood of the point $t = 0$.

§ 6. Operator $1/(1-\beta h^{\lambda})$. In applications we often encounter series

$$1+\beta h^{\lambda}+\beta^2 h^{2\lambda}+\ldots,$$

where β is a complex number and λ a positive number. Multiplying such a series by $1-\beta h^{\lambda}$, we obtain

$$(1-\beta h^{\lambda})(1+\beta h^{\lambda}+\beta^2 h^{2\lambda}+\ldots)$$
$$=(1+\beta h+\beta^2 h^{2\lambda}+\ldots)-(\beta h^{\lambda}+\beta^2 h^{2\lambda}+\ldots)=1.$$

It follows hence that

$$\frac{1}{1-\beta h^{\lambda}}=1+\beta h^{\lambda}+\beta^2 h^{2\lambda}+\ldots$$

Consequently the operator $1/(1-\beta h^{\lambda})$ can be interpreted as the masses $1, \beta, \beta^2, \ldots$ distributed at the points $0, \lambda, 2\lambda, \ldots$ (fig. 112 a, b and c). Such an operator multiplied by l gives jump curves whose shape depends on the values β and λ (fig. 113 a, b and c).

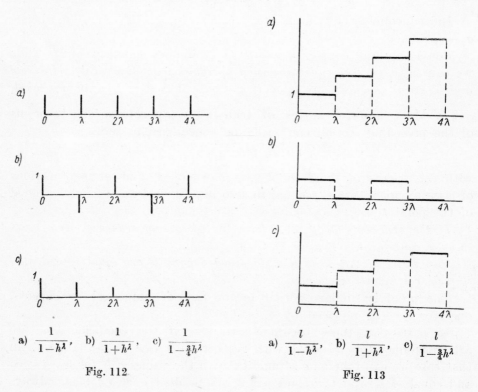

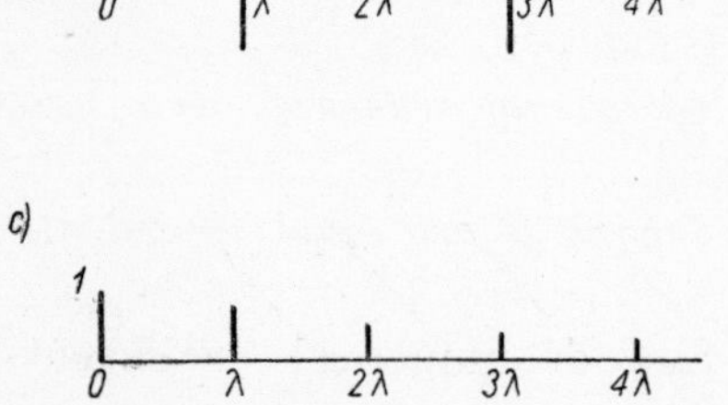

a) $\frac{1}{1-h^{\lambda}}$, b) $\frac{1}{1+h^{\lambda}}$, c) $\frac{1}{1-\frac{3}{4}h^{\lambda}}$

Fig. 112

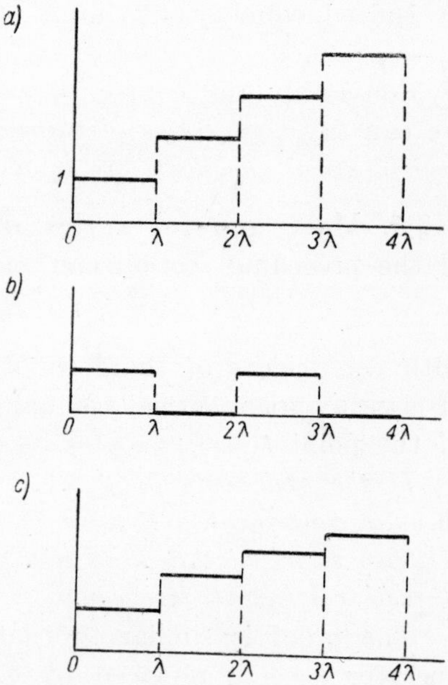

a) $\frac{l}{1-h^{\lambda}}$, b) $\frac{l}{1+h^{\lambda}}$, c) $\frac{l}{1-\frac{3}{4}h^{\lambda}}$

Fig. 113

If we multiply by the operator $1/(1-h^{\beta})$ a function f which outside the interval $0\leqslant t<\beta$ is equal to zero, we obtain a function whose graph is found by repeating infinitely many times that fragment of the graph of the function $\{f(t)\}$ which corresponds to the interval $0 \leqslant t < \beta$ (figs. 114 and 115).

Thus operator (6.2) represents a periodic function for $0 \leqslant t < \infty$ (provided the function f is equal to 0 outside the interval $0 \leqslant t \leqslant \lambda$).

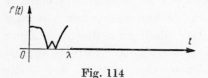

Fig. 114

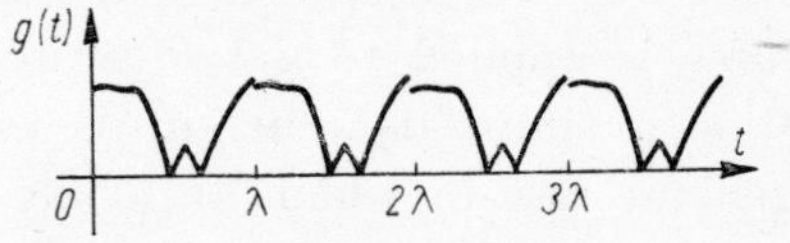

Fig. 115

On the other hand, if we are given a periodic function g whose period is λ, the expression

$$f = (1-h^\lambda)g$$

represents a function equal to zero for $t > \lambda$. Thus we have the following theorem:

A function $g = \{g(t)\}$ $(t \geqslant 0)$ *is periodic for* $0 \leqslant t < \infty$ *if and only if it can be represented in the form*

$$g = f/(1-h^\lambda),$$

where λ *is a positive number and the function* $f = \{f(t)\}$ *is equal to zero for* $t > \lambda$. *Number* λ *is the period of the function* g.

In particular, assuming $\lambda = 2\pi$ and $\{f(t)\} = \dfrac{1}{1+s^2}(1+h^\pi)$ (see example 6, p. 119), we obtain (on simplifying) the operator

$$\frac{1}{(1+s^2)(1-h^\pi)},$$

which is a function with the graph represented in fig. 116.

This operator can be applied in electrical engineering since it represents a rectified half-wave.

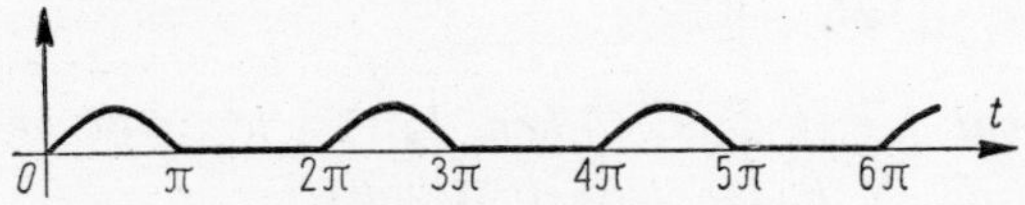

Fig. 116

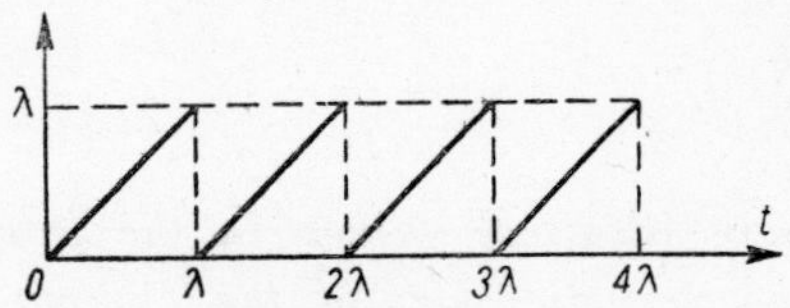

Fig. 117

It is easy to give the operational form for a *saw* (fig. 117). It suffices to multiply the operator representing the tooth of the saw (see example 5, p. 119) by $1/(1-h^\lambda)$, which gives

$$\frac{1-(\lambda s+1)h^\lambda}{s^2(1-h^\lambda)}.$$

Exercise. Give the graphs corresponding to the following operators:

$$(\alpha)\quad \frac{h^\lambda}{s(1+h^\lambda)},\qquad (\beta)\quad \frac{s}{(s^2+1)(1-h^\pi)},\qquad (\gamma)\quad \frac{s-1}{3s^2(1-h)}.$$

§ 7. Electrical systems excited periodically. In §§ 33 and 39 of Part I we discussed the particular case where a sinusoidal electromotive force is applied to a two-terminal network. In this case after a certain time a sinusoidal current is established. We shall now discuss a more general case in which an arbitrary periodic electromotive force is applied to a network with a given impedance. Then, after a time, a periodic current is established. Our task is to calculate that current and the transient current.

It follows from the periodicity of the electromotive force that it is of the form

$$E = E_0/(1-h^\lambda)$$

where λ is the period and E_0 the electromotive force having the same values as E in the interval $0 \leqslant t < \lambda$ and equal to 0 outside this interval.

Suppose that $Z = P/Q$ where P and Q are polynomials of s. We represent the current in the form

$$I = \frac{I_0}{1-h^\lambda} + \frac{N}{P}, \tag{7.1}$$

where N is a polynomial of s of degree less by 1 than P.

Hence on the grounds of formula $ZI = E$ we obtain

$$I_0 = \frac{E_0}{Z} - \frac{N}{P}(1-h^\lambda). \tag{7.2}$$

The polynomial N can always be chosen so that the functions

$$\frac{E_0}{Z} \quad \textit{and} \quad \frac{N}{P}(1-h^\lambda) \tag{7.3}$$

have identical values in the interval $\lambda < t < \infty$. Then $I_0/(1-h^\lambda)$ will be the periodic part of the current and N/P the transient part.

Proof. The fraction $1/Z$ can always be represented in the form $Q_0 + Q_1/P$ where Q_0 and Q_1 are polynomials, Q_1 being of lower degree than P. If Q has a lower degree than P, then $Q_0 = 0$. Since $P = a_n s^n + \ldots + a_0$, the functions $f = Q_1/P$ and $g = N/P$ satisfy the homogeneous equation

$$a_n x^{(n)} + \ldots + a_0 x = 0 \qquad (a_n \neq 0) \tag{7.4}$$

in the interval $0 \leqslant t < \infty$. In the partial interval $\lambda < t < \infty$ this equation is also satisfied by functions (7.3) since the first of them can be represented in the form $Q_0 E_0 + \dfrac{Q_1}{P} E_0$ and thus has the values $\int_0^\lambda E_0(\tau) f(t-\tau)\, d\tau$ in this interval (for the values of $Q_0 E_0$ vanish there together with E_0), and the second has the values $g(t) - g(t-\lambda)$. It follows hence that the coefficients of the polynomial N can always be chosen so that functions (7.3) have identical values in the interval $\lambda \leqslant t < \infty$.

The second part of the theorem is a consequence of the first.

Owing to the above theorem we can always calculate the periodic current and the transient current in practice. For this purpose we must first calculate the values of functions (7.3) in the interval $\lambda < t < \infty$ and, by comparing them, determine the coefficients of the polynomial N. In this way we find the current N/P. The variation of I_0 in the interval $0 \leqslant t < \lambda$ will be found from the equality

$$I_0 = \frac{E_1}{z} - \frac{N}{P} \tag{7.5}$$

if we take for E_1 an arbitrary function having in the interval $0 \leqslant t < \lambda$ the same values as P. Equality (7.5) is used here instead of (7.2) because it is simpler and more convenient on account of E_1 being arbitrary, which makes it possible to simplify calculations in certain cases. It

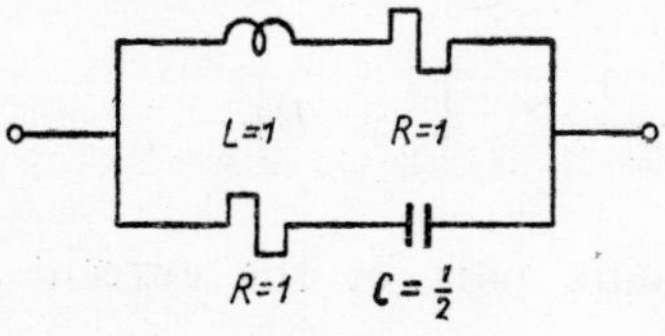

Fig. 118

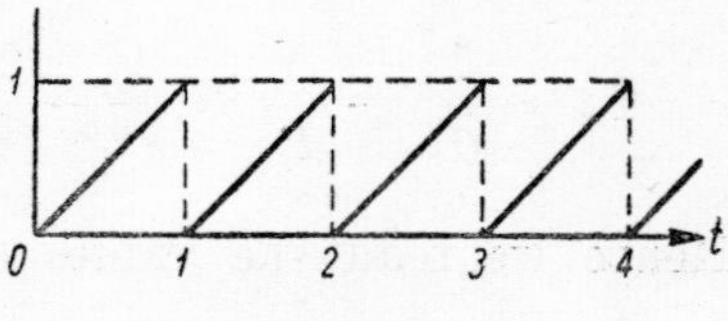

Fig. 119

should be remembered, however, that equality (7.5) can be used to calculate the values of I_0 only in the interval $0 \leqslant t < \lambda$ since elsewhere it is false.

Example 1. To a network with the impedance

$$Z = \frac{(s+1)(s+2)}{s^2 + 2s + 2}$$

(fig. 118) we have applied an electromotive force with period 1, whose variation in the interval $0 \leqslant t < 1$ is given by the function t (fig. 119).

We shall find $1/Z$ by decomposing it into simple fractions

$$(7.6) \qquad \frac{1}{Z} = 1+\frac{1}{s+1}-\frac{2}{s+2} = 1+\{e^{-t}-2e^{-2t}\}.$$

Denote by E_0 the electromotive force with values t in the interval $0 \leqslant t < 1$ and elsewhere equal to 0. The values E_0/Z in the interval $1 < t < \infty$ are expressed, in view of (7.6), by the integral

$$(7.7) \qquad \int_0^1 \tau[e^{-(t-\tau)}-2e^{-2(t-\tau)}]d\tau = e^{-t}-\tfrac{1}{4}e^{-2t}.$$

On the other hand, we have

$$\frac{N}{P} = \frac{A}{s+1}+\frac{B}{s+2} = \{Ae^{-t}+Be^{-2t}\}$$

and hence the values of the function $N(1-h)/P$ for $1 < t < \infty$ are

$$(7.8) \quad (Ae^{-t}+Be^{-2t})-(Ae^{-(t-1)}-Be^{-2(t-1)}) = \{-A(e-1)e^{-t}-B(e^2-1)e^{-2t}\}.$$

By comparing the coefficients in (7.7) and (7.8) we obtain

$$A = -\frac{1}{e-1} \quad \text{and} \quad B = \frac{1}{4(e^2-1)}.$$

In order to find the variation of I_0 in the interval $0 \leqslant t < 1$ we take $E_1 = 1/s^2$ and thus have

$$I_0 = \frac{1}{s^2 z}-\frac{N}{P} = \frac{1}{s^2}-\frac{1}{s}+(1-A)\frac{1}{s+1}+\left(\frac{1}{2}-B\right)\frac{1}{s+2}.$$

Hence we read the values of the periodic part of the current

$$t-\frac{1}{2}+\frac{e}{e-1}e^{-t}-\frac{2e^2-1}{4(e^2-1)}e^{-2t} \quad \text{for} \quad 0 \leqslant t < 1;$$

the transient part has the values

$$-\frac{1}{e-1}e^{-t}+\frac{1}{4(e^2-1)}e^{-2t} \quad \text{for} \quad 0 \leqslant t < \infty.$$

EXAMPLE 2. To a network with self-induction L and resistance R we apply electromotive impulses μ at time intervals λ.

Thus the impedance and the voltage have the form

$$Z = Ls+R, \qquad E = \mu/(1-h^\lambda).$$

Consequently

$$(7.9)\qquad \frac{E_0}{Z} = \frac{\mu}{Ls+R} = \frac{\mu}{E}\{e^{-at}\} \qquad \left(a = \frac{R}{L}\right).$$

Since

$$\frac{N}{P} = \frac{A}{Ls+R} = \frac{A}{L}(e^{-at}),$$

the values of $N(1-h^{\lambda})/P$ are

$$(7.10)\qquad \frac{A}{L}e^{-at} - \frac{A}{L}e^{-a(t-\lambda)} = \frac{A}{L}(1-e^{a\lambda})e^{-at} \qquad \text{for} \qquad \lambda < t < \infty.$$

By comparing (7.9) and (7.10) we obtain $A = \mu/(1-e^{a\lambda})$. From the equality

$$I_0 = \frac{\mu}{Ls+R} - \frac{N}{P} = \frac{e^{a\lambda}}{e^{a\lambda}-1}\,\frac{1}{Ls+R}$$

we read the values of the periodic part of the current

$$\frac{\mu}{L}\cdot\frac{e^{a\lambda}}{e^{a\lambda}-1}e^{-at} \qquad \text{for} \qquad 0 \leqslant t < \lambda;$$

the transient part has the values

$$\frac{\mu}{L}\,\frac{1}{1-e^{a\lambda}}e^{-at}.$$

Exercise. Find the periodic part and the transient part of the current which will flow through the network of Example 2 under the voltage of Example 1 and vice versa: through the network of Example 1 under the voltage of Example 2.

CHAPTER III

DIFFERENCE EQUATIONS

§ 8. Examples of difference equations. The simplest type of a difference equation is the equation

$$x(t+\lambda)-x(t) = f(t). \tag{8.1}$$

Introducing functions of class $\mathcal{U}$ (see § 66, Part I) we can write this equation in the operational form

$$h^\lambda x - x = f,$$

whence we easily get the solution

$$x = \frac{f}{h^\lambda - 1} = -f(1+h^\lambda+h^{2\lambda}+\ldots).$$

Similarly more general equations can be solved, for instance

$$a_0 x(t)+a_1 x(t+\lambda)+\ldots+a_n x(t+\lambda n) = f(t).$$

This kind of applications of the operational calculus are not particularly interesting since the solutions they give are in the form of infinite series, which are of little practical use.

In technical literature, particularly in the field of electrical engineering, we find methods of solving other difference equations, in which the variable runs over integer values only.

Suppose for instance that we are to solve the equation

$$2\xi_n+3\xi_{n+1}+\xi_{n+2} = 1 \tag{8.2}$$

with the initial conditions

$$\xi_0 = 1, \quad \xi_1 = 0. \tag{8.3}$$

Thus we have to find a sequence of numbers $\xi_0, \xi_1, \xi_2, \ldots$, which satisfy equation (8.2) beginning from 1, 0.

Introducing the operator

$$F = \sum_{h=0}^{\infty} \xi_n h^n = \xi_0+\xi_1 h+\xi_2 h^2+\ldots \tag{8.4}$$

we have

$$\frac{1}{h}(F-\xi_0) = \xi_1+\xi_2 h+\xi_3 h^2+\ldots,$$

$$\frac{1}{h}(F-\xi_0-\xi_1 h) = \xi_2+\xi_3 h+\xi_4 h^2+\ldots;$$

since

$$\frac{1}{1-h} = 1+h+h^2+\ldots,$$

we have by (8.2) and (8.3)

$$2F+\frac{3}{h}(F-1)+\frac{1}{h^2}(F-1) = \frac{1}{1-h}.$$

Solving this equation with respect to F and expanding the expression obtained into simple fractions, we have

$$F = \frac{1+2h-2h^2}{(1-h)(1+h)(1+2h)} = \frac{1}{6}\cdot\frac{1}{1-h}-\frac{3}{2}\cdot\frac{1}{1+h}-\frac{2}{3}\cdot\frac{1}{1+2h}.$$

Expanding the right side fractions into series, we have

$$F = \sum_{n=0}^{\infty}\left(\tfrac{1}{6}+\tfrac{3}{2}(-1)^n-\tfrac{2}{3}(-2)^n\right)h^n.$$

Hence, by a comparison with formula (8.4), we obtain the solution in the form

$$\xi_n = \tfrac{1}{6}+\tfrac{3}{2}(-1)^n-\tfrac{2}{3}(-2)^n.$$

A similar method can be used in solving, for instance, the problem of § 48, Part I. If we denote by E_{n-1} and I_{n-1} the voltage and the current at the input of the n-th successive four-terminal network, and by E_n and I_n the tension and the current at its output, then, on the basis of Kirchhoff's laws (or of the theory of four-terminal networks), we obtain the equations

$$E_{n-1} = (1+a)E_n+(2a+a^2)2I_n,$$

$$I_{n-1} = \frac{1}{Z}E_n+(1+a)I_n.$$

Introducing the notation

$$e_n = \frac{E_n}{E_0}, \quad i_n = \frac{\operatorname{sh}\beta\cdot ZI_n}{E_0} \qquad (1+a = \operatorname{ch}\beta,\ n = 1, 2\ldots),$$

we can write

$$(8.6)\qquad \begin{aligned} e_{n-1} &= \operatorname{ch}\beta\cdot e_n+\operatorname{sh}\beta\cdot i_n,\\ i_{n-1} &= \operatorname{sh}\beta\cdot e_n+\operatorname{ch}\beta\cdot i_n. \end{aligned}$$

We introduce the operators

$$(8.7)\qquad \begin{aligned} E &= \sum_{n=0}^{\infty} e_n h^n = e_0+e_1h+e_2h^2+\dots,\\ I &= \sum_{n=0}^{\infty} i_n h^n = i_0+i_1h+i_2h^2+\dots \end{aligned}$$

Since

$$\begin{aligned} hE &= e_0h+e_1h^2+e_2h^3+\dots,\\ hI &= i_0h+i_1h^2+i_2h^3+\dots, \end{aligned}$$

we have by (8.6)

$$\begin{aligned} hE &= \operatorname{ch}\beta\cdot(E-e_0)+\operatorname{sh}\beta\cdot(I-i_0),\\ hI &= \operatorname{sh}\beta\cdot(E-e_0)+\operatorname{ch}\beta\cdot(I-i_0). \end{aligned}$$

We find hence

$$E=\frac{(1-h\operatorname{ch}\beta)e_0-h\operatorname{sh}\beta\cdot i_0}{1-2h\operatorname{ch}\beta+h^2},\qquad I=\frac{-h\operatorname{sh}\beta\cdot e_0+(1-h\operatorname{ch}\beta)i_0}{1-2h\operatorname{ch}\beta+h^2}.$$

Since $1-2h\operatorname{ch}\beta+h^2=(1-he^{\beta})(1-he^{-\beta})$, we obtain by decomposition into simple fractions and their expansion into series

$$\frac{1-h\operatorname{ch}\beta}{1-2h\operatorname{ch}\beta+h^2}=\frac{1}{2}\left(\frac{1}{1-he^{\beta}}+\frac{1}{1-he^{-\beta}}\right)=\sum_{n=0}^{\infty}\operatorname{ch}n\beta\cdot h^n,$$

$$\frac{\operatorname{sh}\beta}{1-2h\operatorname{ch}\beta+h^2}=\frac{1}{2}\left(\frac{1}{1-he^{\beta}}-\frac{1}{1-he^{-\beta}}\right)=\sum_{n=0}^{\infty}\operatorname{sh}n\beta\cdot h^n.$$

Consequently

$$E=\sum_{n=0}^{\infty}(e_0\operatorname{ch}n\beta-i_0\operatorname{sh}n\beta)h^n,\qquad I=\sum_{n=0}^{\infty}(-e_0\operatorname{sh}n\beta+i_0\operatorname{ch}n\beta)h^n$$

and by (8.7)

$$e_n=e_0\operatorname{ch}n\beta-i_0\operatorname{sh}n\beta,\qquad i_n=-e_0\operatorname{sh}n\beta+i_0\operatorname{ch}n\beta.$$

Finally, using formulas (8.5), we get

$$E_0=E_n\operatorname{ch}n\beta+I_nZ\operatorname{sh}\beta\operatorname{sh}n\beta,\qquad I_0=\frac{E_n}{Z}\,\frac{\operatorname{sh}n\beta}{\operatorname{sh}}+I_n\operatorname{ch}n\beta.$$

Thus we have obtained on different lines the same result as on p. 89.

§ 9. Operators $1/(1-\beta h^{\lambda})^k$. In solving certain difference equations operators of the type $1/(1-\beta h^{\lambda})^k$ occur. It will be shown in this section how they are expanded into a series.

From the equality

$$(1-\beta h^{\lambda})(1+2\beta h^{\lambda}+3\beta^2 h^{\lambda}+\ldots)$$
$$=(1+2\beta h^{\lambda}+3\beta^2 h^{2\lambda}+\ldots)-(\beta h^{\lambda}+2\beta^2 h^{2\lambda}+\ldots)$$
$$=1+\beta h^{\lambda}+\beta^2 h^{2\lambda}+\ldots=\frac{1}{1-ph^{\lambda}}$$

it follows that

$$\frac{1}{(1-\beta h^{\lambda})^2}=1+2\beta h^{\lambda}+3\beta^2 h^{2\lambda}+\ldots=\sum_{n=0}^{\infty}(n+1)\beta^n h^{n\lambda}.$$

Similarly we find the formula

$$\frac{1}{(1-\beta h^{\lambda})^3}=\sum_{n=0}^{\infty}\frac{(n+1)(n+2)}{1\cdot 2}\beta^n h^{n\lambda}$$

and generally

$$\frac{1}{(1-\beta h^{\lambda})^{1+k}}=\sum_{n=0}^{\infty}\binom{n+k}{k}\beta^n h^{n\lambda}$$ (β — complex number, k — natural number) where $\binom{n+k}{k}=\frac{(n+1)(n+2)\ldots(n+k)}{1\cdot 2\ldots k}$. This formula is also valid for $k=0$ if we assume that $\binom{n}{0}=1$ for every natural n.

This formula can also be deduced from the theorem on differentiating power series, which will be proved in the next section.

§ 10. Difference equations of arbitrary order. We shall now discuss the solution of the difference equation

$$(10.1)\qquad a\xi_{n+k}+a_1\xi_{n+k-1}+\ldots+a_k\xi_n=\delta_n\qquad(n=0,1,2,\ldots)$$

where k is a fixed natural number, $a_0,\ldots,a_k$ and δ_n being arbitrary complex numbers. Such an equation is often termed a *recurrence equation*. If $a_0\neq 0$, the equation is of order k.

Introducing the operator

$$(10.2)\qquad X=\xi_0+\xi_1 h+\xi_2 h^2+\ldots=\sum_{n=0}^{\infty}\xi_n h^n,$$

we have the equalities

$$\frac{1}{h}(X-\xi_0)=\sum_{n=0}^{\infty}\xi_{n+1}h^n,\quad\ldots,\quad\frac{1}{h^k}(X-\xi_0-\ldots-\xi_{k-1}h^{k-1})=\sum_{n=0}^{\infty}\xi_{n+k}h^n.$$

Hence by (10.1)

$$(10.3)\qquad \frac{\alpha_0}{h^k}(X-\xi_0-\ldots-\xi_{k-1}h^{k-1})+\ldots+\frac{\alpha_k-1}{h}(X-\xi_0)+\alpha_k X=\sum_{n=0}^{\infty}\delta_n h^n$$

and finally

$$(10.4)\qquad X=\frac{\beta_{k-1}h^{k-1}+\ldots+\beta_0}{\alpha_k h^k+\ldots+\alpha_0}+\frac{h^k}{\alpha_k h^k+\ldots+\alpha_0}\sum_{n=0}^{\infty}\delta_n h^n,$$

where

$$\beta_\nu=\alpha_0\xi_\nu+\alpha_1\xi_{\nu-1}+\ldots+\alpha_\nu\xi_0.$$

If we manage to expand the second component on the right-hand side of formula (10.4) into a power series of the operator h, then by comparison with series (10.2) we shall obtain the unknown coefficients ξ_n. This is conveniently done if the operator on the right-hand side of (10.3) can be represented in the form of an operator rational with respect to h,

$$(10.5)\qquad \frac{\varepsilon_p h^p+\ldots+\varepsilon_1 h+\varepsilon_0}{\eta h^q+\ldots+\eta_1 h+\eta_0},$$

where ε_n and η_n are complex numbers. Then, calculating the operator X from equation (10.3), we shall obtain it also as a rational expression of h. It is known from algebra that every expression of this kind can be decomposed into a polynomial of h and simple fractions of the form

$$\frac{1}{(1-\beta h)^n}.$$

These fractions in turn can be expanded into a power series of h, and in this manner the unknowns ξ_n can be found.

Let us solve, for instance, the equation

$$\xi_{n+2}-5\xi_{n+1}+6\xi_n=n.$$

In this case we have

$$\frac{1}{h^2}(X-\xi_0-\xi_1 h)-\frac{5}{h}(X-\xi_0)+6X=\sum_{n=0}^{\infty}nh^n=\frac{h}{(1-h)^2}.$$

Hence

$$X=\frac{(-5\xi_0+\xi_1)h+\xi_0}{6h^2-5h+1}+\frac{h^3}{(6h^2-5h+1)(1-h)^2}$$

$$=\frac{A}{1-3h}+\frac{B}{1-2h}+\frac{4}{4}\,\frac{1}{1-h}+\frac{1}{2}\,\frac{1}{(1-h)^2},$$

where

$$A=\tfrac{1}{4}-2\xi_0+\xi_1,\qquad B=-1+3\xi_0-\xi_1.$$

Expanding simple fractions into a series we obtain

$$X = \sum_{n=0}^{\infty} [A\cdot 3^n + B\cdot 2^n + \tfrac{1}{4} + \tfrac{1}{2}(n+1)]h^n,$$

whence by comparison with series (10.2)

$$A\cdot 3^n + B\cdot 2^n + \frac{n}{2} + \frac{3}{4} \qquad (n = 2, 3, \ldots).$$

The values of ξ_0 and ξ_1 may be arbitrary.

Exercise. A *Fibonacci sequence* is defined by reduction:

$$\xi_{n+2} = \xi_{n+1} + \xi_n, \qquad \xi_0 = \xi_1 = 1.$$

Find the general term of this sequence.

§ 11. Reduction of the complex form of a solution to the real form. Let us solve the equation

$$\xi_{n+2} - 2\xi_{n+1} + 2\xi_n = 0$$

under the assumption that $\xi_0 = 0$ and $\xi_1 = 1$.

Now we have

$$\frac{1}{h^2}(X-h) - \frac{2}{h}X + 2X = 0,$$

whence

$$X = \frac{h}{2h^2 - 2h + 1} = \frac{i}{2}\left(\frac{1}{1-(1-i)h} - \frac{1}{1-(1+i)h}\right)$$

$$= \frac{i}{2}\sum_{n=0}^{\infty}[(1-i)^n - (1+i)^n]h^n$$

and finally

(11.1) $$\xi_n = \frac{i}{2}[(1-i)^n - (1+i)^n].$$

It can be seen from this example that the method discussed in the preceding section sometimes gives the solution in a complex form though all the coefficients and initial values are real.

In such cases it is always possible to reduce the solution to the real form by the use of the sine and cosine functions. It is known from algebra that if we encounter in the decomposition of expression (10.4) (with real coefficients) into simple fractions a fraction $A/(1-\beta h)^{k+1}$

where β is not a real number, then we shall also find in it a fraction $\bar{A}/(1-\bar{\beta}h)^{k+1}$ where the numbers $\bar{A}$ and $\bar{\beta}$ are conjugate to A and β. These fractions have the expansion

$$\sum_{n=1}^{\infty}\binom{k+n}{n}(A\beta^n+\bar{A}\bar{\beta}^n)h^n.$$

Introducing the notation

$$A = \tfrac{1}{2}(B+Ci), \quad \beta = \varrho(\cos\varphi+i\sin\varphi) \quad (B, C, \varrho, \varphi \text{ real numbers})$$

we shall obtain the real form

$$A\beta^n+\bar{A}\bar{\beta}^n = (B\cos n\varphi - C\sin n\varphi)\,\varrho^n.$$

For (11.1), for instance, we can take $B = 0$, $C = -1$, $\varrho = \sqrt{2}$, $\varphi = -\frac{1}{4}\pi$; consequently

$$\xi_n = \sin\tfrac{1}{4}n\pi\cdot 2^{n/2}.$$

This method need not be applied in a stereotyped manner: in certain cases we may simplify the calculation by writing at once

$$\frac{1}{(1+h^2)^{k+1}} = \sum_{n=0}^{\infty}\binom{k+n}{n}(-1)^n h^{2n},$$

without the use of sines and cosines.

§ 12. General remarks. The method of solving difference equations which has been discussed above is not connected in any essential way with the operational calculus. In this chapter we have used only the following properties of the operator h:

I. If $\sum_{n=0}^{\infty}\xi_n h^n = \sum_{n=0}^{\infty}\eta_n h^n$, then $\xi_n = \eta_n$;

II. $\sum_{n=0}^{\infty}\xi_n h^n + \sum_{n=0}^{\infty}\eta_n h^n = \sum_{n=0}^{\infty}(\xi_n+\eta_n)h^n$;

III. $a\sum_{n=0}^{\infty}\xi_n h^n = \sum_{n=0}^{\infty}a\xi_n h^n$;

IV. $\dfrac{1}{(1-\beta h^{\lambda})^{k+1}} = \sum_{n=0}^{\infty}\binom{n+k}{k}\beta^n h^{n\lambda}.$

Moreover, we have availed ourselves of the fact that every power series of h is convergent.

Properties I-IV characterize also ordinary power series, in which h may denote a real or a complex variable. As regards convergence, all the series under consideration have been expansions of rational functions, *i. e.*, treated in the ordinary way they have been convergent for small values of the argument. Thus the method of solving difference equations which has been described here is actually a *method of power series*, and the operator h has been used only to enable us to disregard from the very beginning the question of convergence of the series. The use of the operator h enables us also to solve difference equations with coefficients that are not numbers but, for instance, operators rational with respect to s. For in that case conditions I-IV are satisfied (condition I being satisfied in virtue of theorem XX, § 5).

Divergent series can also be treated correctly without the use of the operational calculus as the so-called *formal power series*. Logically they are nothing else than sequences of coefficients on which certain operations are defined. This treatment has the advantage of permitting the solution of difference equations with arbitrary coefficients (even such as are not rational operators with respect to s).

The method of solving difference equations which has been discussed in this chapter is connected by some authors with the theory of Laplace transformations, jump functions being used instead of series (see Gardner--Barnes [1]). Such treatment is much more complicated both from the theoretical point of view and in applications. Moreover, it is less general and even does not comprise all series with numerical coefficients.

CHAPTER IV

POWER SERIES

§ 13. Power series of a numerical variable with operational coefficients. Let $f_0, f_1, \dots$ be a sequence of functions of class $\mathcal{C}$. We shall prove that *if the series*

$$(13.1) \qquad f_0+f_1\lambda+f_2\lambda^2+\dots$$

is for a certain fixed number $\lambda=\lambda_1$ convergent almost uniformly (with respect to the variable t), then the series

$$(13.2) \qquad |f_0|+|f_1\lambda|+|f_2\lambda^2|+\dots$$

and with it also series (13.1), *regarded as a series of functions of two variables λ and t, are uniformly convergent in every domain*

$$(13.3) \qquad |\lambda|\leqslant\lambda_0<\lambda_1, \qquad 0\leqslant t\leqslant t_0.$$

Proof. For any fixed $t_0>0$ series (13.2) is convergent in the whole domain (13.3). It must only be shown that the convergence is uniform.

It follows from the almost uniform convergence of series (13.1) that for a fixed t_0 there exists such a number M that $|f_n\lambda_1^n|$ for $0\leqslant t\leqslant t_0$. Consequently we have in the domain (13.3) the inequality

$$|f_{n+1}|\lambda_0^{n+1}+|f_{n+2}|\lambda_0^{n+2}+\dots\leqslant M\left[\left(\frac{\lambda_0}{|\lambda_1|}\right)^{n+1}+\left(\frac{\lambda_0}{|\lambda_1|}\right)^{n+2}+\dots\right]$$

$$=\frac{M}{1-\dfrac{\lambda_0}{|\lambda_1|}}\left(\frac{\lambda_0}{|\lambda_1|}\right)^{n+1},$$

which proves the uniform convergence of (13.2) in the domain (13.3) since the last term on the right side tends to zero.

Now let $a_0, a_1, a_2, \dots$ be an arbitrary sequence of operators.

If the series

$$(13.4) \qquad a_0+a_1\lambda+a_2\lambda^2+\dots$$

is convergent for a certain number $\lambda=\lambda_1$, then it is convergent in the circle $|\lambda|<\lambda_1$.

Indeed, we can then write

$$a_0 + a_1\lambda + a_2\lambda^2 + \ldots = q(f_0 + f_1\lambda + f_2\lambda^2 \ldots) \qquad (f_n \in \mathcal{C})$$

where the series on the right side is convergent almost uniformly for $\lambda = \lambda_1$ and thus also for every fixed λ satisfying the inequality $|\lambda| < \lambda_1$, which follows from the theorem proved just now. And this signifies the convergence of series (13.4) for $|\lambda| < |\lambda_1|$ in the operational sense.

The upper bound of the real values of λ for which series (13.4) is convergent is termed its *convergence radius* ϱ. In certain cases we may have $\varrho = 0$ or $\varrho = \infty$. Series (13.4) is convergent inside the convergence circle, *i. e.*, for $|\lambda| < \varrho$.

§ 14. Multiplication of power series. Given two sequences of operators

$$a_0 + a_1 + a_2, \ldots \quad \text{and} \quad b_0, b_1, b_2, \ldots$$

we introduce the operators

$$\begin{aligned} c_0 &= a_0 b_0, \\ c_1 &= a_0 b_1 + a_1 b_0, \\ c_2 &= a_0 b_2 + a_1 b_1 + a_2 b_0, \\ &\ldots\ldots\ldots\ldots\ldots \end{aligned}$$

The following theorem holds:

If the series

$$a_0 + a_1\lambda + a_2\lambda^2 + \ldots \quad \textit{and} \quad b_0 + b_1\lambda + b_2\lambda^2 + \ldots \tag{14.1}$$

are convergent for $|\lambda| < \lambda_1$, *then also the series*

$$c_0 + c_1\lambda + c_2\lambda^2 + \ldots$$

is convergent for $|\lambda| < \lambda_1$ *and equal to the product of the preceding series, i. e.*,

$$(a_0 + a_1\lambda + a_2\lambda^2 + \ldots)(b_0 + b_1\lambda + b_2\lambda^2 + \ldots) = c_0 + c_1\lambda + c_2\lambda^2 + \ldots$$

Proof. We can write

$$(a_0 + \ldots + a_n\lambda^n)(b_0 + \ldots + b_n\lambda^n) = c_0 + \ldots + c_n\lambda^n + R_n$$

where

$$R_n = (a_1 b_n + a_2 b_{n-1} + \ldots + a_n b_1)\lambda^{n+1} + \\ + (a_2 b_n + a_3 b_{n-1} + \ldots + a_n b_2)\lambda^{n+2} + \ldots + a_n b_n \lambda^{2n}.$$

It suffices to prove that for $|\lambda| < \lambda_1$ we have $\lim\limits_{n\to\infty} R_n = 0$.

We fix numbers λ and λ_0 in such a way that $|\lambda| < \lambda_0 < \lambda_1$. In view of the convergence of series (14.1) for $\lambda = \lambda_0$ we can write

$$\sum_{n=0}^{\infty} a_n \lambda_0^n = q_1 \sum_{n=0}^{\infty} f_n \lambda_0^n, \qquad \sum_{n=0}^{\infty} b_n \lambda_0^n = q_2 \sum_{n=0}^{\infty} g_n \lambda_0^n \qquad (f_n, g_n \in \mathcal{C})$$

where the series on the right sides of the equalities are almost uniformly convergent. Hence follows the existence for every fixed number $t_0 > 0$ of such positive numbers M_1 and M_2 that

$$|f_n(t)|\lambda_0^n < M_1 \quad \text{and} \quad |g_n(t)|\lambda_0^n < M_2 \quad \text{for} \quad 0 \leqslant t < t_0.$$

Consequently

$$F_n = |(f_1 g_n + f_2 g_{n-1} + \ldots + f_n g_1)\lambda^{n+1} + \\ + (f_2 g_n + f_3 g_{n-1} + \ldots + f_n g_2)\lambda^{n+2} + \ldots + f_n g_n \lambda^{2n}|$$

$$\leqslant M_1 M_2 t_0 \left[n \left| \frac{\lambda}{\lambda_0} \right|^{n+1} + (n-1) \left| \frac{\lambda}{\lambda_0} \right|^{n+2} + \ldots + \left| \frac{\lambda}{\lambda_0} \right|^{2n} \right]$$

$$\leqslant M_1 M_2 t_0 \cdot n \left(\left| \frac{\lambda}{\lambda_0} \right|^{n+1} + \left| \frac{\lambda}{\lambda_0} \right|^{n+2} + \ldots \right) = \frac{M_1 M_2 t_0^2}{1 - \left| \dfrac{\lambda}{\lambda_0} \right|} n \left| \frac{\lambda}{\lambda_0} \right|^{n+1}.$$

Since $\lim\limits_{n\to\infty} n \left| \dfrac{\lambda}{\lambda_0} \right|^{n+1} = 0$, the sequence F_n almost uniformly tends to zero. Consequently the sequence $R_n = q_1 q_2 F_n$ tends to zero in the operational sense, q. e. d.

This theorem is a generalization of an analogical theorem on ordinary power series and is reducible to it under the assumption that all the operators $a_0, a_1, a_2, \ldots$ and $b_0, b_1, b_2, \ldots$ are numbers.

§ 15. Power series of operators with numerical coefficients. In applications we find power series of the form

(15.1) $$\Phi(w) = \alpha_0 + \alpha_1 w + \alpha_2 w^2 + \ldots,$$

where $\alpha_1, \alpha_2, \ldots$ are numerical (real or complex) coefficients and w an operator. Such series may be regarded as a particular case of the series discussed in the preceding section since we can take $a_n = \alpha_n w^n$ and $\lambda = 1$.

If $w = h$, we are dealing with the series considered in Chapters II and III.

If $w = \lambda$ (λ a complex number), then series (15.1) is reduced to an ordinary power series

(15.2) $$\Phi(\lambda) = \alpha_0 + \alpha_0 \lambda + \alpha_2 \lambda^2 + \ldots$$

In this section we shall deal with a series in which w is a function of class $\mathcal{C}$:

$$\Phi(f) = \alpha_0 + \alpha_1 f + \alpha_2 f^2 + \dots \quad (f \in \mathcal{C}). \tag{15.3}$$

We have the following theorem:

If the convergence radius of series (15.2) *is positive, then series* (15.3) *is operationally convergent for every function f of class $\mathcal{C}$.*

Since the addition or subtraction of the one term, α_0, does not affect the convergence of the series, this theorem results immediately from the following auxiliary theorem:

If the convergence radius of series (15.2) *is positive, then the series*

$$\alpha_1 \lambda f + \alpha_2 \lambda^2 f^2 + \dots \quad (f \in \mathcal{C}) \tag{15.4}$$

regarded as a series of two variables, λ and t, is uniformly convergent in every domain

$$0 \leqslant \lambda \leqslant \lambda_0, \quad 0 \leqslant t \leqslant t_0. \tag{15.5}$$

Proof of the auxiliary theorem. Denote by M the maximum absolute value of $f(t)$ in an arbitrarily fixed interval $0 \leqslant t \leqslant t_0$. Moreover, introduce the notation

$$f^n = \{f^n(t)\} \quad (n = 1, 2, \dots).$$

Then for $0 \leqslant t \leqslant t_0$

$$|f^1(t)| \leqslant M_1,$$

$$|f^2(t)| = \left|\int_0^t f^1(t-\tau) f^1(\tau)\, d\tau\right| \leqslant \int_0^t M \cdot M\, d\tau = M^2 \frac{t}{1!},$$

$$|f^3(t)| = \left|\int_0^t f^1(t-\tau) f^2(\tau)\, d\tau\right| \leqslant \int_0^t M \cdot M^2 \frac{\tau}{1!}\, d\tau = M^3 \frac{t^2}{2!},$$

and generally

$$|f^n(t)| \leqslant M^n \frac{t^{n-1}}{(n-1)!} \leqslant M^n \frac{t_0^{n-1}}{(n-1)!} \quad (n = 1, 2, \dots).$$

The sequence $\left(\dfrac{2\lambda_0}{\varrho}\right)^n M^n \dfrac{t_0^{n-1}}{(n-1)!}$ tends to zero, *i. e.*, it is bounded by a certain number K. Consequently

$$|\alpha_n \lambda^n f^n(t)| \leqslant \left|\alpha_n \lambda^n M^n \frac{t_0^{n-1}}{(n-1)!}\right| = \left|\left(\frac{2\lambda_0}{\varrho}\right)^n M^n \frac{t_0^{n-1}}{(n-1)!}\, \alpha_n \left(\frac{0}{2}\right)^n\right| \leqslant K|\alpha_n| \left(\frac{\varrho}{2}\right)^n.$$

Since ϱ is the convergence radius of series (15.2), the series

$$K|\alpha_1|\frac{\varrho}{2}+K_2|\alpha_2|\left(\frac{\varrho}{2}\right)^2+\ldots$$

is convergent. Hence follows the uniform convergence of series (15.4) in the domain (15.5).

Example 1. The series

$$\frac{1}{1-\lambda}=1+\lambda+\lambda^2+\ldots$$

has the convergence radius equal to 1. The series

$$\frac{1}{s-a}=\frac{l}{1-al}=l+al^2+a^2l^3+\ldots=\left\{1+\frac{at}{1!}+\frac{a^2t^2}{2!}+\ldots\right\}$$

is convergent for every complex a. This implies also the formula

$$\frac{1}{s-a}=\{e^{at}\},$$

worked out in a different manner on p. 33.

Example 2. Series

$$\cos\lambda=1-\frac{\lambda^2}{2!}+\frac{\lambda^4}{4!}-\ldots$$

has the convergence radius $+\infty$. It follows hence, for example, that the series

$$\cos\frac{1}{s^2}=1-\frac{1}{2!s^4}+\frac{1}{4!s^8}-\ldots$$

is convergent.

The theorem on series (15.3) can be generalized to functions of class $\mathcal{K}$ and even to wider classes of operators. We shall prove that *if series* (15.2) *has a positive convergence radius, then the series*

$$\alpha_0+\frac{\alpha_1}{s^\beta}+\frac{\alpha_2}{s^{2\beta}}+\ldots \tag{15.6}$$

is convergent for every $\beta>0$.

Proof. We have the equalities

$$\frac{1}{s}\left(\alpha_0+\alpha_1\frac{1}{s^\beta}+\alpha_2\frac{1}{s^{2\beta}}+\ldots\right)=\frac{\alpha_0}{s}+\frac{\alpha_1}{s^{1+\beta}}+\frac{\alpha_2}{s^{1+2\beta}}+\ldots \tag{15.7}$$

$$=\left\{\alpha_0+\alpha_1\frac{t^\beta}{\Gamma(1+\beta)}+\alpha_2\frac{t^{2\beta}}{\Gamma(1+2\beta)}+\ldots\right\}.$$

But for every number $\gamma > 0$ we have

$$\Gamma(1+n\beta) = \int_0^\infty t^{n\beta} e^{-t} dt > \int_\gamma^{1+\gamma} t^{n\beta} e^{-t} dt > \int_\gamma^{1+\gamma} \gamma^{n\beta} e^{-1-\gamma} dt = \gamma^{n\beta} e^{-1-\gamma}$$

$$(n = 0, 1, 2, \ldots).$$

If we take an arbitrary fixed interval $0 \leqslant t \leqslant t_0$, then for $\gamma^\beta = 2t_0^\beta/\varrho$ we shall have

$$\left| \frac{t^{n\beta}}{\Gamma(1+n\beta)} \right| < e^{1+\gamma} \left(\frac{\varrho}{2} \right)^n.$$

It follows hence that series (15.6), as a series of functions of the variable t, is uniformly convergent in the interval $0 \leqslant t \leqslant t_0$, *i. e.*, it is operationally convergent.

Exercise. Prove the formula

$$\sin \frac{1}{s} = \left\{ \frac{1}{1!} - \frac{t^2}{3!2!} + \frac{t^4}{5!4!} - \ldots \right\}.$$

§ 16. Powers with arbitrary real exponents. If n is a natural number, then by the *power* a^n we understand the product $a \ldots a$ composed of n factors. In this way the power a^n is defined for every operator a. A power with a negative exponent is also defined for every operator $a \neq 0$ by the formula $a^{-n} = 1/a^n$. Non-integer powers, on the other hand, have so far been defined only for operators of the form $s - a$ (see p. 111), for translation operators and for operators which are ordinary numbers.

Using the known expansion

$$(1+\lambda)^\beta = \sum_{\nu=0}^{\infty} \binom{\beta}{\nu} \lambda^\nu \qquad (|\lambda| < 1),$$

we can define powers with any real exponents λ also for operators of the form $1+f$ ($f \in \mathcal{C}$), writing

$$(1+f)^\beta = \sum_{\nu=0}^{\infty} \binom{\beta}{\nu} f^\nu.$$

Since $(1+\lambda)^\beta(1+\lambda)^{\beta_2} = (1+\lambda)^{\beta_1+\beta_2}$, *i. e.*,

$$\sum_{\nu=0}^{\infty} \binom{\beta_1}{\nu} \lambda^\nu \sum_{\nu=0}^{\infty} \binom{\beta^2}{\nu} \lambda^\nu = \sum_{\nu=0}^{\infty} \binom{\beta_1+\beta_2}{\nu} \lambda^\nu,$$

from the theorem on multiplying operational series (see p. 167) follows the formula

(16.1) $$(1+f)^{\beta_1}(1+f)^{\beta_2} = (1+f)^{\beta_1+\beta_2}.$$

Hence for $\beta = \beta_1 = -\beta_2$ we have

$$(1+f)^{-\beta} = 1/(1+f)^{\beta}.$$

Having defined the powers of the operators a and b, we define the power of their product ab by the formula

$$(ab)^{\beta} = a^{\beta} b^{\beta}.$$

In virtue of this formula we can write

$$\frac{1}{(s-a)^{\beta}} = \frac{1}{s^{\beta}}\,\frac{1}{(1-al)^{\beta}} = \sum_{\nu=0}^{\infty}\binom{-\beta}{\nu}(-al)^{\nu+\beta} = \left\{\frac{t^{\beta-1}}{\Gamma(\beta)}\sum_{\nu=0}^{\infty}\frac{(at)^{\nu}}{\nu!}\right\} = \left\{\frac{t^{\beta-1}}{\Gamma(\beta)}e^{at}\right\}$$

(see Exercise 2 on p. 113) according to the definition on p. 111.

Any operator rational with respect to s can be raised to an arbitrary power by writing

$$\left(\frac{\gamma_m s^m + \ldots + \gamma_0}{\delta_n s^n + \ldots + \delta_0}\right)^{\beta} = s^{(m-n)\beta}\left(\frac{\gamma_m}{\delta_n}\right)^{\beta}\frac{(1+f_1)^{\beta}}{(1+f_2)^{\beta}},$$

where

$$f_1 = \frac{\gamma_{m-1}}{\gamma_m}l + \ldots + \frac{\gamma_0}{\gamma_m}l^m, \qquad f_2 = \frac{\delta_{n-1}}{\delta_n}l + \ldots + \frac{\delta_0}{\delta_n}l^n.$$

The power g^{β} with an arbitrary exponent β is also defined for every function g with a positive value at the point 0 and with a derivative g' continuous for $0 \leqslant t < \infty$:

$$g^{\beta} = \frac{1}{s^{\beta}}(sg)^{\beta} = \frac{1}{s^{\beta}}[g(0)+g']^{\beta} = \frac{[g(0)]^{\beta}}{s}\sum_{\nu=0}^{\infty}\binom{\beta}{\nu}\left(\frac{g'}{g(0)}\right)^{\nu}.$$

In the case of $\beta = 1/n$ (n being natural) we write

$$\sqrt[n]{1+f} = (1+f)^{\frac{1}{n}}$$

and in the case of $n = 2$ we omit the exponent 2 above the root sign. It follows from formula (16.1) that the operator $\sqrt{1+f}$ satisfies the equation $x^2 = 1+f$; it is also the operator $-\sqrt{1+f}$ that satisfies this equation. Similarly, the operator $\sqrt[n]{1+f}$ and every operator $\varepsilon\sqrt[n]{1+f}$ where $\varepsilon^n = 1$ satisfy the equation $x^n = 1+f$.

More generally, if an operator x_0 satisfies the equation

$$x^n = a, \tag{16.2}$$

then each of the operators $\varepsilon_1 x_0, \ldots, \varepsilon_n x_0$, where ε_ν are the solutions of the equation $x^n = 1$, also satisfies that equation.

These are the only solutions of equations (16.2). Indeed, by the theorems of algebra we have the identity

$$\prod_{\nu=1}^{n} (x - \varepsilon_\nu x_0) = x^n - a;$$

if an operator x_1 satisfies equation (16.2), then by substituting it in the above identity we obtain the equality $\prod_{\nu=n}^{n} (x_1 - \varepsilon_\nu x_0) = 0$, which implies that at least one factor in the product is equal to zero, *i. e.*, that x_1 is equal to one of the roots $\varepsilon_\nu x_0$.

We can prove a more general proposition, namely that *the algebraic equation of the n-th degree*

$$a_n x^n + \ldots + a_1 x + a_0 = 0 \qquad (a_n \neq 0)$$

whose coefficients a_ν are operators has at least n solutions. It cannot be maintained, however, that every equation of the n-th degree has n solutions. For instance, there exists no solution of the equation

(16.3) $$x^2 = f \quad \text{where} \quad f = \{t \sin \ln t\}.$$

Indeed, let the operator x be called *real* if it can be represented in the form p/q where p and q are real functions. It is easy to prove that every operator x may be represented in one and only one manner as $x_1 + ix_2$, x_1 and x_2 being real operators.

Suppose that an operator $x = x_1 + ix_2$ satisfies equation (16.3). Then $x_1^2 - x_2^2 + 2ix_1x_2 = f$, whence it follows that $x_1 = 0$ or $x_2 = 0$, f being real.

Let us introduce an operation U defining it for every operator $a = \{p(t)\}/\{q(t)\}$ $(p, q \in \mathcal{C})$ by the equality

$$Ua = \frac{\{p(e^\pi t)\}}{\{q(e^\pi t)\}}.$$

It is easy to verify that

$$U(ab) = (Ua)(Ub)$$

and that

$$Up = e^\pi \{p(e^\pi t)\} \qquad (p \in \mathcal{C}).$$

If x satisfies equation (16.3), then

$$(Ux)^2 = U(x^2) = \{e^{2\pi} t \sin \ln (e^\pi t)\} = -e^{2\pi} f = -e^{2\pi} x^2.$$

Hence $Ux = \pm ie^\pi x$, which is impossible since the operators Ux and x are simultaneously real and imaginary.

§ 17. A problem in electrical engineering. Roots of operators may occur in certain electrical calculations as has been seen in § 47 of Part I. Namely, if we apply to a four-terminal network with the matrix $\begin{bmatrix} a & b \\ c & d \end{bmatrix}$ a network with impedance Z, we obtain a network with impedance $\dfrac{aZ+b}{cZ+d}$. If we demand that the two impedances be equal,

$$Z = \frac{aZ+b}{cZ+d},$$

we obtain a solution containing a root,

$$Z = \frac{a-d \pm \sqrt{(a-d)^2+4bc}}{2c}.$$

Suppose that a four-terminal network has the form given in fig. 120. Then its matrix is

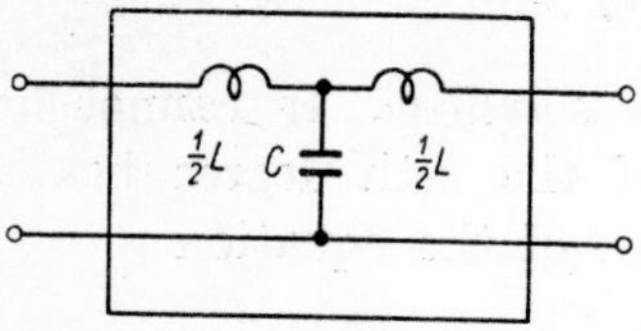

Fig. 120

$$\begin{bmatrix} 1 & \frac{1}{2}Ls \\ 0 & 1 \end{bmatrix} \begin{bmatrix} 1 & 0 \\ Cs & 1 \end{bmatrix} \begin{bmatrix} 1 & \frac{1}{2}Ls \\ 0 & 1 \end{bmatrix},$$

i. e., the multiplication performed,

$$\begin{bmatrix} 1+\frac{1}{2}LCs^2 & Ls+\frac{1}{4}L^2Cs^3 \\ Cs & 1+\frac{1}{2}LCs^2 \end{bmatrix},$$

whence we obtain

$$Z = \tfrac{1}{2}L\sqrt{s^2+a^2}, \quad \text{where} \quad a = 2/\sqrt{Lc}.$$

If we apply to a network with this impedance an electromotive force E, we shall obtain the current

$$I = \frac{2E}{L} \cdot \frac{1}{\sqrt{s^2+a^2}}.$$

§ 18. The Bessel function J_0. The operator obtained in the preceding section may be expanded into an infinite series,

$$\frac{1}{\sqrt{s^2+a^2}} = \frac{l}{\sqrt{1+(al)^2}} = l\sum_{\nu=0}^{\infty}\binom{-\frac{1}{2}}{\nu}(al)^{2\nu} = l\sum_{\nu=0}^{\infty}\frac{(-1)^\nu(2\nu)!}{2^{2\nu}(\nu!)^2}a^{2\nu}l^{2\nu}$$

$$= \left\{\sum_{\nu=0}^{\infty}(-1)^\nu\frac{a^{2\nu}t^{2\nu}}{2^{2\nu}(\nu!)^2}\right\}.$$

Introducing the *Bessel function of order zero*,

$$J_0(t) = \sum_{\nu=0}^{\infty}(-1)^\nu\frac{t^{2\nu}}{2^{2\nu}(\nu!)^2}, \tag{18.1}$$

we can write

$$(18.2)\qquad \frac{1}{\sqrt{s^2+a^2}} = \{J_0(at)\}.$$

It is convenient to calculate the values of the Bessel function from formula (18.1) since it represents a series converging very rapidly. In particular, it can be seen that $J_0(0) = 1$. Substituting it for t in formula (18.1) and a for ia in formula (18.2), we have

$$J_0(it) = \sum_{\nu=0}^{\infty} \frac{t^{2\nu}}{2^{2\nu}(\nu!)^2}, \qquad \frac{1}{\sqrt{s^2-a^2}} = \{J_0(iat)\}.$$

§ 19. A more general problem in electrical engineering. The problem discussed in § 17 may be given a different interpretation. Let us consider an infinite chain of four-terminal networks with the matrix $\begin{bmatrix} a & b \\ c & d \end{bmatrix}$. The problem consists in finding the current which will flow through the input wires of the chain under the voltage impulse E.

In order to approach this problem mathematically we must first make clear what we mean by an infinitely long chain, since such a chain does not really exist. We mean a chain containing so many links that adding or disconnecting one link does not practically affect the course of the phenomenon. Thus, supposing that if we apply an electromotive force E a current I will flow, we assume that after the addition of one more four-terminal network and a repetition of the experiment there will again flow a current which cannot by measurement be distinguished from I.

Treating the input wires of the chain of four-terminal networks as the terminals of a two-terminal network with the impedance Z, we obtain on connecting another four-terminal network a two-terminal network with impedance $\dfrac{aZ+b}{cZ+d}$. The assumption of the chain being infinite signifies that

$$Z = \frac{aZ+b}{cZ+d}.$$

Applying to the chain the electromotive force E, we obtain in the case of a chain consisting of the four-terminal networks shown in fig. 120

$$(19.1)\qquad I = \frac{2L}{L}\frac{1}{\sqrt{s^2+a^2}}, \qquad \text{where} \qquad a = \frac{2}{\sqrt{LC}},$$

just as in § 17.

For the same infinite chain (consisting of the networks shown in fig. 120) we shall now solve a more general problem: what current flows at the output of the n-th successive network under the conditions of the preceding experiment?

Denote by E_1 and I_1 the voltage and the current at the output of the first network. We have the relations

$$E = aE_1 + bI_1, \qquad I = cE_1 + dI_1,$$

whence in the case of a network with determinant 1

$$E_1 = dE - bI, \qquad I_1 = -cE + aI.$$

In particular, for the network under consideration we have by (19.1)

$$E_1 = (1 + \tfrac{1}{2}LCs^2)E - (Ls + \tfrac{1}{4}L^2Cs^3)\frac{2E}{L}\cdot\frac{1}{\sqrt{s^2+a^2}},$$

$$I_1 = -CsE + (1 + \tfrac{1}{2}LCs^2)\frac{2E}{L}\cdot\frac{1}{\sqrt{s^2+a^2}},$$

and, after an easy algebraical calculation,

$$E_1 = \frac{E}{a^2}(\sqrt{s^2+a^2} - s)^2, \qquad I_1 = \frac{2E}{La^2}\,\frac{(\sqrt{s^2+a^2}-s)^2}{\sqrt{s^2+a^2}}.$$

Obviously we can formally obtain E_1 and I_1 multiplying E and I by the operator $(\sqrt{s^2+a^2}-s)/a^2$. On the grounds of this remark we easily find for the voltage E_2 and current I_2 at the output of the second network the formulas

$$E_2 = dE_1 - bI_1 = (dE - bI)\cdot\frac{1}{a^2}(\sqrt{s^2+a^2}-s) = E_1\cdot\frac{1}{a^2}(\sqrt{s^2+a^2}-s),$$

$$I_2 = -cE_1 + aI_1 = (-cE + aI)\cdot\frac{1}{a^2}(\sqrt{s^2+a^2}-s) = I_1\cdot\frac{1}{a^2}(\sqrt{s^2+a^2}-s),$$

whence

$$E_2 = \frac{E}{a^4}(\sqrt{s^2+a^2}-s)^4, \qquad I_2 = \frac{2E}{La^4}\,\frac{(\sqrt{s^2+a^2}-s)^4}{\sqrt{s^2+a^2}}.$$

In the same way we obtain the general formulas,

$$E_n = \frac{E}{a^{2n}}(\sqrt{s^2+a^2}-s)^{2n}, \qquad I_n = \frac{2E}{La^{2n}}\,\frac{(\sqrt{s^2+a^2}-s)}{\sqrt{s^2+a^2}},$$

expressing the voltage and the current at the output of the n-th network.

§ 20. Bessel functions J_n with an arbitrary natural n. In order to evaluate the operators obtained in the preceding section we shall use the expansion

$$(20.1)\qquad (\sqrt{1+\lambda}-1)^n = n\sum_{\nu=0}^{\infty}(-1)^\nu \frac{(n+2\nu-1)!}{2^{n+2\nu}\nu!(n+\nu)!}\lambda^{n+\nu}\qquad (|\lambda|<1).$$

This formula can be proved in the following manner. Writing

$$(20.2)\qquad \varphi_n(\lambda) = (\sqrt{1+\lambda}-1)^n \qquad (n=1,2,\ldots)$$

we can easily find that

$$\varphi_{n+1}'(\lambda) = \frac{n+1(\sqrt{1+\lambda}-1)^n}{2\sqrt{1+\lambda}},$$

$$[\lambda^{-n/2}\varphi_n(\lambda)]' = \frac{n}{2}\lambda^{-n/2-1}\frac{(\sqrt{1+\lambda}-1)^n}{\sqrt{1+\lambda}}.$$

Hence

$$\varphi_{n+1}'(\lambda) = \frac{n+1}{n}\lambda^{n/2+1}[\lambda^{-n/2}\varphi_n(\lambda)]'$$

and

$$(20.3)\qquad \varphi_{n+1}(\lambda) = \frac{n+1}{n}\int_0^\lambda \lambda^{n/2+1}[\lambda^{-n/2}\varphi_n(\lambda)]'d\lambda$$

since (20.2) shows that $\varphi_n(0)=0$.

But from Newton's formula we have

$$\varphi_1(\lambda) = \sqrt{1+\lambda}-1 = \sum_{\nu=0}^{\infty}(-1)^\nu\frac{(2\nu)!}{2^{1+2\nu}\nu!(1+\nu)!}\lambda^{1-\nu};$$

thus using the recurrence formula (20.3) we easily find expansion (20.1) by induction.

Formula (20.1) implies that

$$(\sqrt{s^2+a^2}-s)^n = s^n(\sqrt{1+a^2l^2}-1)^n$$

$$= n\sum_{\nu=0}^{\infty}(-1)^\nu\frac{(n+2\nu-1)!}{2^{n+2\nu}\nu!(n+\nu)!}a^{2(n+\nu)}l^{n+2\nu},$$

i. e.,

$$(20.4)\qquad (\sqrt{s^2+a^2}-s)^n = \left\{n\sum_{\nu=0}^{\infty}(-1)^\nu\frac{a^{2(n+\nu)}t^{n+2\nu-1}}{2^{n+2\nu}\nu!(n+\nu)!}\right\}\qquad (n=1,2,\ldots).$$

If we substitute $n+1$ for n in formula (20.4) and then differentiate it and divide it by $(n+1)a$, we shall obtain

$$\frac{(\sqrt{s^2+a^2}-s)^n}{\sqrt{s^2+a^2}} = \left\{ \sum_{\nu=0}^{\infty} (-1)^\nu \frac{a^{2(n+\nu)} t^{n+2\nu}}{2^{n+2\nu}\, \nu!\,(n+\nu)!} \right\} \qquad (n = 0, 1, 2, \ldots). \tag{20.5}$$

Introducing the *Bessel function of order n*:

$$\mathrm{J}_n(t) = \sum_{\nu=0}^{\infty} (-1)^\nu \frac{t^{n+2\nu}}{2^{n+2\nu}\, \nu!\,(n+\nu)!} \qquad (n = 0, 1, 2, \ldots) \tag{20.6}$$

we can write formulas (20.4) and (20.6) in the form

$$(\sqrt{s^2+a^2}-s)^n = \left\{ \frac{n a^n}{t} \mathrm{J}_n(at) \right\} \qquad (n = 1, 2, \ldots),$$

$$\frac{(\sqrt{s^2+a^2}-s)^n}{\sqrt{s^2+a}} = \{ a^n \mathrm{J}_n(at) \} \qquad (n = 0, 1, 2, \ldots),$$

these formulas being valid for all complex a.

PART THREE

THE OPERATIONAL DIFFERENTIAL CALCULUS

CHAPTER I

OPERATIONAL FUNCTIONS AND THEIR DERIVATIVES

§ 1. Operational functions. Let us consider the operator l^λ (p. 111). Since we can take any real number as λ, we are dealing here in fact with a certain function which assigns operators to numbers λ. The symbol l^λ denotes the value of this function at the point λ.

Generally, we shall deal with functions $f(\lambda)$ which assign arbitrary operators to numbers λ. Such functions will be termed *operational functions*. The symbol $f(\lambda)$ itself, not preceded by the word function, will denote the value of the function in question for a given number λ, *i. e.*, the operator assigned to that number. Moreover, we shall frequently use the term *operational function* $f(\lambda)$, or shortly *function* $f(\lambda)$ without introducing a separate symbol for it.

If λ is fixed and positive, then the operator l^λ is a function of the variable t,

$$l^\lambda = \left\{\frac{t^{\lambda-1}}{\Gamma(\lambda)}\right\} \qquad (\lambda > 0).$$

It will be observed that two variables, λ and t, appear within the braces, and that the braces cancel only the variable t, which does not appear on the left side of the formula.

Generally, given a function of two variables $f(\lambda, t)$ defined for $t \geqslant 0$ and for some values of λ, we shall write

$$f(\lambda) = \{f(\lambda, t)\} \tag{1.1}$$

in the same way as we write $a = \{a(t)\}$. Formula (1.1) defines an operational function of a peculiar kind, namely a function which assigns operators that are functions of the variable t to the values of λ. Such a function $f(\lambda)$ will be termed *parametric*. For instance the operational function l^λ is parametric in the interval $0 < \lambda < \infty$. The function $f(\lambda) = \{\lambda^2 + t^2\}$ is parametric for all values of λ.

With regard to parametric operational functions we shall always assume that their values are functions of the variable t belonging to class $\mathcal{K}$ (p. 108).

Another peculiar type of operational functions are those functions whose values are numerical operators, *i. e.*, simply numbers; we shall term them *numerical functions.* The function $f(\lambda) = \lambda^2$ is an example of a numerical function for all values, while the function l^λ is numerical only at one point, $\lambda = 0$, since $l^0 = 1$. For $\lambda < 0$ the function l^λ is neither parametric nor numerical.

Exercises. Prove the equalities

(α) $\{\lambda + t\} = l^2\lambda^2 + 2l^3\lambda + l^4$; (β) $\{\lambda^2 + t^2\}\{\lambda^2 - t^2\} = l^2\lambda^2 - 4l^6$;

(γ) $\{e^{\alpha\lambda+\beta t}\} = \dfrac{e^{\alpha\lambda}}{s-\beta}$; (δ) $\{\cos(\lambda - t)\} = \dfrac{1}{1+s^2}(\sin\lambda + s\cos\lambda)$.

§ 2. Continuity of the operational function. An operational function $f(\lambda)$ will be termed *continuous in a finite* (open or closed) *interval I* (fig. 121) if it can be represented in that interval as a product of a certain operator q and a parametric function $f_1(\lambda) = \{f_1(\lambda, t)\}$ such that the function of two variables $f_1(\lambda, t)$ is continuous (in the usual sense) in the domain D $(\lambda \in I,\ 0 \leqslant t < \infty)$,

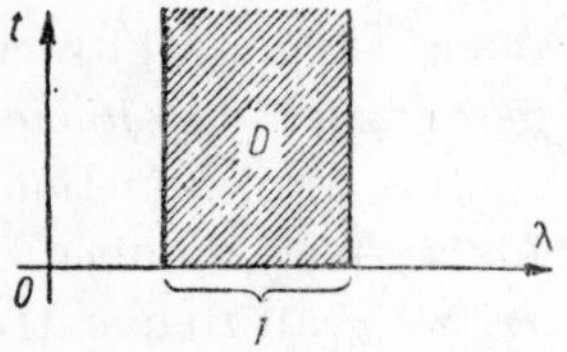

Fig. 121

$$f(\lambda) = qf_1(\lambda).$$

Thus, owing to the factor q, the concept of continuity of an operational function is reduced to the concept of ordinary continuity of a function of two variables.

The function $f(\lambda) = \{\lambda^2 + t^2\}$, for instance, is continuous in every finite interval I, for we can write

$$f(\lambda) = 1 \cdot \{\lambda^2 + t^2\}$$

where the function $\lambda^2 + t^2$ is continuous in the domain D. Here we have simply taken number 1 as the factor q.

If the function of two variables $f(\lambda, t)$ is continuous (in the usual sense) in the domain D, then the parametric operational function

$$f(\lambda) = \{f(\lambda, t)\} \tag{2.1}$$

is continuous in the interval I.

It may occur that a function $f(\lambda, t)$ is not continuous in the domain D and yet the operational function $f(\lambda) = \{f(\lambda, t)\}$ is continuous in the sense of the definition given at the beginning. For instance the function

$$H_\lambda(t) = \begin{cases} 0 & \text{for} \quad 0 \leqslant t < \lambda, \\ 1 & \text{for} \quad 0 \leqslant \lambda < t \end{cases}$$

(see p. 116) regarded as a function of two variables, λ and t, is discontinuous on the straight line $\lambda = t$ (fig. 122), and nevertheless the operational function $H_\lambda = \{H^\lambda(t)\}$ is continuous since we can write

$$H_\lambda = s\{h_1(\lambda_1 t)\} \tag{2.2}$$

where the function $h_1(\lambda, t)$ is continuous in the usual sense and defined by the equalities

$$h_1(\lambda, t) = \begin{cases} 0 & \text{for} \quad 0 \leqslant t < \lambda, \\ t-\lambda & \text{for} \quad 0 \leqslant \lambda \leqslant t. \end{cases} \tag{2.3}$$

In order to verify formula (2.2) it suffices to write

$$l\{H_\lambda(t)\} = \left\{\int_0^t H_\lambda(\tau)\,d\tau\right\} = \{h_1(t)\}.$$

The function H_λ is defined for $\lambda \geqslant 0$ and continuous in every finite interval.

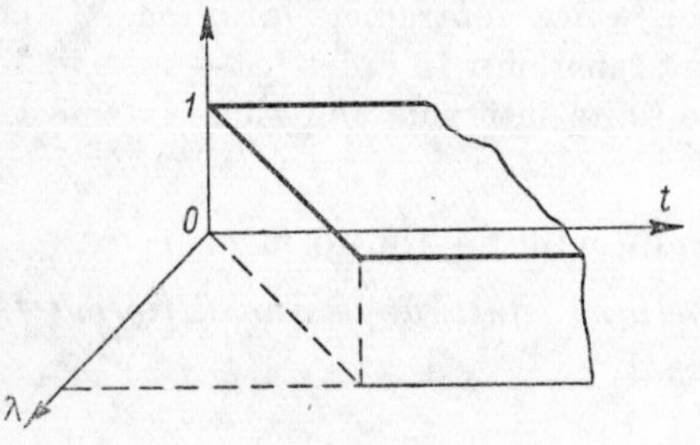

Fig. 122. Function $H_\lambda(t)$

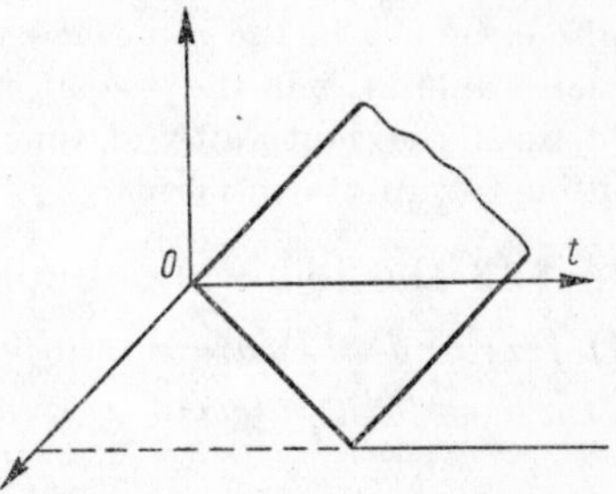

Fig. 123. Function $h_1(\lambda, t)$

The function $h^\lambda = sH_\lambda$ ($\lambda \geqslant 0$) is no longer a parametric function, its values being operators irreducible to functions of t. Yet it is continuous in every finite interval since we can of course write

$$h^\lambda = s^2\{h_1(\lambda, t)\}. \tag{2.4}$$

For the function h^λ we have proved (see p. 117) the formula

$$h^\lambda \cdot h^\mu = h^{\lambda+\mu}. \tag{2.5}$$

The function h^λ resembles an ordinary exponential function e^λ, which also satisfies the functional equation analogical to (2.5),

$$e^\lambda \cdot e^\mu = e^{\lambda+\mu};$$

moreover, we have $e^0 = 1$. Both functions, h^λ and e^λ, belong to a wider class of exponential functions, which will be discussed in a more detailed way in § 9. Here let us observe that function h^λ is continuous in every finite interval $\alpha \leqslant \lambda \leqslant \beta$. Indeed, we can write

$$h^\lambda = h^\alpha \cdot h^{\lambda-\alpha}$$

and by (2.4)

$$h^\lambda = h^\alpha \cdot s^2 \cdot \{h_1(\lambda-\alpha, t)\},$$

which in itself proves continuity.

We shall now extend the definition of continuity to arbitrary infinite intervals. An operational function will be termed *continuous in a given infinite interval* if it is continuous in every finite interval contained in that interval.

The function h^λ is continuous in the interval $(-\infty, +\infty)$.

If we adopted for the infinite interval a direct definition of continuity of a function, such as has been given for the finite interval, then the function h^λ would not be continuous in the interval $(-\infty, +\infty)$ since such an operator q that $h^\lambda = q\{h_1(\lambda, t)\}$ and that the function $h_1(\lambda, t)$ is continuous for $0 \leqslant t < \infty$ and for all real λ does not exist. Thus the function h would be continuous in every finite interval and discontinuous in the interval $(-\infty, +\infty)$, which contradicts intuition. A similar situation would arise in the case of many other functions. In order to avoid it we have first defined the continuity of functions for finite intervals and then extended the definition to infinite intervals.

In § 13 the following simple theorem will be found useful:

If $f(\lambda)$ and $g(\lambda)$ are operational functions continuous and different from zero in a certain interval I and such that

$$f(\lambda)^2 = g(\lambda)^2,$$

then either $f(\lambda) = g(\lambda)$ in the whole interval I or $f(\lambda) = -g(\lambda)$ in the whole interval I.

It is obvious that for every point λ taken separately we have $f(\lambda) = g(\lambda)$ or $f(\lambda) = -g(\lambda)$. If the first equality held for a certain point λ_1 of a given interval and the second equality held for another point, λ_2, of that interval, then from the assumption of the functions being always different from zero it would follow that one of the functions $f(\lambda)$ and $g(\lambda)$ is discontinuous between the points λ_1 and λ_2. We omit the details of the proof, which are easy to reconstruct.

Finally, it will be observed that if the operational function $f(\lambda)$ is numerical, then the definition given in this section is identical with the ordinary definition of continuity. Indeed, we can then write $f(\lambda) = s\{f(\lambda)\}$. From the ordinary continuity of the function $f(\lambda)$ it follows that it is also continuous as a function of two variables, λ and t (constant with respect to t), and *vice versa*.

The concept of continuity is connected with that of the *limit of a function*, which can be defined as follows: a function $f(\lambda)$ has a limit g at the point $\lambda = \lambda_0$ if it becomes continuous after the substitution of g for the values of $f(\lambda_0)$. In this sense there exist, for instance, limits (64.2) and (65.2) in §§ 64 and 65 of Part One. The concept of limit may also be given a direct interpretation.

§ 3. Continuous derivative of an operational function. For applications of the operational calculus the concept of *continuous derivative* is sufficient. To begin with, let us define such a derivative, leaving a more general definition until § 7.

An operational function $f(\lambda)$ will be said to be *continuously differentiable* in a finite interval I if we can write

$$f(\lambda) = qf_1(\lambda) \qquad (q \neq 0) \tag{3.1}$$

where q is an operator and $f_1(\lambda)$ a parametric function $\{f_1(\lambda, t)\}$ having a partial derivative $\left\{\frac{\partial}{\partial\lambda} f_1(\lambda_1 t)\right\}$ continuous in the whole domain D $(\lambda \in I,\ 0 \leqslant t < \infty)$.

The function $f(\lambda)$ will then be said *to have in the interval I a continuous derivative*:

$$f'(\lambda) = q\left\{\frac{\partial}{\partial\lambda} f_1(\lambda, t)\right\}. \tag{3.2}$$

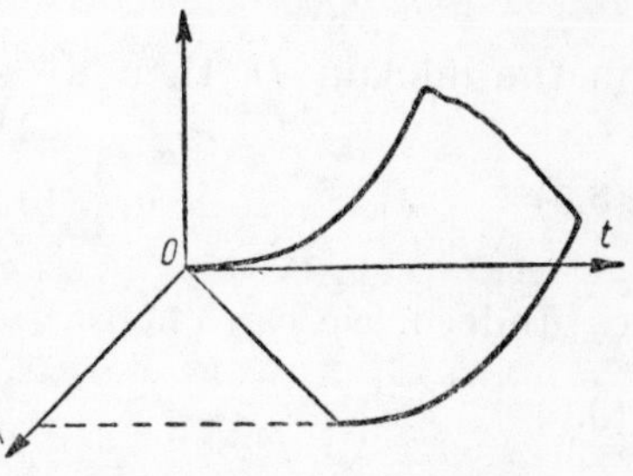

Fig. 124. Function $h_2(\lambda, t)$

As an example it will be shown that the function h^λ has a continuous derivative in every finite interval $0 \leqslant \lambda \leqslant \lambda_0$. Indeed, by (2.4), we can write for $\lambda \geqslant 0$

$$h^\lambda = s^3 \cdot l\{h_1(\lambda, t)\} = s^3\{h_2(\lambda, t)\},$$

where the function $h_2(\lambda, t)$ is defined by the equalities

$$h_2(\lambda, t) = \begin{cases} 0 & \text{for} \quad 0 \leqslant t \leqslant \lambda, \\ \frac{1}{2}(t-\lambda)^2 & \text{for} \quad 0 \leqslant \lambda < t, \end{cases}$$

and has a partial derivative $\dfrac{\partial}{\partial\lambda} h_2(\lambda, t)$ continuous in the domain D $(0 \leqslant \lambda < \infty,\ 0 \leqslant t < \infty)$. Hence

$$(h^\lambda)' = s^3\left\{\frac{\partial}{\partial\lambda} h_2(\lambda, t)\right\} \quad \text{for} \quad 0 \leqslant \lambda \leqslant \lambda_0, \tag{3.3}$$

where λ_0 is an arbitrary positive number.

If the function $f(\lambda)$ is differentiable (continuously) in the interval I, then the derivative $f'(\lambda)$ can be represented in the form (3.2) in infinitely many ways. Indeed, let a be an arbitrary function of class $\mathcal{C}$ different from 0; we can then write

$$f(\lambda) = \frac{q}{a} f_2(\lambda),$$

where the function $f_2(\lambda) = \{\int_0^t a(t-\tau) f_1(\lambda, \tau)\, d\tau\}$ is still parametric and has a continuous partial derivative in the domain D. Consequently the derivative of the function can also be written in the form

$$f'(\lambda) = \frac{q}{a}\left\{\frac{\partial}{\partial\lambda} f_2(\lambda, t)\right\}.$$

It may seem uncertain whether the definition of the derivative is unique. Therefore we must ascertain that if the function $f(\lambda)$ can be represented in the interval I in two ways,

$$(3.4) \qquad f(\lambda) = q_1\{f_1(\lambda, t)\} \quad \text{and} \quad f(\lambda) = q_2\{f_2(\lambda, t)\},$$

so that the partial derivatives $\frac{\partial}{\partial\lambda} f_1(\lambda, t)$ and $\frac{\partial}{\partial\lambda} f_2(\lambda, t)$ are continuous in the domain D, then we shall always have

$$(3.5) \qquad q_1\left\{\frac{\partial}{\partial\lambda} f_1(\lambda, t)\right\} = q_2\left\{\frac{\partial}{\partial\lambda} f_2(\lambda, t)\right\}.$$

Indeed, we can choose such functions a_1, a_2 and $c \neq 0$ of class $\mathcal{C}$ that

$$(3.6) \qquad q_1 = a_1/c \quad \text{and} \quad q_2 = a_2/c.$$

Then it follows from (3.4) that

$$a_1\{f_1(\lambda, t)\} = a_2\{f_2(\lambda, t)\},$$

i. e.,

$$\int_0^t a_1(t-\tau) f_1(\lambda, \tau)\, d\tau = \int_0^t a_2(t-\tau) f_2(\lambda, \tau)\, d\tau \quad \text{in the domain } D.$$

Hence by differentiation with respect to λ we obtain

$$\int_0^t a_1(t-\tau) \frac{\partial}{\partial\lambda} f_1(\lambda, \tau)\, d\tau = \int_0^t a_2(t-\tau) \frac{\partial}{\partial\lambda} f_2(\lambda, \tau)\, d\tau,$$

i. e.,

$$a_1\left\{\frac{\partial}{\partial\lambda} f_1(t, \lambda)\right\} = a_2\left\{\frac{\partial}{\partial\lambda} f_2(t, \lambda)\right\}.$$

Dividing this equality by c we obtain equality (3.5). We have thus proved the unicity of the definition.

It will be observed that if the function $f(\lambda)$ is numerical, then the above definition is identical with the usual definition of the continuous derivative. Indeed, we can then write $f(\lambda) = s\{f(\lambda)\}$; provided the ordinary derivative $\frac{d}{d\lambda} f(\lambda)$ is continuous, we have

$$f'(\lambda) = s\left\{\frac{\partial}{\partial\lambda} f(\lambda)\right\} = s\left\{\frac{d}{d\lambda} f(\lambda)\right\} = \frac{d}{d\lambda} f(\lambda).$$

It follows hence in particular that *the derivative of a numerical function is always a numerical function.*

4. Properties of the continuous derivative.

PROPERTY I. *If the function $f(\lambda)$ is constant in a certain interval I, i. e., if one and the same operator c is assigned to each value of λ in that interval, then $f'(\lambda) = 0$. Conversely, if $f'(\lambda) = 0$ in I, then the function $f(\lambda)$ is constant.*

Indeed, every operator c is of the form a/b where $a, b \in \mathcal{C}$, $b \neq 0$. Thus if $f(\lambda) = c$, we can write

$$f'(\lambda) = \frac{1}{b}\left\{\frac{\partial}{\partial\lambda} a(t)\right\} = \frac{1}{b}\{0\} = 0.$$

Conversely, if $f'(\lambda) = 0$, then in formula (3.2) we have $\frac{\partial}{\partial\lambda} f_1(\lambda, t) = 0$ for λ and t belonging to the domain D, whence if follows that $f_1(\lambda, t)$ is independent of λ, i. e., that the function represented by formula (2.1) is constant.

PROPERTY II. *If the operational functions $f(\lambda)$ and $g(\lambda)$ have continuous derivatives $f'(\lambda)$ and $g'(\lambda)$ in the interval I, then their sum and their difference also have continuous derivatives in that interval and*

$$[f(\lambda) \pm g(\lambda)]' = f'(\lambda) \pm g'(\lambda).$$

Indeed, it follows from the assumption of the existence of the continuous derivative that

$$f(\lambda) = q_1 f_1(\lambda) \quad \text{and} \quad g(\lambda) = q_2 g_1(\lambda),$$

where $f_1(\lambda)$ and $g_2(\lambda)$ are parametric functions with partial derivatives with respect to λ continuous in the domain D. We can then write (3.6) and consequently

$$f(\lambda) = \frac{1}{c} f_2(\lambda) \quad \text{and} \quad g(\lambda) = \frac{1}{c} g_2(\lambda)$$

where $f_2(\lambda) = a_1 f_1(\lambda)$ and $g_2(\lambda) = a_2 g_1(\lambda)$. Thus

$$f(\lambda) \pm g(\lambda) = \frac{1}{c}\{f_2(\lambda, t) \pm g_2(\lambda, t)\},$$

whence

$$\begin{aligned}
[f(\lambda) \pm g(\lambda)]' &= \frac{1}{c}\left\{\frac{\partial}{\partial\lambda}[f_2(\lambda, t) \pm g_2(\lambda, t)]\right\} \\
&= \frac{1}{c}\left\{\frac{\partial}{\partial\lambda} f_2(\lambda, t)\right\} \pm \frac{1}{c}\left\{\frac{\partial}{\partial\lambda} g_2(\lambda, t)\right\} \\
&= f'(\lambda) \pm g'(\lambda).
\end{aligned}$$

Property III. *If the functions $f(\lambda)$ and $g(\lambda)$ have continuous derivatives $f'(\lambda)$ and $g'(\lambda)$ in the interval I, then their product also has a continuous derivative in that interval and the following formula holds:*

$$[f(\lambda)g(\lambda)]' = f'(\lambda)g(\lambda) + f(\lambda)g'(\lambda).$$

Indeed, we have

$$\begin{aligned}
[f(\lambda)g(\lambda)]' &= q_1 q_2 \left\{\frac{\partial}{\partial\lambda}\int_0^t f_1(\lambda, t-\tau) g_1(\lambda, \tau)\,d\tau\right\} \\
&= q_1 q_2 \left\{\int_0^t \frac{\partial}{\partial\lambda} f_1(\lambda, t-\tau) g_1(\tau, \lambda)\,d\tau + \int_0^t f_1(\lambda, t-\tau)\frac{\partial}{\partial\lambda} g_1(\lambda, \tau)\,d\tau\right\} \\
&= q_1 q_2 \left\{\frac{\partial}{\partial\lambda} f_1(\lambda, t)\right\} g_1(\lambda) + q_1 q_2 f_1(\lambda)\left\{\frac{\partial}{\partial\lambda} g_1(\lambda, t)\right\} \\
&= f'(\lambda)g(\lambda) + f(\lambda)g'(\lambda).
\end{aligned}$$

Property IV. *If c is an arbitrary operator and the operational function $f(\lambda)$ has a continuous derivative in the interval I, then the product $cf(\lambda)$ also has a continuous derivative in that interval and the following formula holds:*

$$[cf(\lambda)]' = cf'(\lambda).$$

This property immediately follows from properties I and III.

Property V. *If the operational functions $g(\lambda)$ and $f(\lambda)/g(\lambda)$ have continuous derivatives in the interval I, then the function $f(\lambda)$ also has a continuous derivative in that interval, and the following formulas hold:*

$$\left[\frac{f(\lambda)}{g(\lambda)}\right]' = \frac{f'(\lambda)g(\lambda) - f(\lambda)g'(\lambda)}{g(\lambda)^2}.$$

This property follows from property III since

$$f'(\lambda)=\left[\frac{f(\lambda)}{g(\lambda)}\,g(\lambda)\right]'=\left[\frac{f(\lambda)}{g(\lambda)}\right]'g(\lambda)+\frac{f(\lambda)}{g(\lambda)}\,g'(\lambda),$$

whence, by an easy transformation, we obtain the required formula.

PROPERTY VI. *If $f(\lambda)$ has a continuous derivative $f'(\lambda)$ in the interval I, and $\varphi(\lambda)$ is a numerical function with values belonging to I having a continuous derivative in the interval K, then the composed function $F(\lambda) = f[\varphi(\lambda)]$ has a continuous derivative in K and the following formula holds:*

$$F'(\lambda)=f'[\varphi(\lambda)]\cdot\varphi'(\lambda).$$

Indeed, by (3.1) and (3.2) we have

$$F(\lambda)=q\{f_1[\varphi(\lambda),t]\}$$

and, denoting $\frac{\partial}{\partial\lambda}f_1(\lambda,t)$ by $f_0(\lambda,t)$,

$$F'(\lambda)=q\left\{\frac{\partial}{\partial\lambda}f_1[\varphi(\lambda),t]\right\}=q\{f_0[\varphi(\lambda),t]\cdot\varphi'(\lambda)\}=q\{f_0[\varphi(\lambda),t]\}\cdot\varphi'(\lambda).$$

Exercise. Find by two methods (first direct from the definition and then on the grounds of the properties proved in this section) the derivatives of the following operational functions:

(α) $f(\lambda)=\{\lambda^2+t^2\}=l\lambda^2+2l^3;$

(β) $f(\lambda)=\{\lambda^4+\lambda^2 t^2+t^4\}=l\lambda^4+2l^3\lambda^2+24l^5;$

(γ) $f(\lambda)=\{\sin(\lambda+t)\}=\dfrac{1}{1+s^2}(s\sin\lambda+\cos\lambda);$

(δ) $f(\lambda)=\dfrac{1}{\{\lambda^2+t^2\}}=\dfrac{1}{l\lambda^2+2l^3}.$

§ 5. Continuous derivatives of higher orders. Let $f'(\lambda)$ be a continuous derivative of the operational function $f(\lambda)$. If $f'(\lambda)$ is continuously differentiable, then its derivative is termed the *second continuous derivative* of the function $f(\lambda)$ and denoted by $f''(\lambda)$. Similarly, by the *third continuous derivative* $f'''(\lambda)$ we understand the continuous derivative of the second continuous derivative, etc.

It can easily be seen that if the function $f(\lambda)$ has its second continuous derivative $f''(\lambda)$ in the interval I, then there exist such an operator q_2

and such a parametric function $\{f_2(\lambda, t)\}$ whose second partial derivative $\left\{\frac{\partial^2}{\partial\lambda^2} f_2(\lambda, t)\right\}$ is continuous in the domain D $(\lambda \in I,\ 0 \leqslant t < \infty)$ that

$$f(\lambda) = q_2\{f_2(\lambda, t)\},$$

$$f''(\lambda) = q_2\left\{\frac{\partial^2}{\partial\lambda^2} f_2(\lambda, t)\right\}.$$

Generally, if the function $f(\lambda)$ has its n-th continuous derivative $f^{(n)}(\lambda)$ in an interval, there exist such an operator q_n and such a parametric function $\{f_n(\lambda, t)\}$ having its n-th partial derivative $\left\{\frac{\partial^n}{\partial\lambda^n} f_n(\lambda, t)\right\}$ continuous in the domain D that

(5.1) $$f(\lambda) = q_n\{f_n(\lambda, t)\}$$

and

(5.2) $$f^{(n)}(\lambda) = q_n\left\{\frac{\partial^n}{\partial\lambda^n} f_n(\lambda, t)\right\}.$$

On the other hand, if condition (5.1) is satisfied for a function $f(\lambda)$ and the partial derivative $\left\{\frac{\partial^n}{\partial\lambda^n} f_n(\lambda, t)\right\}$ is continuous in the domain D, that implies the existence of the n-th continuous derivative $f^{(n)}(\lambda)$ defined by formula (5.2). Thus for operational functions conditions (5.1) and (5.2) may serve as an equivalent definition of the n-th continuous derivative.

Exercise. Find the second and the third continuous derivatives of the operational functions given in the exercises of the preceding section.

§ 6. The continuous derivative in an infinite interval. Hitherto it has been assumed that the interval I is finite. The definition of the continuous derivative can be extended to infinite intervals in the same way as the definition of continuity of a function. Namely, an operational function $f(\lambda)$ is said to have a *continuous derivative* $f'(\lambda)$ *in an infinite interval* I if $f'(\lambda)$ is a continuous derivative in every finite interval contained in I.

Properties I-VI of § 4 can immediately be extended to derivatives in infinite intervals.

The definition of continuous derivatives of any order is extended to infinite intervals in exactly the same manner.

In § 3 we have proved that the function h^λ has a continuous derivative in every finite interval $0 \leqslant \lambda \leqslant \lambda_0$. Formula (3.3) implies moreover that

(6.1) $$(h^\lambda)' = s^3\{-h_1(\lambda, t)\} = -sh^\lambda \quad (0 \leqslant \lambda \leqslant \lambda_0).$$

If $[\alpha, \beta]$ is an arbitrarily fixed finite interval, then by formula (2.5), which has been shown to be true for any real λ and μ, we can write

$$h^{\lambda} = h^{\alpha} h^{\lambda-\alpha}.$$

Introducing the notation $k(\lambda) = (h^{\lambda})'$, we can write in view of properties IV and VI of § 4

$$k(\lambda) = h^{\lambda} k(\lambda - \alpha).$$

Hence follows the existence of the continuous derivative $(h^{\lambda})'$ in the interval $[\alpha, \beta]$. Since this interval can be established arbitrarily, we have proved the operational function h^{λ} to have a continuous derivative in the infinite interval $(-\infty, \infty)$.

By (3.3) we can again write

$$k(\lambda) = h^{\alpha}[-sk(\lambda-\alpha)] = -sh^{\lambda};$$

consequently for any real values of λ we have the formula

$$(h^{\lambda})' = -sh^{\lambda}. \tag{6.2}$$

§ 7. General definition of the derivative. The considerations of this section will be more theoretical in character, and the reader who is interested only in applications may pass them over entirely.

We have seen in § 3 that if $f(\lambda)$ is a numerical function which has a continuous operational derivative $f'(\lambda)$, then $f'(\lambda)$ is also a derivative in the usual sense, continuous of course. Here we are going to show how to give a more general definition of the operational derivative, which in the case of numerical functions is identical with the usual definition of the derivative, not necessarily continuous.

A function $f(\lambda)$ is said to be *differentiable at a point* λ_0 if it can be represented in the neighbourhood of that point as the product

$$f(\lambda) = q\{f_1(\lambda, t)\},$$

where q is an operator and $\{f_1(\lambda, t)\}$ a parametric function such that the quotient

$$\frac{f_1(\lambda, t) - f_1(\lambda_0, t)}{\lambda - \lambda_0} \tag{7.1}$$

uniformly tends to the limit for $\lambda \to \lambda_0$ in every finite interval $0 \leqslant t \leqslant t_0$.

This limit is of course equal to the partial derivative $\dfrac{\partial}{\partial \lambda} f_1(\lambda_0, t)$, which is continuous with respect to t. Now the existence of a partial derivative, even if it is continuous with respect to t, does not by itself imply the *uniform* existence of a limit of quotient (7.1). The product

$q\left\{\frac{\partial}{\partial\lambda} f_1(\lambda_0, t)\right\}$ will be termed the *derivative of the operational function* $f(\lambda)$ *at the point* λ_0 and denoted by $f'(\lambda_0)$.

Such a derivative is a generalization of the continuous derivative since the assumption of the function $\frac{\partial}{\partial\lambda} f_1(\lambda, t)$ being continuous (with respect to both variables) implies the uniform existence of a limit of quotient (7.1) in every interval $0 \leqslant t \leqslant t_0$. Indeed, quotient (7.1) is equal to the derivative $\left[\frac{\partial}{\partial\lambda} f(\lambda, t)\right]_{\lambda=\xi}$ where ξ is contained between λ_0 and λ. As $\lambda \to \lambda_0$, this derivative uniformly tends to the limit in the interval $0 \leqslant t \leqslant t_0$.

The derivative generalized in this way retains all the properties I-VI. If we did not assume the uniform continuity of the quotient, we could not prove all of those properties.

CHAPTER II

EXPONENTIAL FUNCTIONS

§ 8. Differential equation $x'(\lambda) = wx(\lambda)$. We shall prove the following theorem:

For given operators w, k *and a real number* λ_0 *there exists at most one operational function* $x(\lambda)$ *satisfying for any real* λ *the equation*

(8.1) $$x'(\lambda) = wx(\lambda) \text{ (1)}$$

and the condition

(8.2) $$x(\lambda_0) = k.$$

Proof. Suppose that there exist two operational functions, $x_1(\lambda)$ and $x_2(\lambda)$, satisfying equation (8.1) and condition (8.2). Then the function

$$x(\lambda) = x_1(\lambda) - x_2(\lambda)$$

also satisfies equation (8.1) and we have

(8.3) $$x(\lambda_0) = 0.$$

It is sufficient to prove that $x(\lambda) = 0$ for any real λ.

Introducing the auxiliary function

$$y(\lambda) = x(\lambda)x(2\mu - \lambda),$$

where μ is an arbitrary fixed real number, we have

$$y'(\lambda) = x'(\lambda)x(2\mu - \lambda) - x(\lambda)x'(2\mu - \lambda).$$

By (8.1) we have

$$y'(\lambda) = wx(\lambda)x(2\mu - \lambda) - x(\lambda)wx(2\mu - \lambda) = 0;$$

thus the function $y(\lambda)$ is constant for any real λ. But by (8.3) we have

$$y(\lambda_0) = x(\lambda_0)x(2\mu - \lambda_0) = 0,$$

whence it follows that $y(\lambda) = 0$ for any λ, *i. e.*, that

$$x(\lambda)x(2\mu - \lambda) = 0.$$

---

(1) From the assumption that the function $x(\lambda)$ has a derivative it follows that it is continuous; equation (8.1) implies further that the derivative $x'(\lambda)$ is continuous.

In particular, substituting $\lambda = \mu$ we obtain hence $x(\mu)^2 = 0$ and finally

$$x(\mu) = 0.$$

Since μ has been fixed arbitrarily, the theorem is proved.

§ 9. Generalized exponential functions. If w is a number, then the exponential function $x(\lambda) = e^{\lambda w}$ satisfies the equation

$$x'(\lambda) = wx(\lambda) \tag{9.1}$$

and the condition

$$x(0) = 1. \tag{9.2}$$

By the theorem proved above this is the only function with these properties (which is known from classical analysis). Thus conditions (9.1) and (9.2) may serve as a definition of the exponential function.

If w is not a number but an arbitrary operator, then conditions (9.11 and (9.2) define generalized exponential functions, for which we shal) henceforth consistently use the symbol $e^{\lambda w}$. In other words, if the operational function $x(\lambda)$ satisfies conditions (9.1) and (9.2) for a given operator w, we shall write

$$x(\lambda) = e^{\lambda w}.$$

In view of the theorem given in the preceding section the values of every exponential function are always different from zero.

The operational function h^λ satisfies the conditions

$$(h^\lambda)' = -sh^\lambda \quad \text{and} \quad h^0 = 1$$

(see § 6); consequently, in accordance with the accepted definition of exponential function, we can write

$$h^\lambda = e^{-\lambda s}.$$

Thus the translation operator may also be denoted by the symbol $e^{-\lambda s}$.

Symbol e^w denotes the value of the exponential function $e^{\lambda w}$ at the point $\lambda = 1$ and its meaning is definite if that exponential function exists.

The only operators w satisfying the equation $e^w = 1$ are the numbers $2k\pi i$ where k is an integer.

Indeed, if $e^w = 1$, then every operator $y = e^{\mu w/\nu}$, where μ and ν are integers ($\nu \neq 0$), satisfies the equation $y^\nu = 1$. Since this equation has n roots which are numbers and has no other roots (see § 16 of Part II), the operator y is always a number. Consequently the function $e^{\lambda w}$ has numerical values for every rational number λ. This function is continuous and thus has numerical values everywhere. Therefore its derivative $(e^{\lambda w})'$ also has numerical values everywhere. Since $w = (e^{\lambda w})'/e^{\lambda w}$, the operator w is a number. And the only numbers satisfying the equation $e^w = 1$ are numbers $2k\pi i$ (k being an integer).

Two facts have been utilized in this proof: 1° If a sequence consists of numbers, its limit in the operational sense is identical with the ordinary limit. Consequently a function with numerical values in a dense set, continuous in the operational sense, has numerical values everywhere; 2° For functions with numerical values an operational derivative is identical with a derivative in the usual sense.

§ 10. Derivatives of power series. We shall now prove that *if a numerical power series*

$$\psi(\lambda) = \alpha_0 + \alpha_1\lambda + \alpha_2\lambda^2 + \dots$$

has a positive radius of convergence, then the function

$$\psi(\lambda f) = \alpha_0 + \alpha_1\lambda f + \alpha_2\lambda^2 f^2 + \dots, \tag{10.1}$$

where $f = \{f(t)\} \in \mathcal{C}$, *has a derivative in the form of a power series,*

$$[\psi(\lambda f)] = 1\alpha_1 f + 2\alpha_2\lambda f^2 + \dots,$$

which is convergent for any complex λ.

Proof. We may assume in the proof that $\alpha_0 = 0$, which does not affect the generality of the theorem.

The power series

$$\psi(\lambda f) = \alpha_1\lambda f + \alpha_2\lambda^2 f^2 + \dots$$

represents the parametric function $\psi(\lambda f) = \{\psi(\lambda, t)\}$ and uniformly converges (in the usual sense) in every domain

$$|\lambda| \leqslant \lambda_0, \quad 0 \leqslant t \leqslant t_0. \tag{10.2}$$

Similarly, series (10.1) represents a parametric function and is uniformly convergent in every domain (10.2). Introducing the notation

$$f^n = \{f^n(t)\} \quad (n = 1, 2, \dots),$$

we can write

$$\alpha_1\lambda f + \alpha_2\lambda^2 f^2 + \dots = \{\alpha_1\lambda f^1(t) + \alpha_2\lambda^2 f^2(t) + \dots\},$$

$$\alpha_1 f + 2\alpha_2\lambda f^2 + \dots = \{\alpha_1 f^1(t) + 2\alpha_2\lambda f^2(t) + \dots\}$$

$$= \left\{\frac{\partial}{\partial\lambda}[\alpha_1\lambda f^1(t) + \alpha_2\lambda^2 f^2(t) + \dots]\right\},$$

whence it follows that

$$[a_1\lambda f+a_2\lambda^2 f^2+\ldots]' = a_1 f+2a_2\lambda f^2+\ldots,$$

which proves our theorem. The main idea of the proof has been the use of the theorem on differentiating ordinary power series of the variable λ term by term, the variable t appearing as a parameter. Owing to the uniform convergence of the series in question in the domain (10.2) this theorem is extended to operational series.

In particular, if

$$\psi(\lambda f) = 1+\frac{\lambda f}{1!}+\frac{\lambda^2 f^2}{2!}+\ldots,$$

then

$$[\psi(\lambda f)]' = f+\frac{\lambda f^2}{1!}+\frac{\lambda^2 f^3}{2!}+\ldots = f\psi(\lambda f).$$

Since $\psi(0)=1$, by the definition of exponential function we have

$$e^{\lambda f} = 1+\frac{\lambda f}{1!}+\frac{\lambda^2 f^2}{2!}+\ldots \tag{10.3}$$

Thus, if $f\in\mathcal{C}$, then the exponential function $e^{\lambda f}$ expands into a power series, just as an ordinary exponential function. It should be observed that in this case the exponential function has the form

$$e^{\lambda f} = 1+g(\lambda)$$

where $g(\lambda) = \{g(\lambda, t)\}$ is a parametric function.

Remark. Also the function $e^{-\lambda\sqrt{s}}$ and many others can be expanded in power series, but proving the convergence of those series is much more difficult (see Ryll-Nardzewski [2]). It is impossible, however, to give a general definition of the exponential function by means of power series since the series for the function $e^{-\lambda s}$, for instance, is not convergent (see Mikusiński and Ryll-Nardzewski [2]).

For $f=-1/s$ expansion (10.3) holds since $-1/s=\{-1\}\in\mathcal{C}$. Thus for $\lambda\geqslant 0$ we have

$$e^{-\lambda/s} = \sum_{n=0}^{\infty}(-1)^n\frac{\lambda^n l^n}{n!} = s\sum_{n=0}^{\infty}(-1)^n\frac{\lambda^n l^{n+1}}{n!}$$

$$= s\left\{\sum_{n=0}^{\infty}(-1)^n\frac{\lambda^n t^n}{(n!)^2}\right\} = s\{J_0(2\sqrt{\lambda t})\}.$$

Hence we have the formula

$$\frac{1}{s}\, e^{-\lambda/s} = \{J_0(2\sqrt{\lambda t})\}.$$

Exercise. Prove that for $\lambda \geqslant 0$ we have the formulas

(α) $\frac{1}{\sqrt{s}}\, e^{-\lambda/s} = \left\{\frac{1}{\sqrt{\pi t}} \cos 2\sqrt{\lambda t}\right\}$; (β) $\frac{1}{\sqrt{s}}\, e^{\lambda/s} = \left\{\frac{1}{\sqrt{\pi t}} \operatorname{ch} 2\sqrt{\lambda t}\right\}$;

(γ) $\frac{1}{s^2} e^{-\lambda/s} = \left\{\sqrt{\frac{t}{\lambda}}\, J_1(2\sqrt{\lambda t})\right\}$.

§ 11. Function $\exp\lambda(s-\sqrt{s^2+a^2})$ and cognate functions. The exponential function $\exp\lambda(s-\sqrt{s^2+a^2})$ can be expanded in a power series,

(11.1) $$\exp\lambda(s-\sqrt{s^2+a^2}) = 1 + \sum_{\nu=1}^{\infty} \frac{1}{(n+1)} (-\lambda)^{n+1} (\sqrt{s^2+a^2}-s)^{n+1}$$

because the operator

$$s-\sqrt{s^2+a^2} = -\sum_{\nu=1}^{\infty} (-1)^{\nu} \binom{\frac{1}{2}}{\nu} a^2 l^{2\nu-1}$$

is a function of class $\mathcal{C}$.

Substituting in formula (20.4) of Part II λ for a, $n+1$ for n and $\nu-n$ for ν we obtain

$$(\sqrt{s^2+a^2}-s)^{n+1} = \left\{(-1)^n (n+1) \sum_{\nu=n}^{\infty} \frac{(-1)^{\nu} a^{2+2\nu} t^{2\nu-n}}{2^{1+2\nu-n}(\nu-n)!\,(\nu+1)!}\right\};$$

substituting this expression in (11.1) and changing the order of summation, we obtain

(11.2) $$\exp\lambda(s-\sqrt{s^2+a^2})$$

$$= 1 - \left\{\lambda \sum_{\nu=0}^{\infty} (-1)^{\nu} \frac{a^{2+2\nu} t^{\nu}}{2^{1+2\nu} \nu!\,(\nu+1)!} \sum_{\varkappa=0}^{\nu} \frac{\nu!\, \lambda^{\varkappa} t^{\nu-\varkappa}}{2^{-\varkappa} (\nu-\varkappa)!\, \varkappa!}\right\}$$

$$= 1 - \left\{\lambda \sum_{\nu=0}^{\infty} (-1)^{\nu} \frac{a^{2+2\nu} t^{\nu}}{2^{1+2\nu} \nu!\,(\nu+1)!} (t+2\lambda)^{\nu}\right\}.$$

In view of definition (20.6) of Part II we can finally write

(11.3) $$\exp\lambda(s-\sqrt{s^2+a^2}) = 1 - \left\{\frac{\lambda}{\sqrt{t^2+2\lambda t}}\, a J_1(a\sqrt{t^2+2\lambda t})\right\}.$$

In this manner we have reduced the exponential function under consideration to the Bessel function J_1. We shall now deduce its simple connection with function J_0. Differentiating equality (11.3) with respect to α and then dividing the result by $-\alpha\lambda$, we obtain

$$\frac{\exp\lambda(s-\sqrt{s^2+\alpha^2})}{\sqrt{s^2+\alpha^2}}=\left\{\sum_{\nu=0}^{\infty}(-1)^{\nu}\frac{\alpha^{2\nu}t^{\nu}}{2^{2\nu}(\nu!)^2}(t+2\lambda)^{\nu}\right\}$$

and by formula (18.1) of Part II

$$\frac{\exp\lambda(s-\sqrt{s^2+\alpha^2})}{\sqrt{s^2+\alpha^2}}=\{J_0(\alpha\sqrt{t^2+2\lambda t})\}. \tag{11.4}$$

Formulas (11.3) and (11.4) are valid for $\lambda\geqslant 0$ and for every complex α. In particular, replacing α by $i\alpha$ in those formulas we have

$$\begin{aligned}\exp\lambda(s-\sqrt{s^2-\alpha^2})&=1-\left\{\frac{\lambda}{\sqrt{t^2+2\lambda t}}\,i\alpha J_1(i\alpha\sqrt{t^2+2\lambda t})\right\}\\ \frac{\exp\lambda(s-\sqrt{s^2-\alpha^2})}{\sqrt{s^2-\alpha^2}}&=\{J_0(i\alpha\sqrt{t^2+2\lambda t})\}.\end{aligned} \tag{11.5}$$

Multiplying expressions (11.3), (11.4) and (11.5) by $e^{-\lambda s}$ we obtain the formulas

$$\exp(-\lambda\sqrt{s^2+\alpha^2})=e^{-\lambda s}-\left\{\begin{matrix}0 & \text{for} & 0\leqslant t<\lambda\\ \dfrac{\lambda}{\sqrt{t^2-\lambda^2}}\,\alpha J_1(\alpha\sqrt{t^2-\lambda^2}) & \text{for} & 0\leqslant\lambda<t\end{matrix}\right\},$$

$$\frac{\exp(-\lambda\sqrt{s^2+\alpha^2}}{\sqrt{s^2+\alpha^2}}=\left\{\begin{matrix}0 & \text{for} & 0\leqslant t<\lambda\\ J_0(\alpha\sqrt{t^2-\lambda^2} & \text{for} & 0\leqslant\lambda<t\end{matrix}\right\},$$

$$\exp(-\lambda\sqrt{s^2-\alpha^2})=e^{-\lambda s}-\left\{\begin{matrix}0 & \text{for} & 0\leqslant t<\lambda\\ \dfrac{\lambda}{\sqrt{t^2-\lambda^2}}\,i\alpha J_1(i\alpha\sqrt{t^2-\lambda^2}) & \text{for} & 0\leqslant\lambda<t\end{matrix}\right\},$$

$$\frac{\exp(-\lambda\sqrt{s^2-\alpha^2})}{\sqrt{s^2+\alpha^2}}=\left\{\begin{matrix}0 & \text{for} & 0\leqslant t<\lambda\\ J_0(i\alpha\sqrt{t^2-\lambda^2}) & \text{for} & 0\leqslant\lambda<t\end{matrix}\right\}.$$

CHAPTER III

DIFFERENTIAL EQUATION $x''(\lambda) = wx(\lambda)$

§ 12. A unicity theorem. We shall prove the following theorem:

If we are given operators w, k_0, k_1 and a real number λ_0, then there exists at most one operational function $x(\lambda)$ satisfying for all real λ the equation

(12.1) $$x''(\lambda) = wx(\lambda)$$

and the conditions

$$x(\lambda_0) = k_0, \quad x'(\lambda_0) = k_1.$$

Proof. Suppose that there exist two such functions, $x_1(\lambda)$ and $x_2(\lambda)$. Then the difference

$$x(\lambda) = x_1(\lambda) - x_2(\lambda)$$

satisfies equation (10.1) and the conditions

(12.2) $$x(\lambda_0) = 0, \quad x'(\lambda_0) = 0.$$

It is sufficient to prove that $x(\lambda) = 0$ for all real λ.

Introducing an auxiliary function

$$y(\lambda) = x'(\lambda)x(2\mu - \lambda) + x(\lambda)x'(2\mu - \lambda)$$

where μ is an arbitrary real number, we have

$$y'(\lambda) = x''(\lambda)x(2\mu - \lambda) - x(\lambda)x''(2\mu - \lambda).$$

By (12.1) we have

$$y'(\lambda) = wx(\lambda)x(2\mu - \lambda) - x(\lambda)xw(2\mu - \lambda) = 0;$$

consequently the function $y(\lambda)$ is constant for all real λ. However, by (12.2) we have

$$y(\lambda_0) = x'(\lambda_0)x(2\mu - \lambda_0) + x(\lambda_0)x'(2\mu - \lambda_0) = 0,$$

whence it follows that $y(\lambda) = 0$ for all λ, *i. e.*, that

$$x'(\lambda)x(2\mu - \lambda) + x(\lambda)x'(2\mu - \lambda) = 0.$$

Since μ has been arbitrarily fixed, this equation must hold for all real λ and μ.

In particular, substituting $\lambda = \mu$, we have

$$2x(\lambda)x'(\lambda) = 0, \quad i.e., \quad [x(\lambda)^2]' = 0.$$

Thus the function $x(\lambda)^2$ is constant, and since $x(\lambda_0)^2 = 0$, $x(\lambda)^2 = 0$ for all λ and consequently $x(\lambda) = 0$ for all λ.

The theorem is proved.

§ 13. Continuation of solutions. We shall now prove the following theorem:

If an operational function $x(\lambda)$ is defined in the interval $a \leqslant \lambda \leqslant \beta$ and satisfies in that interval the equation

$$x'(\lambda) = wx(\lambda), \tag{13.1}$$

where w is an operator, then it can be continued outside the interval $a \leqslant \lambda \leqslant \beta$ in such a way that it will satisfy the same equation for all real λ.

Proof. If the function $x(\lambda)$ is identically equal to zero for $a \leqslant \lambda \leqslant \beta$, the theorem is obvious, since it is then possible to continue the function so as to make it equal to zero also outside that interval. If it is not identically equal to zero, then by the continuity of $x(\lambda)$ there exists inside the interval $a < \lambda < \beta$ a point γ at which $x(\gamma) \neq 0$.

Introducing an auxiliary function

$$y(\lambda) = px(\lambda - \beta + \gamma) \quad \text{for} \quad \beta \leqslant \lambda \leqslant \beta_1 = \gamma + 2(\beta - \gamma)$$

we can easily verify that $y(\lambda)$ satisfies equation (13.1) in the interval $\beta \leqslant \lambda \leqslant \beta_1$ whatever operator p is established. Let us choose p so that $y(\beta) = x(\beta)$, i. e., let us take $p = \dfrac{x(\beta)}{x(\gamma)}$. Then, by equation (13.1), we have

$$y'(\beta) = \frac{x(\beta)}{x(\gamma)} x'(\gamma) = \frac{x(\beta)}{x(\gamma)} wx(\gamma) = wx(\beta) = x'\beta.$$

Since the values of the functions $x(\lambda)$ and $y(\lambda)$ and the values of their derivatives coincide at the point β, these functions can be joined into one function, defined in the whole interval $a \leqslant \lambda \leqslant \beta_1$, and satisfying equation (13.1) in it.

This function may be continued in the same way in the interval $a \leqslant \lambda \leqslant \beta_2$, where $\beta_2 = \gamma + 2(\beta_1 - \gamma) = \gamma + 4(\beta - \gamma)$, and so forth indefinitely.

In a similar way the function may be continued to the left up to $-\infty$. The proof is thus complete.

This theorem and the theorem proved in § 8 (p. 191) imply that *if a function $x(\lambda)$ is known to satisfy equation (13.1) in a finite interval $a \leqslant \lambda \leqslant \beta$, then it is uniquely defined in it by its value at an arbitrarily fixed point of that interval.*

The theorem on the continuation of solutions holds also for the equation of the second order:

If an operational function $x(\lambda)$ is defined in the interval $a \leqslant \lambda \leqslant \beta$ and satisfies in it the equation

$$x''(\lambda) = wx(\lambda) \tag{13.2}$$

then it may be continued beyond the interval $a \leqslant \lambda \leqslant \beta$ so as to satisfy the same equation for all real λ.

Proof. If the function $x(\lambda)$ is identically equal to zero for $a \leqslant \lambda \leqslant \beta$, then the theorem is obvious. Suppose, therefore, that $x(\gamma) \neq 0$ for a certain point γ, which in view of the continuity of the function may be assumed to lie inside the interval $a < \lambda < \beta$.

Introducing the auxiliary function

$$\Delta(\lambda) = w[x(\lambda)]^2 - [x'(\lambda)]^2$$

we have

$$\Delta'(\lambda) = 2wx(\lambda)x'(\lambda)x''(\lambda) = 0,$$

whence it follows in particular that

$$w[x(\lambda)]^2 - [x'(\lambda)]^2 = c \quad \text{for} \quad a \leqslant \lambda \leqslant \beta,$$

where c is a constant operator.

We shall distinguish two cases:

1° $c = 0$. Then

$$[x'(\lambda)]^2 = w[x(\lambda)]^2$$

and in particular

$$[x'(\gamma)]^2 = w[x(\gamma)]^2.$$

Writing briefly

$$u = \frac{x'(\gamma)}{x(\gamma)} \tag{13.3}$$

we have $u^2 = w$ and

$$[x'(\lambda)]^2 = [ux(\lambda)]^2.$$

Let (α_1, β_1) be the largest open interval lying in $[\alpha_1, \beta_1]$, containing the point γ and such that $x(\lambda) \neq 0$ in (α_1, β_1). Since the function $x(\lambda)$ is continuous, we must always have $x'(\lambda) = ux(\lambda)$ or $x'(\lambda) = -ux(\lambda)$ (see § 2). By (13.3) only the equality

$$x'(\lambda) = ux(\lambda) \qquad (\alpha_1 < \lambda < \beta_1) \tag{13.4}$$

is possible.

But the continuity of $x(\lambda)$ and $x'(\lambda)$ implies that equation (13.4) will also be satisfied at the end points of the interval, *i. e.*, in the whole closed interval $[\alpha_1, \beta_1]$. If we had $x(\alpha_1) = 0$ or $x(\beta_1) = 0$, then we should have $x(\lambda) = 0$ in the whole interval $[\alpha_1, \beta_1]$, which is not true. Consequently, $x(\alpha_1) \neq 0$ and $x(\beta_1) \neq 0$, whence it follows that $\alpha_1 = \alpha$ and $\beta_1 = \beta$.

Since $x(\lambda)$ satisfies equation (13.4) in the whole interval $[\alpha, \beta]$, it may be continued so as to make the equation satisfied for all real λ. But then $x(\lambda)$ will also satisfy equation (13.2) for all real λ since

$$x''(\lambda) = ux'(\lambda) = u\cdot ux(\lambda) = wx(\lambda).$$

2° $c \neq 0$. We can easily verify that the function

$$y(\lambda) = px(\lambda-\beta+\gamma)+qx'(\lambda-\beta+\gamma) \qquad (\beta \leqslant \lambda \leqslant \beta_1 = \gamma+2(\beta-\gamma))$$

satisfies equation (13.2) in $[\beta, \beta_1]$ whatever operators p and q are chosen. They may be chosen in such a way that $y(\beta) = x(\beta)$ and $y'(\beta) = x'(\beta)$, *i. e.*, that

$$px(\gamma)+qx'(\gamma) = x(\beta),$$
$$px'(\gamma)+qwx(\gamma) = x'(\beta),$$

since the determinant

$$\begin{vmatrix} x(\gamma) & x'(\gamma) \\ x'(\gamma) & wx(\gamma) \end{vmatrix} = c$$

is different from zero. We then have

$$y''(\beta) = p\cdot wx(\gamma)+qwx'(\gamma) = wx(\beta) = x''(\beta).$$

The values of the functions $x(\lambda)$ and $y(\lambda)$ and the values of their first and second order derivatives coinciding at the point β, those functions may be joined into one function defined in the whole interval $[\alpha_1, \beta_1]$ and satisfying equation (13.2) in it.

This function may be further continued in the same way over the interval $[\alpha, \beta_2]$ where $\beta_2 = \gamma+4(\beta-\gamma)$, and so forth to infinity. It may similarly be continued to the left up to $-\infty$.

We have proved continuation to be possible in any case.

The last theorem implies that the unicity theorem, proved in the preceding section for the infinite interval, is also valid for the finite interval.

CHAPTER IV

VIBRATIONS OF A STRING

§ 14. Operational equation of the vibrating string. Suppose that a string whose length is λ_0 has been stretched along an axis λ from the point 0 to the point λ_0. The function $x(\lambda, t)$ denoting the displacement of the point of the string with the abscissa λ at the instant t satisfies the partial differential equation

$$x_{\lambda\lambda}(\lambda, t) = \alpha^2 x_{tt}(\lambda, t) \tag{14.1}$$

where $\alpha = \sqrt{\mu/P}$; P is the tension of the string and μ the mass per unit of length. In working out this equation we assume the string to be perfectly elastic and its displacements so small that they do not change the tension P, which is taken to be constant.

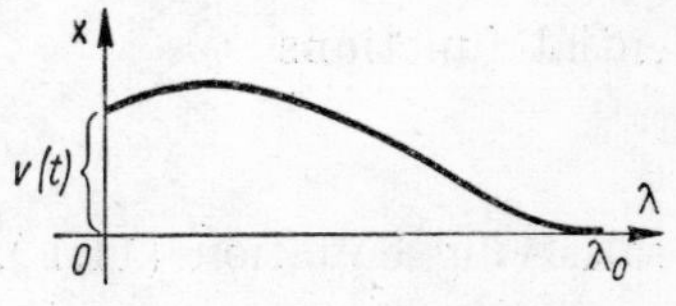

Fig. 125. The shape of the string at the instant t

Let us assume that at the instant $t = 0$ the string coincides with the λ axis and its particles have no velocity; this is expressed by the assumption

$$x(\lambda, 0) = 0 \quad \text{and} \quad x_t(\lambda, 0) = 0 \quad (0 \leqslant \lambda \leqslant \lambda_0). \tag{14.2}$$

Then suppose that one end of the string moves in a direction perpendicular to the λ axis and its motion is defined by the function $v(t)$; suppose moreover that the other end of the string is held fast. This is expressed by the assumption

$$x(0, t) = v(t) \quad \text{and} \quad x(\lambda_0, t) = 0 \quad (0 \leqslant t < \infty). \tag{14.3}$$

We shall determine the motion of the remaining particles of the string and show that this motion is uniquely defined by the conditions stated. To use mathematical language, we shall solve the partial equation (14.1) under the given conditions (14.2) and (14.3) and show that the solution obtained is unique.

By assumption (14.2), the operational form of equation (14.1) is

$$x''(\lambda) = a^2 s^2 x(\lambda) \quad (a > 0) \tag{14.1'}$$

where $x(\lambda) = \{x(\lambda, t)\}$; conditions (14.2) are contained in equation (14.1'). Conditions (14.3), on the other hand, now have the form

$$x(0) = v \quad \text{and} \quad x(\lambda_0) = 0, \tag{14.3'}$$

where $v = \{v(t)\}$.

To begin with, let us find exponential functions $e^{\lambda w}$ satisfying equation (14.1'), *i, e.*, such that

$$(e^{\lambda w})'' = a^2 s^2 e^{\lambda w}.$$

Integrating this we have

$$w^2 e^{\lambda w} = a^2 s^2 e^{\lambda w}$$

and dividing it by $e^{\lambda w}$ (an exponential function being everywhere different from zero) we obtain

$$w^2 = a^2 s^2.$$

Hence $w = -as$ or $w = as$. Thus there exist two (and only two) exponential functions

$$e^{-a\lambda s} \quad \text{and} \quad e^{a\lambda s}$$

satisfying equation (14.1').

It is easy to verify that every operational function of the form

$$x(\lambda) = c_1 e^{-a\lambda s} + c_2 e^{a\lambda s} \tag{14.4}$$

satisfies equation (14.1') whatever operators c_1 and c_2 are chosen. Let us choose these operators so as to satisfy conditions (14.3'), *i. e.*, to have

$$\begin{aligned} x(0) &= c_1 + c_2 = v, \\ x(\lambda_0) &= c_1 e^{-a\lambda s} + c_2 e^{a\lambda s} = 0. \end{aligned} \tag{14.5}$$

Solving this system of equations we obtain

$$c_1 = \frac{v}{1 - e^{-2a\lambda_0 s}} \quad \text{and} \quad c_2 = \frac{e^{-2a\lambda_0 s} v}{1 - e^{-2a\lambda_0 s}}.$$

Hence we have the required solution

$$x(\lambda) = \frac{(e^{-a\lambda s} - e^{-a(2\lambda_0 - \lambda)s})v}{1 - e^{-2a\lambda_0 s}} \quad (0 \leqslant \lambda \leqslant \lambda_0). \tag{14.6}$$

Knowing the properties of the translation operator we can write this solution by means of symbols of classical analysis; however, the formulas obtained in this way are rather complicated and therefore it is best to make use in the discussion of the operational solution, which is clearer.

For example let us discuss solution (14.6) under the assumption that

$$a = \tfrac{1}{2}, \qquad \lambda_0 = 10,$$

(14.7) $$v = \begin{cases} t & \text{for} \quad 0 \leqslant t < 4 \\ 4 & \text{for} \quad 4 \leqslant t < \infty \end{cases}.$$

Substituting various values for λ we can easily analyse the motion of the individual particles of the string. For example, for $\lambda = 2$ we have

(14.8) $$x(2) = \frac{(e^{-s} - e^{-9s})v}{1 - e^{-10s}}.$$

For the operator $(e^{-s} - e^{-9s})v$ we have the graph in fig. 126; whence by a superposition of waves translated by 10, 20, 30, ... units we find

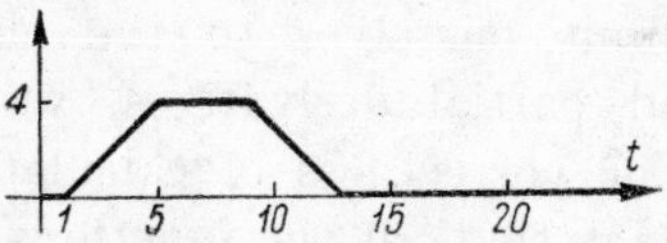

Fig. 126

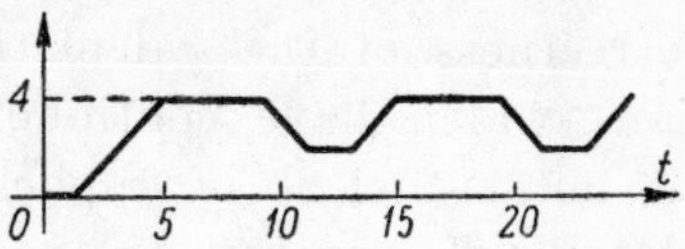

Fig. 127

for $x(2)$ the graph 127. This graph represents the motion of the string particle with the abscissa 2.

Figs. 128 and 129 show the graphs for the points $\lambda = 5$ and $\lambda = 8$, which can be obtained in a similar way.

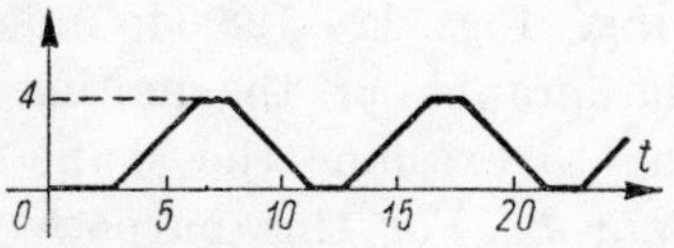

Fig. 128

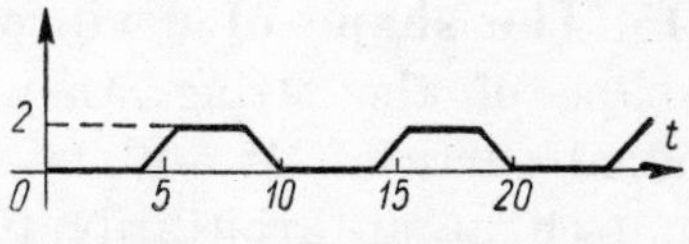

Fig. 129

Curiously enough in the example discussed above the string moves in such a manner that the function $x(\lambda, t)$ does not satisfy at all the partial differential equation (14.1). It does not do so for the simple reason that the motion of string particles is defined by polygonal lines, and thus it is not everywhere that the function $x(\lambda, t)$ has derivatives (even those of the first order).

We could say that in reality the string never bends at an acute angle and $x(\lambda, t)$ can always be regarded as a function with continuous second derivatives, figs 125-128 being only an approximation and a certain simplification.

In practice, however, such bends often lie within the limits of the measurement error; consequently it is unprofitable to consider minute details, particularly since their introduction to the calculation would complicate it greatly without making the final result any more accurate. Under such conditions it is even desirable to neglect in the calculations slight disturbances which are not essential to the characterization of the whole phenomenon.

Our calculation has been carried out in this very manner and it is quite correct from the mathematical point of view, provided we regard the operational equation (14.1′) as the fundamental equation of a vibrating string.

The solutions of this equation are simultaneously the solutions of the partial equation (14.1), but only when they have continuous second partial derivatives. Thus the partial equation cannot be regarded as the general equation of a vibrating string unless we are indifferent to the correctness of the calculation or limit ourselves to the class of functions which have continuous second partial derivatives, which in turn is not sufficient in applications. The correctness of calculation in the domain of operators is due to the fact that all the functions under consideration are operationally differentiable (even an arbitrary number of times).

According to the classification adopted in the theory of partial equations equation (14.1) belongs to the hyperbolic type. It is for this reason that the operational function $e^{-\lambda s}$, which is closely connected with this equation, can be termed the *hyperbolic exponential function*.

§ 15. The shape of a vibrating string. Figs. 124-128 do not show the shape of the string: they give the graphs of the motion of its individual particles. It will be interesting to examine the shape of the string itself at an arbitrarily fixed instant t_0. For this purpose let us expand the solution (14.6) (under the assumption (14.7) in an infinite series

$$x(\lambda) = \sum_{n=0}^{\infty} \{\exp[-(10n+\tfrac{1}{2}\lambda)s] - \exp[-(10n+10-\tfrac{1}{2}\lambda)s]\} v.$$

Suppose that we wish to examine the shape of the string at an instant $t_0 < 10$. Those terms of the series in which the coefficient of s is greater than 10 will then have no significance because they represent functions equal to 0 in the interval $0 \leqslant t < 10$. Thus, instead of examining $x(\lambda)$ we can examine the function

$$\{\exp(-\tfrac{1}{2}\lambda s) - \exp[-(10-\tfrac{1}{2}\lambda)s]\}v.$$

Let us examine separately the functions

$$x_1(\lambda) = \{x_1(\lambda, t)\} = [\exp(-\tfrac{1}{2}\lambda s)]v, \quad x_2(\lambda) = \{x_2(\lambda, t)\} = \{\exp[-(10-\tfrac{1}{2}\lambda)s]\}v;$$

by equality (14.7) and the properties of the translation operator we have

$$x_1(\lambda, t) = \begin{cases} 0 & \text{for} \quad 0 \leqslant t < \tfrac{1}{2}\lambda, \\ t-\tfrac{1}{2}\lambda & \text{for} \quad \tfrac{1}{2}\lambda \leqslant t < \tfrac{1}{2}\lambda+4, \\ 4 & \text{for} \quad \tfrac{1}{2}\lambda+4 \leqslant t; \end{cases}$$

$$x_2(\lambda, t) = \begin{cases} 0 & \text{for} \quad 0 \leqslant t < 10-\tfrac{1}{2}\lambda, \\ t-10+\tfrac{1}{2}\lambda & \text{for} \quad 10-\tfrac{1}{2}\lambda \leqslant t < 14-\tfrac{1}{2}\lambda, \\ 4 & \text{for} \quad 14-\tfrac{1}{2}\lambda \leqslant t. \end{cases}$$

Choosing an arbitrary $t = t_0$ we find the graphs for the functions $x_1(\lambda, t_0)$ and $x_2(\lambda, t_0)$; the graph of the function x_1 is represented in fig. 130 by a continuous line and the graph of the function x_2 by a broken line.

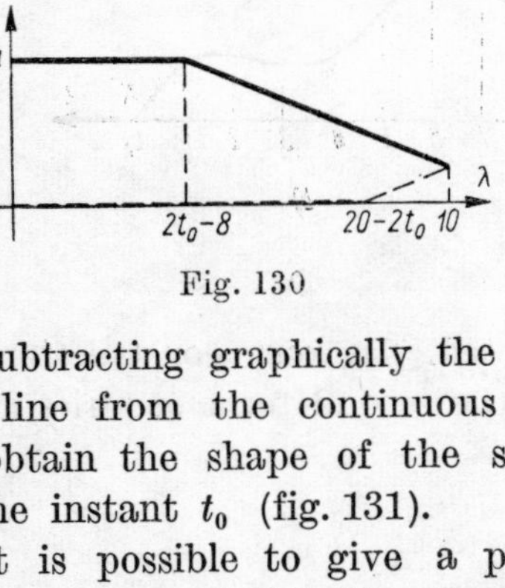

Fig. 130

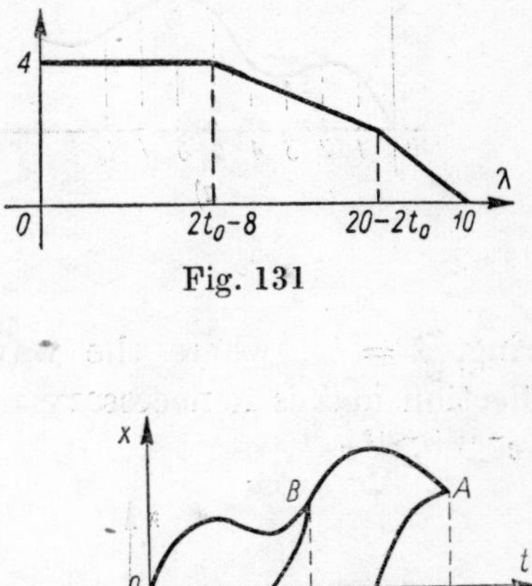

Fig. 131

Subtracting graphically the broken line from the continuous line we obtain the shape of the string at the instant t_0 (fig. 131).

It is possible to give a purely graphical method of finding the shape of the string at an instant t if we have the graph of the function v. In order to work out that method let us write the general solution (14.6) in the form of an infinite series,

$$(15.1) \qquad x(\lambda) = \sum_{n=0}^{\infty} \left(e^{-(2na\lambda_0+a\lambda)s} - e^{-[2(n+1)a\lambda_0-a\lambda]s}\right)v.$$

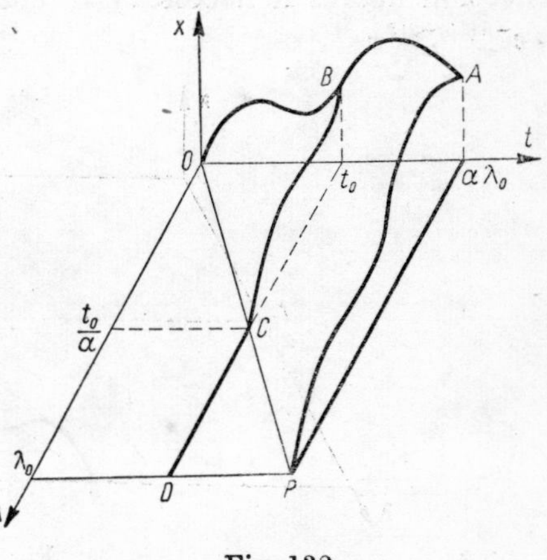

Fig. 132

If $0 \leqslant t < a\lambda_0$, then it is sufficient to consider only one term of the series, namely

$$e^{-a\lambda s} v = \begin{cases} 0 & \text{for} \quad 0 \leqslant t < a\lambda \\ v(t - a\lambda) & \text{for} \quad a\lambda \leqslant t \end{cases}; \tag{15.2}$$

fig. 132 shows the surface which corresponds to that term.

The surface arises by guiding a straight line parallel to OP along the curve OBA representing the graph of the function $x = v(t)$. In order to obtain the shape of the string at the instant t_0 it is sufficient to intersect the surface by a plane perpendicular to the t axis and passing through the point t_0; the shape of the string is shown by the intersection curve BCD.

Hence follows a simple plane construction, ilustrated by figs. 133 a and 133 b. The thick line in fig. 133 a pictures the motion of the initial point of the string, and the thick line in fig. 133 b pictures the shape of the string at the instant t_0. The construction requires no explanations.

It can be seen from the above construction that as the time t goes on, the curve OA' moves to the right like a wave with the velocity $1/a$. At the instant $t = a\lambda_0$ the wave front reaches the end point of the

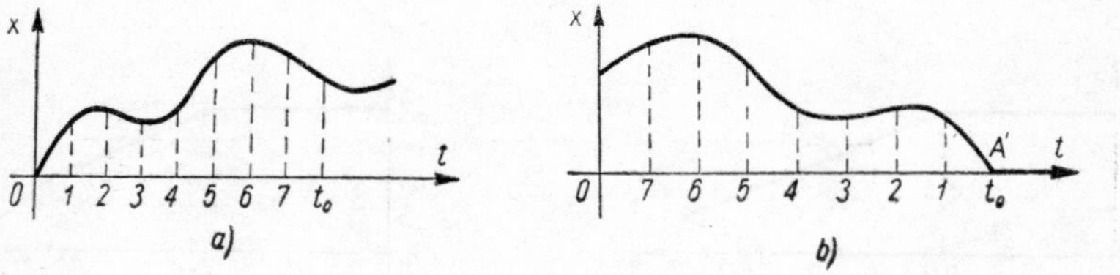

Fig. 133

string, $\lambda = \lambda_0$, where the wave is reflected. In our construction the reflection makes it necessary to consider the second term of series (15.1), $-e^{-a(2\lambda_0 - \lambda)s} v$.

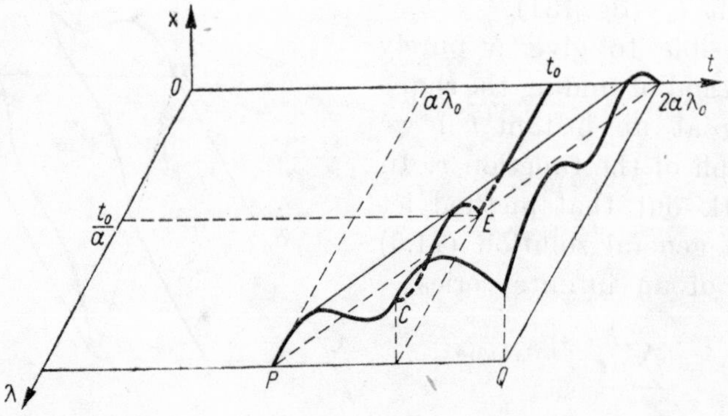

Fig. 134

To the operator

$$(15.3)\qquad e^{-a(2\lambda_0-\lambda)s}v = \begin{cases} 0 & \text{for} \quad 0 \leqslant t < a(2\lambda_0-\lambda) \\ v(t-2a\lambda_0+a\lambda) & \text{for} \quad a(2\lambda_0-\lambda) \leqslant t \end{cases}$$

corresponds the surface represented in fig. 134.

In order to obtain the shape of the string at the instant t we first find, in the manner described above, the shape of the curve corresponding to the operator (15.3). It is the curve $A'O$ of fig. 133 b translated to the right up to the point t_0/a, which under the present assumption lies to the right of the point λ_0; on translating it we shall have the curve $ABCD$ given in fig. 135 (in order to draw it we must know of course the behaviour of the function v for the values of t greater than $a\lambda_0$). From its part ABC, corresponding to the interval $0 \leqslant \lambda \leqslant \lambda_0$, we must subtract the arc marked with the letters t_0EC in fig. 134. This arc is transferred to fig. 135 and marked with the letters OEC; it is a symmetrical reflection of the arc CD with respect to the straight line CF.

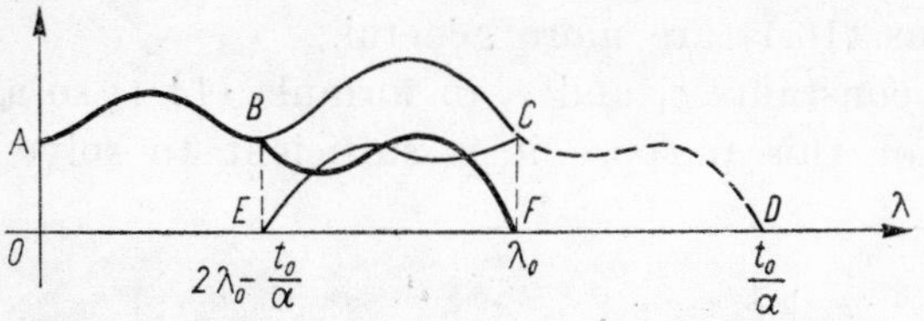

Fig. 135

The definite shape of the string is shown in fig. 135 by the thick line ABF.

The bend of this line at the point B comes from the reflection of the wave and passes to the left with the velocity $1/a$; at the instant $2a\lambda_0$ the bend reaches the initial point of the string and the wave is reflected for the second time. Then the third term of series (15.1) comes into the picture, and the shape of the string at a later instant may by found by a suitable combination of three arcs.

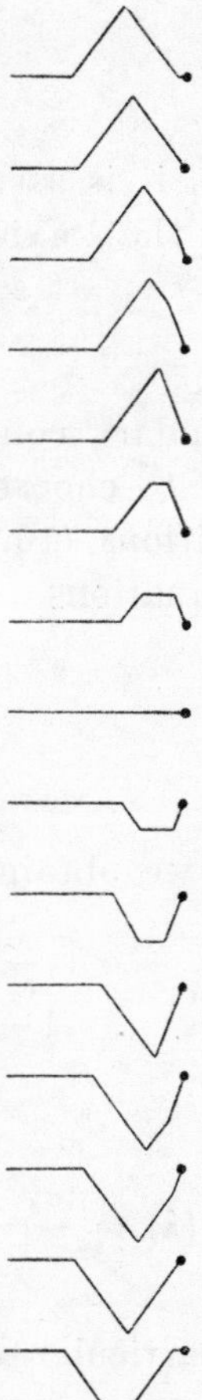

Fig. 136. Reflection of a symmetric wave

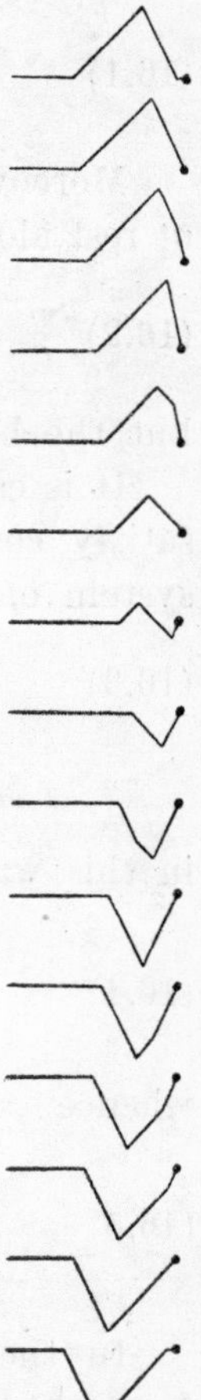

Fig. 137. Reflection of an asymmetric wave

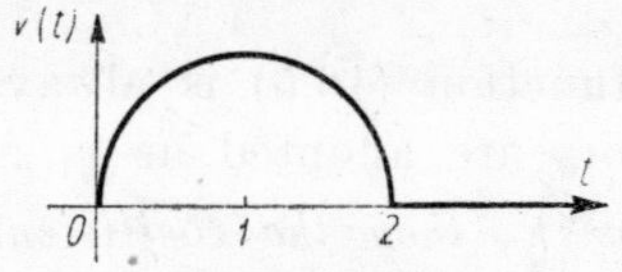

Fig. 138

Applying the graphical method of reflection we may easily examine the reflection of a wave if its shape is given. Figs 136 and 137 present, in the kinematographic manner, the reflection of a simple symmetric wave and of an asymmetric one.

Example. Examine by the graphical method the reflection of a wave if $a = 1$, the graph of v being given in fig. 138.

§ 16. More general boundary conditions. Let us also examine the motion of the string when an arbitrary motion defined by the functions $v_1 = \{v_1(t)\}$ and $v_2 = \{v_2(t)\}$ is imparted to its two ends. If the length of the string is λ_0, this is expressed by the assumption

$$(16.1) \qquad x(0) = v_1, \quad x(\lambda_0) = v_2.$$

Moreover, it is assumed that at the instant $t = 0$ the string is lying at rest along the λ axis. We must then solve the same equation as before,

$$(16.2) \qquad x''(\lambda) = a^2 s^2 x(\lambda),$$

but the boundary conditions (16.1) are more general.

It is easy to choose the constants c_1 and c_2 in formula (14.4) so as to satisfy conditions (16.1). For this purpose it is sufficient to solve the system of equations

$$(16.3) \qquad c_1 + c_2 = v_1,$$

$$c_1 e^{-a\lambda_0 s} + c_2 e^{a\lambda_0 s} = v_2;$$

in this way we obtain

$$(16.4) \qquad c_1 = \frac{v_1 - e^{-a\lambda_0 s} v_2}{1 - e^{-2a\lambda_0 s}}, \quad c_2 = \frac{-e^{-2a\lambda_0 s} v_1 + e^{-a\lambda_0 s} v_2}{1 - e^{-2a\lambda_0 s}},$$

whence

$$(16.5) \qquad x(\lambda) = \frac{(e^{-a\lambda s} - e^{-a(2\lambda_0 - \lambda)s}) v_1 + (e^{-a(\lambda_0 - \lambda)s} - e^{-(\lambda_0 + \lambda)s}) v_2}{1 - e^{-2a\lambda_0 s}}.$$

In the particular case of $v_2 = 0$ this formula assumes the simpler form (14.6).

Apart from its physical sense, function (16.5) is always a solution of equation (16.2) whatever operators are adopted as v_1 and v_2.

If v_1 and v_2 are functions of class $\mathcal{K}$, then the coefficients c_1 and c_2 defined by formula (16.4) *are also functions of class $\mathcal{K}$.*

Indeed, a function of class $\mathcal{K}$ multiplied by the translation operator remains a function of class $\mathcal{K}$. Since a sum and a difference of functions of class $\mathcal{K}$ are again functions of class $\mathcal{K}$, the numerators of the expressions (16.4) are functions of class $\mathcal{K}$ for any fixed $\lambda_0 > 0$. Those numerators are divided by the denominator $1-e^{-2a\lambda_0 s}$ or, which is the same, multiplied by the series

$$1+e^{-2a\lambda_0 s}+e^{-4a\lambda_0 s}+\ldots;$$

in effect this gives again functions of class $\mathcal{K}$.

The following theorem may be proved in a similar manner:

If v_1 and v_2 are functions of class $\mathcal{C}$ equal to zero at the point $t = 0$, then the coefficients (16.4) *are also functions of class $\mathcal{C}$ equal to zero at the point $t = 0$.*

The function $x(\lambda)$ satisfying equation (16.2) and conditions (16.1) can always be represented as the sum

$$x(\lambda) = x_1(\lambda)+x_2(\lambda),$$

where $x_1(\lambda)$ and $x_2(\lambda)$ satisfy the same equation (16.2) and the conditions

$$x_1(0) = v_1, \quad x_1(\lambda_0) = 0,$$
$$x_2(0) = 0, \quad x_2(\lambda_0) = v_1.$$

The function $x_1(\lambda)$ represents the motion of a string whose end point is fixed, and the function $x_2(\lambda)$ represents the motion of a string whose initial point is motionless. In both cases the shape of the string may be found by means of the construction given in the preceding section (with a suitable orientation of the drawings, of course). The shape of a string with both ends moving can be found by simply putting together the two graphs.

Exercise. Find by the graphical method the shape of the string at the instant $t = \frac{1}{2}a\lambda_0$ assuming that at the instant $t = 0$ the string lies motionless on the λ axis and the same motion is imparted simultaneously to both its ends, the graph of that motion being given in fig. 139.

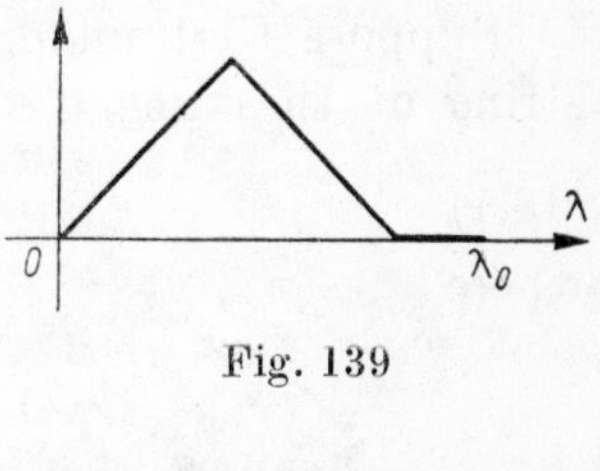

Fig. 139

§ 17. Unicity of solution. We shall prove that every operational function $y(\lambda)$ satisfying equation (14.1') is of the form (14.4). Indeed, this function satisfies at the point $\lambda = 0$ certain initial conditions,

$$y(0) = k_0 \quad \text{and} \quad y'(0) = k_1.$$

But in formula (14.4) we can always choose the coefficients c_1 and c_2 so that

$$x(0) = c_1 + c_2 = k_0,$$
$$x'(0) = -c_1 as + c_2 as = k_1,$$

since the determinant

$$\begin{vmatrix} 1 & 1 \\ -as & as \end{vmatrix} = 2as$$

is different from zero. With the values of c_1 and c_2 chosen in this way, we have, on the strength of the final remark of § 13, $y(\lambda) = x(\lambda)$ for all the λ of the interval under consideration.

Expression (14.4) will be termed the *general solution* of equation (14.1'); there appear in it two arbitrary constants, c_1 and c_2.

It is easy to prove now that *conditions* (14.3') *or, more generally, conditions* (16.1) *define the solution of equation* (14.1') *uniquely*. Indeed, the solution must have the form (14.4); on the other hand, in view of conditions (16.1), equalities (16.3) must be satisfied, those equalities defining the constants c_1 and c_2 uniquely since

$$\begin{vmatrix} 1 & 1 \\ e^{-a\lambda_0 s} & e^{a\lambda_0 s} \end{vmatrix} = e^{a\lambda_0 s} - e^{-a\lambda_0 s} \neq 0.$$

The unicity of the solutions is thus proved.

Hence it follows in particular that if there exists a function satisfying the partial equation (14.1) and conditions (14.2) and (14.3), or more generally conditions (14.2) and

$$x(0, t) = v_1(t) \quad \text{and} \quad x(\lambda_0, t) = v_2(t) \quad (0 \leqslant t < \infty),$$

then it is unique.

§ 18. An infinitely long string. No such string exists in reality. What we want to express is this.

Suppose that under the conditions discussed in § 14 we observe the string at the time $0 \leqslant t < a\lambda_0$. Writing solution (14.6) in the form

$$x(\lambda) = e^{-a\lambda s} v + b(\lambda), \tag{18.1}$$

where

$$b(\lambda) = e^{-a\lambda_0 s} \frac{(e^{-a(\lambda_0+\lambda)s} - e^{-a(\lambda_0-\lambda)s})v}{1 - e^{-2a\lambda_0 s}},$$

we see that the function $b(\lambda) = \{b(\lambda, t)\}$ is equal to zero for $0 \leqslant \lambda \leqslant \lambda_0$ and $0 \leqslant t < a\lambda_0$. Consequently the term $b(\lambda)$ in formula (18.1) may be neglected and the investigation restricted to the function

$$x(\lambda) = e^{-a\lambda s} v. \tag{18.2}$$

We then have

$$x(\lambda, t) = \begin{cases} 0 & \text{for} \quad 0 \leqslant t < a\lambda, \\ v(t-a\lambda) & \text{for} \quad 0 \leqslant a\lambda < t. \end{cases}$$

It can be seen that at the instant t the front of the wave moving from the initial point of the string is at the point $\lambda = t/a$; the wave moves with the velocity $1/a = \sqrt{P/\mu}$. The velocity of the wave is proportional to the square root of the tension of the string and inversely proportional to the square root of the linear density of the string.

If the string is very long, then solution (17.2) is accepted as the equation of its motion and the string is said – not quite correctly – to be *infinitely long.*

Let us now find a solution $x(\lambda)$ of the equation

$$x''(\lambda) = a^2 s^2 x(\lambda),$$

which is a parametric function in the *infinite* interval $0 \leqslant \lambda < \infty$; moreover the condition

(18.3) $$x(0) = q$$

is imposed.

The general solution of this equation has the form

$$x(\lambda) = c_1 e^{-a\lambda s} + c_2 e^{a\lambda s}.$$

If $x(\lambda)$ is to be a parametric function, its value at the point 0 and at an arbitrary fixed point λ_0 must be a function of class $\mathcal{K}$; consequently the coefficients c_1 and c_2 must also be functions of class $\mathcal{K}$ (see § 16). Hence it follows that $c_2 = 0$, since otherwise for large values of λ the component $c_2 e^{a\lambda s}$ would cease to be a function of class $\mathcal{K}$ and $x(\lambda)$ would not be a parametric function.

Hence our solution is reduced to the form (18.2); since condition (18.3) implies $e_1 = v$, function (18.2) is the desired solution.

Thus for an infinite string it is possible to solve the equation at once in an infinite interval: the calculation is shorter and the same result is obtained.

Interpreting this fact from the point of view of partial differential equations, we see that the only function satisfying the equation

$$x_{\lambda\lambda}(\lambda, t) = a^2 x_{tt}(\lambda, t)$$

in the domain $0 \leqslant \lambda < \infty$, $0 \leqslant t < \infty$ with the conditions

(18.4) $$\begin{aligned} x(\lambda, 0) &= x_t(\lambda, 0) = 0 \qquad (0 \leqslant \lambda < \infty), \\ x(0, t) &= v(t) \qquad\qquad\quad (0 \leqslant t < \infty) \end{aligned}$$

is the function

$$x(\lambda, t) = \begin{cases} 0 & \text{for} \quad 0 \leqslant t < a\lambda, \\ v(t - a\lambda) & \text{for} \quad 0 \leqslant a\lambda < t. \end{cases}$$

Some textbooks of the operational calculus give, besides conditions (18.4), also the condition

(18.5) $$\lim_{\lambda\to\infty} x(\lambda, t) = 0.$$

As can be seen from the above discussion, this condition is entirely superfluous (¹). Intuitively it is obvious since, the velocity of the wave being finite, no disturbance in infinity can reach us after a finite period of time.

§ 19. Spring vibrations in the case of certain particular initial positions. Suppose that a string is fixed at the points $\lambda = 0$ and $\lambda = \lambda_0$ and that its shape at the instant $t = 0$ is given by the function

(19.1) $$x(\lambda, 0) = \mu \sin\frac{k\pi\lambda}{\lambda_0} \qquad (0 \leqslant \lambda \leqslant \lambda_0),$$

where μ is a positive number and k a natural number (fig. 140).

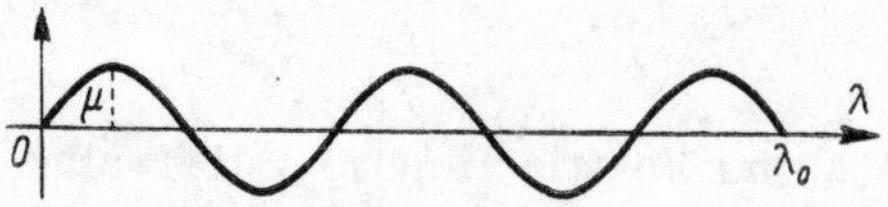

Fig. 140. The shape of the string at the instant $t = 0$ $(k = 5)$

The particles of the string are assumed to have no velocity at the instant $t = 0$, *i. e.*,

(19.2) $$x_t(\lambda, 0) = 0 \qquad (0 \leqslant \lambda \leqslant \lambda_0).$$

The assumption of the string being fixed at the ends is expressed by the conditions

(19.3) $$x(0, t) = 0 \quad \text{and} \quad x(\lambda_0, t) = 0 \qquad (0 \leqslant t \leqslant \infty).$$

Finally it is assumed that neither the force of gravity nor any other external force acts upon the string. Thus the partial differential equation of the string has the form

$$x_{\lambda\lambda}(\lambda, t) = a^2 x_{tt}(\lambda, t).$$

(¹) The textbooks in question apply the method of Laplace transformations; it should be observed that if that method is used, even the introduction of condition (18.5) does not make it possible to prove that the solution obtained is unique.

By (19.1) and (19.2) we have

$$\{x_{tt}(\lambda, t)\} = s^2\{x(\lambda, t)\} - s\mu \sin\frac{k\pi\lambda}{\lambda_0};$$

consequently the operational equation has the form

$$x''(\lambda) - a^2 s^2 x(\lambda) = -a^2 \mu s \sin\frac{k\pi\lambda}{\lambda_0} \qquad (0 \leqslant \lambda \leqslant \lambda_0) \tag{19.4}$$

and conditions (19.3) can be written down in the form

$$x(0) = 0 \quad \text{and} \quad x(\lambda_0) = 0. \tag{19.5}$$

We shall find out whether the operator c can be determined in such a way as to make the function

$$x(\lambda) = c \sin\frac{k\pi\lambda}{\lambda_0}, \tag{19.6}$$

which is similar in shape to the right side of equation (19.4), constitute the solution of that equation. Substituting (19.6) in (19.4) and dividing it by $-\sin\dfrac{k\pi\lambda}{\lambda_0}$ we obtain

$$c\frac{k^2\pi^2}{\lambda_0^2} + ca^2s^2 = a^2\mu s,$$

whence

$$c = \frac{\mu s}{s^2 + \dfrac{k^2\pi^2}{a^2\lambda_0^2}} = \left\{\mu \cos\frac{k\pi t}{a\lambda_0}\right\}.$$

The coefficient c being determined in this manner, function (19.6) satisfies equation (19.4); but it obviously also satisfies conditions (19.5). The motion of the string is thus defined by the formula

$$x(\lambda, t) = \mu \cos\frac{k\pi t}{a\lambda_0} \sin\frac{k\pi\lambda}{\lambda_0} \qquad (0 \leqslant \lambda \leqslant \lambda_0,\ 0 \leqslant t < \infty).$$

Hence it can be seen that the string always has the shape of a sinusoid, while the amplitude changes. At the instant $t = \dfrac{(1+2n)a\lambda_0}{2k}$ $(n = 0, 1, \ldots)$ the amplitude is equal to zero and the string is wholly straightened. The vibration frequency is

$$n = \frac{k}{2a\lambda_0}.$$

For $n = \lambda_0/k, \ldots, (k-1)\lambda_0/k$ it is always $x(\lambda, t) = 0$; at those points, called the nodes, the string is always motionless. The number of nodes is $k-1$; the larger it is, the higher the vibration frequency.

The conditions of our problem may be approximately realized in musical string instruments. In these the string tension is so high that the force of gravity plays an insignificant part. By holding the string back with the finger at a suitable point, we can create nodes, owing to which the string will produce a much higher tone than it does normally. These are the so called flageolet tones. In reality we can never make the string absolutely motionless at the nodes, and that is why additional lower harmonic tones arise, giving to the flageolet tones a peculiarly soft quality, very pleasant to the ear.

§ 20. String vibrations in case of an arbitrarily fixed initial position. Let $\varphi(\lambda)$ be an arbitrary numerical function, continuous for all real λ and such that

(20.1) $$-\varphi(-\lambda) = \varphi(\lambda) = \varphi(\lambda + 2\lambda_0);$$

the function $\varphi(\lambda)$ is thus odd and periodic with the period $2\lambda_0$ (fig. 141). These properties imply that $\varphi(k\lambda_0) = 0$ for every integer k.

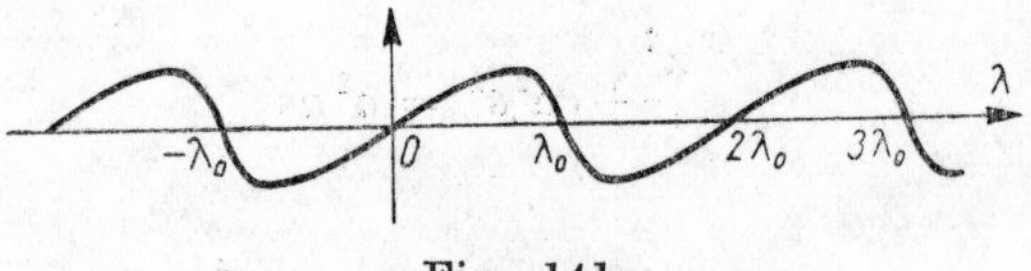

Fig. 141

It is easy to verify that the operational function $x_1(\lambda) = \{\varphi(\lambda + t/a)\}$ $(a \neq 0)$ has a continuous derivative $x_1'(\lambda)$ and that

$$x_1'(\lambda) = asx_1(\lambda) - a\varphi(\lambda);$$

indeed, we can write

$$x_1(\lambda) = s\left\{\int_0^t \varphi\left(\lambda + \frac{\tau}{a}\right) d\tau\right\} = s\left\{\int_{a\lambda}^{a\lambda+t} \varphi\left(\frac{\tau}{a}\right) d\tau\right\},$$

whence

$$x_1'(\lambda) = s\left\{\frac{\partial}{\partial\lambda}\int_{a\lambda}^{a\lambda+t} \varphi\left(\frac{\tau}{a}\right) d\tau\right\} = as\left\{\varphi\left(\lambda + \frac{t}{a}\right) - \varphi(\lambda)\right\} = asx_1(\lambda) - a\varphi(\lambda).$$

Similarly the operational function $x_2(\lambda) = \{\varphi(\lambda - t/a)\}$ $(a \neq 0)$ has a continuous derivative

$$x_2'(\lambda) = -asx_2(\lambda) + a\varphi(\lambda).$$

Hence it follows that the function

$$x(\lambda) = \tfrac{1}{2}[x_1(\lambda)+x_2(\lambda)]$$

has a continuous derivative

$$x'(\lambda) = \tfrac{1}{2}as[x_1(\lambda)-x_2(\lambda)]$$

and besides another continuous derivative

$$x''(\lambda) = \tfrac{1}{2}a^2s^2[x_1(\lambda)+x_2(\lambda)]-a^2s\varphi(\lambda).$$

We have thus proved that the function

(20.2) $$x(\lambda) = \{x(\lambda, t)\} = \tfrac{1}{2}\left\{\varphi\left(\lambda+\frac{t}{a}\right)+\varphi\left(\lambda-\frac{t}{a}\right)\right\}$$

satisfies the operational differential equation

(20.3) $$x''(\lambda) = a^2s^2x(\lambda)-a^2s\varphi(\lambda);$$

it is the string equation with the initial conditions

$$x(\lambda, 0) = \varphi(\lambda), \quad x_t(\lambda, 0) = 0 \quad (0 \leqslant \lambda \leqslant \lambda_0).$$

By (20.1) it is obvious that

$$x(0, t) = \tfrac{1}{2}\left[\varphi\left(\frac{t}{a}\right)+\varphi\left(-\frac{t}{a}\right)\right] = 0,$$

$$x(\lambda_0, t) = \tfrac{1}{2}\left[\varphi\left(\lambda_0+\frac{t}{a}\right)+\varphi\left(\lambda_0-\frac{t}{a}\right)\right] = \tfrac{1}{2}\left[\varphi\left(\lambda_0+\frac{t}{a}\right)+\varphi\left(-\lambda_0-\frac{t}{a}\right)\right] = 0$$

i. e., in the operational form,

(20.4) $$x(0) = 0 \quad \text{and} \quad x(\lambda_0) = 0.$$

Thus function (20.2) represents the motion of a string whose end points are fixed and whose initial position is arbitrarily fixed, the particles of the string having no velocity at the instant $t = 0$.

Solution (20.2) was already known to d'Alembert. The advantage of the operational treatment lies in the possibility of taking as $\varphi(\lambda)$ in equation (20.3) any continuous function (satisfying condition (20.1)), not necessarily differentiable. Now if we start from the partial equation

$$x_{\lambda\lambda}(\lambda, t) = a^2x_{tt}(\lambda, t),$$

then function (20.2) may be regarded as the solution if and only if the function $\varphi(\lambda)$ is differentiable twice, which is not sufficient for applications (see § 14).

Moreover, the operational calculus ensures the unicity of solution. Indeed, if there existed besides $x(\lambda)$ another solution, $x_1(\lambda)$, of equation (20.3) satisfying (20.4), then the difference $y(\lambda) = x(\lambda) - x_1(\lambda)$ would satisfy the homogeneous equation

$$y''(\lambda) = a^2 s^2 y(\lambda),$$

and consequently we should have

$$y(\lambda) = c_1 e^{-a\lambda s} + c_2 e^{a\lambda s}.$$

But

$$c_1 + c_2 = y(0) = x(0) - x_1(0) = 0 - 0 = 0,$$

$$c_1 e^{-a\lambda_0 s} + c_2 e^{a\lambda_0 s} = y(\lambda_0) = x(\lambda_0) - x_0(\lambda_0) = 0 - 0 = 0;$$

hence $c_1 = c_2 = 0$ and consequently $y(\lambda) = 0$, *i. e.*, $x(\lambda) - x_0(\lambda) = 0$. Solution (20.2) is thus unique.

Formula (20.2) is extremely suitable for the graphical examination of string motion. Suppose for instance that at the instant $t = 0$ the string is plucked at one fourth of it length. The graph given in fig. 142 then corresponds to its initial position.

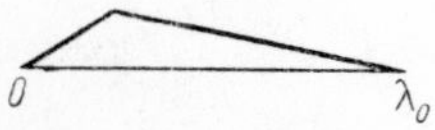

Fig. 142

The graph shows the function $\varphi(\lambda)$ in the interval $0 \leqslant \lambda \leqslant \lambda_0$. The function is continued to $-\infty$ and $+\infty$ according to formulas (20.1) (fig. 143).

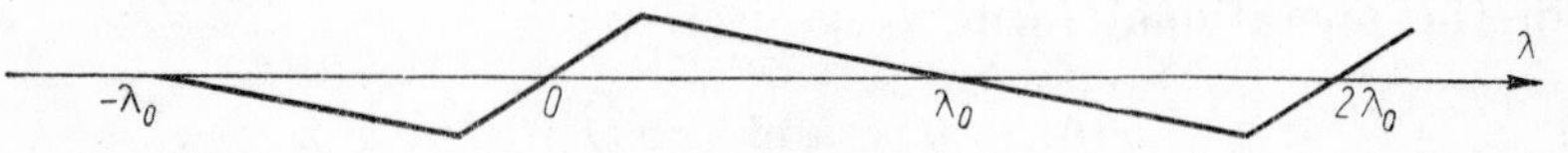

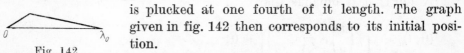

Fig. 143

In order to find the shape of the string at the instant t it is sufficient to translate the graph of the continued function by the length t/a to the left and by the same length to the right and to find graphically the arithmetic mean of the two translated graphs (fig. 144).

Fig. 144

This method is general.

In fig. 145 we give the shape of a string, found by this method, during half of the vibration period.

Exercises.

1. Using formula (**20.2**), find the solution in the case of

$$x(\lambda, 0) = \mu\lambda(\lambda_0 - \lambda)$$

and compare it with the solution obtained in § 19.

2. Using the graphical method, examine the motion of a string with the initial position shown in fig. 146.

§ 21. String vibrations with given initial velocity. We shall now determine the motion of a string if the given conditions are

$$x(\lambda, 0) = 0, \quad x_t(\lambda, 0) = \psi(\lambda) \quad (0 \leqslant \lambda \leqslant \lambda_0),$$
$$x(0, t) = 0, \quad x(\lambda_0, t) = 0 \quad (0 \leqslant t < \infty)$$

under the assumption that no external forces act upon it.

The operational equation will then have the form

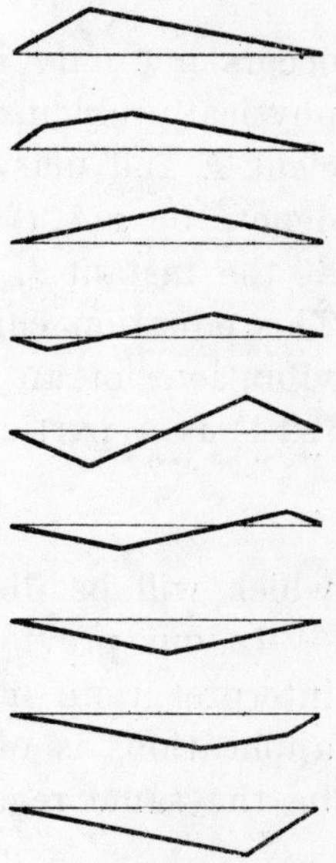

Fig. 145

$$x''(\lambda) = a^2 s^2 x(\lambda) - a^2 \psi(\lambda), \tag{21.1}$$

and the conditions – the form

$$x(0) = 0, \quad x(\lambda_0) = 0. \tag{21.2}$$

It will be observed that if $x(\lambda)$ satisfies equation (21.1) with conditions (21.2), then the function

$$y(\lambda) = s x(\lambda)$$

satisfies the equation

$$y''(\lambda) = a^2 s^2 y(\lambda) - a^2 s \psi(\lambda)$$

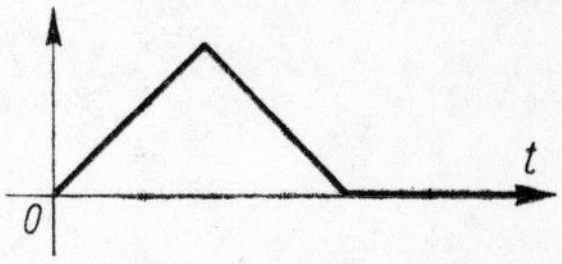

Fig. 146

with the same conditions (21.2). Thus

$$y(\lambda) = \tfrac{1}{2}\left\{\psi\left(\lambda + \frac{t}{a}\right) + \psi\left(\lambda - \frac{t}{a}\right)\right\},$$

whence

$$x(\lambda) = \tfrac{1}{2}\left\{\int_0^t \left[\psi\left(\lambda + \frac{\tau}{a}\right) + \psi\left(\lambda - \frac{\tau}{a}\right)\right] d\tau\right\}.$$

§ 22. Other interpretations. The partial equation

$$x_{\lambda\lambda}(\lambda, t) = a^2 x_{tt}(\lambda, t) \tag{22.1}$$

occurs not only in the vibrating string theory out also in many other physical problems. Suppose for instance that a bar with the torsion coefficient E and mass δ per unit of length is placed along an axis λ. If we denote by $x(\lambda, t)$ the angular deflection of the bar with the coordinate λ at the instant t, we shall again obtain equation (22.1) where $a^2 = E/\delta$. This equation can also be regarded as the equation of the longitudinal vibrations of an elastic bar. Finally, it will be observed that equation (22.1) is a particular case of the equation of telegraphy

$$x''(\lambda) = (Ls+R)(Cs+G)x(\lambda),$$

which will be discussed at greater length in Chapter VIII.

In our previous discussion we limited ourselves to a single physical interpretation, namely to the case of a vibrating string. The range of applications is of course much wider, since the calculations will always be the same regardless of their physical interpretation.

CHAPTER V

THE EQUATION OF HEAT

§ 23. The parabolic exponential function. The parabolic exponential function $e^{-\lambda\sqrt{s}}$ will play a similar role in the *equation of heat*, dealt with in this Chapter, to that played by the hyperbolic exponential function in the theory of the vibrating string.

In order to introduce the parabolic exponential function we take the parametric function

$$F(\lambda) = \{F(\lambda, t)\} = \left\{\frac{\lambda}{2\sqrt{\pi t^3}} \exp\left(-\frac{\lambda^2}{4t}\right)\right\} \qquad (0 < \lambda < \infty).$$

We have the equality

$$l^{1/2}F(\lambda) = \left\{\frac{\lambda}{2\pi}\int_0^t (t-\tau)^{-1/2}\tau^{-3/2}\exp\left(-\frac{\lambda^2}{4\tau}\right)d\tau\right\},$$

and substituting $\dfrac{\lambda^2}{4\tau} = \dfrac{\lambda^2}{4t} + \sigma^2$

$$\text{(23.1)} \qquad l^{1/2}F(\lambda) = \left\{\frac{2}{\pi\sqrt{t}}\exp\left(-\frac{\lambda^2}{4t}\right)\int_0^\infty e^{-\sigma^2}d\sigma\right\} = \left\{\frac{1}{\sqrt{\pi t}}\exp\left(-\frac{\lambda^2}{4t}\right)\right\}.$$

Further we have

$$\text{(23.2)} \qquad l^{3/2}F(\lambda) = \left\{\int_0^t \frac{1}{\sqrt{\pi t}}\exp\left(-\frac{\lambda^2}{4\tau}\right)d\tau\right\}.$$

The partial derivative

$$\frac{\partial}{\partial\lambda}\int_0^t \frac{1}{\sqrt{\pi\tau}}\exp\left(-\frac{\lambda^2}{4\tau}\right)d\tau = -\int_0^t \frac{\lambda}{2\sqrt{\pi\tau^3}}\exp\left(-\frac{\lambda^2}{4\tau}\right)d\tau$$

being continuous for $0 < \lambda < \infty$, $0 \leqslant t < \infty$, we can write $l^{3/2}F'(\lambda) = -lF(\lambda)$, and consequently

$$\text{(23.3)} \qquad F'(\lambda) = -\sqrt{s}\,F(\lambda).$$

The operational function $F(\lambda)$ can be continued over all real values of λ in such a way that equation (23.3) will still be satisfied (see § 13). Then, by (23.2), we shall have

$$F(0) = s^{3/2}\left\{\int_0^t \frac{d\tau}{\sqrt{\pi\tau}}\right\} = s^{3/2}(l\cdot l^{1/2}) = 1.$$

Hence it follows that the continued function $F(\lambda)$ is an exponential function,

$$F(\lambda) = e^{-\lambda\sqrt{s}}.$$

For positive values of λ this function is reduced to the parametric function

$$e^{-\lambda\sqrt{s}} = \left\{\frac{\lambda}{\sqrt{\pi t^3}}\exp\left(-\frac{\lambda^2}{4t}\right)\right\}. \tag{23.4}$$

The function $e^{-\lambda\sqrt{s}}$ will be termed the *parabolic exponential function* on account of its connection with the equation of heat, which according to the general classification of partial equations is assigned to the parabolic type.

We should also note the formula

$$\frac{1}{\sqrt{s}}\,e^{-\lambda\sqrt{s}} = \left\{\frac{1}{\sqrt{\pi t}}\exp\left(-\frac{\lambda^2}{4t}\right)\right\},$$

which follows immediately from (23.1).

The parabolic exponential function is closely connected with the *error function* (p. 113). Indeed for $\lambda > 0$ we have

$$\frac{1}{s}\,e^{-\lambda\sqrt{s}} = \left\{\int_0^t \frac{1}{2\sqrt{\pi\tau^3}}\exp\left(-\frac{\lambda^2}{4\tau}\right)d\tau\right\}; \tag{23.5}$$

substituting in the last integral $\sigma = \lambda/2\sqrt{\tau}$, we obtain

$$\frac{1}{s}\,e^{-\lambda\sqrt{s}} = \left\{\operatorname{cerf}\frac{\lambda}{2\sqrt{t}}\right\}, \tag{23.6}$$

where

$$\operatorname{cerf} t = \frac{2}{\sqrt{\pi}}\int_t^\infty e^{-\sigma^2}d\sigma = 1-\operatorname{erf} t.$$

The function cerf (fig. 147) is continuous and decreases in the interval $0 \leqslant t < \infty$ from 1 to 0 (see § 58, Part I).

In view of cerf $0 = 1$ formula (23.6) is obviously true not only for $\lambda > 0$ but also for $\lambda = 0$ (unlike formula (23.5), which for $\lambda = 0$ gives $1/s$ on the left side and 0 on the right).

The symbol cerf is to denote the complement of the function erf (just as for instance ctg denotes the complement of the function tg).

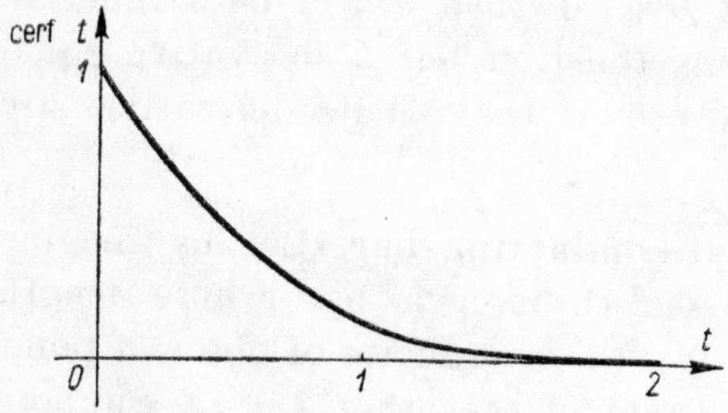

Fig. 147

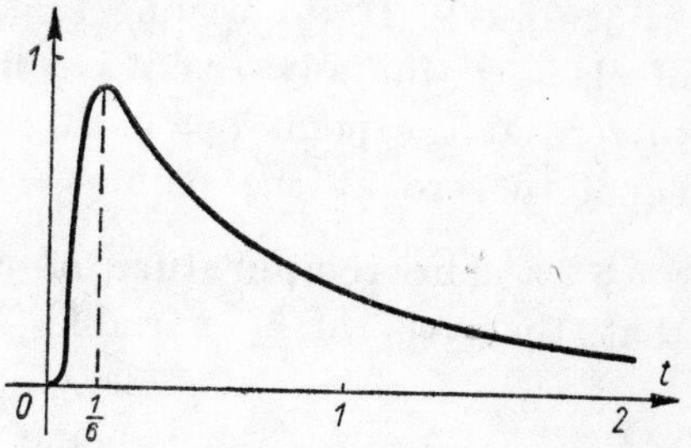

Fig. 148

§ 24. Some analytic properties of the parabolic exponential function. For any fixed $\lambda > 0$ the operator $e^{-\lambda\sqrt{s}}$ represents a function of the variable t defined by the formula

$$F(\lambda, t) = \frac{\lambda}{2\sqrt{\pi t^3}} \exp\left(-\frac{\lambda^2}{4t}\right). \tag{24.1}$$

Let us examine the shape of this function.

It is a positive function for $0 < t < \infty$. We also see that

$$\lim_{t \to 0+} F(\lambda, t) = 0 \quad \text{and} \quad \lim_{t \to \infty} F(\lambda, t) = 0,$$

whence it follows that the maximum of $F(\lambda, t)$ is reached inside the interval $0 < t < \infty$. In order to find that maximum, we make the derivative with respect to t,

$$\frac{\partial}{\partial t} F(\lambda, t) = (\lambda^2 - 6t) \frac{\lambda}{8\sqrt{\pi t^7}} \exp\left(-\frac{\lambda^2}{4t}\right), \tag{24.2}$$

equal to zero. This shows that the maximum is reached at the point $t = \frac{1}{6}\lambda^2$ and is equal to

$$F(\lambda, \tfrac{1}{6}\lambda^2) = \frac{3}{\lambda^2}\sqrt{\frac{6}{\pi e^3}}. \tag{24.3}$$

Formula (24.3) shows also that

$$\lim_{t\to 0+} \frac{\partial}{\partial t} F(\lambda, t) = 0;$$

this means that the tangent to the curve becomes horizontal as the point t approaches zero.

Fig. 148 gives the graph of function (24.1) for $\lambda = 1$.

Remark. If we assume that $F(\lambda, 0) = 0$, then F will be a function of class $\mathcal{C}$ (for any fixed $\lambda > 0$). This function has a derivative equal to zero at the point $t = 0$. It can be proved that all its derivatives are equal to zero at the point $t = 0$.

§ 25. The temperature of a heat-conducting bar. Let us imagine that the axis of a variable λ passes through a bar whose length is λ_0 (fig. 149), the coordinate of one end point being $\lambda = 0$ and of the other $\lambda = \lambda_0$. Suppose that k denotes the heat conductibility, c the specific heat and δ the density of the bar. Further suppose that the lateral surface of the bar is perfectly insulated, so that the heat can only flow in and flow out through the ends of the bar. If we denote by $x(\lambda, t)$ the temperature of a layer of the bar with the coordinate λ at the instant t, then the partial equation

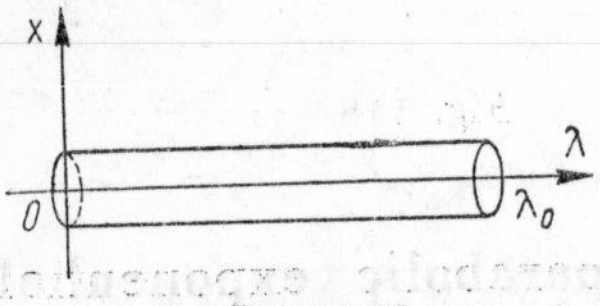

Fig. 149

(25.1) $$x_{\lambda\lambda}(\lambda, t) = a^2 x_t(\lambda, t),$$

where $a = \sqrt{c\delta/K}$, will be satisfied.

Suppose that at the instant $t = 0$ the temperature in the whole bar is 0,

(25.2) $$x(\lambda, 0) = 0 \quad (0 < \lambda < \lambda_0)$$

and that we know the variations of temperature at both ends of the bar, namely

(25.3) $$x(0, t) = v(t), \quad x(\lambda_0, t) = 0 \quad (0 \leqslant t < \infty).$$

The problem consists in determining the distribution of temperature at an arbitrary instant $t > 0$. Mathematically this means that we must solve the differential equation (25.1) with the given conditions (25.2) and (25.3).

By assumption (25.2), equation (25.1) can be written by means of operational symbols in the following way:

(25.4) $$x''(\lambda) = a^2 s x(\lambda);$$

the conditions

$$x(0) = v, \quad x(\lambda_0) = 0 \tag{25.5}$$

correspond to conditions (25.3).

To begin with, we seek exponential functions $e^{\lambda w}$ satisfying equation (25.4), *i. e.*, such that

$$(e^{w\lambda})'' = a^2 s e^{\lambda w}.$$

Differentiating we obtain

$$w^2 e^{\lambda w} = a^2 s e^{\lambda w},$$

whence

$$w^2 = a^2 s$$

and $w = -a\sqrt{s}$ or $w = a\sqrt{s}$. Thus there exist two (and only two) exponential functions,

$$e^{-a\lambda\sqrt{s}} \quad \text{and} \quad e^{a\lambda\sqrt{s}},$$

satisfying equation (25.4).

Every operational function of the form

$$x(\lambda) = c_1 e^{-a\lambda\sqrt{s}} + c_2 e^{a\lambda\sqrt{s}} \tag{25.6}$$

also satisfies equation (25.4) whatever operators c_1 and c_2 are fixed. We shall choose those operators in such a way that

$$\begin{aligned} x(0) &= c_1 + c_2 = v, \\ x(\lambda_0) &= c_1 e^{-a\lambda_0\sqrt{s}} + c_2 e^{a\lambda\sqrt{s}} = 0. \end{aligned} \tag{25.7}$$

Solving this system of equations we obtain

$$c_1 = \frac{v}{1-e^{-2a\lambda_0\sqrt{s}}} \quad \text{and} \quad c_2 = \frac{-e^{-2a\lambda_0\sqrt{s}}\cdot v}{1-e^{-2a\lambda_0\sqrt{s}}}.$$

Hence the required solution of equation (25.4):

$$x(\lambda) = \frac{(e^{-a\lambda\sqrt{s}} - e^{-a(2\lambda_0-\lambda)\sqrt{s}})v}{1-e^{-2a\lambda_0\sqrt{s}}}. \tag{25.8}$$

It is easy to prove that every operational function $y(\lambda)$ satisfying equation (25.4) is of the form (25.6). Indeed, this function satisfies at the point $\lambda = 0$ the conditions

$$y(0) = k_0 \quad \text{and} \quad y'(0) = k.$$

But we can always choose the coefficients c_1 and c_2 in formula (25.6) in such a way that

$$x(0) = c_1 + c_2 = k_0,$$
$$x'(0) = -c_1 a\sqrt{s} + c_2 a\sqrt{s} = k_1,$$

since the determinant

$$\begin{vmatrix} 1 & 1 \\ -a\sqrt{s} & a\sqrt{s} \end{vmatrix} = 2a\sqrt{s}$$

is different from zero. The values c_1 and c_2 being chosen in this way, we have $y(\lambda) = x(\lambda)$ for all λ (see §§ 12 and 13).

Each solution of equation (25.4) being of the form (25.6), the only solution satisfying conditions (25.5) is the function (25.8) since the coefficients have been uniquely determined from equations (25.7).

Solution (25.8) can easily be adapted to numerical calculations if we expand it in an infinite series. In order to do this correctly let us recall certain points from the classical theory of series.

§ 26. Expanding the solution in an infinite series. Since

$$\frac{1}{1-e^{-2\lambda_0\sqrt{s}}} = 1 + \sum_{\nu=1}^{\infty} e^{-2\nu a\lambda_0\sqrt{s}} = 1 + \left\{\sum_{\nu=1}^{\infty} \frac{\nu a\lambda_0}{\sqrt{\pi t^3}} \exp\left(-\frac{\nu^2 a^2 \lambda_0^2}{t}\right)\right\},$$

solution (25.8) can be represented in the form

$$x(\lambda) = v\left(\sum_{\nu=0}^{\infty} e^{-a(2\nu\lambda_0+\lambda)\sqrt{s}} - \sum_{\nu=1}^{\infty} e^{-a(2\nu\lambda_0-\lambda)\sqrt{s}}\right)$$

or

$$x(\lambda, t) = \sum_{\nu=0}^{\infty} \int_0^t v(t-\tau) \frac{a(2\nu\lambda_0+\lambda)}{2\sqrt{\pi\tau^3}} \exp\left(-\frac{a^2(2\nu\lambda_0+\lambda)^2}{4\tau}\right) d\tau -$$
$$- \sum_{\nu=1}^{\infty} \int_0^t v(t-\tau) \frac{a(2\nu\lambda_0-\lambda)}{2\sqrt{\pi\tau^3}} \exp\left(-\frac{a^2(2\nu\lambda_0-\lambda)^2}{4\tau}\right) d\tau.$$

In particular let us denote by $G(\lambda)$ the solution of the equation in the case of $v = 1/s$. We can then write

$$G(\lambda) = \frac{1}{s}\left(\sum_{\nu=0}^{\infty} e^{-a(2\nu\lambda_0+\lambda)\sqrt{s}} - \sum_{\nu=1}^{\infty} e^{-a(2\nu\lambda_0-\lambda)\sqrt{s}}\right)$$

or

$$G(\lambda, t) = \sum_{\nu=0}^{\infty} \operatorname{cerf} \frac{a(2\nu\lambda_0+\lambda)}{2\sqrt{t}} - \sum_{\nu=1}^{\infty} \operatorname{cerf} \frac{a(2\nu\lambda_0-\lambda)}{2\sqrt{t}}. \tag{26.1}$$

The function $G(\lambda, t)$ represents the distribution of temperature in the bar, which had temperature 0 at the initial instant, its initial point $\lambda = 0$ being constantly held at temperature 1 and its end point $\lambda = \lambda_0$ at temperature 0.

With the aid of the function G we can also write the solution in the general case, when the temperature of the bar is defined by conditions (25.3). Indeed, by formula (25.8), we can write

$$x(\lambda,t) = \frac{d}{dt}\int_0^t v(t-\tau)G(\lambda, \tau)\,d\tau.$$

§ 27. Inequalities and the module. Generally it is impossible to say that one of two operators is larger than the other, just as we cannot always say this about complex numbers. In the particular case of a and b being functions of class $\mathcal{K}$ with real values we shall understand by the symbol

$$a \leqslant b$$

that

$$a(t) \leqslant b(t)$$

for all values of $t \geqslant 0$ for which both functions are continuous.

Thus for instance

$$e^{-\lambda\sqrt{s}} \leqslant 3\sqrt{\frac{6}{\pi e^3}}\cdot\frac{1}{\lambda^2 s} \qquad (\lambda > 0), \tag{27.1}$$

which follows form the calculation performed in § 24.

Similarly we have

$$\frac{s}{s^2+1} \leqslant \frac{1}{s},$$

since $\cos t \leqslant 1$; but between $s/(s^2+1)$ and $1/2s$ we cannot establish any sign of inequality, $\sin t$ being greater than $\frac{1}{2}$ at some points and less than $\frac{1}{2}$ at other points.

By the *module* $|a|$ of a function a of class $\mathcal{K}$ we shall simply understand

$$|a| = |\{a(t)\}| = \{|a(t)|\};$$

the module $|a|$ is thus again a function of class $\mathcal{K}$. If a and b are functions of class $\mathcal{K}$, then

$$|a+b| \leqslant |a|+|b|, \qquad |a\cdot b| \leqslant |a|\cdot|b|,$$

since

$$|a(t)+b(t)| \leqslant |a(t)|+|b(t)|,$$

$$\left|\int_0^t a(t-\tau)b(\tau)\,d\tau\right| \leqslant \int_0^t |a(t-\tau)|\cdot|b(\tau)|\,d\tau.$$

Remark. The equality $|a\cdot b| = |a|\cdot|b|$ generally does not hold. For if that were the case, we should have for $a = l$

$$\left|\int_0^t b(\tau)\,d\tau\right| = \int_0^t |b(\tau)|\,d\tau,$$

which need not be true at all.

Suppose that a_n $(n = 1, 2, \ldots)$ and a are functions of class $\mathcal{C}$.

If there exist a function $g \in \mathcal{C}$ and a numerical sequence ε_n tending to zero such that

(27.2) $$|a_n - a| \leqslant \varepsilon_n g \quad (n = 1, 2, \ldots),$$

then the sequence a_n is uniformly convergent to a in every finite interval $0 \leqslant t \leqslant t_0$, i. e., it is also convergent in the operational sense.

Indeed, the continuity of g implies that for every finite interval $0 \leqslant t \leqslant t_0$ there exists a number M satisfying the inequality

$$|g(t)| \leqslant M \quad \text{for} \quad 0 \leqslant t \leqslant t_0,$$

whence

$$|a_n(t) - a(t)| \leqslant \varepsilon_n M \quad \text{for} \quad 0 \leqslant t \leqslant t_0,$$

which denotes uniform convergence in the interval $0 \leqslant t \leqslant t_0$.

We can also prove the converse theorem, namely that *if a sequence a_n of functions of class $\mathcal{C}$ tends to a uniformly in every interval $0 \leqslant t \leqslant t_0$, then there exist a function $g \in \mathcal{C}$ and a numerical sequence ε_n tending to zero such that inequalities* (27.2) *hold.*

Exercise. Prove the inequalities

$$(\alpha)\quad \frac{1}{s^2+a^2} \leqslant \frac{1}{as} \quad (a > 0); \qquad (\beta)\quad \frac{1}{\sqrt{s}}\, e^{-\lambda\sqrt{s}} \leqslant \frac{1}{\sqrt{\pi e}} \cdot \frac{\sqrt{2}}{\lambda s} \quad (\lambda > 0).$$

§ 28. An infinitely long bar.

Formula (25.8) can be written in the form

(28.1) $$x(\lambda) = v e^{-a\lambda\sqrt{s}} + b(\lambda),$$

where

$$b(\lambda) = v\left(\sum_{\nu=1}^{\infty} e^{-a(2\nu\lambda_0-\lambda)\sqrt{s}} - \sum_{\nu=1}^{\infty} e^{-a(2\nu\lambda_0-\lambda)\sqrt{s}}\right).$$

But by (27.1) we have

$$|b(\lambda)| \leqslant |v| \cdot 3\sqrt{\frac{6}{\pi e^3}} \cdot \frac{1}{s} \sum_{\nu=1}^{\infty} \left(\frac{1}{(2\nu\lambda_0 + \lambda)^2} + \frac{1}{(2\nu\lambda_0 - \lambda)^2} \right)$$

$$\leqslant |v| \cdot 3\sqrt{\frac{6}{\pi e^3}} \cdot \frac{2}{\lambda_0^2 s} \sum_{\nu=1}^{\infty} \frac{1}{(2\nu-1)^2} = \frac{K}{\lambda_0^2} \cdot \frac{|v|}{s},$$

where $K = 6\sqrt{\frac{6}{\pi e^3}} \cdot \sum_{\nu=1}^{\infty} \frac{1}{(2\nu-1)^2}$.

Hence it can be seen that if $\lambda_0 \to \infty$, then $b(\lambda)$ decreases to zero.

Assuming the bar to be very long we can neglect the term $b(\lambda)$ in formula (28.1) and write the solution in the form

(28.2) $$x(\lambda) = v e^{-a\lambda\sqrt{s}} \qquad (\lambda \geqslant 0)$$

or

(28.3) $$x(\lambda, t) = \frac{a\lambda}{2\sqrt{\pi}} \int_0^t v(t-\tau)\tau^{-3/2} \exp\left(-\frac{a^2\lambda^2}{4\tau}\right) d\tau \qquad \begin{pmatrix} 0 \leqslant \lambda < \infty \\ 0 < t < \infty \end{pmatrix}.$$

This function represents the distribution of heat in an infinite bar under the assumption that the temperature of the bar was 0 at the instant $t = 0$ and that the temperature at the point $\lambda = 0$ is given by the function v. An infinite bar is of course a mere idea just as an infinite string was (see § 18).

If the temperature at the initial point of the bar is constant, $v = \omega/s$, then solution (28.2) can be written in the form

$$x(\lambda) = \frac{w}{s} e^{-a\lambda\sqrt{s}} \qquad (0 \leqslant \lambda < \infty)$$

or

(28.4) $$x(\lambda, t) = \omega \operatorname{cerf} \frac{a\lambda}{2\sqrt{t}} \qquad (0 \leqslant \lambda < \infty,\ 0 < t < \infty).$$

Remark. Function (28.4) is undetermined on the straight line $t = 0$; however, if we assume

$$x(\lambda, 0) = \lim_{t \to 0} x(\lambda, t) = 0,$$

we shall make it continuous in the whole quarter of the plane

$$0 \leqslant \lambda < \infty, \quad 0 \leqslant t < \infty$$

except one point, $\lambda = t = 0$ (if $\omega \neq 0$). Consequently no partial derivatives exist at t and equation (25.1) cannot be satisfied at that point. This difficulty is avoided if we take the operational equation (25.4) as the fundamental equation of heat, since for any real λ each of its solutions has derivatives, even ones of arbitrarily high order.

In the establishing of formula (28.3) an essential part has been played by the second condition of (25.3), *i. e.*, by the condition

$$x(\lambda_0, t) = 0 \quad (0 \leqslant t < \infty); \tag{28.5}$$

it was only after taking this condition into account that we passed to the limit as $\lambda_0 \to \infty$.

The same formula, (28.3), can be obtained by solving equation (25.1) for the whole quarter $0 \leqslant \lambda < \infty$, $0 \leqslant t < \infty$ at once and replacing condition (28.5) by an analogous condition,

$$\lim_{\lambda\to\infty} x(\lambda, t) = 0 \quad (0 \leqslant t < \infty) \tag{28.6}$$

under the assumption that the limit exists uniformly. We can weaken condition (28.6), assuming only that the function $x(\lambda, t)$ is bounded in a certain way.

Strictly speaking, we shall have to find a solution $x(\lambda, t)$ of equation (25.1)

$$x_{\lambda\lambda}(\lambda, t) = a^2 x_t(\lambda, t),$$

which will satisfy the conditions

$$x(\lambda, 0) = 0 \quad (0 \leqslant \lambda < \infty), \tag{28.7}$$

$$x(0, t) = v(t) \quad (0 < t < \infty),$$

$$|x(\lambda, t)| \leqslant m(t) \quad (0 \leqslant \lambda < \infty,\ 0 \leqslant t < \infty), \tag{28.8}$$

where v and m are given functions of class $\mathcal{C}$. The function m will not figure in the solution itself since the significance of condition (28.8) consists only in a certain limitation of the function $x(\lambda, t)$ which ensures the unicity of the solution.

In the operational treatment the present problem consists in finding a parametric function $x(\lambda)$ satisfying equation (25.4),

$$x''(\lambda) = a^2 s x(\lambda),$$

and the conditions

$$x(0) = v, \tag{28.9}$$

$$|x(\lambda)| \leqslant m \quad (0 \leqslant \lambda < \infty). \tag{28.10}$$

The general solution of the equation in question has the form

$$x(\lambda) = c_1 e^{-a\lambda\sqrt{s}} + c_2 e^{-2a\lambda\sqrt{s}}.$$

We shall prove that if $x(\lambda)$ is assumed to be a parametric function satisfying condition (28.10) we must have $c_2 = 0$.

Indeed, we can write

$$c_2 = x(\lambda)e^{-a\lambda\sqrt{s}} - c_1 e^{-2a\lambda\sqrt{s}}; \tag{28.11}$$

but in view of

$$0 \leqslant e^{-a\lambda\sqrt{s}} \leqslant 3\sqrt{\frac{6}{\pi e^3}}\frac{1}{a^2\lambda^2 s}$$

we have

$$\lim_{\lambda\to\infty} e^{-a\lambda\sqrt{s}} = \lim_{\lambda\to\infty} e^{-2a\lambda\sqrt{s}} = 0,$$

whence, under assumption (28.10), it follows that the right side of formula (28.11) tends to zero as $\lambda \to \infty$. Therefore we must have $c_2 = 0$.

In this manner the solution is reduced to the form

$$x(\lambda) = c_1 e^{-a\lambda\sqrt{s}}.$$

Condition (28.9) implies further that $c_1 = v$, whence we obtain the required solution,

$$x(\lambda) = ve^{-a\lambda\sqrt{s}},$$

i. e., solution (28.3) in the ordinary, not the operational form.

The obtained solution is unique.

It can be shown that if assumption (28.8) or (28.10) is neglected there still exist other solutions. Thus we have here a different situation from that existing in the case of an infinite string, where the condition of boundedness of the solution was of no importance. In the present case the condition of boundedness cannot be neglected.

However, it can be replaced by the following weaker condition: for every number $t_0 > 0$ there exists such a number β_0 that

$$\lim_{\lambda\to\infty} [e^{-\beta_0\lambda^2} \max_{0\leqslant t\leqslant t_0} |x(\lambda, t)|] = 0.$$

In that case the theorem on unicity still holds then. The proof will be found in Tychonoff's paper [1] on the equation of heat.

In order to illustrate the manner of heat propagation in a more concrete way let us imagine a long bar of silver with the initial temperature 0° C; this bar is constantly heated at one end up to the temperature 100° C.

The following physical constants for silver are needed:

specific heat $c = 0{,}055$,

conductibility $k = 1{,}01$,

density $\delta = 10{,}5$.

Hence we have

$$a = \sqrt{\frac{0{,}055 \cdot 10{,}5}{1{,}01}} \approx 0{,}76 .$$

Changes of temperature are thus defined by the formula

$$x(\lambda, t) = 100 \operatorname{cerf}\left(0{,}38 \frac{\lambda}{\sqrt{t}}\right).$$

When one second has elapsed, the temperature at a distance of 10 centimetres from the initial point of the bar will rise (theoretically) by no more than 0,00001° C, which of course cannot be verified experimetally. Using a thermometer which reacts to the variations of 0,1° C we can ascertain after one second a rise of temperature at a distance of not more than 4,8 cm. Using a more sensitive thermometer, which indicates changes of 0,001° C, we shall ascertain a rise of temperature at a distance of 8,2 cm.

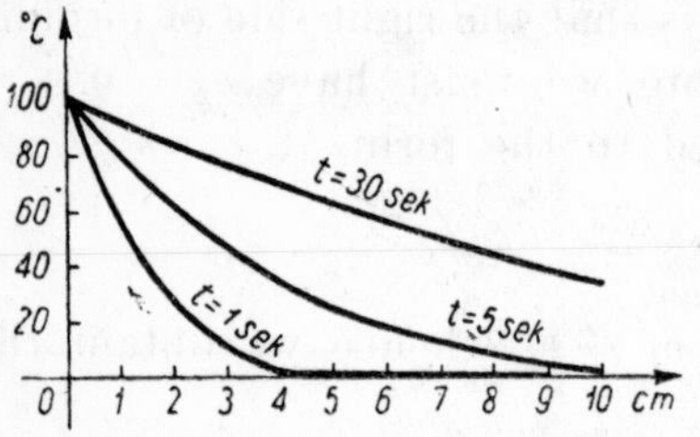

Fig. 150. Heat propagation in a silver bar

Fig. 150 shows, in the form of a graph, the distribution of temperature in the bar when one, five and thirty seconds have elapsed.

§ 29. A bar without an outgoing flow of heat. We shall now solve the equation

$$x_{\lambda\lambda}(\lambda, t) = a^2 x_t(\lambda, t) \qquad (0 \leqslant \lambda \leqslant \lambda_0,\ 0 \leqslant t < \infty)$$

under the assumptions

$$x(\lambda, 0) = 0 \qquad (0 \leqslant \lambda \leqslant \lambda_0),$$

$$x(0, t) = v(t), \qquad x_\lambda(\lambda_0, t) = 0 \qquad (0 \leqslant t < \infty).$$

In the physical interpretation the first derivative, $x_\lambda(\lambda_0, t)$ denotes the amount of heat flowing through the point λ_0. The assumption of this derivative being equal to zero means that one end of the bar (as well as the whole of its lateral surface) is perfectly insulated against its environment. This assumption has been introduced instead of the assumption of § 25, according to which one end of the bar, $\lambda = \lambda_0$, is constantly kept at temperature 0.

The operational equation retains the form

$$x''(\lambda) = a^2 s x(\lambda)$$

but the conditions at the ends of the bar are defined by the equalities

$$x(0) = v, \quad x'(\lambda_0) = 0.$$

The general solution of the equation is the function

$$x(\lambda) = c_1 e^{-a\lambda\sqrt{s}} + c_2 e^{a\lambda\sqrt{s}};$$

the constants c_1 and c_2 are determined from the conditions

$$x(0) = c_1 + c_2 = v,$$

$$x'(\lambda_0) = -c_1 a\sqrt{s}e^{-a\lambda_0\sqrt{s}} + c_2 a\sqrt{s}e^{a\lambda_0\sqrt{s}} = 0;$$

in this way we obtain

$$c_1 = \frac{v}{1+e^{-2a\lambda_0\sqrt{s}}}, \quad c_2 = \frac{ve^{-2a\lambda_0\sqrt{s}}}{1+e^{-2a\lambda_0\sqrt{s}}},$$

and finally

$$x(\lambda) = \frac{(e^{-a\lambda\sqrt{s}} + e^{-a(2\lambda_0-\lambda)\sqrt{s}})v}{1+e^{-2a\lambda_0\sqrt{s}}}.$$

The only difference between this solution and (25.8) is that now we have sums and not differences in the numerator and in the denominator. In this case we can also use expansions into series, starting from the formula

$$\frac{1}{1+e^{-2a\lambda_0\sqrt{s}}} = 1 + \sum_{\nu=1}^{\infty}(-1)^\nu e^{-2\nu a\lambda_0\sqrt{s}}.$$

The proof of convergence is the same as before. The formulas found in this way will differ from the previous ones only in signs; we shall not write them in detail.

§ 30. Trigonometric series. A *trigonometric series* is the term given to a series

$$f(x) = \frac{a_0}{2} + \sum_{n=1}^{\infty}(a_n \cos nx + b_n \sin nx),$$

where a_n and b_n are real or complex numbers and x is a variable which is supposed to assume real values.

There exist general conditions which make it possible to ascertain in a great many cases whether a given function $f(x)$ can be represented in the form of a trigonometric series. The formulas for the coefficients of that series have also been known for a long time.

Here we shall make no use of the general theory: we shall limit ourselves to the consideration of a few simple cases, which will be needed in the sequel.

To begin with, we shall prove that

$$(30.1)\qquad \sum_{n=1}^{\infty}(-1)^{n-1}\frac{\sin nx}{n}=\frac{x}{2}\quad \text{for}\quad -\pi<x<\pi$$

and that the convergence of this series is uniform in every closed interval $[-x_0, x_0]$ contained in $(-\pi, \pi)$.

By the identity

$$2\cos kx\cos\tfrac{x}{2}=\cos(k-\tfrac{1}{2})x+\cos(k+\tfrac{1}{2})x$$

we have

$$\begin{aligned}2[\cos x-\cos 2x+\ldots+(-1)^{k-1}\cos kx]\cos\tfrac{x}{2}\\ =[\cos\tfrac{x}{2}+\cos\tfrac{3x}{2}]-[\cos\tfrac{3x}{2}+\cos\tfrac{5x}{2}]+\ldots+\\ +(-1)^{k-1}[\cos(k-\tfrac{1}{2})x+\cos(k+\tfrac{1}{2})x]\\ =\cos\tfrac{x}{2}+(-1)^{k-1}\cos(k+\tfrac{1}{2})x,\end{aligned}$$

whence

$$\sum_{k=1}^{k}(-1)^{n-1}\cos nx=\tfrac{1}{2}+(-1)^{k-1}\frac{\cos(k+\frac{1}{2})x}{2\cos\frac{1}{2}x}.$$

Integrating the last equality from 0 to x we get

$$(30.2)\qquad \sum_{n=1}^{\infty}(-1)^{n-1}\frac{\sin nx}{n}=\tfrac{1}{2}x+(-1)^{k-1}I_k(x),$$

where

$$I_k(x)=\int_0^x\frac{\cos(k+\frac{1}{2})\xi}{2\cos\frac{1}{2}\xi}\,d\xi.$$

Integrating by parts we obtain

$$I_k(x)=\frac{1}{2k+1}\left[\frac{\sin(k+\frac{1}{2})x}{\cos\frac{1}{2}x}-\tfrac{1}{2}\int_0^x\frac{\sin\frac{1}{2}\xi\sin(k+\frac{1}{2})\xi}{\cos^2\frac{1}{2}\xi}\,d\xi\right],$$

whence we have for $|x|\leqslant x_0<\pi$

$$|I_k(x)|\leqslant\frac{1}{2k+1}\left[\frac{1}{\cos\frac{1}{2}x_0}+\tfrac{1}{2}\int_0^{x_0}\frac{d\xi}{\cos^2\frac{1}{2}\xi}\right]=\frac{1}{2k+1}\left(\sec\frac{x_0}{2}+\operatorname{tg}\frac{x_0}{2}\right).$$

This inequality proves that the sequence $I_k(x)$ uniformly tends to zero in the interval $[-x_0, x_0]$ as $k\to\infty$. Hence follows the theorem.

For $x = \pm\pi$ series (30.1) is obviously also convergent but this time to zero and not to $x/2$. Moreover, the periodicity of $\sin nx$ shows that series (30.1) tends to the periodic function given in fig. 151.

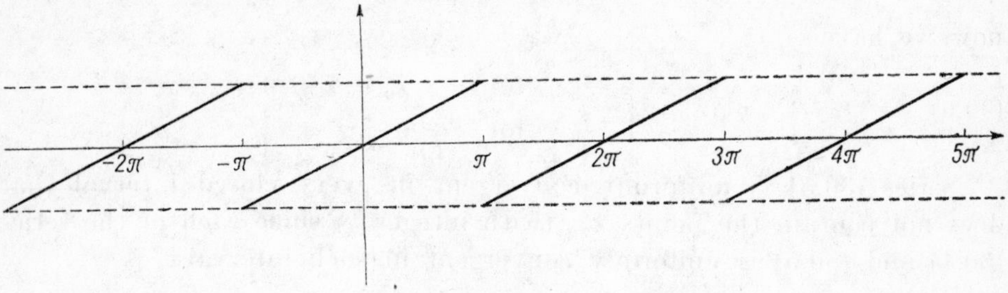

Fig. 151

Many other trigonometric series can be derived from series (30.1). For example, the series

$$\varphi_1(\lambda) = \frac{2\lambda_0}{\pi} \sum_{n=1}^{\infty} \frac{(-1)^{n-1}}{n} \sin \frac{n\pi\lambda}{\lambda_0} \tag{30.3}$$

can be obtained from series (30.1) by substituting $x = \pi\lambda/\lambda_0$.

Series (30.3) is uniformly convergent in every closed interval that does not contain the points $(2k-1)\lambda_0$ (with integer k).

We have of course

$$\varphi_1(\lambda) = \lambda \quad \text{for} \quad -\lambda_0 < \lambda < \lambda_0.$$

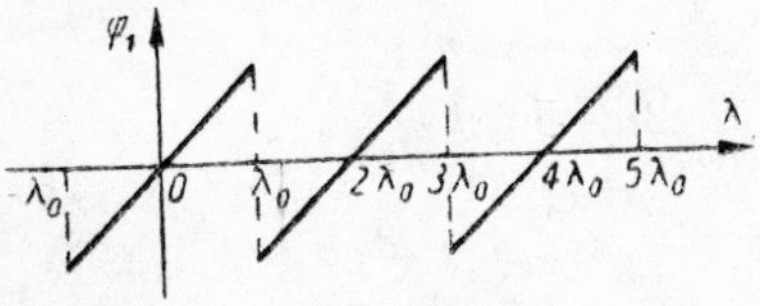

Fig. 152. $\varphi_1(\lambda) = \dfrac{2\lambda_0}{\pi} \sum_{n=1}^{\infty} (-1)^{n-1} \dfrac{1}{n} \sin \dfrac{n\pi\lambda}{\lambda_0}$

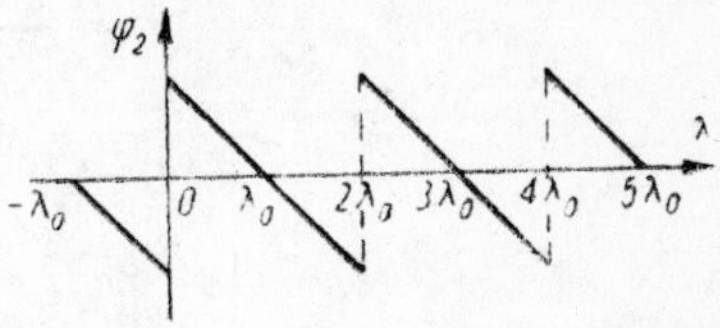

Fig. 153. $\varphi_2(\lambda) = \dfrac{2\lambda_0}{\pi} \sum_{n=1}^{\infty} \dfrac{1}{n} \sin \dfrac{n\pi\lambda}{\lambda_0}$

Replacing in series (30.3) λ by $\lambda_0 - \lambda$ we obtain a new function,

$$\varphi_2(\lambda) = \varphi_1(\lambda_0 - \lambda) = \frac{2\lambda_0}{\pi} \sum_{n=1}^{\infty} \frac{1}{n} \sin \frac{n\pi\lambda}{\lambda_0}, \tag{30.4}$$

such that

$$\varphi_2(\lambda) = \lambda_0 - \lambda \quad \text{for} \quad 0 < \lambda < 2\lambda_0.$$

Series (30.4) is uniformly convergent in every closed interval that does not contain the points $2l\lambda_0$ (with integer k).

Adding the series (30.3) and (30.4) we obtain (fig. 154)

$$\varphi_3(\lambda) = \varphi_1(\lambda)+\varphi_2(\lambda) = \frac{4\lambda_0}{\pi}\sum_{n=1}^{\infty}\frac{1}{2n-1}\sin\frac{(2n-1)\pi\lambda}{\lambda_0}; \tag{30.5}$$

now we have

$$\varphi_3(\lambda) = \begin{cases} -\lambda_0 & \text{for} \quad -\lambda_0<\lambda<0, \\ \lambda_0 & \text{for} \quad 0<\lambda<\lambda_0. \end{cases} \tag{30.6}$$

Series (30.5) is uniformly convergent in every closed interval that does not contain the points $k\lambda_0$ (with integer k) since each of the series (30.4) and (30.5) is uniformly convergent in such intervals.

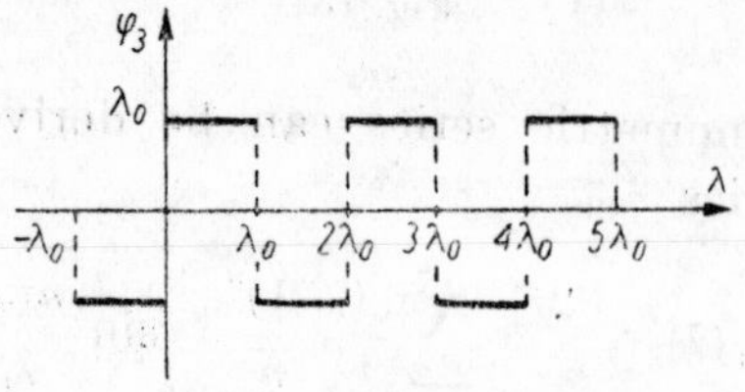

Fig. 154. $\varphi_3(\lambda) = \frac{4\lambda_0}{\pi}\sum_{n=1}^{\infty}\frac{1}{2n-1}\sin\frac{(2n-1)\pi\lambda}{\lambda_0}$

Consequently series (30.5) can be integrated term by term:

$$\int_0^{\lambda}\varphi_3(t)\,dt = \frac{4\lambda_0}{\pi}\int_0^{\lambda}\sum_{n=1}^{\infty}\frac{1}{2n-1}\sin\frac{(2n-1)\pi t}{\lambda_0}\,dt \tag{30.7}$$

$$= \frac{4\lambda_0}{\pi}\sum_{n=1}^{\infty}\int_0^{\lambda}\frac{1}{2n-1}\sin\frac{(2n-1)\pi t}{\lambda_0}\,dt$$

$$= \frac{4\lambda_0^2}{\pi^2}\sum_{n=1}^{\infty}\frac{1}{(2n-1)^2} - \frac{4\lambda_0^2}{\pi^2}\sum_{n=1}^{\infty}\frac{1}{(2n-1)^2}\cos\frac{(2n-1)\pi\lambda}{\lambda_0}.$$

This equality holds for any real λ since the integrated series is uniformly convergent in every closed interval that does not contain the points $k\lambda_0$ (with integer k), and the series obtained after the integration is uniformly convergent in any interval.

We shall make use of this example in deducing certain relations which will be needed in the sequel. Namely, by formula (30.6), we have

$$\int_0^{\lambda_0/2}\varphi_3(t)\,dt = \frac{\lambda_0^2}{2}.$$

Substituting $\lambda = \frac{1}{2}\lambda_0$ in equality (30.7) we shall thus have

$$\frac{1}{2}\lambda_0^2 = \frac{4\lambda_0^2}{\pi^2}\sum_{n=1}^{\infty}\frac{1}{(2n-1)^2},$$

whence

$$\sum_{n=1}^{\infty}\frac{1}{(2n-1)^2} = \frac{1}{1^2}+\frac{1}{3^2}+\frac{1}{5^2}+\ldots = \frac{\pi^2}{8}. \tag{30.8}$$

Substituting (30.8) in formula (30.7) we obtain

$$\int_0^\lambda \varphi_3(t)\,dt = \frac{\lambda_0^2}{2} - \frac{4\lambda_0^2}{\pi^2}\sum_{n=1}^{\infty}\frac{1}{(2n-1)^2}\cos\frac{(2n-1)\pi\lambda}{\lambda_0},$$

and by (30.6)

$$\sum_{n=1}^{\infty}\frac{1}{(2n-1)^2}\cos\frac{(2n-1)\pi\lambda}{\lambda_0} = \frac{\pi^2}{8}\left(1-\frac{2\lambda}{\lambda_0}\right) \qquad (0\leqslant\lambda\leqslant\lambda_0). \tag{30.9}$$

This formula will be made use of in § 35.

Formula (30.8) has been found by Euler. It should also be noted that

$$\frac{1}{1^2}+\frac{1}{2^2}+\frac{1}{3^2}+\ldots = \left(\frac{1}{1^2}+\frac{1}{3^2}+\frac{1}{5^2}+\ldots\right)+\left(\frac{1}{2^3}+\frac{1}{4^2}+\frac{1}{6^2}+\ldots\right)$$

$$= \frac{\pi^2}{8}+\frac{1}{4}\left(\frac{1}{1^2}+\frac{1}{2^2}+\frac{1}{3^2}+\ldots\right),$$

whence follows

$$\frac{1}{1^2}+\frac{1}{2^2}+\frac{1}{3^2}+\ldots = \frac{\pi^2}{6}.$$

This formula has also been given by Euler.

§ 31. Changes of temperature in a bar with a given initial temperature. Suppose that the temperature distribution in a bar whose length is λ_0 is given at the instant $t = 0$ by the function

$$x(\lambda, 0) = \sin\frac{n\pi\lambda}{\lambda_0} \qquad (0\leqslant\lambda\leqslant\lambda_0),$$

where n is a natural number, and that both ends of the bar are kept at temperature 0,

$$x(0, t) = 0, \qquad x(\lambda_0, t) = 0 \qquad (0\leqslant t<\infty).$$

Since

$$\{x_t(\lambda, t)\} = s\{x(\lambda, t)\} - \sin\frac{n\pi\lambda}{\lambda_0},$$

the operational equation expressing this case will be non-homogeneous,

$$x''(\lambda) - a^2 s x(\lambda) = -a^2 \sin\frac{n\pi\lambda}{\lambda_0}; \tag{31.1}$$

this equation must be solved with the boundary conditions

$$x(0) = 0, \quad x(\lambda_0) = 0. \tag{31.2}$$

This problem formally resembles the one we have solved in § 19 for the vibrating string. We shall solve it in a similar manner, seeking a function of the form

$$x(\lambda) = c \sin\frac{n\pi\lambda}{\lambda_0} \tag{31.3}$$

which would satisfy equation (31.1).

Substituting (31.3) in (31.1) and dividing by $-\sin\frac{n\pi\lambda}{\lambda_0}$, we obtain

$$c\frac{n^2\pi^2}{\lambda_0^2} + ca^2 s = a^2,$$

whence

$$c = \frac{1}{s + n^2\beta^2} = \{\exp(-n^2\beta^2 t)\},$$

where $\beta = \pi/a\lambda_0$.

With the coefficient c chosen thus, function (31.3) satisfies equation (31.1); simultaneously it satisfies conditions (31.2). Therefore the temperature distribution in the bar is defined by the formula

$$x(\lambda, t) = \exp(-n^2\beta^2 t) \sin\frac{n\pi\lambda}{\lambda_0}.$$

This shows that at any instant t the curve of temperature distribution is a sinusoid whose amplitude rapidly tends to zero.

If the initial temperature distribution is given by the function

$$x(\lambda, t) = \sum_{n=1}^{k} \mu_n \sin\frac{n\pi\lambda}{\lambda_0} \quad (0 \leqslant \lambda \leqslant \lambda_0),$$

the operational equation will have the form

$$x''(\lambda) - a^2 s x(\lambda) = -a^2 \sum_{n=1}^{k} \mu_n \sin\frac{n\pi\lambda}{\lambda_0}.$$

Leaving conditions (31.2) unchanged, we shall have a solution in the form of a sum,

$$x(\lambda) = \sum_{n=1}^{k} \frac{\mu_n}{s+n^2\beta^2} \sin\frac{n\pi\lambda}{\lambda_0}.$$

Finally, suppose that the initial temperature distribution is given by the function

$$x(\lambda, 0) = \varphi(\lambda),$$

which is continuous in a closed interval and can be expanded inside that interval in the trigonometric series

$$\varphi(\lambda) = \sum_{n=1}^{\infty} \mu_n \sin\frac{n\pi\lambda}{\lambda_0} \qquad (0 < \lambda < \lambda_0).$$

This series is uniformly convergent in every interval $[\lambda_1, \lambda_2]$ contained in $(0, \lambda_0)$.

The operational equation has the form

$$x''(\lambda) - a^2 s x(\lambda) = -a^2 \varphi(\lambda). \tag{31.4}$$

If we leave conditions (31.2) unchanged, the formal solution will also have the form of an infinite series,

$$x(\lambda) = \sum_{n=1}^{\infty} \frac{\mu_n}{s+n^2\beta^2} \sin\frac{n\pi\lambda}{\lambda_0}. \tag{31.5}$$

Writing this solution in the ordinary, non-operational form, we have

$$x(\lambda, t) = \sum_{n=1}^{\infty} \mu_n \exp\left(-\frac{n^2\pi^2}{a^2\lambda_0^2}\right) \sin\frac{n\pi\lambda}{\lambda_0}.$$

This shows in particular that as $t \to \infty$ the temperature of the bar rapidly tends to zero everywhere.

§ 32. Checking the correctness of the solution. It is easy to prove that the sequence μ_n tends to zero. Indeed, in view of the uniform convergence of the series $\sum_{n=1}^{\infty} \sin\frac{n\pi\lambda}{\lambda_0}$, there exists such a sequence $\gamma_1, \gamma_2, \ldots$ tending to zero that

$$\left|\mu_n \sin\frac{n\pi\lambda}{\lambda_0}\right| \leqslant \gamma_n \qquad (n = 1, 2, \ldots) \tag{32.1}$$

for all λ from the interval (λ_1, λ_2). For any sufficiently large n we can find such a value of λ from the interval (λ_1, λ_2) that $\sin\frac{n\pi\lambda}{\lambda_0} = 1$; for that value of λ inequality (32.1) is reduced to $|\mu_n| \leqslant \gamma_n$, whence it follows that the sequence μ_n tends to zero.

Series (31.5) can be written in the following form:

$$x(\lambda) = \frac{s^2}{\beta^4}\sum_{n=1}^{\infty}\frac{\mu_n}{n^4}\left(\frac{n^2\beta^2}{s^2} - \frac{1}{s} + \frac{1}{s+n^2\beta^2}\right)\sin\frac{n\pi\lambda}{\lambda_0} = a^2 s^2\{\Phi(\lambda, t)\},$$

where

$$(32.2) \qquad \Phi(\lambda, t) = \frac{\lambda_0^2 t}{\pi^2}\sum_{n=1}^{\infty}\frac{\mu_n}{n^2}\sin\frac{n\pi\lambda}{\lambda_0} - \frac{a^2\lambda_0^4}{\pi^4}\sum_{n=1}^{\infty}\frac{\mu_n}{n^4}(1-e^{-n^2\beta^2 t})\sin\frac{n\pi\lambda}{\lambda_0}.$$

The sequence μ_n tending to zero, both series occuring in formula (32.2) converge uniformly in the whole domain $D(0 \leqslant \lambda \leqslant \lambda_0,\ 0 \leqslant t < \infty)$ and function (32.2) is continuous in that domain. Hence it follows that series (31.5) converges operationally in the interval $0 \leqslant \lambda \leqslant \lambda_0$ and represents a continuous operational function there.

Differentiating formally series (32.2) twice with respect to λ, we obtain

$$(32.3) \qquad \frac{\partial^2}{\partial\lambda^2}\Phi(\lambda, t) = -t\sum_{n=1}^{\infty}\mu_n\sin\frac{n\pi\lambda}{\lambda_0} + \sum_{n=1}^{\infty}\frac{a^2\lambda_0^2}{\pi^2}\cdot\frac{\mu_n}{n^2}(1-e^{-n^2\beta^2 t})\sin\frac{n\pi\lambda}{\lambda_0}.$$

The first series of (32.3) by hypothesis converges to $\varphi(\lambda)$ uniformly in every interval $[\lambda_1, \lambda_2]$ contained in $(0, \lambda_0)$ and the second series converges uniformly in the domain D to a function $\psi(\lambda, t)$ continuous in that domian. Thus, by the theorem on differentiating function series, we have

$$(32.4) \qquad \frac{\partial^2}{\partial\lambda^2}\Phi(\lambda, t) = -t\varphi(\lambda) + \psi(\lambda, t)$$

in the domain

$$D'(0 < \lambda < \lambda_0,\ 0 \leqslant t < \infty).$$

Since the right side of formula (32.4) represents a function continuous in the whole domain D, formula (32.4) holds in the whole of that domain.

This follows from the double application of the following simple lemma:

If the derivative $f'(\lambda)$ of a (numerical) function $f(\lambda)$, continuous in the interval $0 \leqslant \lambda \leqslant \lambda_0$, exists in the open interval $0 < \lambda < \lambda_0$ and is equal in it to a function $g(\lambda)$, continuous in the interval $0 \leqslant \lambda \leqslant \lambda_0$, then the derivative $f'(\lambda)$ also exists in the closed interval $0 \leqslant \lambda \leqslant \lambda_0$ and is equal to $g(\lambda)$ in that interval.

This lemma follows immediately from Rolle's theorem since

$$\frac{f(h)-f(0)}{h}=f'(\xi)=\lambda(\xi) \qquad (0<\xi<h),$$

whence $f'(0)=g(0)$. Similarly $f'(\lambda_0)=g(\lambda_0)$ is found.

We can write

$$\{\psi(\lambda, t)\}=\frac{a^2\lambda_0^2}{\pi^2}\sum_{n=1}^{\infty}\frac{\mu_n}{n^2}\left(\frac{1}{s}-\frac{1}{s+n^2\beta^2}\right)\sin\frac{n\pi\lambda}{\lambda_0}$$

$$=\frac{1}{s}\sum_{n=1}^{\infty}\frac{\mu_n}{s+n^2\beta^2}\sin\frac{n\pi\lambda}{\lambda_0}=\frac{1}{s}x(\lambda),$$

whence

$$x''(\lambda)=a^2s^2\left\{\frac{\partial^2}{\partial\lambda^2}\Phi(\lambda, t)\right\}=a^2s^2\{-t\varphi(\lambda)+\psi(\lambda, t)\}=-a^2\varphi(\lambda)+a^2sx(\lambda).$$

We have thus verified that series (31.5) is the actual solution of equation (31.4) satisfying conditions (31.2).

§ 33. Certain particular cases. For $0<\lambda<\lambda_0$ we have

$$\lambda_0-\lambda=\frac{2\lambda_0}{\pi}\sum_{n=1}^{\infty}\frac{1}{n}\sin\frac{n\pi\lambda}{\lambda_0};$$

whence it follows in view of § 31 that the solution $x_1(\lambda)$ of the operational equation

$$x''(\lambda)-a^2sx(\lambda)=-a^2(\lambda_0-\lambda) \tag{33.1}$$

satisfying the conditions

$$x_1(0)=0, \quad x_1(\lambda_0)=0 \tag{33.2}$$

is given by the function

$$x_1(\lambda)=\frac{2\lambda_0}{\pi}\sum_{n=1}^{\infty}\frac{1}{n(s+n^2\beta^2)}\sin\frac{n\pi\lambda}{\lambda_0} \qquad \left(\beta=\frac{\pi}{a\lambda_0}\right). \tag{33.3}$$

It can easily be observed that the function

$$x_2(\lambda)=(\lambda_0-\lambda)/s \tag{33.4}$$

also satisfies equation (33.1), but instead of (33.2) it satisfies the conditions

$$x_2(0)=\lambda_0/s \quad \text{and} \quad x_2(\lambda_0)=0.$$

Hence it follows that the function $x(\lambda) = [x_2(\lambda) - x_1(\lambda)]/\lambda_0$ satisfies the homogeneous equation

$$x''(\lambda) - a^2 s x(\lambda) = 0$$

with the conditions

$$x(0) = 1/s \quad \text{and} \quad x(\lambda_0) = 0.$$

The latter problem, however, has already been solved in § 26 and the solution $G(\lambda)$ obtained there has been shown to be unique. It follows hence that $G(\lambda) = x(\lambda)$. By formulas (33.3) and (33.4) we obtain a different expansion for $G(\lambda)$ from that obtained in § 26:

$$G(\lambda) = \frac{1}{s}\left(1 - \frac{\lambda}{\lambda_0}\right) - \frac{2}{\pi}\sum_{n=1}^{\infty} \frac{1}{n(s+n^2\beta^2)} \sin\frac{n\pi\lambda}{\lambda_0}.$$

Consequently we also have

$$G(\lambda, t) = 1 - \frac{\lambda}{\lambda_0} - \frac{2}{\pi}\sum_{n=1}^{\infty} \frac{1}{n} \exp\left(-\frac{n^2\pi^2 t}{a^2\lambda_0^2}\right) \sin\frac{n\pi\lambda}{\lambda_0}; \tag{33.5}$$

this formula is suitable for practical calculation particularly in case of large t, the series converging then very rapidly. For t close to zero formula (26.1) is more convenient.

§ 34. A bar insulated at one end. If the initial distribution of temperature in the bar is given by the function

$$x(\lambda, 0) = \sin\frac{(n-\frac{1}{2})\pi\lambda}{\lambda_0} \qquad (0 < \lambda < \lambda_0,\ n \text{ being an integer}),$$

then the operational equation has the form

$$x''(\lambda) - a^2 s x(\lambda) = -a^2 \sin\frac{(n-\frac{1}{2})\pi\lambda}{\lambda_0}. \tag{34.1}$$

Seeking the solution of the form

$$x(\lambda) = c \sin\frac{(n-\frac{1}{2})\pi\lambda}{\lambda_0},$$

we substitute this expression in (34.1) and divide the equality obtained by $-\sin\frac{(n-\frac{1}{2})\pi\lambda}{\lambda_0}$. We thus obtain

$$c\frac{(n-\frac{1}{2})^2\pi^2}{\lambda_0^2} + ca^2 s = a^2,$$

whence $c = \dfrac{1}{s+(n-\frac{1}{2})^2\beta^2}$ where $\beta = \dfrac{\pi}{a\lambda_0}$. The required solution thus has the form

$$x(\lambda) = \frac{1}{s+(n-\frac{1}{2})^2\beta^2} \sin\frac{(n-\frac{1}{2})\pi\lambda}{\lambda_0};$$

it satisfies the boundary conditions

$$x(0) = 0 \quad \text{and} \quad x'(\lambda_0) = 0. \tag{34.2}$$

Let us now solve the same problem assuming the initial distribution of temperature in the bar to be given arbitrarily,

$$x(\lambda, 0) = \varphi(\lambda) \qquad (0 \leqslant \lambda \leqslant \lambda_0);$$

as regards the function $\varphi(\lambda)$ we shall only assume that it is continuous in the interval $[0, \lambda_0]$ and that it can be expanded inside that interval in the series

$$\varphi(\lambda) = \sum_{n=1}^{\infty} \mu_n \sin\frac{(n-\frac{1}{2})\pi\lambda}{\lambda_0} \qquad (0 < \lambda < \lambda_0),$$

which uniformly tends to $\varphi(\lambda)$ in every closed interval $[\lambda_1, \lambda_2]$ contained in $(0, \lambda_0)$.

The operational equation has the form

$$x''(\lambda) - a^2 s x(\lambda) = -a^2\varphi(\lambda).$$

If the boundary conditions are left unchanged, the solution will have the form of an infinite series,

$$x(\lambda) = \sum_{n=1}^{\infty} \frac{\mu}{s+(n-\frac{1}{2})^2\beta^2} \sin\frac{(n-\frac{1}{2})\pi\lambda}{\lambda_0},$$

and in ordinary notation

$$x(\lambda, t) = \sum_{n=1}^{\infty} \mu_n \exp\left(-\frac{(n-\frac{1}{2})^2\pi^2}{a^2\lambda^2} t\right) \sin\frac{(n-\frac{1}{2})\pi\lambda}{\lambda_0};$$

we can examine the convergence of this series and its derivatives by the same method as that used in § 33.

By formula (30.5) and (30.6) we have

$$1 = \frac{1}{\lambda_0}\varphi_3\left(\frac{\lambda}{2}\right) = \frac{2}{\pi}\sum_{n=1}^{\infty} \frac{1}{n-\frac{1}{2}} \sin\frac{(n-\frac{1}{2})\pi\lambda}{\lambda_0} \qquad (0 < \lambda < 2\lambda_0);$$

this series is uniformly convergent in every closed interval contained in $(0, 2\lambda_0)$.

Consequently the solution of the equation

$$x''(\lambda)-a^2 s x(\lambda) = -\frac{a}{s}-a^2, \tag{34.3}$$

satisfying conditions (34.2) has in the interval $0<\lambda\leqslant\lambda_0$ the form

$$x_1(\lambda)=\frac{2}{\pi}\sum_{n=1}^{\infty}\frac{1}{n-\frac{1}{2}}\,\frac{1}{s+(n-\frac{1}{2})^2\beta^2}\sin\frac{(n-\frac{1}{2})\pi\lambda}{\lambda_0}.$$

On the other hand, the function

$$x_2(\lambda)=1/s$$

satisfies also the differential equation (34.3) but with different boundary conditions, namely

$$x_2(0)=1/s \quad \text{and} \quad x_2'(\lambda_0)=0.$$

Hence it follows that the function $x(\lambda)=x_2(\lambda)-x_1(\lambda)$, *i. e.*, the function

$$x(\lambda)=\frac{1}{s}-\frac{2}{\pi}\sum_{n=1}^{\infty}\frac{1}{n-\frac{1}{2}}\,\frac{1}{s+(n-\frac{1}{2})^2\beta^2}\sin\frac{(n-\frac{1}{2})\pi\lambda}{\lambda_0} \tag{34.4}$$

satisfies the homogeneous equation

$$x''(\lambda)-a^2 s x(\lambda)=0 \tag{34.5}$$

with the conditions

$$x(0)=1/s \quad \text{and} \quad x'(\lambda_0)=0.$$

Writing (34.4) in the ordinary, non-operational form, we have

$$x(\lambda,t)=1-\frac{2}{\pi}\sum_{n=1}^{\infty}\frac{1}{n-\frac{1}{2}}\exp\left(-\frac{(n-\frac{1}{2})^2\pi^2}{a^2\lambda^2}t\right)\sin\frac{(n-\frac{1}{2})\pi\lambda}{\lambda_0};$$

this function represents the changes of temperature in a bar which at the instant $t=0$ had temperature 0 everywhere, with one end of the bar, say $\lambda=0$, constantly heated up to a temperature 1 and the other end, $\lambda=\lambda_0$, insulated. It can be seen that after a long lapse of time the temperature of the whole bar very slightly differs from 1.

Exercises.

1. Show that the function

$$X(\lambda)=svx(\lambda), \tag{34.6}$$

where $x(\lambda)$ is defined by formula (34.4), satisfies equation (34.5) with the boundary conditions

$$x(0)=v, \quad x'(\lambda_0)=0.$$

Give the physical interpretation.

2. Write the function (34.6) in the ordinary, non-operational form.

§ 35. Heat inflow regulated at one end. Suppose now that the initial distribution of temperature in the bar is given by the function

$$x(\lambda, 0) = \cos\frac{(n-\frac{1}{2})\pi\lambda}{\lambda_0} \qquad (0 < \lambda < \lambda_0,\ n \text{ being an integer});$$

we then have the operational equation

$$x''(\lambda) - a^2 s x(\lambda) = -a^2 \cos\frac{(n-\frac{1}{2})\pi\lambda}{\lambda_0}.$$

As before, we can see that the function

$$x(\lambda) = \frac{1}{s+(n-\frac{1}{2})^2\beta^2}\cos\frac{(n-\frac{1}{2})\pi\lambda}{\lambda_0}$$

is a solution of this equation such that

(35.1) $$x'(0) = 0 \quad\text{and}\quad x(\lambda_0) = 0.$$

With the same boundary conditions (35.1) we shall now solve the equation

(35.2) $$x''(\lambda) - a^2 s x(\lambda) = -a^2(\lambda_0 - \lambda).$$

Replacing in formula (30.9) λ by $\frac{1}{2}\lambda$ we have

$$\frac{1}{4}\sum_{n=1}^{\infty}\frac{1}{(n-\frac{1}{2})^2}\cos\frac{(n-\frac{1}{2})\pi\lambda}{\lambda_0} = \frac{\pi^2}{8}\left(1-\frac{\lambda}{\lambda_0}\right),$$

whence

$$\lambda_0 - \lambda = \frac{2\lambda_0}{\pi^2}\sum_{n=1}^{\infty}\frac{1}{(n-\frac{1}{2})^2}\cos\frac{(n-\frac{1}{2})\pi\lambda}{\lambda_0};$$

consequently the solution can be written in the form of the infinite series

$$x_1(\lambda) = \frac{2\lambda_0}{\pi^2}\sum_{n=1}^{\infty}\frac{1}{(n-\frac{1}{2})^2}\,\frac{1}{s+(n-\frac{1}{2})^2\beta^2}\cos\frac{(n-\frac{1}{2})\pi\lambda}{\lambda_0} \qquad (0 \leqslant \lambda \leqslant \lambda_0).$$

On the other hand, the function

$$x_2(\lambda) = \frac{\lambda_0 - \lambda}{s}$$

satisfies the differential equation (35.2) with the conditions

$$x_2'(0) = -1/s \quad\text{and}\quad x_2(\lambda_0) = 0.$$

It follows hence that the function $x(\lambda) = x_2(\lambda) - x_1(\lambda)$, *i. e.*, the function

(35.3) $$x(\lambda) = \frac{\lambda_0 - \lambda}{s} - \frac{2\lambda_0}{\pi^2} \sum_{n=1}^{\infty} \frac{1}{(n-\frac{1}{2})^2} \frac{1}{s + (n-\frac{1}{2})^2 \beta^2} \cos \frac{(n-\frac{1}{2})\pi\lambda}{\lambda_0}$$

satisfies the homogeneous equation

(35.4) $$x''(\lambda) - a^2 s x(\lambda) = 0$$

with the boundary conditions

$$x'(0) = -1/s, \quad x(\lambda_0) = 0.$$

Writing function (35.3) in the ordinary, non-operational form, we have

$$x(\lambda, t) = \lambda_0 - \lambda - \frac{2\lambda_0}{\pi^2} \sum_{n=1}^{\infty} \frac{1}{(n-\frac{1}{2})^2} \exp\left(-\frac{(n-\frac{1}{2})^2\pi^2}{a^2\lambda_0^2}\right) \cos \frac{(n-\frac{1}{2})\pi\lambda}{\lambda_0}.$$

This function represents the changes of temperature in a bar in which the inflow of heat through the point $\lambda = 0$ is constantly regulated in such a way that it is equal to 1:

$$-\left[\frac{\partial}{\partial\lambda} x(\lambda, t)\right]_{\lambda=0} = 1,$$

while the end $\lambda = \lambda_0$ is constantly kept at temperature 0; at the instant $t = 0$ the whole bar has temperature 0.

Exercise.

1. Show that the function

(35.5) $$X(\lambda) = -svx(\lambda),$$

where $x(\lambda)$ is defined by formula (35.3), satisfies equation (35.4) with the boundary conditions

$$X'(0) = v, \quad X(\lambda_0) = 0.$$

Give the physical interpretation.

2. Write function (35.5) in the ordinary, non-operational form.

§ 36. A heat-conducting ring. We shall now investigate the changes of temperature in a heat-conducting ring, being given the distribution of temperature at the instant $t = 0$. It will be assumed that there is no external inflow or outflow of heat.

If the length of the ring is λ_0, we can regard it in calculation as a bar whose length is λ_0 and consider the equation

(36.1) $$x''(\lambda) - a^2 s x(\lambda) = -a^2 \varphi(\lambda),$$

where the function $\varphi(\lambda)$, defined in the interval $[0, \lambda_0]$, represents the initial distribution of temperature.

Suppose that the function $\varphi(\lambda)$ expands in the trigonometric series

$$\varphi(\lambda) = \frac{\alpha_0}{2} + \sum_{n=1}^{\infty} \left(\alpha_n \cos \frac{2n\pi\lambda}{\lambda_0} + \beta_n \sin \frac{2n\pi\lambda}{\lambda_0} \right)$$

uniformly convergent in the interval $[0, \lambda_0]$.

Seeking a solution also in the form of a trigonometric series,

$$x(\lambda) = \frac{a_0}{0} + \sum_{n=1}^{\infty} \left(a_n \cos \frac{2n\pi\lambda}{\lambda_0} + b_n \sin \frac{2n\pi\lambda}{\lambda_0} \right),$$

we obtain, by the same method as the one used in §§ 31 and 34,

$$a_n = \frac{\alpha_n}{s+4n^2\beta^2}, \quad b_n = \frac{\beta_n}{s+4n^2\beta^2} \quad \left(\beta = \frac{\pi}{a\lambda_0} \right).$$

Consequently the required solution has the form

$$x(\lambda) = \frac{\alpha_0}{2s} + \sum_{n=1}^{\infty} \frac{1}{s+4n^2\beta^2} \left(\alpha_n \cos \frac{2n\pi\lambda}{\lambda_0} + \beta_n \sin \frac{2n\pi\lambda}{\lambda_0} \right)$$

or in ordinary notation

$$x(\lambda, t) = \frac{\alpha_0}{2} + \sum_{n=1}^{\infty} \exp\left(-\frac{4n^2\pi^2}{a^2\lambda_0^2} t \right) \cdot \left(\alpha_n \cos \frac{2n\pi\lambda}{\lambda_0} + \beta_n \sin \frac{2n\pi\lambda}{\lambda_0} \right).$$

We shall prove that this solution is unique.

Indeed, for every solution the conditions of concordance must hold:

$$x(0) = x(\lambda_0), \quad x'(0) = x'(\lambda_0) \quad \text{and} \quad x''(0) = x''(\lambda_0);$$

consequently every solution can be continued periodically outside the interval $[0, \lambda_0]$. We shall thus limit ourselves to the discussion of periodical solutions of equation (36.1), assuming that the function $\varphi(\lambda)$ is periodic with the period λ_0.

Suppose that equation (36.1) has two periodic solutions, $x_1(\lambda)$ and $x_2(\lambda)$. Then the difference

$$x_0(\lambda) = x_1(\lambda) - x_2(\lambda)$$

satisfies the homogeneous equation

$$x''(\lambda) - a^2 s x(\lambda) = 0,$$

and consequently must have the form

$$x_0(\lambda) = c_1 e^{-a\lambda\sqrt{s}} + c_2 e^{a\lambda\sqrt{s}}.$$

But this difference is also a periodic function and in particular

$$x_0(0) = x_0(\lambda_0) = x_0(2\lambda_0),$$

i. e.,

$$(36.2) \qquad c_1 + c_2 = c_1 e^{-a\lambda_0\sqrt{s}} + c_2 e^{a\lambda_0\sqrt{s}} = c_1 e^{-2a\lambda_0\sqrt{s}} + c_2 e^{2a\lambda_0\sqrt{s}}.$$

Solving this system of equations we obtain

$$c_1 = c_2 = 0.$$

The solution of system (36.2) may be carried out conveniently with the aid of determinants by introducing an auxiliary unknown c_0 and writing

$$\begin{aligned} c_0 + c_1 \qquad\quad + c_2 \qquad\quad &= 0, \\ c_0 + c_1 e^{-a\lambda_0\sqrt{s}} + c_2 e^{a\lambda_0\sqrt{s}} &= 0, \\ c_0 + c_1 e^{-2a\lambda\sqrt{s}} + c_2 e^{2a\lambda_0\sqrt{s}} &= 0. \end{aligned}$$

The determinant

$$\begin{vmatrix} 1 & 1 & 1 \\ 1 & e^{-a\lambda_0\sqrt{s}} & e^{a\lambda_0\sqrt{s}} \\ 1 & e^{-2a\lambda_0\sqrt{s}} & e^{2a\lambda_0\sqrt{s}} \end{vmatrix} = (e^{a\lambda_0\sqrt{s}} - e^{-a\lambda_0\sqrt{s}})(e^{a\lambda_0\sqrt{s}} - 1)(e^{-a\lambda_0\sqrt{s}} - 1)$$

being different from zero, we must have $c_0 = c_1 = c_2 = 0$.

It follows hence that we have $x_0(\lambda) = 0$ identically, q. e. d.

§ 37. Operation T^a and its application. In certain cases we can simplify calculation by introducing an operation T^a, which is defined by the equality

$$T^a a = T^a\{a(t)\} = \{e^{at} a(t)\},$$

where α may be an arbitrary complex number and a an arbitrary function of class $\mathcal{K}$.

It can easily be seen that the operation T^a has the following properties:

$$(37.1) \qquad T^\alpha T^\beta a = T^{\alpha+\beta} a, \qquad T^\alpha(a+b) = T^\alpha a + T^\alpha b.$$

The second equality expresses the distributivity of the operation T^α with respect to addition. It is easy to prove that it has also the property of distributivity with respect to multiplication:

$$(37.2) \qquad T^\alpha(a \cdot b) = T^\alpha a \cdot T^\alpha b.$$

Indeed

$$T^a(a\cdot b) = \left\{e^{at}\int_0^t a(t-\tau)b(\tau)\,d\tau\right\} = \left\{\int_0^t e^{a(t-\tau)}a(t-\tau)\cdot e^{a\tau}b(\tau)\,d\tau\right\} = T^a a\cdot T^a b.$$

We generalize the operation T^a to arbitrary operators $a = p/q\ (p, q \in \mathcal{C})$, writing

$$T^a a = \frac{T^a p}{T^a q}.$$

It is easy to verify that properties (37.1) and (37.2) are retained for arbitrary operators a and b.

In particular we have for the numerical operator γ

$$T^a\gamma = \gamma,$$

since

$$T^a\gamma = T^a\frac{\{\gamma\}}{\{1\}} = \frac{\{e^{at}\gamma\}}{\{e^{at}\}} = \frac{\gamma\{e^{at}\}}{\{e^{at}\}} = \gamma;$$

moreover, by (37.2),

$$T^a(\gamma a) = \gamma T^a a,\qquad T^a\frac{1}{a} = \frac{1}{T^a a}.$$

For the differential operator s we have the formula

$$T^a s = s - a,$$

since

$$T^a s = T^a\frac{1}{\{1\}} = \frac{1}{\{e^{at}\}} = s - a.$$

By formula (37.2) we have $T^a s^2 = (T^a s)^2 = (s-a)^2$ and more generally $T^a s^n = (s-a)^n$. If $R(s)$ is an arbitrary rational expression of the operator s,

$$R(s) = \frac{\alpha_m s^m + \ldots + \alpha_0}{\beta_n s^n + \ldots + \beta_0},$$

then

(37.3) $$T^a R(s) = R(s-a).$$

In particular we have

$$\{e^{at}\cos\beta t\} = T^a\{\cos\beta t\} = T^a\frac{s}{s^2+\beta^2} = \frac{s-a}{(s-a)^2+\beta^2};$$

this formula has been deduced on different lines on p. 34.

It will also be observed that in view of the formula

$$\frac{1}{(s-\alpha)^{\lambda}} = \left\{e^{\alpha t}\cdot\frac{t^{\lambda-1}}{\Gamma(\lambda)}\right\} \qquad (\lambda > 0)$$

(see p. 112) we also have

$$\frac{1}{(s-\alpha)^{2}} = T^{\alpha}\frac{1}{s^{\lambda}}$$

and, in particular,

$$T^{\alpha}\sqrt{s} = \sqrt{s-\alpha}. \tag{37.4}$$

By formulas (37.2) and (37.4) we have for instance

$$T^{\alpha}\sqrt{s^2-\beta^2} = T^{\alpha}\sqrt{s-\beta}\,T^{\alpha}\sqrt{s+\beta} = \sqrt{(s-\alpha)-\beta}\sqrt{(s-\alpha)+\beta} = \sqrt{(s-\alpha)^2-\beta^2}$$

We shall also prove that if the function $f(\lambda)$ has an operational derivative continuous in a certain interval, then the function $T^{\alpha}f(\lambda)$ also has an operational derivative continuous in that interval and

$$[T^{\alpha}f(\lambda)]' = T^{\alpha}f'(\lambda). \tag{37.5}$$

Indeed, if $f(\lambda) = qf_1(\lambda)$, where $f_1(\lambda) = \{f_1(\lambda, t)\}$ is a parametric function with a continuous partial derivative with respect to λ, then

$$[T^{\alpha}f(\lambda)]' = [T^{\alpha}q\{e^{\alpha t}f_1(\lambda, t)\}]' = T^{\alpha}q\left\{e^{\alpha t}\frac{\partial\lambda}{\partial}f_1(\lambda, t)\right\}$$

$$= T^{\alpha}qT^{\alpha}\left\{\frac{\partial}{\partial\lambda}f_1(\lambda, t)\right\} = T^{\alpha}\left[q\left\{\frac{\partial}{\partial\lambda}f_1(\lambda, t)\right\}\right] = T^{\alpha}f'(\lambda).$$

From (37.5) and from the definition of exponential function follows the formula

$$T^{\alpha}e^{\lambda w} = e^{\lambda T^{\alpha}w}, \tag{37.6}$$

since

$$[T^{\alpha}e^{\lambda w}]' = T^{\alpha}(we^{\lambda w}) = T^{\alpha}wT^{\alpha}e^{\lambda w},$$

$$T^{\alpha}e^{0\cdot w} = T^{\alpha}1 = 1.$$

Formulas (37.3) and (37.4) are easy to remember if we observe that the performance of the operation T^{α} brings about the replacement of the operator s by $s-\alpha$.

Making use of the formulas deduced we can easily transform more complicated expressions, for instance

$$T^{-\gamma}\frac{e^{-\alpha\lambda\sqrt{s}} - e^{-\alpha(2\lambda_0-\lambda)\sqrt{s}}}{1-e^{-2\alpha\lambda_0\sqrt{s}}} = \frac{e^{-\alpha\lambda\sqrt{s-\gamma}} - e^{-\alpha(2\lambda_0-\lambda)\sqrt{s+\gamma}}}{1-e^{-2\alpha\lambda_0\sqrt{s+\gamma}}}.$$

By means of the operation T^a we shall prove some more formulas, which will be used later on.

To begin with, let us take the formulas

(37.7)
$$e^{-\lambda\sqrt{s-a}} = \left\{\frac{\lambda}{2\sqrt{\pi t^3}}\exp\left(at-\frac{\lambda^2}{4t}\right)\right\},$$
$$\frac{1}{\sqrt{s-a}}e^{-\lambda\sqrt{s-a}} = \left\{\frac{1}{\sqrt{\pi t}}\exp\left(at-\frac{\lambda^2}{4t}\right)\right\};$$

they result from the following simple calculation:

$$e^{-\lambda\sqrt{s-a}} = e^{-\lambda T^a\sqrt{s}} = T^a e^{-\lambda\sqrt{s}},$$
$$\frac{1}{\sqrt{s-a}}e^{-\lambda\sqrt{s-a}} = \frac{1}{T^a\sqrt{s}}e^{-\lambda T^a\sqrt{s}} = T^a\left(\frac{1}{\sqrt{s}}e^{-\lambda\sqrt{s}}\right).$$

We shall prove that for any complex α and any positive real β the following formulas hold:

(37.8)
$$\left\{\operatorname{erf}\left(\alpha\sqrt{t}+\frac{\beta}{\sqrt{t}}\right)\right\} = \frac{1}{s}e^{-2\alpha\beta}\left(\frac{\alpha}{\sqrt{s+\alpha^2}}-1\right)e^{-2\beta\sqrt{s+\alpha^2}}+\frac{1}{s},$$

(37.9)
$$\left\{\operatorname{erf}\left(\alpha\sqrt{t}-\frac{\beta}{\sqrt{t}}\right)\right\} = \frac{1}{s}e^{-2\alpha\beta}\left(\frac{\alpha}{\sqrt{s+\alpha^2}}+1\right)e^{-2\beta\sqrt{s+\alpha^2}}-\frac{1}{s}.$$

Indeed, writing

$$f(t) = \operatorname{erf}\left(\alpha\sqrt{t}+\frac{\beta}{\sqrt{t}}\right) = \frac{2}{\sqrt{\pi}}\int_0^{\alpha\sqrt{t}+\beta/\sqrt{t}} e^{-\tau^2}d\tau,$$

we have

$$f'(t) = e^{-2\alpha\beta}e^{-\alpha^2 t}\left(\frac{\alpha}{\sqrt{\pi t}}e^{-\beta^2/t}-\frac{\beta}{\sqrt{\pi t^3}}e^{-\beta^2/t}\right)$$

and

$$\{f'(t)\} = e^{-2\alpha\beta}T^{-\alpha^2}\left(\frac{\alpha}{\sqrt{s}}e^{-2\beta\sqrt{s}}-e^{-2\beta\sqrt{s}}\right) = e^{-2\alpha\beta}\left(\frac{\alpha}{\sqrt{s+\alpha^2}}-1\right)e^{-2\beta\sqrt{s+\alpha^2}}.$$

Hence follows formula (37.8) since $f(0+) = 1$.

Similarly, writing

$$g(t) = \operatorname{erf}\left(\alpha\sqrt{t}-\frac{\beta}{\sqrt{t}}\right) = \frac{2}{\sqrt{\pi}}\int_0^{\alpha\sqrt{t}-\beta/\sqrt{t}} e^{-\tau^2}d\tau,$$

we have

$$\{g'(t)\} = e^{2\alpha\beta}\left(\frac{\alpha}{\sqrt{s+\alpha^2}}+1\right)e^{-2\beta\sqrt{s+\alpha^2}},$$

whence follows formula (37.9) since $g(0+) = -1$.

From (37.8) and (37.9) easily follow the formulas

(37.10)
$$\frac{a}{s\sqrt{s+a^2}}e^{-2\beta\sqrt{s+a^2}} = \left\{\frac{1}{2}e^{-2a\beta}\operatorname{erf}\left(a\sqrt{t}-\frac{\beta}{\sqrt{t}}\right)+\frac{1}{2}e^{2a\beta}\operatorname{erf}\left(a\sqrt{t}+\frac{\beta}{\sqrt{t}}\right)-\operatorname{sh}2a\beta\right\},$$

(37.11)
$$\frac{1}{s}e^{-2\beta\sqrt{s+a^2}} = \left\{\frac{1}{2}e^{-2a\beta}\operatorname{erf}\left(a\sqrt{t}-\frac{\beta}{\sqrt{t}}\right)-\frac{1}{2}e^{2a\beta}\operatorname{erf}\left(a\sqrt{t}+\frac{\beta}{\sqrt{t}}\right)-\operatorname{ch}2a\beta\right\}.$$

Since
$$s-\sqrt{(s-a)^2+\beta^2} = a+T^a\left(s-\sqrt{s^2+\beta^2}\right),$$
by (11.3) and (11.4) we have

(37.12)
$$\exp\lambda\left(s-\sqrt{(s-a)^2+\beta^2}\right) = e^{a\lambda}-\left\{\frac{\lambda}{\sqrt{t^2+2\lambda t}}e^{a(\lambda+t)}\beta J_1\left(\beta\sqrt{t^2+2\lambda t}\right)\right\},$$
$$\frac{\exp\lambda\left(s-\sqrt{s^2+2as}\right)}{\sqrt{(s-a)^2+\beta^2}} = \left\{e^{a(\lambda+t)}J_0\left(\beta\sqrt{t^2+2\lambda t}\right)\right\}.$$

Replacing in formulas (37.12) a by β and β by ia, we have

(37.13)
$$\exp\lambda\left(s-\sqrt{s^2+2as}\right) = e^{-a\lambda}-\left\{\frac{\lambda}{\sqrt{t^2+2\lambda t}}e^{-a(\lambda+t)}iaJ_1\left(ia\sqrt{t^2+2\lambda t}\right)\right\}$$
$$\frac{\exp\lambda\left(s-\sqrt{s^2+2as}\right)}{\sqrt{s^2+2as}} = \left\{e^{-a(\lambda+t)}J_0\left(i\beta\sqrt{t^2+2\lambda t}\right)\right\}.$$

Multiplying expressions (37.12) and (37.13) by $e^{-\lambda s}$, we obtain the formulas

$$\exp\left(-\lambda\sqrt{(s-a)^2+\beta^2}\right) = e^{a\lambda}e^{-\lambda s}-\left\{\begin{matrix} 0 & \text{for} & 0\leqslant t<\lambda \\ \dfrac{\lambda}{\sqrt{t^2-\lambda^2}}e^{at}\beta J_1\left(\beta\sqrt{t^2-\lambda^2}\right) & \text{for} & 0\leqslant\lambda<t\end{matrix}\right\},$$

$$\frac{\exp\left(-\lambda\sqrt{(s-a)^2+\beta^2}\right)}{\sqrt{(s-a)^2+\beta^2}} = \left\{\begin{matrix} 0 & \text{for} & 0\leqslant t<\lambda \\ e^{at}J_0\left(\beta\sqrt{t^2-\lambda^2}\right) & \text{for} & 0\leqslant\lambda<t\end{matrix}\right\},$$

$$\exp\left(-\lambda\sqrt{s^2+2as}\right. = e^{a\lambda}e^{-\lambda s}-\left\{\begin{matrix} 0 & \text{for} & 0\leqslant t<\lambda \\ e^{at}J_0\left(ia\sqrt{t^2-\lambda^2}\right) & \text{for} & 0\leqslant\lambda<t\end{matrix}\right\},$$

$$\frac{\exp\left(-\lambda\sqrt{s^2+2as}\right)}{\sqrt{s^2+2as}} = \left\{\begin{matrix} 0 & \text{for} & 0\leqslant t<\lambda \\ e^{-at}J_0\left(ia\sqrt{t^2-\lambda^2}\right) & \text{for} & 0\leqslant\lambda<t\end{matrix}\right\}.$$

Exercise. Prove the formulas

(α) $T^{-1}\sqrt{s^2-3s+2} = \sqrt{s^2-s}$; (β) $T^1\sqrt{s^2+s+1} = \sqrt{s^2-s+1}$;

(γ) $T^a\sqrt[3]{s^3-1} = \sqrt[3]{(s-a)^3-1}$.

(Hint. Decompose the polynomials under the radical sign into linear components).

§ 38. Non-insulated heat conductor. In §§ 25-36 we dealt with heat conductibility in a bar or a ring under the assumption of its perfect insulation from environment. Now we shall assume that the bar is not insulated and that the loss of heat at each point of the bar is proportional to the difference of temperatures between the bar and the environment. We shall assume moreover that the temperature of the environment is equal to 0. We shall then have the equation

$$x_{\lambda\lambda}(\lambda, t) - a^2 x_t(\lambda, t) - \beta x(\lambda, t) = 0,$$

where β is a suitably chosen coefficient. Suppose also that at the instant $t = 0$ the temperature of the bar is equal to 0. Then the operational equation has the form

(38.1) $$x''(\lambda) - (a^2 s + \beta) x(\lambda) = 0.$$

Finally, suppose that the initial point of the bar $\lambda = 0$ is kept at temperature $v = \{v(t)\}$ and its end point at temperature 0; this is expressed by the boundary conditions

(38.2) $$x(0) = v \quad \text{and} \quad x(\lambda_0) = 0.$$

In order to solve the problem we seek exponential functions satisfying equation (38.1). Substituting e^w in equation (38.1) and dividing by e^w we obtain

$$w^2 - (a^2 s + \beta) = 0,$$

whence

$$w = -a\sqrt{s+\gamma} \quad \text{or} \quad w = a\sqrt{s+\gamma},$$

where $\gamma = \beta/a^2$.

Thus there exist two exponential functions,

$$e^{-a\lambda\sqrt{s+\gamma}} \quad \text{and} \quad e^{a\lambda\sqrt{s+\gamma}},$$

satisfying equation (38.1). Hence it follows that the expression

$$x(\lambda) = c_1 e^{-a\lambda\sqrt{s+\gamma}} + c_2 e^{a\lambda\sqrt{s+\gamma}}$$

is the general solution of equation (38.1). Adapting it to conditions (38.2) we obtain, as in § 25,

$$x(\lambda) = \frac{\left(e^{-a\lambda\sqrt{s+\gamma}} - e^{-a(2\lambda_0-\lambda)\sqrt{s+\gamma}}\right)v}{1 - e^{-a\lambda_0 2\sqrt{s+\gamma}}}.$$

Using the notation of § 37 we can write

$$T^{\gamma}x(\lambda) = \frac{(e^{-\alpha\lambda s} - e^{-\alpha(2\lambda_0-\lambda)\sqrt{s}})v_0}{1 - e^{-2\alpha\lambda_0\sqrt{s}}},$$

where

$$v_0 = T^{\gamma}v.$$

Obviously the operational function $y(\lambda) = T^{\gamma}x(\lambda)$ has the same form as function (25.8) on p. 223. We could have foreseen it in view of

$$y''(\lambda) = \alpha^2 s y(\lambda)$$

and

$$y(0) = v_0, \quad y(\lambda_0) = 0.$$

When the bar is very long, it can be assumed, as in § 28, that

$$y(\lambda) = v_0 e^{-\alpha\lambda\sqrt{s}}$$

and consequently that

$$x(\lambda) = ve^{-\alpha\lambda\sqrt{s+\gamma}}. \tag{38.3}$$

Hence in the ordinary form we have the formula

$$x(\lambda, t) = \frac{\alpha\lambda}{2\sqrt{\pi}}\int_0^t v(t-\tau)\tau^{-3/2}\exp\left(-\frac{\beta\tau}{\alpha^2} - \frac{\alpha^2\lambda^2}{4\tau}\right)d\tau.$$

In particular if the function v is constant,

$$v = \omega/s,$$

solution (38.3) can be written in the form

$$x(\lambda) = \omega e^{-\alpha\lambda\sqrt{s+\gamma}}/s$$

or, by formula (37.11),

$$x(\lambda, t) = \frac{\omega}{2}\left[e^{-\lambda\sqrt{\beta}}\operatorname{erf}\left(\frac{\sqrt{\beta t}}{\alpha} - \frac{\alpha\lambda}{2\sqrt{t}}\right) - e^{\lambda\sqrt{\beta}}\operatorname{erf}\left(\frac{\sqrt{\beta t}}{\alpha} + \frac{\alpha\lambda}{2\sqrt{t}}\right) - 2\operatorname{ch}2\lambda\sqrt{\beta}\right].$$

This form of the solution is convenient in view of the possibility of using the tables of the erf function.

CHAPTER VI

THE EQUATION OF TELEGRAPHY

§ 39. The general form of the equation of telegraphy. The theory of electrical circuits which was discussed in Chapter V of Part I, concerns so called *short lines*. In the case of *long lines* (for instance telegraphic lines) the finite velocity of current transmission must be taken into account, which brings us to the consideration of partial differential equations, *i. e.*, in the operational treatment, to operational differential equations.

Let us imagine an electric cable consisting of two parallel wires stretched along the axis λ. Denote by $U(\lambda, t)$ and $I(\lambda, t)$ the voltage and the current at a point of the cable with the coordinate λ at the instant t. The following relations hold between the functions U and I:

$$U_\lambda = -LI_t - RI, \quad I_\lambda = -CU_t - GU, \tag{39.1}$$

where R denotes resistance, G — leak-conductance, L — self-induction and C — capacity; these quantities are measured on the unit of length of the cable.

Suppose also that at the instant $t = 0$ no current flows through the cable and the voltage is everywhere equal to zero:

$$U(\lambda, 0) = 0, \quad I(\lambda, 0) = 0.$$

Equations (39.1) then have the following operational form:

$$U'(\lambda) = -(Ls+R)I(\lambda), \tag{39.2}$$

$$I'(\lambda) = -(Cs+G)U(\lambda). \tag{39.3}$$

Differentiating (39.2) with respect to λ we obtain

$$U''(\lambda) = -(Ls+R)I'(\lambda)$$

and, by (39.3),

$$U''(\lambda) = (Ls+R)(Cs+G)U(\lambda);$$

this is the *equation of telegraphy* in the operational form. Performing the multiplication and carrying over all the terms to the left side, we can write

$$U''(\lambda) - [LCs^2 + (RC+LG)s + RG]U(\lambda) = 0.$$

Eliminating $U(\lambda)$ from (39.2) and (39.3) we easily verify that the function $I(\lambda)$ satisfies the same equation,

$$I''(\lambda) - [LCs^2 + (RC+LG)s + RG]I(\lambda) = 0.$$

To begin with, let us discuss this equation for certain particular cases.

§ 40. Conductance without loss. Conductance never takes place without losses. They are due to the resistance R and the leak-conductance G of the current. However, if the quantities R and G are small, self-induction i and capacity C being large, we can assume approximately that

$$R = 0 \quad \text{and} \quad G = 0.$$

The equation of telegraphy is then reduced to the form

$$U''(\lambda) - LCs^2 U(\lambda) = 0 \qquad (L > 0,\ C > 0).$$

If we assume that the cable is very long and that an electromotive force $E = \{E(t)\}$ is applied at its initial point,

$$U(0) = E,$$

then the mathematical problem is the same as in the case of an infinitely long vibrating string. Consequently, in view of § 18, we can at once write the solution, assuming that $a^2 = LC$,

$$U(\lambda) = E\exp(-\lambda s\sqrt{LC}),$$

i. e.,

$$U(\lambda, t) = \begin{cases} 0 & \text{for} \quad 0 \leqslant t < \lambda\sqrt{LC}, \\ E(t - \lambda\sqrt{LC}) & \text{for} \quad 0 \leqslant \lambda\sqrt{LC} < t. \end{cases}$$

In the case under consideration the voltage wave moves with the velocity $1/\sqrt{LC}$.

It is also easy to determine the current intensity since by (39.2) we have

$$I(\lambda) = -\frac{1}{Ls}U'(\lambda) = \sqrt{\frac{C}{L}}E\exp(-\sqrt{LC}\,\lambda s),$$

i. e.,

$$I(\lambda, t) = \begin{cases} 0 & \text{for} \quad 0 \leqslant t < \lambda\sqrt{LC}, \\ \sqrt{\dfrac{C}{L}}E(t - \lambda\sqrt{LC}) & \text{for} \quad 0 \leqslant \lambda\sqrt{LC} < t. \end{cases}$$

§ 41. Conductance without deformation. Heaviside was the first to point out that in the more general case

$$\frac{R}{L} = \frac{G}{L} \qquad (L > 0, \ C > 0)$$

the voltage and the current are transferred in the same way as in the case of conductance without loss, the only difference being the fact that the wave amplitude is exponentially damped as the wave moves forward.

Indeed, in that case the equation of telegraphy has the form

$$U''(\lambda) - (as+\beta)^2 U(\lambda) = 0 \qquad \left(a = \sqrt{LC}, \ \beta = \sqrt{RG}\right).$$

Seeking exponential functions $e^{\lambda w}$ satisfying this equation we obtain the equality

$$w^2 - (as+\beta)^2 = 0,$$

whence

$$w = -as - \beta \quad \text{or} \quad w = as + \beta.$$

Thus there exist two such functions,

$$e^{-(as+\beta)\lambda} \quad \text{and} \quad e^{(as+\beta)\lambda},$$

whence we have the general solution

$$U(\lambda) = c_1 e^{-(as+\beta)\lambda} + c_2 e^{(as+\beta)\lambda}.$$

If we assume that $U(\lambda)$ is a parametric function for any $\lambda \geqslant 0$ and that $U(0) = E$, then, as in § 18, we obtain the formula

$$U(\lambda) = Ee^{-(as+\beta)\lambda}.$$

This solution can also be found by considering that the function

$$V(\lambda) = T^{\gamma} U(\lambda) \qquad (\gamma = \beta/a)$$

satisfies the equation

$$V''(\lambda) - a^2 s^2 V(\lambda) = 0$$

and the equation

$$V(0) = T^{\gamma} E.$$

Thus the problem is reduced to the one solved in the preceding section, and we have

$$V(\lambda) = T^{\gamma} Ee^{-a\lambda s},$$

whence

$$U(\lambda) = T^{-\gamma} V(\lambda) = ET^{-\gamma} e^{-a\lambda s} = Ee^{-(as+\beta)\lambda}.$$

Writing the solutions in the ordinary, non-operational form, we have

$$U(\lambda, t) = \begin{cases} 0 & \text{for} \quad 0 \leqslant t < \lambda\sqrt{LC}, \\ \exp(-\lambda\sqrt{RG})\cdot E(t-\lambda\sqrt{LC}) & \text{for} \quad 0 \leqslant \lambda\sqrt{LC} < t, \end{cases}$$

and by (39.2)

$$I(\lambda) = -\frac{1}{Ls+R}U'(\lambda) = \frac{\alpha s+\beta}{Ls+R}e^{-(\alpha s+\alpha)\lambda} = \sqrt{\frac{C}{L}}e^{-(\alpha s+\beta)\lambda}E,$$

$$I(\lambda, t) = \begin{cases} 0 & \text{for} \quad 0 \leqslant t < \lambda\sqrt{LC}, \\ \sqrt{\dfrac{C}{L}}\exp(-\lambda\sqrt{RG})\cdot E(t-\lambda\sqrt{LC}) & \text{for} \quad 0 \leqslant \lambda\sqrt{LC} < t. \end{cases}$$

§ 42. The Thomson cable. With long telegraphic lines and low current frequency the importance of self-inductance L and leak-conductance G decreases and it can be assumed approximately that

$$L = 0 \quad \text{and} \quad G = 0 \quad (R > 0,\ C > 0).$$

Under these assumptions William Thomson (later Lord Kelvin) calculated, with sufficient accuracy for practical purposes, the propagation of current in a transoceanic cable.

In this case the equation of telegraphy is reduced to the form

$$T''(\lambda) = RCs\,U(\lambda),$$

and thus it is formally identical with the equation of heat; having assumed the line to be long, we can make use of the solution given in § 28. Assuming that

$$U(0) = E,$$

we shall thus have

$$U(\lambda) = Ee^{-\lambda\sqrt{RC}\sqrt{s}}$$

where $E = \{E(t)\}$ is the electromotive force at the initial point of the cable.

In particular if the electromotive force is constant,

$$E = \{E_0\},$$

then the solution has the form

$$U(\lambda) = \frac{E_0}{s}e^{-\lambda\sqrt{RC}\sqrt{s}},$$

i. e.,

$$U(\lambda, t) = E_0 \operatorname{cerf}\frac{\lambda}{2}\sqrt{\frac{RC}{t}}.$$

By (39.2) we have

$$I(\lambda) = -\frac{1}{R} U'(\lambda) = E_0 \sqrt{\frac{C}{R}} \cdot \frac{1}{\sqrt{s}} e^{-\lambda\sqrt{RC}\sqrt{s}},$$

i. e.,

$$I(\lambda, t) = E_0 \sqrt{\frac{C}{\pi R t}} \exp\left(-\frac{RC\lambda^2}{4t}\right).$$

§ 43. A cable without self-induction. Let us now consider the case where

$$L = 0 \quad (R > 0,\ C > 0,\ G > 0).$$

The equation of telegraphy then has the form

$$U''(\lambda) = (RCs + RG)\, U(\lambda);$$

assuming that the cable is very long and that the electromotive force at its initial point is constant $E = \{E_0\}$, we shall have an analogical solution to that given in § 38:

$$U(\lambda) = \frac{E_0}{s} \exp(-\lambda\sqrt{RCs + RG}),$$

$$U(\lambda, t) = \frac{E_0}{2}\left[e^{-\lambda\sqrt{RG}} \operatorname{erf}\left(\sqrt{\frac{Gt}{C}} - \frac{\lambda}{2}\sqrt{\frac{RC}{t}}\right) - \right.$$

$$\left. - e^{\lambda\sqrt{RG}} \operatorname{erf}\left(\sqrt{\frac{Gt}{C}} + \frac{\lambda}{2}\sqrt{\frac{RC}{t}}\right) - 2\operatorname{ch}\lambda\sqrt{RG}\right].$$

By (39.2) we have

$$I(\lambda) = -\frac{1}{R} U'(\lambda) = \frac{E_0\sqrt{RCs + RG}}{Rs} \exp(-\lambda\sqrt{RCs + RG})$$

$$= E_0\left(\frac{C}{\sqrt{RCs + RG}} + \frac{G}{s\sqrt{RCs + RG}}\right) \exp(-\lambda\sqrt{RCs + RG});$$

whence by formulas (37.7) and (37.10)

$$I(\lambda, t) = \sqrt{\frac{C}{R}} \frac{E_0}{\sqrt{\pi t}} \exp\left(-\frac{Gt}{C} - \frac{RC\lambda^2}{4t}\right) +$$

$$+ \sqrt{\frac{G}{R}} \cdot \frac{E_0}{2}\left[e^{-\lambda\sqrt{RG}} \operatorname{erf}\left(\sqrt{\frac{Gt}{C}} - \frac{\lambda}{2}\sqrt{\frac{RC}{t}}\right) + \right.$$

$$\left. + e^{\lambda\sqrt{RG}} \operatorname{erf}\left(\sqrt{\frac{Gt}{C}} + \frac{\lambda}{2}\sqrt{\frac{RC}{t}}\right) - 2\operatorname{sh}\lambda\sqrt{RG}\right].$$

§ 44. A cable without leak-conductance. Next we shall consider the case where

$$G = 0 \quad (L > 0,\ C > 0,\ R > 0).$$

This case frequently occurs in practice because in a great many calculations the leakage of the current is so small that it can be disregarded.

Now the equation of telegraphy has the form

$$U''(\lambda) = (LCs^2 + RCs)\,U(\lambda), \tag{44.1}$$

of course under the assumption that at the instant $t = 0$ there is no voltage and no current on the line.

The general solution of this equation is the expression

$$U(\lambda) = c_1 e^{-\lambda\sqrt{LCs^2+RCs}} + c_2 e^{\lambda\sqrt{LCs^2+RCs}}.$$

If the solution is to be a parametric function in the interval $0 \leqslant \lambda < \infty$, we must have $c_2 = 0$. Indeed, we have

$$\sqrt{LCs^2+RCs} = s\sqrt{LC} + a$$

where $a = \sum_{n=0}^{\infty} \binom{\frac{1}{2}}{n} \left(\frac{R}{L}\right)^n l^n$ is an element of class $\mathcal{C}$; consequently we can write

$$e^{-a\lambda} U(\lambda) - c_1 e^{-\sqrt{LC}\lambda s} e^{-2\lambda a} = c_2 e^{\sqrt{LC}\lambda s}.$$

If $U(\lambda)$ is a parametric function in the interval $0 \leqslant \lambda < \infty$ then the expression on the left side of the equality is also a parametric function in that interval. And this implies that $c_2 = 0$ (see § 18).

Thus, assuming the telegraphic line to be long, we shall have a solution of the form

$$U(\lambda) = E \exp(-\lambda\sqrt{LCs^2+RCs}),$$

where $E = \{E(t)\}$ is the voltage at the initial point $\lambda = 0$ of the line in question.

Let us also discuss the case where the electromotive force is constant,

$$E = \{E_0\} = E_0/s.$$

Then the solution has the form

$$U(\lambda) = \frac{E_0}{s} \exp(-\lambda\sqrt{LCs^2+RCs}).$$

By (39.2) we can easily find the current,

$$I(\lambda) = -\frac{U'(\lambda)}{Ls+R} = \frac{E_0 C}{\sqrt{LCs^2+RCs}}\exp(-\lambda\sqrt{LCs^2+RCs}).$$

Hence, assuming that $a = \frac{1}{2}\sqrt{R/L}$ and using the formulas of § 38, we obtain for $0 \leqslant t < \sqrt{LC\lambda}$:

$$U(\lambda, t) = E_0\left(e^{-a\lambda\sqrt{LC}} - \frac{1}{2}\int\limits_{\sqrt{LC\lambda}}^{t}\frac{\sqrt{RC\lambda}}{\sqrt{\tau^2-LC\lambda^2}}e^{-a\tau}i\mathrm{J}_1(ia\sqrt{\tau^2-LC\lambda^2})\,d\tau\right),$$

$$I(\lambda, t) = E_0\sqrt{\frac{C}{L}}\,e^{-at}\mathrm{J}_0(ia\sqrt{t^2-LC\lambda^2}).$$

For $0 \leqslant t < \sqrt{LC}$ the two functions, $U(\lambda,t)$ and $I(\lambda,t)$, have the value 0.

Hence it can be seen that in the present case the current wave moves with velocity $1/\sqrt{LC}$. When the wave front reaches the point with the coordinate λ, the voltage and the current have the values

$$E_0\exp(-\tfrac{1}{2}\sqrt{R/L}\lambda) \quad\text{and}\quad E_0\sqrt{C/L}\exp(-\tfrac{1}{2}\sqrt{RC}\lambda)$$

respectively.

§ 45. The case where all the four conductance parameters are positive. Introducing the notation

$$a = \frac{1}{2}\left(\frac{R}{4}+\frac{G}{C}\right), \qquad \beta = \frac{1}{2}\left(\frac{R}{L}-\frac{G}{C}\right),$$

we can write the equation of telegraphy in the form

$$U''(\lambda)-LC[(s+a)^2-\beta^2]\,U(\lambda) = 0.$$

Hence the solution

$$U(\lambda) = c_1\exp(-\lambda\sqrt{LC}\sqrt{(s+a)^2-\beta^2})+c_2\exp(\lambda\sqrt{LC}\sqrt{(s+a)^2-\beta^2}).$$

If the line is very long, then, reasoning as in the preceding case, we can assume that $c_2 = 0$ and $c_1 = E$ (the electromotive force at the initial point of the cable). In particular if $E = \{E_0\} = E_0/s$, then

$$U(\lambda) = \frac{E_0}{s}\exp(-\lambda\sqrt{LC}\sqrt{(s+a)^2-\beta^2}).$$

By (39.2) we have

$$I(\lambda) = -\frac{U'(\lambda)}{Ls+R} = E_0\frac{\sqrt{LC}\sqrt{(s+a)^2-\beta^2}}{s(Ls+R)}\exp(-\lambda\sqrt{LC}\sqrt{(s+a)^2-\beta^2}$$

$$= E_0\sqrt{\frac{C}{R}}\left(1+\frac{G}{Cs}\right)\frac{\exp(-\lambda\sqrt{LC}\sqrt{(s+a)^2-\beta^2}}{(s+a)^2-\beta^2}.$$

Hence for $0 \leqslant t < \sqrt{LC}\lambda$ we have

$$U(\lambda, t) = E_0\left(e^{-a\lambda\sqrt{LC}} - \int\limits_{\sqrt{LC}\lambda}^{t} \frac{\lambda\sqrt{LC}}{\sqrt{\tau^2-\lambda^2 LC}}\, e^{-a\tau} i\beta \mathrm{J}_1(i\beta\sqrt{\tau^2-LC\lambda^2})\,d\tau\right),$$

$$I(\lambda, t) = E_0\sqrt{\frac{C}{L}}\left(e^{-at}\mathrm{J}_0(i\beta\sqrt{t^2-LC\lambda^2}) + \frac{G}{C}\int\limits_{\sqrt{LC}\lambda}^{t} e^{-a\tau}\mathrm{J}_0(i\beta\sqrt{\tau^2-LC\lambda^2})\,d\tau\right).$$

For $0 \leqslant t < \sqrt{LC}$ both functions, $U(\lambda, t)$ and $I(\lambda, t)$, have the value 0.

Obviously with the growth of λ the greater the number a the faster the voltage and the current decrease; that is why number a is called the *damping coefficient*. Number β is termed the *deformation coefficient*; we have seen in § 41 that if $\beta = 0$, the wave is only damped and not deformed at all.

CHAPTER VII

THE ALGEBRAIC DERIVATIVE

§ 46. Definition and properties. In § 37 we have defined the operation T^{a} (dependent on the parameter a), which, when applied to functions of class $\mathcal{K}$, involves the multiplication of their values by e^{at}. We shall now introduce an operation D (independent of any parameter), which, when applied to functions of class $\mathcal{K}$, involves the multiplication of their values by $-t$. Thus if $\{a = a(t)\} \in \mathcal{K}$, then

$$Da = D\{a(t)\} = \{-ta(t)\}.$$

If a and b belong to class $\mathcal{K}$, then

(46.1)
$$D(a+b) = Da+Db,$$
$$D(ab) = Da\cdot b + a\cdot Db.$$

Indeed,

$$D(a+b) = \{-t[a(t)+b(t)]\} = \{-ta(t)\}+\{-tb(t)\} = Da+Db,$$

$$D(ab) = \left\{-t\int_0^t a(t-\tau)b(\tau)\,d\tau\right\}$$

$$= \left\{\int_0^t (-t+\tau)a(t-\tau)b(\tau)\,d\tau + \int_0^t a(t-\tau)\cdot(-\tau)b(\tau)\,d\tau\right\}$$

$$= Da\cdot b + a\cdot Db.$$

Formulas (46.1) show that the operation D has the characteristic properties of a derivative. It will be termed the *algebraic derivative*.

We shall now extend the definition of algebraic derivative to any operators $a = p/q$ ($p, q \in \mathcal{C}$, $q \neq 0$) assuming that

$$D\left(\frac{p}{q}\right) = \frac{Dp\cdot q - p\cdot Dq}{q^2}.$$

It is easy to verify that the operation generalized in this manner retains properties (46.1), where a and b may be any operators.

For every numerical operator a we have the formula

$$Da = 0.$$

Indeed, we can write

$$a = \frac{\{a\}}{\{1\}};$$

consequently

$$Da = \frac{\{1\}\{-at\} - \{-t\}\{a\}}{\{1\}^2} = \frac{\left\{-\frac{at^2}{2}\right\} - \left\{-\frac{at^2}{2}\right\}}{\{1\}^2} = 0.$$

On account of the second formula of (46.1) we have so far

$$D(ab) = a \cdot Db \tag{46.2}$$

for every numerical operator a and any operator b.

Further, it follows that for any operators a and b we have

$$D(a-b) = Da - Db,$$

because

$$D(a-b) = D[a+(-1)b] = Da + (-1)Db = Da - Db.$$

We shall also prove that for any operators a and b ($b \neq 0$) we have the formula

$$D\left(\frac{a}{b}\right) = \frac{Da \cdot b - a \cdot Db}{b^2}. \tag{46.3}$$

Namely, writing $a = m/n$ and $b = p/q$ ($m, n, p, q \in \mathcal{C}$; $p, q \neq 0$), we have

$$D\left(\frac{a}{b}\right) = D\left(\frac{mq}{np}\right) = \frac{D(mq)np - mqD(np)}{n^2p^2}$$

$$= \frac{(Dm \cdot q + m \cdot Dq)np - mq(Dn \cdot p + n \cdot Dp)}{n^2p^2};$$

$$\frac{Da \cdot b - a \cdot Db}{b^2} = \frac{\frac{Dm \cdot n - m \cdot Dq}{n^2} \cdot \frac{p}{q} - \frac{m}{n} \cdot \frac{Dp \cdot q - p \cdot Dq}{q^2}}{\frac{p^2}{q^2}}$$

$$= \frac{(Dm \cdot n - m \cdot Dn)pq - mn(Dp \cdot q - p \cdot Dq)}{n^2p^2}.$$

Hence it is easy to obtain formula (46.3).

In particular we have

$$Ds = D\left(\frac{1}{\{1\}}\right) = \frac{D1 \cdot \{1\} - 1 \cdot D\{1\}}{\{1\}^2} = \frac{0 \cdot \{1\} - 1 \cdot \{-1\}}{\{1\}^2} = \frac{\{t\}}{\{t\}} = 1.$$

Thus the algebraic derivative of the differential operator is equal to number 1:

$$Ds = 1. \tag{46.4}$$

By the second formula of (46.1) we have

$$Ds^2 = Ds \cdot s + s \cdot Ds = 1 \cdot s + s \cdot 1 = 2s,$$

$$Ds^3 = D(s \cdot s^2) = Ds \cdot s^2 + s \cdot Ds^2 = 1 \cdot s^2 + s \cdot 2s = 3s^2,$$

and generally

$$Ds^n = ns^{n-1}$$

for every natural number n.

If

$$W = a_n s^n + \ldots + a_1 s + a_0,$$

then by formulas (46.2) and (46.4) we have

$$DW = na_n s^{n-1} + \ldots + a_1.$$

Thus it can be seen that the algebraic derivative of the polynomial of the differential operator s is found by formal differentiation of that polynomial with respect to s.

Similarly, the algebraic derivative of an arbitrary expression of the rational operator s

$$\frac{a_n s^n + \ldots + a_0}{\beta_n s^n + \ldots + \beta_0}$$

can be calculated by formal differentiation with respect to the operator s.

The algebraic derivative can also be termed the *derivative with respect to the operator* s and denoted by the symbol $\frac{d}{ds}$ instead of D. For instance

$$\frac{d}{ds}\frac{1}{s+\lambda} = -\frac{1}{(s+\lambda)^2}.$$

§ 47. Powers of the operator $1/(s^2+\beta^2)$. By means of the algebraic derivative we can easily deduce formulas for the powers of the operator $1/(s^2+\beta^2)$. Namely we have

$$\frac{d}{ds}\frac{s}{s^2+\beta^2} = \frac{2\beta^2}{(s^2+\beta^2)^2} - \frac{1}{s^2+\beta^2},$$

whence

$$\frac{1}{(s^2+\beta^2)^2} = \frac{1}{2\beta^2}\left(\frac{1}{s^2+\beta^2} + \frac{d}{ds}\frac{s}{s^2+\beta^2}\right),$$

i. e.,

$$(47.1) \qquad \frac{1}{(s^2+\beta^2)^2} = \left\{\frac{1}{2\beta^2}\left(\frac{1}{\beta}\sin\beta t - t\cos\beta t\right)\right\}.$$

Let us write generally for $n = 1, 2, \ldots$

$$(47.2) \qquad \frac{1}{(s^2+\beta^2)^n} = \left\{\frac{1}{(2\beta^2)^{n-1}}\left[A_n(\beta^2t^2)\frac{1}{\beta}\sin\beta t - B_n(\beta^2t^2)\cdot t\cos\beta^2\right]\right\}$$

where $A_n(x)$ and $B_n(x)$ are the functions to be determined. Since

$$\frac{1}{s^2+\beta^2} = \left\{\frac{1}{\beta}\sin\beta t\right\},$$

we have

$$(47.3) \qquad A_1(x) = 1, \quad B_1(x) = 0,$$

by (47.1) we have

$$(47.4) \qquad A_1(x) = 1, \quad B_2(x) = 1.$$

On the other hand, we have

$$\frac{d^2}{ds^2}\frac{1}{(s^2+\beta^2)^{n-1}} = \frac{2(2n-1)(n-1)}{(s^2+\beta^2)^n} - \frac{4\beta^2 n(n-1)}{(s^2+\beta^2)^{n+1}},$$

whence

$$\frac{1}{(s^2+\beta^2)^{n+1}} = \left\{\frac{2n-1}{2\beta^2 n}\frac{1}{(2\beta^2)^{n-1}}\cdot\left[A_n(\beta^2t^2)\frac{1}{\beta}\sin\beta t - B_n(\beta^2t^2)\cdot t\cos\beta t\right]\right\}$$

and by formula (47.2)

$$\frac{1}{(s^2+\beta^2)^{n+1}} = \left\{\frac{2n-1}{2\beta^2 n}\frac{1}{(2\beta^2)^{n-1}}\left[A_n(\beta^2t^2)\frac{1}{\beta}\sin\beta t - B_n(\beta^2t^2)\cdot t\cos\beta t\right]\right\} -$$

$$-\left\{\frac{t^2}{4\beta^2 n(n-1)}\frac{1}{(2\beta^2)^{n-2}}\left[A_{n-1}(\beta^2t^2)\frac{1}{\beta}\sin\beta t - B_{n-1}(\beta^2t^2)\cdot t\cos\beta t\right]\right\},$$

i. e.,

$$\frac{1}{(s^2+\beta^2)^{n+1}} = \left\{\frac{1}{(2\beta^2)^n}\left[\left(\frac{2n-1}{n}A_n(\beta^2t^2) - \frac{\beta^2t^2}{n(n-1)}A_{n-1}(\beta^2t^2)\right)\frac{1}{\beta}\sin\beta t -\right.\right.$$

$$\left.\left. -\left(\frac{2n-1}{n}B_n(\beta^2t^2) - \frac{\beta^2t^2}{n(n-1)}B_{n-1}(\beta^2t^2)\right)t\cos\beta t\right]\right\}.$$

By formula (47.2) we must have

$$\begin{aligned} A_{n+1}(x) &= \frac{2n-1}{n} A_n(x) - \frac{x}{n(n-1)} A_{n-1}(x), \\ B_{n+1}(x) &= \frac{2n-1}{n} B_n(x) - \frac{x}{n(n-1)} B_{n-1}(x), \end{aligned} \qquad (n = 2, 3, \ldots) \tag{47.5}$$

By formulas (47.3), (47.4) and (47.5) we can successively find the functions $A_3, A_4, \ldots$ and $B_3, B_4, \ldots$ Obviously they are all polynomials. Those polynomials, up to $n = 10$ inclusively, are listed in a table supplied at the end of the book.

Using that table and formula (47.2) we can, for instance, write at once

$$\frac{1}{(s^2+\beta^2)^4} = \left\{\frac{1}{(2\beta^2)^3}\left[\left(\frac{5}{2}-\beta^2t^2\right)\frac{1}{\beta}\sin\beta t - \frac{1}{2}\left(5-\frac{\beta^2t^2}{3}\right)t\cos\beta t\right]\right\}.$$

Finding the algebraic derivative from formula (47.2) we obtain for $n = 1, 2, \ldots$

$$-\frac{2ns}{(s^2+\beta^2)^{n+1}} = \left\{\frac{-t}{(2\beta^2)^{n-1}}\left[A_n(\beta^2t^2)\frac{1}{\beta}\sin\beta t - B_n(\beta^2t^2)\cdot t\cos\beta t\right]\right\},$$

whence, for $n = 2, 3, \ldots,$

$$\frac{s}{(s^2+\beta^2)^n} = \frac{1}{2(n-1)(2\beta^2)^{n-2}}\left[A_{n-1}(\beta^2t^2)\cdot\frac{t}{\beta}\sin\beta t - B_{n-1}(\beta^2t^2)t^2\cos\beta t\right]\Bigg\}. \tag{47.6}$$

Thus we have for instance

$$\frac{s}{(s^2+\beta^2)^4} = \left\{\frac{1}{48\beta^4}\left[(3-\beta^2t^2)\frac{t}{\beta}\sin\beta t - 3t^2\cos\beta t\right]\right\}.$$

Applying the operation T^a (see § 37) to formulas (47.2) and (47.6) we obtain more general formulas:

$$\frac{1}{[(s-a)^2+\beta^2]^n} = \left\{\frac{e^{at}}{(2\beta^2)^{n-1}}\left[A_n(\beta^2t^2)\cdot\frac{1}{\beta}\sin\beta t - B_n(\beta^2t^2)\cdot t\cos\beta t\right]\right\}$$

for $n = 1, 2, \ldots$ and

$$\frac{s}{[(s-a)^2+\beta^2]^n} = \left\{\frac{e^{at}}{2(n-1)(2\beta^2)^{n-2}}\left[A_{n-1}(\beta^2t^2)\cdot\frac{t}{\beta}\sin\beta t - B_{n-1}(\beta^2t^2)\cdot t^2\cos\beta t\right]\right\}$$

for $n = 2, 3, \ldots$

PART FOUR

AN OUTLINE OF THE GENERAL THEORY OF LINEAR DIFFERENTIAL EQUATIONS WITH CONSTANT COEFFICIENTS

CHAPTER I

HOMOGENEOUS EQUATIONS

§ 1. Introductory remarks. The equation of a vibrating string, the equation of heat and the equation of telegraphy are examples of linear differential equations with constant coefficients; they have the form

$$x'' - a^2 s^2 x = 0, \qquad x'' - asx = 0, \qquad x'' - (Ls+R)(Cs+G)x = 0.$$

Now we shall deal with more general equations:

$$a_m x^{(m)} + \ldots + a_0 x = f(\lambda); \tag{1.1}$$

the coefficients $a_m, \ldots, a_0$ ($a_m \neq 0$) may be arbitrary operators and $f(\lambda)$ an arbitrary continuous operational function; $x = x(\lambda)$ is an unknown operational function. In the particular case where the operators $a_m, \ldots, a_0$ are numbers and $f(\lambda)$ a numerical function, equation (1.1) may be regarded as an ordinary differential equation with constant coefficients; consequently the theory which we are going to outline here may be regarded as a generalization of the classical theory of such equations.

In Chapter I we shall discuss homogeneous equations, *i. e.*, equations in which the function $f(\lambda)$ is identically equal to zero.

§ 2. Characteristic equations. In order to solve the homogeneous equation

$$a_m x^{(m)} + \ldots + a_0 x = 0 \qquad (a_m \neq 0), \tag{2.1}$$

we first seek the solutions in the form of exponential functions $x = e^{\lambda u}$. Therefore we substitute in equation (2.1) $x = e^{\lambda u}$:

$$a_m u^m e^{\lambda u} + \ldots + a_0 e^{\lambda u} = 0;$$

the exponential function being different from zero for every λ, we can divide this equality by $e^{\lambda u}$. We thus obtain the equation

(2.2) $$a_m u^m + \ldots + a_0 = 0,$$

which is termed the *characteristic equation* of the differential equation (2.1). The polynomial

$$P(u) = a_m u^m + \ldots + a_0$$

will be termed the *characteristic polynomial.*

An equation of the form (2.2), where $a_m, \ldots, a_0$ are arbitrary operators, is not always solvable, *i. e.*, an operator u satisfying that equation does not always exist [1]. Considering differential equations we shall constantly assume that their characteristic equation has m roots, *i. e.*, as many as is their degree; these roots are not necessarily different from one another. To be more accurate, we shall constantly assume that the characteristic polynomial $P(u)$ is decomposable into m linear factors,

(2.3) $$P(u) = a_m \prod_{\mu=1}^{m} (u - w_\mu)$$

(a decomposition into such factors is always unique).

This assumption is felt to be justified in view of the fact that in all applications we deal with polynomials which can be effectively decomposed into factors. For instance in the case of the equation of heat, $x'' - a^2 s x = 0$, the characteristic polynomial $u^2 - a^2 s$ is decomposable into the factors $(u + a\sqrt{s})(u - a\sqrt{s})$.

§ 3. On exponential functions. Having obtained the roots $w_1, \ldots, w_m$ of the characteristic equation we must form the exponential functions $e^{\lambda w_\mu}$. This involves a new difficulty since such functions do not always exist. Namely, for certain operators w a function identically equal to zero may happen to be the only solution of the differential equation $x' = wx$; consequently the additional condition $x(0) = 1$, which should be satisfied by every exponential function, cannot be satisfied.

For instance there exists no exponential function $e^{i\lambda s}$ (for real λ). For if it existed, then for a suitably chosen operator $q \neq 0$ the function $y(\lambda) = q e^{i\lambda s}$ would be parametric,

$$y(\lambda) = \{y(\lambda, t)\}$$

in the interval $0 \leqslant \lambda \leqslant 1$ and would satisfy in it the equation $y'(\lambda) = isy(\lambda)$. Thus it would satisfy the equation $y''(\lambda) + s^2 y(\lambda) = 0$ or, which

(1) An example of an unsolvable equation is given in § 16 of Part II.

is the same, the function of two variables $y(\lambda, t)$ would satisfy the partial differential equation

$$(3.4) \qquad y_{\lambda\lambda}(\lambda, t) + y_{tt}(\lambda, t) = 0 \quad (0 \leqslant \lambda \leqslant 1,\ 0 \leqslant t < \infty)$$

with the initial conditions

$$(3.5) \qquad y(\lambda, 0) = 0, \quad y_t(\lambda, 0) = 0 \quad (0 \leqslant \lambda \leqslant 1).$$

The functions satisfying equation (3.4) are termed *harmonic functions*. It is known from the theory of those functions that if conditions (3.5) are satisfied, $y(\lambda, t)$ is identically equal to zero. Hence $e^{i\lambda s} = y(\lambda)/q = 0$ in the interval $[0, 1]$, which is impossible.

Thus an exponential function $e^{i\lambda s}$ does not exist. Consequently the symbol $e^{i\lambda s}$ has no meaning at all, just as for instance the symbol $\frac{1}{0}$. It would be wrong to say that the function $e^{i\lambda s}$ is identically equal to zero because the condition $x(0) = 1$ is inherent in the definition of every exponential function.

From the non-existence of $e^{i\lambda s}$ follows the non-existence of the function $e^{-i\lambda s}$. For if $e^{-i\lambda s}$ existed, the function $x(\lambda) = 1/e^{-i\lambda s}$ would satisfy the equation

$$x'(\lambda) = isx(\lambda)$$

with the condition $x(0) = 1$ and thus would be an exponential function $e^{i\lambda s}$.

If there exist exponential functions $e^{\lambda w_1}$ *and* $e^{\lambda w_2}$ (λ *being real*), *then there exists also an exponential function* $e^{\lambda(w_1+w_2)}$ *and is equal to the product* $e^{\lambda w_1} e^{\lambda w_2}$.

Indeed, writing $x(\lambda) = e^{\lambda w_1} e^{\lambda w_2}$ we have

$$x'(\lambda) = w_1 e^{\lambda w_1} \cdot e^{\lambda w_2} + e^{\lambda w_1} \cdot w_2 e^{\lambda w_2} = (w_1 + w_2) e^{\lambda w_1} \cdot e^{\lambda w_2}$$

and $x(0) = 1 \cdot 1 = 1$, which proves the theorem.

If there exists an exponential function $e^{\lambda w}$ (λ *being real*) *then for every real* a *the function* $e^{\lambda a w}$ *is also exponential.*

This follows immediately from the formula for the differentiation of a composed function.

It follows from the above two theorems that *if there exist exponential functions* $e^{\lambda w_1}$ *and* $e^{\lambda w_2}$, *then for any real* a_1 *and* a_2 *the exponential function* $e^{\lambda(a_1 w_1 + a_2 w_2)}$ *also exists.*

Remark. We might try to find such a generalization of the notion of operators that would make the exponential function $e^{\lambda w}$ always existent. However, the very fact of non-existence of certain exponential functions is advantageous from the practical point of view: it enables us, for instance, to classify partial equations in a manner that facilitates the choice of solving methods for them.

§ 4. Logarithms. The operators w for which the exponential function $e^{\lambda w}$ exists will be termed *logarithmic*. For example the operators a and $\sqrt{s}$ are logaritmic, while the operator is is not. Every complex number is logarithmic.

The theorems given in the preceding section imply that *if w_1 and w_2 are logarithmic and a_1 and a_2 arbitrary real numbers, then the operator $a_1 w_1 + a_2 w_2$ is also logarithmic.*

For instance the operators

$$i+\sqrt{s}, \qquad 2s-3\sqrt{s}$$

are logarithmic.

If w_1 is logarithmic and w_2 is not, then the operator $a_1 w_1 + a_2 w_2$ ($a_1, a_2 \neq 0$ being real numbers) is never logarithmic. Indeed, if it were logarithmic, then also the operator

$$w_2 = -\frac{a_1}{a_2} w_1 + \frac{1}{a_2}(a_1 w_1 + a_2 w_2)$$

would be logarithmic, contrary to our assumption. For instance the operators

$$(1+i)s, \qquad \frac{1}{2} - \frac{\sqrt{3}}{2} is, \qquad \frac{1}{2} + \frac{\sqrt{3}}{2} is$$

are not logarithmic.

It follows from the calculation performed in § 2 that if a root w_μ of the characteristic equation (2.2) is logarithmic, then the exponential function $e^{\lambda w_\mu}$ satisfies the differential equation (2.1).

§ 5. Multiple roots of the characteristic equation. The root w_μ of equation (2.2) is termed *$\varkappa$-tuple* if the polynomial $P(u)$ contains $\varkappa$ factors of the form $u - w_\mu$. For instance the operator $-s$ is a double root of the equation

(5.1) $$u^3 + su^2 - s^2 u - s^3 = 0$$

because $u^3 + su^2 - su^2 - s^3 = (u+s)^2(u-s)$. Now the root s is simple because the factor $u-s$ occurs only once.

If the operator w_μ, which is logarithmic, is a $\varkappa$-tuple root of equation (2.2), then each of the functions

(5.2) $$e^{\lambda w_\mu}, \lambda e^{\lambda w_\mu}, \ldots, \lambda^{\varkappa-1} e^{\lambda w_\mu}$$

satisfies equation (2.1).

Proof. If $x(\lambda) = \lambda^\sigma e^{\lambda w_\mu}$ (σ being natural), then by Leibnitz's theorem on differentiating a product we have

$$x^{(k)}(\lambda) = \sum_{j=0}^{k} \binom{k}{j} (\lambda^\sigma)^{(j)} (e^{\lambda w_\mu})^{(k-j)}$$

$$= \sum_{j=0}^{k} \binom{k}{j} \frac{\sigma!}{(\sigma-j)!} \lambda^{\sigma-j} w_\mu^{k-j} e^{\lambda w_\mu}$$

$$= e^{\lambda w_\mu} \sum_{j=0}^{k} \frac{k!}{(k-j)!} \binom{\sigma}{j} \lambda^{\sigma-j} w_\mu^{k-j},$$

where we must assume $\dfrac{\sigma!}{(\sigma-j)!} = 0$ and $\dbinom{\sigma}{j} = 0$ provided $j > \sigma$.

Consequently

$$\sum_{k=0}^{m} a_k x^{(k)}(\lambda) = \sum_{k=0}^{m} a_k e^{\lambda w_\mu} \sum_{j=0}^{m} \frac{k!}{(k-j)!} \binom{\sigma}{j} \lambda^{\sigma-j} w_\mu^{k-j}$$

$$= e^{\lambda w_\mu} \sum_{j=0}^{m} \binom{\sigma}{j} \lambda^{\sigma-j} \sum_{j=0}^{m} a_k \frac{k!}{(k-j)!} w_\mu^{k-j}$$

$$= e^{\lambda w_\mu} \sum_{j=0}^{\sigma} \binom{\sigma}{j} \lambda^{\sigma-j} \sum_{k=0}^{m} a_k \frac{k!}{(k-j)!} w_\mu^{k-j}.$$

It is known from algebra that if a polynomial $P(w) = \sum_{k=0}^{m} a_k u^k$ decomposed into linear factors contains $\varkappa$ identical factors $u - w_\mu$, then its j-th derivative $(0 \leqslant j \leqslant \varkappa - 1)$

$$\sum_{k=0}^{m} a_k \frac{k!}{(k-j)!} u^{k-j}$$

is equal to zero for $u = w_\mu$. Thus if $0 \leqslant \sigma \leqslant \varkappa - 1$, we have the equality

$$\sum_{k=0}^{m} a_k x^{(k)}(\lambda) = 0$$

in the whole interval under consideration. Consequently the function $x(\lambda)$ satisfies equation (2.1).

Example. The equation

$$x''' + sx'' - s^2 x' - s^3 x = 0 \tag{5.3}$$

has the characteristic equation (5.1) for which the operator $-s$ is a double root. Consequently each of the functions

$$e^{-\lambda s} \quad \text{and} \quad \lambda e^{-\lambda s}$$

satisfies equation (5.3), which can easily be verified by substitution.

§ 6. The general solution. According to the theorem which has been proved, for every root w_μ which is logarithmic the number of solutions (5.2) is equal to its multiplicity. Thus if the characteristic equation (2.2) totals p logarithmic roots (counted according to multiplicity), then we can write down p solutions; let us denote them by

$$x_1(\lambda), \ldots, x_p(\lambda).$$

If $c_1, \ldots, c_p$ are arbitrary operators, then the function

$$x(\lambda) = c_1 x_1(\lambda) + \ldots + c_p x_p(\lambda) \tag{6.1}$$

is also a solution of equation (2.1). Expression (6.1) is termed the general solution of equation (2.1); the number of arbitrary constants contained in it is equal to the number of logarithmic roots of the characteristic equation.

EXAMPLES. 1. For the equation

$$x''' + sx'' - s^2 x' - s^3 x = 0$$

the characteristic equation is

$$u^3 + su^2 - s^2 u - s^3 = 0.$$

It has one simple root s and one double root $-s$; both of them are logarithmic. Thus the general solution contains three arbitrary constants and has the form

$$x(\lambda) = c_1 e^{\lambda s} + c_2 e^{-\lambda s} + c_3 \lambda e^{-\lambda s}.$$

EXAMPLE 2. For the equation

$$x''' + sx'' + s^2 x' + s^3 x = 0$$

the characteristic equation is

$$u^3 + su^2 + s^2 u + s^3 = 0.$$

It has three roots, is, $-is$, and $-s$, only the last of them being logarithmic. Consequently the general solution contains only one arbitrary constant

$$x(\lambda) = ce^{-\lambda s}.$$

EXAMPLE 3. For the equation

$$x'' + s^2 x = 0$$

we have the characteristic equation

$$u^2 + s^2 = 0.$$

Neither of its roots, is and $-is$, is logarithmic. Consequently the general solution is reduced to the form

$$x(\lambda) = 0$$

and is independent of any constant.

We shall distinguish three types of differential equations according to the number of logarithmic roots.

A differential equation is

logarithmic if all the roots of the characteristic equation are logarithmic;

pure if none of the roots of the characteristic equation is logarithmic;

mixed if some of the roots of the characteristic equation are logarithmic and others are not.

In the case where the coefficients of equation (2.1) are numbers, we obtain the classical differential equation with constant coefficients. It is logarithmic and consequently the general solution always has m arbitrary constants, *i. e.*, their number is equal to the order of the differential equation.

Generally however, as has been shown by the above examples, the number of arbitrary constants ocurring in the general solution may be smaller than the order of the equation.

The following theorem is very important: *every solution of equation* (2.1) *that exists in a certain interval* (α, β) *can be obtained from the general solution by a suitable choice of the constants* $c_1, \ldots, c_p$.

The proof of this theorem is based on a certain theorem on unicity, which will be dealt with in the next section.

Exercise. Write the general solutions of the following differential equations:

(α) $x''' + 4sx'' + 4sx' + 16s^3 x = 0$; ($\beta$) $x''' + s^3 x = 0$; (γ) $x^{(4)} - s^4 x = 0$;

(δ) $sx''' + (s^2 + s + 1)(x'' + x') + sx = 0$; ($\varepsilon$) $x^{(4)} + s^4 x = 0$.

§ 7. Theorem on the unicity of solution.

THEOREM. *For given operators* $k_0, \ldots, k_{m-1}$ *and a point* λ_0 *of the interval* (α, β) *there exists at most one operational function* $x(\lambda)$ *satisfying in* (α, β) *equation* (2.1) *and the conditions*

(7.1) $$x(\lambda_0) = k_0, \quad x'(\lambda_0) = k_1, \quad \ldots, \quad x^{(m-1)}(\lambda_0) = k_{m-1}.$$

Proof. Suppose that there exist two such functions, $x_1(\lambda)$ and $x_2(\lambda)$. Then their difference,

$$x(\lambda) = x_1(\lambda) - x_2(\lambda),$$

also satisfies equation (2.1) in the interval (α, β) and the conditions

$$(7.2) \qquad x(\lambda_0) = 0, \quad x'(\lambda_0) = 0, \quad \ldots, \quad x^{(m-1)}(\lambda_0) = 0.$$

Thus it is sufficient to prove that every function $x(\lambda)$ satisfying in (α, β) equation (2.1) and conditions (7.2) is equal to zero in (α, β).

In the case of $m = 0$ the theorem is obvious; in the case of $m = 1$ it has been proved in § 17, Part II. Reasoning by induction, let us assume the theorem to be true for equations of the order $0, 1, \ldots, m-1$; we shall prove that this implies the validity of the theorem for equations of order m.

Let us introduce an auxiliary function,

$$(7.3) \qquad y(\lambda) = \sum_{i=0}^{m-1} a_i [x^{(m-1)}(\lambda) x^{(i)}(\mu-\lambda) + \\ + x^{(m-2)}(\lambda) x^{i+1}(\mu-\lambda) + \ldots + x^{(i)}(\lambda) x^{(m-1)}(\mu-\lambda)],$$

where μ is an arbitrarily fixed number such that

$$(7.4) \qquad \alpha < \mu - \lambda_0 < \beta.$$

Then

$$y'(\lambda) = \sum_{i=0}^{m-1} a_i [x^{(m)}(\lambda) x^{(i)}(\mu-\lambda) - x^{(i)}(\lambda) x^{(m)}(\mu-\lambda)]$$

$$= x^{(m)}(\lambda) \sum_{i=0}^{m-1} a_i x^{(i)}(\mu-\lambda) - x^{(m)}(\mu-\lambda) \sum_{i=0}^{m-1} a_i x^{(i)}(\lambda).$$

But by (2.1) we have

$$\sum_{i=0}^{m-1} a_i x^{(i)}(\lambda) = -a_m x^{(m)}(\lambda)$$

and, replacing λ by $\mu - \lambda$,

$$\sum_{i=0}^{m-1} a_i x^{(i)}(\mu-\lambda) = -a_m x^{(m)}(\mu-\lambda);$$

consequently

$$y'(\lambda) = -x^{(m)}(\lambda) a_m x^{(m)}(\mu-\lambda) + x^{(m)}(\mu-\lambda) a_m x^{m}(\lambda) = 0.$$

This equality holds for those values of λ from the interval (α, β) for which $\mu - \lambda$ also belongs to (α, β), *i. e.*, it holds in the common part I

of the intervals (α, β) and $(\mu-\beta, \mu-\alpha)$. Hence it follows that the function $y(\lambda)$ is constant in I. Since the point λ_0 belongs to I and since conditions (7.2) imply that $y(\lambda_0) = 0$, we must have $y(\lambda) = 0$ identically in I, *i. e.*, we must have

$$\text{(7.5)} \qquad \sum_{i=0}^{m-1} a_i [x^{(m-1)}(\lambda) x^{(i)}(\mu-\lambda) + x^{(m-2)}(\lambda) x^{(i+1)}(\mu-\lambda) + \\ + \ldots + x^{(i)}(\lambda) x^{(m-1)}(\mu-\lambda)] = 0,$$

provided inequalities (7.4),

$$\alpha < \lambda < \beta \quad \text{and} \quad \alpha < \mu-\lambda < \beta,$$

are satisfied.

Substituting $\varkappa = \mu-\lambda$ in (7.5) and making the terms containing the derivative $x^{(m-1)}(\lambda)$ precede the sign of summation, we shall obtain

$$\text{(7.6)} \qquad [a_{m-1} x^{(m-1)}(\varkappa) + \ldots + a_0 x(\varkappa) x^{(m-1)}(\lambda) + \\ + \sum_{i=0}^{m-1} a_i [x^{(m-2)}(\lambda) x^{(i-1)}(\varkappa) + \ldots + x^{(i)}(\lambda) x^{(m-1)}(\varkappa)] = 0;$$

this equality is satisfied provided

$$\text{(7.7)} \qquad \alpha < \varkappa < \beta, \quad \alpha < \lambda < \beta, \quad \text{and} \quad \alpha < \varkappa-\lambda_0+\lambda < \beta.$$

Let $\bar{\lambda}$ be an arbitrary point inside the interval (α, β); we shall prove that $x(\bar{\lambda}) = 0$. Therefore we shall distinguish two cases:

1° In every neighbourhood of the point λ_0 there exist values of $\varkappa$ for which

$$a_{m-1} x^{(m-1)}(\varkappa) + \ldots + a_0 x(\varkappa) \neq 0.$$

Among those values we choose one for which $|\varkappa-\lambda_0|$ is less than any of the numbers

$$\lambda_0-\alpha, \quad \bar{\lambda}-\alpha, \quad \beta-\lambda_0 \quad \text{and} \quad \beta-\bar{\lambda}.$$

Then

$$\alpha+|\varkappa-\lambda_0| < \lambda_0 < \beta-|\varkappa-\lambda_0|$$

and

$$\alpha+|\varkappa-\lambda_0| < \bar{\lambda} < \beta-|\varkappa-\lambda_0|.$$

If λ belongs to the interval

$$\text{(7.8)} \qquad \alpha+|\varkappa-\lambda_0| < \lambda < \beta-|\varkappa-\lambda_0|,$$

then inequalities (7.7) are satisfied. Consequently equation (7.6) is satisfied for every λ from the interval (7.8); it is an equation of the order $m-1$ because the coefficient of the highest derivative, $x^{(m-1)}(\lambda)$, is different from zero. Since the point λ_0 belongs to the interval (7.8) and the inequalities

$$(7.9) \qquad x_0(\lambda_0) = 0, \quad \ldots, \quad x^{(m-2)}(\lambda_0) = 0$$

are satisfied at that point, it follows, in virtue of the inductive assumption of the validity of the theorem for equations of the order $\leqslant m-1$, that $x(\lambda) = 0$ for every λ from the interval (7.8). Now the point $\bar{\lambda}$ belongs to that interval, and thus we have in particular $x(\bar{\lambda}) = 0$, q. e. d.

2° There exists such a neighbourhood of the point λ_0 that for all $\varkappa$ belonging to that neighbourhood we have

$$a_{m-1}x^{(m-1)}(\varkappa) + \ldots + a_0 x(\varkappa) = 0.$$

Let us temporarily assume that at least one of the coefficients $a_{m-1}, \ldots, a_0$ is different from 0, and denote by (α_0, β_0) the largest interval (containing the point λ_0) in which this equality is satisfied. Then it follows from equality (7.9) and the inductive assumption that $x(\lambda) = 0$ in the interval (α_0, β_0). If $\bar{\lambda}$ is outside the interval (α_0, β_0), then we can establish λ_1 from the interval (α_0, β_0) and $\varkappa$ outside that interval in such a way that equality (7.6) will hold inside a certain interval containing the points λ and $\bar{\lambda}$. Since $x(\lambda_1) = 0$, we must have $x(\bar{\lambda}) = 0$, as in case 1°.

It remains to get rid of the assumption that at least one of the coefficients $a_{m-1}, \ldots, a_0$ is different from zero. But if they are all equal to zero, equation (2.1) is reduced (on being divided by a_m) to the form $x^{(m)}(\lambda) = 0$. Thus the function $x^{(m-1)}(\lambda)$ must be constant in (α, β). Since $x^{(m-1)}(\lambda_0) = 0$, we have $x^{(m-1)}(\lambda) = 0$ everywhere in (α, β). Hence by induction $x(\lambda) = 0$ in (α, β). We have thus completed the proof of the theorem.

§ 8. The logarithmic equation. In the case of a logarithmic equation all the roots of the characteristic equation are logarithmic and the general solution has m arbitrary constants,

$$x(\lambda) = c_1 x_1(\lambda) + \ldots + c_m x_m(\lambda).$$

Given arbitrary operators $k_0, \ldots, k_{m-1}$ and a point λ_0 we can choose the constants $c_1, \ldots, c_m$ in such a way as to satisfy conditions (7.1). For this purpose it is sufficient to solve with respect to $c_1, \ldots, c_m$ the system of equations

$$\begin{aligned}
&c_1 x_1(\lambda)_0 + \ldots + c_m x_m(\lambda_0) = k_0, \\
&c_1 x_1'(\lambda_0) + \ldots + c_m x_m'(\lambda_0) = k_1, \\
&\ldots\ldots\ldots\ldots\ldots\ldots\ldots\ldots \\
&c_1 x_1^{(m-1)}(\lambda_0) + \ldots + c_m x_m^{(m-1)}(\lambda_0) = k_{m-1}.
\end{aligned}$$

For the solvability of this system it is necessary and sufficient that the determinant

$$(8.1)\qquad \begin{vmatrix} x_1(\lambda_0) & \dots x_m(\lambda_0) \\ x_1'(\lambda_0) & \dots x_m'(\lambda_0) \\ \dots & \dots \\ x_1^{(m-1)}(\lambda_0) & \dots x_m^{(m-1)}(\lambda_0) \end{vmatrix}$$

be different from zero. It is easy to verify that the determinant is different from zero if all the roots of the characteristic equation are different from one another. For in that case we have

$$x_1(\lambda) = e^{\lambda w_1}, \quad \dots, \quad x_m(\lambda) = e^{\lambda w_m}$$

and determinant (8.1) has the form

$$\begin{vmatrix} e^{\lambda_0 w_1} & \dots e^{\lambda_0 w_m} \\ w_1 e^{\lambda_0 w_1} & \dots w_m e^{\lambda_0 w_m} \\ \dots & \dots \\ w_1^{m-1} e^{\lambda_0 w_1} & \dots w_m^{m-1} e^{\lambda_0 w_m} \end{vmatrix} = e^{\lambda_0(w_1+\dots+w_m)} \begin{vmatrix} 1 & \dots 1 \\ w_1 & \dots w_m \\ \dots & \dots \\ w_1^{m-1} & \dots w_m^{m-1} \end{vmatrix};$$

the last determinant, termed the *Vandermonde determinant*, is known to be different from zero provided the elements $w_1, \dots, w_m$ are all different from one another.

If the roots of the characteristic equation do not all differ from one another, then some of the functions $x_1(\lambda), \dots, x_m(\lambda)$ will be of the form $\lambda^\varkappa e^{w_\nu \lambda}$ where $\varkappa \geqslant 1$. The calculation of determinant (8.1) is then more complicated but also in that case the determinant is always different from zero (see Mikusiński [2] and [6]).

Now if $x_0(\lambda)$ is any function satisfying equation (2.1) in a certain interval, then the coefficients $c_1, \dots, c_m$ can always be chosen is such a way that

$$x(\lambda_0) = x_0(\lambda_0), \quad \dots, \quad x^{(m-1)}(\lambda_0) = x_0^{(m-1)}(\lambda_0)$$

for a certain point λ_0 of the interval (α, β).

But then, by the theorem on unicity, the functions $x(\lambda)$ and $x_0(\lambda)$ must be identical in the whole interval in question. Thus if the equation is logarithmic, each of its solutions can be obtained by substituting suitable values for the constants $c_1, \dots, c_m$ in the general solution.

In order to prove an analogous theorem for non-logarithmic equations we shall first consider certain properties of linear differential expressions.

§ 9. Linear differential expressions. Denote the left side of the differential equation (2.1) by Lx,

$$Lx = \sum_{\mu=0}^{m} a_\mu x^{(\mu)}, \tag{9.1}$$

the symbol Lx will be termed a *linear differential expression*. If, in such an expression, we substitute for x an operational function $x(\lambda)$ (having a continuous m-th derivative), then $Lx(\lambda)$ will represent a continuous operational function.

If $Lx(\lambda) = 0$ identically in a certain interval, it follows that the function $x(\lambda)$ has infinitely many derivatives in that interval. Indeed, we can then write

$$x^{(m)}(\lambda) = -\frac{1}{a_m}\sum_{\mu=0}^{m-1} a_\mu x^\mu(\lambda); \tag{9.2}$$

since on the right side only derivatives up to the order $m-1$ occur, a continuous derivative exists for the right side and thus also for the left side:

$$x^{(m+1)}(\lambda) = -\frac{1}{a_m}\sum_{\mu=0}^{m-1} a_\mu x^{(\mu+1)}(\lambda). \tag{9.3}$$

The derivative $x^{(m)}(\lambda)$, appearing now on the right side of formula (9.3), can be replaced by expression (9.2); thus the derivative $x^{(m+1)}(\lambda)$ will be expressed solely by derivatives of an order lower than m. Consequently $x^{(m+1)}(\lambda)$ can again be differentiated. Repeating the same procedure a suitable number of times, we can obtain derivatives of an arbitrarily high order. The function $x(\lambda)$ is thus indefinitely differentiable.

If $Lx(\lambda) = 0$ identically in an interval, then also $Lx^{(n)}(\lambda) = 0$ identically in that interval, whatever natural n is taken. This immediately follows from the obvious equality $Lx^{(n)}(\lambda) = [Lx(\lambda)]^{(n)}$. Thus if $x(\lambda)$ is a solution of a homogeneous differential equation $Lx = 0$, *i. e.*, of the equation

$$a_m x^{(m)} + \ldots + a_0 x = 0,$$

then every derivative $x^{(n)}(\lambda)$ is also a solution of this equation.

§ 10. Operations on linear differential expressions. By the *sum* $(L_1+L_2)x$ of two linear expressions L_1x and L_2x we understand the expression L_1x+L_2x. For instance if

$$L_1 x = a_2 x'' + a_1 x' + a_0 x, \qquad L_2 x = b_1 x' + b_0 x, \tag{10.1}$$

then

$$(L_1+L_2)x = ax'' + (a_1+b_1)x' + (a_0+b_0)x.$$

By the *product* L_1L_2x of two linear expressions we understand the expression $L_1(L_2x)$. For instance if we assume (10.1), then

$$\begin{aligned} L_1L_2x &= a_2(L_2x)''+a_1(L_2x)'+a_0(L_2x) \\ &= a_2(b_1x'''+b_0x'')+a_1(b_1x''+b_0x')+a_0(b_1x'+b_0x) \\ &= a_0b_1x'''+(a_2b_0+a_1b_1)x''+(a_1b_0+a_0b_1)x'+a_0b_0x. \end{aligned}$$

§ 11. Characteristic polynomials of linear differential expressions. With every linear expression (9.1) a characteristic polynomial

$$P(u) = \sum_{\mu=0}^{m} a_\mu u^\mu$$

is connected. For example the characteristic polynomials for expressions (10.1) are

$$P_1(u) = a_2u^2+a_1u+a_0 \quad \text{and} \quad P_2(u) = b_1u+b_0.$$

It is obvious that the sum

$$P_1(u)+P_2(u) = a_2u^2+(a_1+b_1)u+(a_0+b_0)$$

is the characteristic polynomial for the sum $(L_1+L_2)x$. Similarly, the product

$$P_1(u)\cdot P_2(u) = a_2b_1u^3+(a_2b_0+a_1b_1)u^2+(a_1b_0+a_0b_1)u+a_0b_0$$

is the characteristic polynomial for the product L_1L_2x.

This is the general rule: *The characteristic polynomial for a sum of linear differential equations is the sum of their characteristic polynomials.* Similarly, *the characteristic polynomial for a product of linear differential expressions is the product of their characteristic polynomials.* This rule makes it possible to perform operations on linear differential expressions in the same way as on polynomials.

This theorem implies in particular that every linear expression (9.1) can be written in the form

$$Lx = a_0L_1 \ldots L_mx$$

where $L_\mu x = x'-w_\mu x$, and w_μ is the root of the characteristic equation $P(u) = 0$.

§ 12. Pure equations. If an equation $Lx = 0$ is pure, then each of the equations

$$L_1x = 0, \quad \ldots, \quad L_mx = 0$$

has only one solution, namely the one identically equal to zero. If $x(\lambda) \neq 0$, then $L_mx(\lambda) \neq 0$. Hence it follows further that $L_{m-1}L_mx(\lambda) \neq 0$,

$L_{m-2}L_{m-1}L_m x(\lambda) \neq 0$ and finally $L_1 \dots L_m x(\lambda) \neq 0$. Consequently $Lx(\lambda) \neq 0$; no function $x(\lambda) \neq 0$ satisfies the equation $Lx = 0$.

Thus we have the theorem:

Pure (homogeneous) equations have the only solutions that are identically equal to zero.

§ 13. Mixed equations. We can easily prove now that *every solution of a mixed equation $Lx = 0$ can be obtained from the general solution by a suitable choice of the constants $c_1, \dots, c_p$.* If p is the number of logarithmic roots of the characteristic equation, then it can be assumed that the equations

$$L_1 x = 0, \quad \dots, \quad L_p x = 0$$

have solutions that are different from zero, and the equations

$$L_{p+1} x = 0, \quad \dots, \quad L_m x = 0$$

have no such solutions. Let us introduce the notation

$$L_{\log} x = L_1 \dots L_p x, \quad L_{cz} x = L_{p+1} \dots L_m x.$$

Then the equation

$$L_{\log} x = 0$$

is logarithmic and each of its solutions has the form

$$c_1 x_1(\lambda) + \dots + c_p x_p(\lambda) \tag{13.1}$$

the significance of the functions $x_1(\lambda), \dots, x_p(\lambda)$ having been discussed in § 6. And the equation

$$L_{cz} x = 0 \tag{13.2}$$

is pure and has an only solution which is identically equal to zero.

The equation $Lx = 0$ can be written in the form

$$L_{cz} L_{\log} x = 0.$$

If a function $x(\lambda)$ is not of the form (13.1), then $L_{\log} x \neq 0$. Consequently we must have $L_{cz} L_{\log} x(\lambda) \neq 0$ and the function $x(\lambda)$ cannot satisfy the equation $Lx = 0$. Thus every solution of the equation $Lx = 0$ has the form (13.1).

§ 14. Adapting the solution to given initial, boundary and other conditions. We have proved that for a differential equation (2.1) of any type every solution can be obtained from the general solution by a suitable choice of the constants c_μ. The general solutions can be adapted to various additional conditions.

EXAMPLE 1. Find a function $x(\lambda)$ satisfying the equation

$$x''' + sx'' - s^2x' - s^3x = 0 \tag{14.1}$$

and the conditions

$$x(0) = 1, \quad x'(0) = s-1, \quad x''(0) = s^2+2s. \tag{14.2}$$

As shown in § 6, the general solution of this equation has the form

$$x(\lambda) = c_1 e^{\lambda s} + (c_2 + c_3\lambda)^{-\lambda s}.$$

Hence

$$x'(\lambda) = c_1 s e^{\lambda s} + (-c_2 s + c_3 - c_3\lambda s)e^{-\lambda s},$$

$$x''(\lambda) = c_1 s^2 e^{\lambda s} + (c_2 s^2 - 2c_3 s + c_3\lambda s^2)e^{-\lambda s}.$$

Taking $\lambda = 0$ and using conditions (14.2) we obtain the equality

$$c_1 + c_2 = 1,$$

$$c_1 s - c_2 s + c_3 = s-1,$$

$$c_1 s + c_2 s^2 - 2c_3 s = s^2 + 2s.$$

Hence we easily find

$$c_1 = 1, \quad c_2 = 0 \quad \text{and} \quad c_3 = -1.$$

Thus the required solution has the form

$$x(\lambda) = e^{s\lambda} - \lambda e^{-\lambda s}.$$

EXAMPLE 2. Find a function $x(\lambda)$ satisfying the differential equation (14.1) and the conditions

$$x(0) = 1/s, \quad x'(0) = 1+1/s, \quad x(1) = 0. \tag{14.3}$$

As before, these conditions lead to the equalities

$$c_1 + c_2 = -1/s,$$

$$c_1 s - c_2 s + c_3 = 1 + 1/s,$$

$$c_1 e^s + (c_2 + c_3)e^{-s} = 0.$$

Hence

$$c_1 = 0, \quad c_2 = -1/s, \quad c_3 = 1/s,$$

and the required solution is

$$x(\lambda) = (\lambda - 1)e^{-\lambda s}/s.$$

EXAMPLE 3. Find a function $x(\lambda)$ satisfying equation (14.1) and the conditions

$$x(0) = 0, \quad x(1) = 0, \quad x(2) = 1.$$

We now have the following system of equations to solve:

$$c_1 + c_2 = 0,$$
$$c_1 e^{s} + c_2 e^{-s} + c_3 e^{-s} = 0,$$
$$c_1 e^{2s} + c_2 e^{-2s} + 2c_3 e^{-2s} = 1;$$

in this way we obtain

$$c_1 = \frac{1}{(e^{s}-e^{-s})^2}, \qquad c_2 = -\frac{1}{(e^{s}-e^{-s})^2}, \qquad c_3 = \frac{1}{e^{-2s}-1}$$

and finally

$$x(\lambda) = \frac{e^{\lambda s}-e^{-\lambda s}}{(e^{s}-e^{-s})^2} + \frac{\lambda e^{-\lambda s}}{e^{-\lambda s}-1}.$$

The conditions given in the first example are termed the *initial conditions*, those of the second example are the *boundary conditions*. Another type of conditions is given in the third example. In all these examples the solution obtained is unique, the constants c_1, c_2, c_3 being uniquely defined.

The number of conditions needed to define uniquely a solution is equal to the number of arbitrary constants in the general solution. In each of the above examples we are given three conditions. The equation considered in those examples is logarithmic. In logarithmic equations the number of conditions needed is always equal to the order of the equation. If the equation is not logarithmic, then the number of conditions determining the solution is less than the order of the equation and equal to the number of logarithmic roots of the characteristic equation, or, which is the same, to the number of constants in the general solution.

Example 4. Find a function $x(\lambda)$ satisfying the equation

$$x''' + sx'' + s^2x' + s^3x = 0$$

and the condition

$$x(1) = s.$$

The general solution now contains one arbitrary constant (see § 6),

$$x(\lambda) = ce^{-\lambda s};$$

we easily determine it by taking into account the given condition, which brings us to the equation

$$ce^{-s} = s.$$

Hence $c = se^{s}$ and the solution is

$$x(\lambda) = se^{(1-\lambda)s}.$$

Exercise. Solve the following equations under the given conditions:

(α) $x''' + 4sx'' + 4s^2x' + 16s^3x = 0, \quad x(0) = 1/s;$

(β) $x''' + s^3x = 0, \quad x(1) = 1;$ (γ) $x^{(4)} - s^4x = 0, \quad x(0) = x(1) = s;$

(δ) $sx''' + (s^2 + s + 1)(x'' + x') + sx = 0, \quad x(0) = 1, \quad x'(0) = 1 - 2/s,$
$x(-1) = 2e^{1/s} - e.$

Are the solutions obtained unique?

CHAPTER II

NON-HOMOGENEOUS EQUATIONS

§ 15. The general solution of a non-homogeneous equation. If functions $x_0(\lambda)$ and $x_1(\lambda)$ satisfy the non-homogeneous equation

(15.1) $$a_m x^{(m)} + \ldots + a_0 x = f(\lambda),$$

then their difference $x(\lambda) = x_0(\lambda) - x_1(\lambda)$ satisfies the homogeneous equation

(15.2) $$a_m x^{(m)} + \ldots + a_0 x = 0.$$

Thus even if we know no more than one solution $x_0(\lambda)$ of (15.1), then after finding the general solution

$$x(\lambda) = c_1 x_1(\lambda) + \ldots + c_p x_p(\lambda)$$

of (15.2) we can at once write the general solution of (15.1) in the form of the sum

(15.3) $$x_0(\lambda) + x(\lambda) = x_0(\lambda) + c_1 x_1(\lambda) + \ldots + c_p x_p(\lambda).$$

Each particular solution of equation (15.1) can be obtained from (15.3) by a suitable choice of the constants $c_1, \ldots, c_p$.

E. g., for the non-homogeneous equation

(15.4) $$x''' + s x'' - s^2 x' - s^3 x = -1$$

we can easily write the general solution using the solution given in the preceding section and the simple observation that the function $x_0(\lambda) = 1/s^3$ satisfies equation (15.4). Thus the general solution in this case has the form

$$x(\lambda) = \frac{1}{s^3} + c_1 e^{-\lambda s} + c_3 e^{\lambda s}.$$

Now the equation

$$x'' + s^2 x = 1$$

has the only solution

$$x(\lambda) = 1/s^2,$$

because the only function satisfying the homogeneous equation $x''+s^2x = 0$ is the function identically equal to zero.

The resolution of a non-homogeneous equation is thus always reduced to the resolution of a homogeneous equation and to the finding of at least one function satisfying the non-homogeneous equation. The finding of that function is generally difficult and in some cases such a function may be non-existent (see Mikusiński [2], p. 233-234). In other cases, if the right side of equation (15.1) is of a peculiar form, it may be easy to find the solution.

§ 16. The case where the right side is a polynomial. Given the equation

$$a_m x^{(m)}+\ldots+a_0 x = b_0+\ldots+b_n\lambda^n \qquad (a_0 \neq 0), \tag{16.1}$$

we can always find the polynomial solution

$$x_0(\lambda) = c_0+\ldots+c_n\lambda^n.$$

It is sufficient to substitute this expression in (16.1) and then to determine $c_0, \ldots, c_n$ by comparing the coefficients of the powers of λ. The polynomial found in this way is the only polynomial satisfying equation (16.1).

E. g., let us determine the polynomial solution for the equation

$$x''+s^2x = s\lambda^3+1. \tag{16.2}$$

Substituting the expression

$$x(\lambda) = c_0+c_1\lambda+c_2\lambda^2+c_2\lambda^3$$

in (16.2) we have

$$(28c_2+bc_3\lambda)+s^2(c_0+c_1\lambda+c_2\lambda^2+c_2\lambda^3) = s\lambda^3+1,$$

whence by comparing the coefficients

$$\begin{aligned} 2c_2+s^2c_0 &= 1, \\ 6c_3+s^2c_1 &= 0, \\ s^2c_2 &= 0, \\ s^2c_3 &= s. \end{aligned}$$

From these equations we easily calculate

$$c_0 = \frac{1}{s^2}, \qquad c_1 = \frac{6}{s^3}, \qquad c_2 = 0, \qquad c_3 = \frac{1}{s};$$

consequently the solution has the form

$$x_0(\lambda) = \frac{1}{s^2} - \frac{6\lambda}{s^3} + \frac{\lambda^3}{s}.$$

This is the only solution of equation (16.2) since the general solution of the homogeneous equation $x''+s^2x=0$ is reduced to zero.

If we have $a_0=0$ in equation (16.1), then, denoting by a_k the last coefficient different from zero, we shall have a polynomial solution of the form

$$x_0(\lambda)=c_0\lambda^k+\ldots+c_n\lambda^{k+n},$$

whose coefficients are determined as in the preceding case. This, however, is not the only polynomial solution, since we can add to it or subtract from it any polynomial of a degree less than k, obtaining other polynomial solutions in this way.

Exercise. Find the polynomial solutions for the equations

(α) $x^{(4)}+sx=a\lambda+b$; (β) $x''-sx'+s^2x=s\lambda^3$; (γ) $x^{(4)}+s^2x''=2\lambda^2+1$.

§ 17. The case where the right side is an exponential function. Given the equation

$$a_m x^{(m)}+\ldots+a_0x=e^{\lambda w} \tag{17.1}$$

where w is an operator such that $a_m w^m+\ldots+a_0=P(w)\neq 0$, we can at once give one of its solutions, viz.

$$x_0(\lambda)=\frac{e^{\lambda w}}{P(w)};$$

it can be directly verified that $x_0(\lambda)$ satisfies (17.1).

E. g., for the equation

$$x'''+sx''+s^2x'+s^3x=e^{\lambda} \tag{17.2}$$

the solution is the function

$$x_0(\lambda)=\frac{e^{\lambda}}{1+s+s^2+s^3}.$$

If $P(w)=0$, then w is a root of the characteristic equation; let q be a multiplicity of that root. Then the function

$$x_0(\lambda)=\frac{\lambda^q e^{\lambda w}}{P^{(q)}(w)} \tag{17.3}$$

satisfies equation (17.1); $P^{(q)}$ denotes the q-th derivative of P.

E. g., for the equation

$$x''+sx''-s^2x'-s^3x=e^{-\lambda s} \tag{17.4}$$

the polynomial $P(u)$ has the form

$$P(u)=u^3+su^2-s^2u-s^2.$$

We easily ascertain that $P(-s) = 0$ and that $-s$ is a double root of the characteristic equation $P(u) = 0$. Consequently the function

$$x_0(\lambda) = \frac{\lambda^2 e^{-s\lambda}}{P''(-s)}$$

satisfies equation (17.4); since

$$P''(u) = 6u+2s, \qquad P''(-s) = -4s,$$

we finally have

$$x_0(\lambda) = -\frac{\lambda^2}{4s} e^{-\lambda s}.$$

It is easy to verify by direct substitution that this function is indeed the solution of the equation.

In order to prove generally that function (17.3) satisfies equation (17.1), let us observe that according to the calculations performed in § 5 we have

$$\sum_{k=0}^{m} a_k x_0^k(\lambda) = \frac{e^{\lambda w}}{P^{(q)}(w)} \sum_{j=0}^{q} \binom{q}{j} \lambda^{q-1} \sum_{k=1}^{m} a_k \frac{k!}{(k-j)!} w^{k-j}$$

$$= \frac{e^{\lambda w}}{P^{(q)}(w)} \sum_{j=0}^{q} \binom{q}{j} \lambda^{q-j} P^{(j)}(w).$$

From the assumption that w is a q-tuple root it follows, as we know from algebra, that $P^{(j)}(w) = 0$ for $j = 0, \ldots, q-1$. Consequently the last sum can be reduced to a single term, namely the last one, and when simplified remains on the right side of the equality $e^{\lambda w}$. This proves the theorem.

Exercise. Give the particular solutions of the following equations:

(α) $x'' + sx' - s^2 x = e^{-\lambda s}$; ($\beta$) $x'' + 2sx' + s^2 x = e^{-\lambda s}$;

(γ) $x'' + 3sx' + 2s^2 x = e^{-\lambda s}$.

§ 18. The case where the right side is a product of a polynomial and an exponential function. This case comprises the two discussed previously:

$$a_m x^{(m)} + \ldots + a_0 x = (b_0 + \ldots + b_n \lambda^n) e^{\lambda w}.$$

It can be proved that if w is a q-tuple root of the characteristic equation, then there always exists a solution of the form

$$x_0(\lambda) = (c_0 \lambda^q + \ldots + c_n \lambda^{q+n}) e^{\lambda w}.$$

In practice the constants $c_0, \ldots, c_n$ are determined by comparing the coefficients of equal powers of λ. *E. g.*, in order to solve the equation

$$x''' + sx'' - s^2 x' - s^3 x = \lambda e^{\lambda s} \tag{18.1}$$

we seek a solution of the form

$$x_0(\lambda) = (c_0\lambda + c_1\lambda^2)e^{\lambda s}$$

since $n = 1$ and $q = 1$ (s being a simple root of the characteristic equation). Substituting $x_0(\lambda)$ in (18.1) we have

$$[3c_0 s^2 + 6c_1 s + (c_0 s^3 + 6c_1 s^2)\lambda + c_1 s^3 \lambda^2]e^{\lambda s} +$$
$$+ s[2c_0 s + 2c_1 + (c_0 s^2 + 4c_1 s)\lambda + c_1 s^2 \lambda^2]e^{\lambda s} -$$
$$- s^2[c_0 + (c_0 s + 2c_1)\lambda + c_1 s\lambda^2]e^{\lambda s} - s^3(c_0\lambda + c_1\lambda^2)e^{\lambda s} = \lambda e^{\lambda s}.$$

Dividing this equality by $e^{\lambda s}$ and comparing the coefficients of equal powers of λ, we obtain the relations

$$4c_0 s^2 + 8c_1 s = 0, \quad 8c_1 s^2 = 1,$$

whence

$$c_0 = -\frac{1}{4s^3}, \quad c_1 = \frac{1}{8s^2}.$$

Thus the required solution is the function

$$x_0(\lambda) = \frac{1}{8}\left(\frac{\lambda^2}{s^2} - \frac{2\lambda}{s^3}\right)e^{\lambda s}.$$

Exercise. Find one particular solution for each of the following equations
(α) $x^{(4)} - 2sx'' + s^2 x = \lambda^2 e^{-\lambda s}$; ($\beta$) $x^{(4)} - 2sx'' + s^2 x = \lambda^2 e^{-\lambda\sqrt{s}}$.

§ 19. The case where the right side is a linear combination of two functions. If the equation is of the form

$$a_m x^{(m)} + \ldots + a_0 x = b_1 f_1(\lambda) + b_2 f_2(\lambda), \tag{19.1}$$

where b_1 and b_2 are arbitrary operators, then it is sufficient to find the solutions of two simpler equations,

$$a_m x^{(m)} + \ldots + a_0 x = f_1(\lambda),$$
$$a_m x^{(m)} + \ldots + a_0 x = f_2(\lambda).$$

Namely if $x_1(\lambda)$ is the solution of the first equation and $x_2(\lambda)$ the solution of the second, then the function

$$x(\lambda) = b_1 x_1(\lambda) + b_2 x_2(\lambda)$$

is the solution of equation (19.1), which can be verified at once by substitution.

This observation may conveniently be used in applications. *E. g.*, for a given equation

(19.2) $$a_m x^{(m)} + \ldots + a_0 x = b_1 e^{\lambda w_1} + b_2 e^{\lambda w_2}$$

where w_1 is a q_1-fold and w_2 a q_2-fold root of the characteristic equation $P(u) = 0$, the function

$$x(\lambda) = \frac{b_1}{P^{(q_1)}(w_1)} \lambda^{q_1} e^{\lambda w_1} + \frac{b_2}{P^{(q_2)}(w_2)} \lambda^{(q_2)} e^{\lambda w_2}$$

is the solution of equation (19.2).

Exercise. Find the particular solutions for the following equations:

(α) $x'' - sx' + s^2 x = s\lambda + e^{\lambda}$; ($\beta$) $x''' + s^3 x = e^{-s\lambda} + e^{s\lambda}$;

(γ) $sx'' + (1+s^2)x' + sx = s + e^{-\lambda} - e^{2\lambda}/s$.

§ 20. The case where the right side is a trigonometric function. Suppose there exists an exponential function $e^{i\lambda w}$ (λ being real). Then there exists also an exponential function $e^{-i\lambda w}$ and we can adopt the definitions

$$\sin \lambda w = \frac{e^{i\lambda w} - e^{-i\lambda w}}{2i}, \qquad \cos \lambda w = \frac{e^{i\lambda w} + e^{-i\lambda w}}{2}.$$

Given the equation

(20.1) $$a_m x^{(m)} + \ldots + a_0 x = \cos \lambda w$$

we can first seek the solutions $x_1(\lambda)$ and $x_2(\lambda)$ for the equations

$$a_m x^{(m)} + \ldots + a_0 x = e^{i\lambda w},$$

$$a_m x^{(m)} + \ldots + a_0 x = e^{-i\lambda w},$$

and then write the solution of equation (20.1) in the form

$$x(\lambda) = \tfrac{1}{2}[x_1(\lambda) + x_2(\lambda)].$$

We can proceed similarly if instead of $\cos \lambda w$ on the right side of the equation we have the function $\sin \lambda w$, or more generally a function of the form

$$b_1 \lambda^{q_1} e^{\lambda w_1} \cos \lambda w_2 + b_2 \lambda^{q_2} e^{\lambda w_3} \sin \lambda w_4.$$

In practice it is often more convenient to apply directly the method of undetermined coefficients. *E. g.*, given the equation

(20.2) $$x'' + sx' + s^2 x = \lambda \cos \lambda s$$

we seek a solution of the form

$$x_0(\lambda) = (c_1 + c_2 \lambda) \cos \lambda s + (c_3 + c_4 \lambda) \sin \lambda s.$$

Substituting this expression in (20.2) and arranging the terms, we have

$$(c_2 s + c_3 s^2 + 2c_4 s + c_4 s^2 \lambda)\cos\lambda s + (-c_1 s^2 - 2c_2 s + c_4 s - c_2 s^2 \lambda)\sin\lambda s = \lambda\cos\lambda s.$$

By comparing the corresponding coefficients we obtain the equations

$$\begin{aligned} c_2 s + c_3 s^2 + 2c_4 s &= 0, \\ c_4 s^2 &= 1, \\ -c_1 s^2 - 2c_2 s + c_4 s &= 0, \\ -c_2 s^2 &= 0, \end{aligned}$$

from which we obtain

$$c_1 = 1/s^3, \quad c_2 = 0, \quad c_3 = -2/s^3, \quad c_4 = 1/s^2,$$

and finally

$$x_0(\lambda) = l^3 \cos\lambda s + (l^2\lambda - 2l^3)\sin\lambda s.$$

Exercise. Find the particular solutions for the following equations:

(α) $x'' + s^2 x = \lambda^2 \sin\lambda s$; (β) $x'' + sx = \lambda\cos\lambda s + e^{\lambda}\sin\lambda s$;

(γ) $x^{(4)} - s^2 x = 1 + 2\cos\lambda\sqrt{s}$.

§ 21. Adapting the solution to additional conditions. Knowing one particular solution of a non-homogeneous equation we can find the general solution by the method given in § 15. We can in turn adapt the constants in the general solution to additional (initial, boundary or other) conditions.

The method is the same as the one used in the case of homogeneous equations; therefore we shall restrict ourselves here to a single example.

We shall solve the equation

(21.1) $$x''' + sx'' - s^2 x' - s^3 x = \lambda e^{\lambda s}$$

satisfying the conditions

(21.1) $$x(0) = \frac{1}{2s^3}, \quad x'(0) = \frac{1}{2s^2}, \quad x(2) = \frac{1}{2s^2} e^{2s} + \frac{1}{2s^3} e^{-2s}.$$

In § 18 we found the following particular solution of equation (21.1):

$$x_0(\lambda) = \frac{1}{8}\left(\frac{\lambda^2}{s^2} - \frac{2\lambda}{s^3}\right)e^{\lambda s};$$

since the general solution of the corresponding homogeneous equation has the form

$$c_1 e^{s\lambda} + c_2 e^{-s\lambda} + c_3 \lambda e^{-s\lambda}$$

(see § 6), we can at once write the general solution of equation (21.1):

$$x(\lambda) = c_1 e^{s\lambda} + c_2 e^{-s\lambda} + c_3 \lambda e^{-s\lambda} + \frac{1}{8}\left(\frac{\lambda^2}{s^2} - \frac{2\lambda}{s^3}\right)e^{\lambda s}.$$

From conditions (21.2) we obtain the relations

$$c_1 + c_2 = \frac{1}{2s^3},$$

$$c_1 s - c_2 s + c_3 - \frac{1}{4s^3} = \frac{1}{2s^2},$$

$$c_1 e^{2s} + c_2 e^{-2s} + 2c_3 e^{-2s} + \frac{1}{2}\left(\frac{1}{s^2} - \frac{1}{s^3}\right)e^{2s} = \frac{1}{2s^2}e^{2s} + \frac{1}{2s^3}e^{-2s},$$

whence

$$c_1 = 1/2s^3, \quad c_2 = 0, \quad c_3 = 1/4s^3.$$

Consequently the solution has the form

$$x(\lambda) = \frac{1}{8}\left(\frac{4}{s^3} - \frac{2\lambda}{s^3} + \frac{\lambda^2}{s^2}\right)e^{\lambda s} + \frac{1}{4s^3}\lambda e^{-\lambda s}.$$

This is the only solution of equation (21.1) that satisfies conditions (21.2).

Exercise. Find the operational functions satisfying the following equations with the given conditions:

(α) $x'' + 5sx' + 6s^2 x = \frac{6}{s}, \quad x(0) = \frac{2}{s^3}, \; x'(0) = \frac{3}{s^2};$

(β) $x'' + 5sx' + 6s^2 x = [1 + 5\lambda s + (2 - 5s + 3s^2)\lambda^2]e^{-2\lambda s}, \; x(0) = -\frac{1}{2}, \; x(1) = 0;$

(γ) $sx''' - x'' - 2s^2 x' + 2sx = 3s \sin\lambda\sqrt{s} - 3s^{5/2}\cos\lambda\sqrt{s},$

$x(-1) = e^{-1/s} - \sin\sqrt{s}, \; x(0) = 1, \; x(1) = e^{1/s} + \sin\sqrt{s};$

(δ) $x^{(4)} + 2(1 + s^2)x'' + 4s^2 x = \sin\lambda\sqrt{2}, \quad x(0) = x(2) = 1/s;$

(ε) $x^{(4)} - 2(1 + s^2)x'' + 4s^2 x = \sin\lambda\sqrt{2},$

$x(0) = 1, \; x(\pi/\sqrt{2}) = e^{\pi}, \quad x(-\pi/\sqrt{2}) = e^{-\pi}, \quad x(\pi\sqrt{2}) = e^{2\pi}.$

Are the solutions obtained unique?

CHAPTER III

APPLICATIONS TO PARTIAL DIFFERENTIAL EQUATIONS

§ 22. Reducing partial operational equations to operational equations. In Part II we reduced certain special partial equations (the vibrating string equation, the equation of heat, the equation of telegraphy) to operational equations. We shall now discuss this question in a more general way. We shall retain our restriction to partial equations with constant coefficients since it is to them that the operational calculus can best be applied. Any such equation can be written in the form

$$\sum_{\mu=0}^{m}\sum_{\nu=0}^{n} a_{\mu\nu}x_{\lambda^\mu t^\nu}(\lambda, t) = \varphi(\lambda, t). \tag{22.1}$$

Using the general formula

$$\{x^{(\nu)}(t)\} = s^\nu\{x(t)\} - s^{\nu-1}x(0) - \ldots - x^{(\nu-2)}(0)$$

we have

$$\{x_{\lambda^\mu t^\nu}(\lambda, t)\} = s^\nu\{x_{\lambda^\mu}(\lambda, t)\} - \sum_{\varkappa=0}^{\nu-1} s^{\nu-\varkappa-1}x_{\lambda^\mu t^\nu}(\lambda, 0) \qquad (\nu \geqslant 1) \tag{22.2}$$

and equation (22.2) can be written in the following operational form:

$$a_m x^{(m)} + \ldots + a_0 x = f(\lambda), \tag{22.3}$$

where

$$a_\mu = a_{\mu n}s^n + \ldots + a_{\mu 0} \qquad (\mu = 0, \ldots, m),$$

$$f(\lambda) = \{\varphi(\lambda, t)\} + \sum_{\mu=0}^{m}\sum_{\nu=1}^{n}\sum_{\varkappa=0}^{\nu-1} \alpha^{\nu-\varkappa-1}x_{\lambda^\mu t^\varkappa}(\lambda, 0) \tag{22.4}$$

and

$$x = x(\lambda) = \{x(\lambda, t)\}.$$

Arranging expression (22.4) according to the powers of s we can write

$$f(\lambda) = \{\varphi(\lambda, t)\} + \sum_{\varkappa=0}^{n=1} s^{n-\varkappa-1}\sum_{\mu=0}^{m}\sum_{\nu=0}^{\varkappa} a_{\mu,n-\varkappa+\nu}x_{\lambda^\mu t^\nu}(\lambda, 0). \tag{22.5}$$

This equality may be obtained in the following way:
The symbol

$$\sum_{\nu=1}^{n}\sum_{\varkappa=1}^{\nu-1} \tag{22.6}$$

denotes summation over all those pairs of indices μ and ν to which correspond the points marked with circles in fig. 155. Introducing new indices, $\varkappa'$, ν', such that $\varkappa = \nu'$,

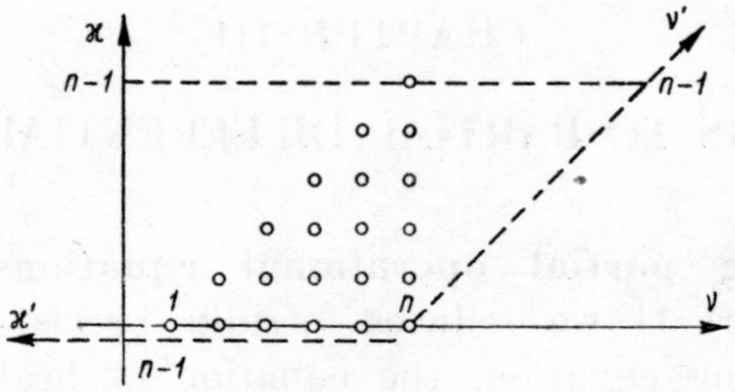

Fig. 155

$\nu = n-\varkappa'+\nu'$ we change the numbering of those points and, as shown in the figure, we must replace the symbol (22.6) by

$$\sum_{\varkappa'=0}^{n=1}\sum_{\nu'=0}^{\varkappa'-1}.$$

Consequently the treble sum in (22.4) can be written in the form

$$\sum_{\mu=0}^{m}\sum_{\varkappa'=0}^{n-1}\sum_{\nu'=0}^{\varkappa'-1} a_{\mu,n-\varkappa'+\nu'}s^{n-\varkappa'-1}x_{\lambda^\mu t^{\nu'}}\quad(\lambda,0),$$

which immediately implies formula (22.5).

Example 1. Find the general solution of the differential equation

$$x_{\lambda\lambda}+x_{tt} = 0 \tag{22.7}$$

satisfying the conditions

$$x(\lambda, 0) = e^{\lambda},\quad x_t(\lambda, 0) = e^{2\lambda}. \tag{22.8}$$

In this case the operational equation has the form

$$x''+sx = sx(\lambda, 0)+x_t(\lambda, 0),$$

i. e., on considering conditions (22.8), we have

$$x''+s^2x = se^{\lambda}+e^{2\lambda}. \tag{22.9}$$

In order to simplify this equation it is best to decompose it into the following two:

$$x''+s^2x_1 = e^{\lambda}\quad\text{and}\quad x''+s^2x_2 = e^{2\lambda};$$

by § 17 the solutions of these equations have the form

$$x_1(\lambda) = \frac{e^{\lambda}}{1+s^2} \quad \text{and} \quad x_2(\lambda) = \frac{e^{2\lambda}}{4+s^2}.$$

Hence we have the solution of equation (22.9):

$$(22.10) \qquad x(\lambda) = sx_1(\lambda) + x_2(\lambda) = \frac{s}{1+s^2}e^{\lambda} + \frac{1}{4+s^2}e^{2\lambda}.$$

In order to find the general solution we must solve the characteristic equation

$$u^2 + s^2 = 0;$$

the roots of this equation are the operators $-is$ and $+is$. But we know that the exponential functions $e^{-i\lambda s}$ and $e^{i\lambda s}$ do not exist. Consequently the general solution is reduced to function (22.10), which is the only solution of equation (22.9).

In the ordinary, non-operational form this function is expressed by the formula

$$x(\lambda, t) = e^{\lambda}\cos t + \tfrac{1}{2}e^{2\lambda}\sin 2t.$$

This is the only solution of equation (22.7) that satisfies conditions (22.8).

Equation (22.7) is called the *harmonic equation.*

EXAMPLE 2. The following equation is termed *biharmonic*:

$$(22.11) \qquad x_{\lambda^4} + 2x_{\lambda^2 t^2} + x_{t^4} = 0.$$

Let us solve it under the conditions

$$(22.12) \qquad x(\lambda, 0) = \lambda\sin\lambda, \quad x_t(\lambda, 0) = 0, \quad x_{t^2}(\lambda, 0) = 0, \quad x_{t^3}(\lambda, 0) = 0.$$

According to (22.2) we have

$$\{x_{\lambda^2 t^2}(\lambda, t)\} = s^2 x'' - s x_{\lambda^2}(\lambda, 0) - x_{\lambda^2 t}(\lambda, 0),$$
$$\{x_{t^4}(\lambda, t)\} = s^4 x - s^3 x(\lambda, 0) - s^2 x_t(\lambda, 0) - s x_{t^2}(\lambda, 0) - x_{t^3}(\lambda, 0).$$

Consequently the operational form of equation (22.11) is

$$x^{(4)} + 2s^2 x'' + s^4 x = s^3 x(\lambda, 0) + s^2 x_t(\lambda, 0) +$$
$$+ s[2x_{\lambda^2}(\lambda, 0) + x_{t^2}(\lambda, 0)] + [2x_{\lambda^2 t}(\lambda, 0) + x_{t^3}(\lambda, 0)].$$

Taking into account conditions (22.12) and the equalities resulting from them,

$$x_{\lambda^2}(\lambda, 0) = 2\cos\lambda - \lambda\sin\lambda, \quad x_{\lambda^2 t}(\lambda, 0) = 0,$$

we have

$$(22.13) \qquad x^{(4)} + 2s^2 x'' + s^4 x = s^3\lambda\sin\lambda + 2s(2\cos\lambda - \lambda\sin\lambda).$$

We seek a solution in the form

$$x(\lambda) = (c_1 + c_2\lambda)\sin\lambda + (c_3 + c_4\lambda)\cos\lambda;$$

substituting this expression in (22.13) and ordering, we have

$$(s^2-1)[(s^2-1)(c_1+c_2\lambda) - 4c_4]\sin\lambda + (s^2-1)[(s^2-1)(c_3+c_4\lambda) + 4c_2]\cos\lambda$$
$$= (s^3-2s)\lambda\sin\lambda + 4s\cos\lambda,$$

and by comparing the coefficients

$$(s^2-1)^2 c_2 = s^3 - 2s,$$
$$(s^2-1)^2 c_4 = 0,$$
$$(s^2-1)[(s^2-1)c_1 - 4c_4] = 0,$$
$$(s^2-1)[(s^2-1)c_3 + 4c_2] = 4s.$$

Hence

$$c_1 = 0, \quad c_2 = \frac{s(s^2-2)}{(s^2-1)^2}, \quad c_3 = \frac{4s}{(s^2-1)^3}, \quad c_4 = 0.$$

Consequently the required solution has the form

$$x(\lambda) = \frac{s(s^2-2)}{(s^2-1)^2}\lambda\sin\lambda + \frac{4s}{(s^2-1)^3}\cos\lambda.$$

Since the characteristic equation

$$u^2 + 2s^2u^2 + s^4 = 0$$

has the (double) roots $-is$, $+is$, and the exponential functions $e^{-i\lambda s}$, $e^{i\lambda s}$ do not exist, the solution obtained is unique.

In view of the equalities

$$\frac{s(s^2-2)}{(s^2-1)^2} = \frac{s}{s^2-1} = \frac{1}{4(s-1)^2} + \frac{1}{4(s+1)^2}$$
$$= \left\{\operatorname{ch}t - \frac{1}{4}te^t + \frac{1}{4}te^{-t}\right\} = \left\{\operatorname{ch}t - \frac{t}{2}\operatorname{sh}t\right\},$$

$$\frac{4s}{(s^2-1)^3} = \frac{1}{4(s-1)^2} - \frac{1}{4(s-1)^2} + \frac{1}{2(s+1)^3} + \frac{1}{2(s-1)^2}$$
$$= \left\{\frac{t}{4}e^{-t} - \frac{t}{4}e^t + \frac{t^2}{4}e^{-t} + \frac{t^2}{4}e^t\right\} = \left\{\frac{t^2}{2}\operatorname{ch}t - \frac{t}{2}\operatorname{sh}t\right\}$$

we can write

$$x(\lambda, t) = \lambda\sin\lambda(\operatorname{ch}t - \tfrac{t}{2}\operatorname{sh}t) + \tfrac{1}{2}\cos\lambda(t^2\operatorname{ch}t - t\operatorname{sh}t).$$

This is the only solution of equation (22.11) that satisfies conditions (22.12).

EXAMPLE 3. Find the solution of the equation

$$x_{\lambda^2} - x_{\lambda t} + x_{t^3} = e^{\lambda - t} \tag{22.14}$$

satisfying the conditions

$$x(\lambda, 0) = 0 \quad \text{and} \quad x_t(\lambda, 0) = 0. \tag{22.15}$$

Since $\{e^{\lambda-t}\} = e^{\lambda}/(s+1)$, the operational equation has the form

$$x'' - sx' + s^2 x = sx(\lambda, 0) + x_t(\lambda, 0) - x_\lambda(\lambda, 0) + e^{\lambda}/(s+1),$$

and by conditions (22.15) and the resulting equation

$$x_\lambda(\lambda, 0) = 0, \tag{22.16}$$

we have

$$x'' - sx' + s^2 x = e^{\lambda}/(s+1)$$

Since $1 - s + s^2 \neq 0$, the function

$$x(\lambda) = e^{\lambda}/(1+s)(1-s+s^2) = e^{\lambda}/(s^3+1).$$

satisfies equation (22.16).

In view of the equality

$$\frac{1}{s^3+1} = \frac{1}{3}\,\frac{1}{s+1} - \frac{1}{3}\,\frac{s-\frac{1}{2}}{(s-\frac{1}{2})^2+\frac{3}{4}} \;\; \frac{1}{2}\,\frac{1}{(s-\frac{1}{2})^2+\frac{3}{4}}$$

$$= \left\{\frac{1}{3}e^{-t} - \frac{1}{3}e^{t/2}\cos\frac{\sqrt{3}t}{2} + \frac{1}{\sqrt{3}}e^{t/2}\sin\frac{\sqrt{3}t}{2}\right\}$$

we can write

$$x(\lambda, t) = \frac{1}{3}e^{\lambda}\left(e^{-t} - e^{t/2}\cos\frac{\sqrt{3}t}{2} + \sqrt{3}\,e^{t/2}\sin\frac{\sqrt{3}t}{2}\right).$$

In order to prove that this is the only solution of equation (22.14) that satisfies conditions (22.15) it is sufficient to observe that the roots of the characteristic equation

$$s^2 - su + s^2 = 0$$

are not logarithmic; indeed, those roots have the form

$$\frac{s}{2} + \frac{\sqrt{3}}{2}is, \quad \frac{s}{2} - \frac{\sqrt{3}}{2}is.$$

EXAMPLE 4. Find the function satisfying the equation

$$x_{\lambda^3} + 3x_{\lambda^2 t} + 3x_{\lambda t^2} + x_{t^3} = 0 \tag{22.17}$$

and the conditions

(22.18) $$x(\lambda, 0) = \lambda^3, \quad x_t(\lambda, 0) = \lambda^2, \quad x_{t^2}(\lambda, 0) = \lambda.$$

Since

$$\{x_{\lambda^3}\} = x''',$$
$$\{x_{\lambda^2 t}\} = sx'' - x_{\lambda^2}(\lambda, 0),$$
$$\{x_{\lambda t^2}\} = s^2 x' - sx_\lambda(\lambda, 0) - x_{\lambda t}(\lambda, 0),$$
$$\{x_{t^3}\} = s^3 x - s^2 x(\lambda, 0) - sx_t(\lambda, 0) - x_{t^2}(\lambda, 0),$$

the operational equation has the form

$$x''' + 3sx''' + 3s^2 x' + s^3 x = s^2 x(\lambda, 0) +$$
$$+ s[3x_\lambda(\lambda, 0) + x_t(\lambda, 0)] + [3x_{\lambda^2}(\lambda, 0) + 3x_{\lambda t}(\lambda, 0) + x_{t^2}(\lambda, 0)],$$

and, taking into account conditions (22.18), we have

(22.19) $$x''' + 3sx'' + 3s^2 x' + s^3 x = s^2\lambda^3 + 10s\lambda^2 + 25\lambda.$$

Using undetermined coefficients we find for equation (22.19) a polynomial solution,

$$x_0(\lambda) = l\lambda^3 + l^2\lambda^2 + l^3\lambda - 15l^4.$$

It is not the only solution of equation (22.19), for the characteristic equation

$$u^3 + 3su^2 + 3s^2 u + s^3 = 0$$

has a treble root $-s$ which is a logarithm. Consequently the general solution of (22.19) has the form

$$x(\lambda) = (c_0 + c_1\lambda + c_2\lambda^2)e^{-\lambda s} + x_0(\lambda)$$

where c_1, c_2 and c are arbitrary operators.

Hence the solution of the partial equation (22.17) is not defined in a unique manner by conditions (22.18). To make it unique we introduce further conditions, *e. g.*,

(22.20) $$x(0, t) = t^3, \quad x_\lambda(0, t) = t^2, \quad x_{\lambda\lambda}(0, t) = t.$$

These conditions correspond to the operational conditions

$$x(0) = 6l^4, \quad x'(0) = 2l^3, \quad x''(0) = l^2;$$

they lead to the equalities

$$x(0) = c_0 - 15l^4 = 6l^4,$$
$$x'(0) = c_1 - sc_0 + l^3 = 2l^3,$$
$$x''(0) = 2c_2 - 2sc_1 + s^2 c_0 + 2l^2 = l^2,$$

from which we obtain

$$c_0 = 21l^4, \quad c_1 = 22l^3, \quad c_2 = 11l^2.$$

Consequently the required solution is the function

$$x(\lambda) = (21l^4+22l^3\lambda+11l^2\lambda^2)e^{-\lambda s}+l\lambda^3+l^2\lambda^2+l^3\lambda-15l^4.$$

Taking into account the meaning of the translation operator $e^{-\lambda s}$, we obtain the formulas

$$x(\lambda, t) = \begin{cases} \lambda^3+t\lambda^2+\frac{1}{2}t^2\lambda-\frac{}{2}t^3 & \text{for} \quad 0 \leqslant t < \lambda, \\ -\frac{5}{2}\lambda^2+\frac{1}{2}t\lambda^2+t^2\lambda+t^3 & \text{for} \quad 0 \leqslant \lambda < t. \end{cases}$$

This is the only solution of equation (22.17) that satisfies conditions (22.18) and (22.20).

§ 23. Remarks on additional conditions. The difference between the last of the above examples and the preceding ones lies in the fact that in the last case, besides conditions (22.18) defining the behaviour of the solution on the t axis, three more conditions are needed to establish the solution uniquely. This is due to the circumstance that the general solution of the operational equation (22.19) contains three arbitrary constants. The number of supplementary conditions will always be equal to the number of arbitrary constants ocurring in the general solution. These conditions may be given upon one or more straight lines parallel to the t axis. *E. g.*, as regards the problems of the vibrating string and of heat conductibility we solved cases in which the supplementary conditions were given on two straight lines. (The number of those lines cannot of course exceed the number of arbitrary constants in the general solution).

Exercise. Solve the following differential equations with the given conditions:

(α) $x_{\lambda\lambda}+x_{tt} = 0$, $x(\lambda, 0) = \lambda$, $x_t(\lambda, 0) = \sin\lambda$;

(β) $x_{\lambda\lambda}+x_{tt} = 1$, $x(\lambda, 0) = 0$, $x_t(\lambda, 0) = \lambda^2 e^{-\lambda}$;

(γ) $x_{\lambda^3}+x_{\lambda^2 t}+3x_{\lambda t^2}+3x_{t^3} = t^2 e^{\lambda}$, $x(\lambda, 0) = x_t(\lambda, 0) = x_{t^2}(\lambda, 0) = 0$,
$x(0, t) = 0$ $(0 \leqslant \lambda < \infty,\ 0 \leqslant t < \infty)$.

§ 24. An incorrect solution. Let us solve the equation

$$x_{\lambda^3 t}+x_{\lambda^2 t}+x_{\lambda t^2}-x_{\lambda t^2}-x_{t^3}-x_t+1 = 0 \tag{24.1}$$

with the conditions

(24.2) $$x(\lambda, 0) = 0, \quad x_t(\lambda, 0) = 1 - e^{-\lambda} \quad (0 < \lambda < \infty),$$

(24.3) $$x(0, t) = 0, \quad x_\lambda(0, t) = 2\sqrt{t/\pi}, \quad x_{\lambda^2}(0, t) = -1 \quad (0 < t < \infty).$$

The corresponding operational equation has the form

$$sx''' + (s+1)x'' - s^2 x' - (s^2+s)x = -s[x_\lambda(\lambda, 0) + x(\lambda, 0)] + \\ + [x_{\lambda^3}(\lambda, 0) + x_{\lambda^2}(\lambda, 0) - x_{\lambda t}(\lambda, 0) - x(\lambda, 0)] - 1/s.$$

From (24.2) we easily find

$$x_\lambda(\lambda, 0) = x_{\lambda 2}(\lambda, 0) = x_{\lambda 2}(\lambda, 0) = 0, \quad x_{\lambda t}(\lambda, 0) = e^{-\lambda};$$

consequently we have

(24.4) $$\begin{gathered} x_\lambda(\lambda, 0) + x(\lambda, 0) = 0, \\ x_{\lambda 3}(\lambda, 0) + x_{\lambda 2}(\lambda, 0) - x_{\lambda t}(\lambda, 0) - x_t(\lambda, 0) - x(\lambda, 0) = -1 \end{gathered}$$

and

(24.5) $$sx''' + (s+1)x'' - s^2 x' - (s^2+s)x = -1 - 1/s.$$

It is easy to find the polynomial solution of equation (24.5); it is reduced to the constant

$$x_0(\lambda) = 1/s^2.$$

The characteristic equation has the form

$$su^3 + (s+1)u^2 - s^2 u - (s^2+s) = 0,$$

and its roots are the operators

$$\sqrt{s}, \quad -\sqrt{s} \quad \text{and} \quad -1/s-1$$

Consequently the general solution of equation (24.5) is the expression

$$x^{(\lambda)} = c_1 e^{\lambda\sqrt{s}} + c_2 e^{-\lambda\sqrt{s}} + c_3 e^{-\lambda(1/s+1)} + 1/s^2.$$

The following operational conditions correspond to conditions (24.3):

$$x(0) = 0, \quad x'(0) = s^{-3/2}, \quad x''(0) = -s^{-1};$$

using them in order to establish the constants c_1, c_2, and c_3, we obtain the equalities

$$x(0) = c_1 + c_2 + c_3 + s^{-2} = 0,$$

$$x'(0) = \sqrt{s}c_1 - \sqrt{s}c_2 - (s^{-1}+1)c_3 = s^{-3/2},$$

$$x''(0) = sc_1 + sc_2 + (s^{-1}+1)^2 c_3 = -s^{-1},$$

whence

$$c_1 = 0, \quad c_2 = -s^{-2}, \quad c_3 = 0,$$

and

$$x(\lambda) = \frac{1}{s^2}(1 - e^{-\lambda\sqrt{s}}).$$

This equality can also be written in the form

$$x(\lambda) = \frac{1}{s}\left(\frac{1}{s} - \frac{1}{s}e^{-\lambda\sqrt{s}}\right) = \frac{1}{s}\left\{1 - \operatorname{cerf}\frac{\lambda}{2\sqrt{t}}\right\} = \frac{1}{s}\left\{\operatorname{erf}\frac{\lambda}{2\sqrt{t}}\right\}.$$

Hence we have the following "solution" of the problem posed at the beginning of this section:

$$x(\lambda, t) = \int_0^t \operatorname{erf}\frac{\lambda}{2\sqrt{\tau}}\,d\tau. \tag{24.6}$$

The word "solution" has been put in inverted commas because what we actually have here is not a solution since the obtained function $x(\lambda, t)$ does not satisfy the required conditions. Indeed, we have

$$x_t(\lambda, t) = \operatorname{erf}\frac{\lambda}{2\sqrt{t}}$$

and in the limit, as $t \to 0$, we have $x_t(\lambda, 0) = 1$, contrary to the second condition of (24.2).

Where does the error lie? — The answer will be given in the next section.

§ 25. Explaining the apparent contradiction. To begin with it will be observed that the operational function obtained, $x(\lambda) = \{x(\lambda, t)\}$, satisfies the operational equation (24.5). That equation has been deduced from equation (24.1) considering conditions (24.2). But those conditions have not been fully exploited, for in passing to the operational form we have used only equalities (24.4).

As can be verified, the function $x(\lambda, t)$ satisfies conditions (24.4) and does not satisfy conditions (24.2). The calculation performed shows that this function is the only solution of equation (24.1) that satisfies conditions (24.3) and (24.4).

Actually it is possible to verify directly that the function $x(\lambda, t)$ satisfies equation (24.1) and conditions (24.3) and (24.4).

Indeed, by

$$x(\lambda, t) = \int_0^t \operatorname{erf}\frac{\lambda}{2\sqrt{\tau}}\,d\tau = \frac{2}{\sqrt{\pi}}\int_0^t d\tau \int_0^{\lambda/2\sqrt{\tau}} e^{-\sigma^2}\,d\sigma \tag{25.1}$$

we obtain in turn the derivatives with respect to λ:

$$x_\lambda(\lambda, t) = \frac{1}{\sqrt{\pi}} \int_0^t \frac{1}{\sqrt{\tau}} \exp\left(-\frac{\lambda^2}{4\tau}\right) d\tau,$$

(25.2) $$x_{\lambda^2}(\lambda, t) = -\frac{1}{2\sqrt{\pi}} \int_0^t \frac{\lambda}{\sqrt{\tau^3}} \exp\left(-\frac{\lambda^2}{4\tau}\right) d\tau - \frac{2}{\sqrt{\pi}} \int_{\lambda/2\sqrt{t}}^{\infty} e^{-\sigma^2} d\sigma = -\operatorname{cerf} \frac{\lambda}{2\sqrt{t}},$$

$$x_{\lambda^3}(\lambda, t) = \frac{1}{\sqrt{\pi t}} \exp\left(-\frac{\lambda^2}{4t}\right).$$

Similarly, from (25.1) we obtain the derivatives with respect to t:

(25.3) $$x_t(\lambda, t) = \operatorname{erf} \frac{\lambda}{2\sqrt{t}} = \frac{2}{\sqrt{\pi}} \int_0^{\lambda/2\sqrt{t}} e^{-\sigma^2} d\sigma,$$

$$x_{t^2}(\lambda, t) = -\frac{\lambda}{2\sqrt{\pi t^3}} \exp\left(-\frac{\lambda^2}{4t}\right).$$

We find in turn the mixed derivatives

$$x_{\lambda t}(\lambda, t) = \frac{1}{\sqrt{\pi t}} \exp\left(-\frac{\lambda^2}{4t}\right),$$

(25.4) $$x_{\lambda t^2}(\lambda, t) = -\left(\frac{1}{2\sqrt{\pi t^3}} + \frac{\lambda^2}{4\sqrt{\pi t^5}}\right) \exp\left(-\frac{\lambda^2}{4t}\right),$$

$$x_{\lambda^2}(\lambda, t) = -\frac{\lambda}{2\sqrt{\pi t^3}} \exp\left(-\frac{\lambda^2}{4t}\right),$$

$$x_{\lambda^3 t}(\lambda, t) = -\left(\frac{1}{2\sqrt{\pi t^3}} + \frac{\lambda^2}{4\sqrt{\pi t^5}}\right) \exp\left(-\frac{\lambda^2}{4t}\right).$$

Substituting suitable values in equation (24.1) and deleting identical terms differing in sign, we obtain on the left side

$$-\operatorname{cerf} \frac{\lambda}{2\sqrt{t}} - \operatorname{erf} \frac{\lambda}{2\sqrt{t}} + 1;$$

in view of the properties of the functions cerf and erf this expression is equal to zero. Equation (24.1) is thus satisfied.

Now substituting $\lambda = 0$, we obtain from formulas (25.1) and (25.2)

$$x(0, t) = 0, \quad x_\lambda(0, t) = \frac{1}{\sqrt{\pi}} \int_0^t \frac{d\tau}{\sqrt{\tau}} = 2\sqrt{\frac{t}{\pi}}, \quad x_{\lambda^2}(0, t) = -1,$$

since cerf $0 = 1$. Obviously conditions (24.3) are satisfied.

Similarly, substituting $\lambda = 0$ in formula (25.1) we obtain

$$x(\lambda, 0) = 0, \tag{25.5}$$

whence

$$x_\lambda(\lambda, 0) = x_{\lambda 2}(\lambda, 0) = x_{\lambda 3}(\lambda, 0) = 0 \tag{25.6}$$

(the last three equalities may also be obtained directly from (25.2) as $t \to 0$). The first formula of (25.3) gives, as $t \to 0$,

$$x_t(\lambda, 0) = \frac{2}{\sqrt{\pi}} \int_0^\infty e^{-\sigma^2} d\sigma = 1, \tag{25.7}$$

whence

$$x_{\lambda t}(\lambda, 0) = 0 \tag{25.8}$$

(the last equality may also be obtained directly from the first formula of (25.4) as $t \to 0$). Substituting the values (25.5) and (25.8) in equalities (24.4), we easily verify that those equalities are satisfied.

If a function satisfies conditions (24.2), then it also satisfies conditions (24.4). Hence it follows that a solution of equation (24.1) satisfying conditions (24.2) and (24.3) does not exist at all.

The problem was thus wrongly posed in the preceding section, the system of conditions (24.2) and (24.3) being, for a given condition, contradictory.

This contradiction vanishes if the conditions on the λ axis are presented at once in the form (24.4). Under those conditions and conditions (24.3), we obtain function (24.6) which is now the unique actual and not the wrong solution of the problem.

Conditions (24.2) and (24.4) are not equivalent. (24.2) imply (24.4) but not *vice versa.*

In all our previous examples conditions analogous to (24.2) and (24.4) were always equivalent and therefore the solutions obtained were correct.

§ 26. The Cauchy conditions and the question of their being equivalent to the general conditions. When passing from the general equation (22.1)

$$\sum_{\mu=0}^{m} \sum_{\nu=0}^{n} a_{\mu\nu} x_{\lambda^\mu t^\nu}(\lambda, t) = \varphi(\lambda, t)$$

to the operational equation (22.3)

$$a_m x^{(m)} + \ldots + a_0 x = f(\lambda),$$

in order to determine the function $f(\lambda)$ it is sufficient to know the form, in a given interval $\alpha < \lambda < \beta$, of the functions

$$(26.1) \qquad \sum_{\mu=0}^{m} \sum_{\nu=0}^{\varkappa} a_{\mu, n-\varkappa+\nu} x_{\lambda^\mu t^\nu}(\lambda, 0) = g_\varkappa(\lambda) \qquad (\varkappa = 0, \ldots, n-1),$$

which determine the behaviour of the solution $x(\lambda, t)$ on the λ axis.

In some cases, as in the examples of § 22, conditions (26.1) may be replaced by simpler conditions

$$(26.2) \qquad x_{t^\varkappa}(\lambda, 0) = h_\varkappa(\lambda) \qquad (\varkappa = 0, \ldots, n-1);$$

conditions of the type (26.2) are termed the *Cauchy conditions.*

But, as was shown in §§ 24 and 25, the Cauchy conditions (26.2) may be introduced instead of the general conditions (26.1) only if they are equivalent to the latter.

If for a certain partial equation conditions (26.1) and (26.2) are not equivalent, the equation will be said to be *restrictive.* In that case the conditions on the λ axis should be given in the form (26.1). If the equation is not restrictive, the conditions on the λ axis may be given either in the form (26.1) or in the Cauchy form (26.2).

It may always be assumed that at least one of the coefficients $a_{0n}, \ldots, a_{mn}$ is different from zero. We then have the following criterion:

Equation (22.1) *is not restrictive if and only if*

$$(26.3) \qquad a_{1n} = \ldots = a_{mn} = 0,$$

or, which is the same, if no partial derivative whose order with respect to t is the highest in the given equation is a mixed derivative.

Proof. If condition (26.3) is satisfied, then $a_{0n} \neq 0$ and equalities (26.1) may be written in the form

$$(26.4) \qquad a_{0n} x(\lambda, 0) = g_0(\lambda),$$

$$(26.5) \qquad a_{0n} x_{t^\varkappa}(\lambda, 0) + \sum_{\mu=0}^{m} \sum_{\nu=0}^{\varkappa-1} a_{\mu n-\varkappa+\nu} x_{\lambda^\mu t^\nu}(\lambda, 0) = g_\varkappa(\lambda) \quad (\varkappa = 1, \ldots, n-1).$$

The function $x(\lambda, 0)$ is uniquely defined by equality (26.4). Taking in (26.5) $\varkappa = 1$ we shall find $x_t(\lambda, 0)$ uniquely since under the sign of double sum we have only functions $x_{\lambda^\mu}(\lambda, 0)$, which are known provided the function $x(\lambda, 0)$ is known. Taking in turn $\varkappa = 2$ we may uniquely find $x_{t^2}(\lambda, 0)$ from (26.5) since under the summation sign we shall have only functions $x(\lambda, 0)$, $x_t(\lambda, 0)$ and their derivatives (with respect to λ). In this manner we shall uniquely obtain all functions $x(\lambda, 0), x_t(\lambda, 0), \ldots, x_{t^{n-1}}(\lambda, 0)$.

Hence it follows that if all functions $g_\varkappa(\lambda)$ are determined, then at the same time all functions $b_\varkappa(\lambda)$ are determined. On the other hand, it is obvious from the form of the equalities (26.1) and (26.2) that if all functions $b_\varkappa(\lambda)$ are determined, then *eo ipso* all functions $g_\varkappa(\lambda)$ are determined. Consequently conditions (26.1) and (26.2) are equivalent.

If condition (26.3) is not satisfied, then at least one of the coefficients $a_{1n}, \ldots, a_{mn}$ is different from zero. Then for $\varkappa = 0$ we can find $x(\lambda, 0)$ from equality (26.1) by solving the (ordinary) differential equation

$$\sum_{\mu=0}^{n} a_{\mu n} x_{\lambda \mu}(\lambda, 0) = g_0(\lambda);$$

the solution is not unique. Having established $x(\lambda, 0)$, we may successively obtain (not necessarily in a unique manner) the functions $x_t(\lambda, 0), \ldots$ $\ldots, x_{t^{n-1}}(\lambda, 0)$. Thus in this case conditions (26.1) and (26.2) are not equivalent. The criterion is thus proved.

It is easy to verify that in all the examples of § 22 condition (26.3) is satisfied. *E. g.*, in equation (22.16) the last term represents a derivative of the highest order with respect to t; that derivative is not mixed. Now in equation (24.1) the terms $x_{\lambda t^2}$ and x_{t^2} are derivatives of the highest (second) order with respect to t; however, the first of them is a mixed derivative, which implies that the equation is restrictive.

§ 27. Solving restrictive equations. The operational method makes it possible to solve both restrictive and non-restrictive equations. An example of a restrictive equation is provided by equation (24.1); the solution of that equation found in § 24 is correct under conditions (24.3) and (24.4).

We shall now discuss another example of a restrictive equation, namely

$$x_{\lambda^3 t} + x_{\lambda t^3} + x_{\lambda^2} + x_{t^2} = e^{\lambda + t}. \tag{27.1}$$

This equation has the corresponding operational equation

$$\begin{aligned} &sx''' + x'' + s^3 x' + s^2 x \\ &= s^2 x_\lambda(\lambda, 0) + s[x_{\lambda t}(\lambda, 0) + x(\lambda, 0)] + [x_{\lambda^3}(\lambda, 0) + x_{\lambda t^2}(\lambda, 0) + x_t(\lambda, 0)] + \frac{e^\lambda}{s-1}. \end{aligned} \tag{27.2}$$

Since in equation (27.1) the derivative of the highest order with respect to t is represented by the term $x_{\lambda t^3}$ and is a mixed derivative, the equation is restrictive. Consequently we shall write the conditions on the λ axis in the form

$$\begin{aligned} x_\lambda(\lambda, 0) &= g_0(\lambda), \\ x_{\lambda t}(\lambda, 0) + x(\lambda, 0) &= g_1(\lambda), \\ x_{\lambda^3}(\lambda, 0) + x_{\lambda t^3}(\lambda, 0) + x_t(\lambda, 0) &= g_2(\lambda). \end{aligned} \tag{27.3}$$

In order to find out how many conditions on the t axis must be given we seek the roots of the characteristic equation

$$su^3+u^2+s^3u+s^2 = 0.$$

They are the operators

$$-1/s, \quad is, \quad -is.$$

Since only one of them (the first) is logarithmic, one condition on the t axis is sufficient:

$$x(0,t) = v(t). \tag{27.4}$$

By (27.3), the operational equation (27.2) assumes the form

$$sx'''+x''+s^3x'+s^2x = s^2g_0(\lambda)+sg_1(\lambda)+g_2(\lambda)+\frac{e^\lambda}{s-1}; \tag{27.5}$$

condition (27.4) may be written in the operational form

$$x(0) = v.$$

Knowing $g_0(\lambda)$, $g_1(\lambda)$, $g_2(\lambda)$ and v, we may solve equation (27.1) by the same method as has been used in solving the examples in § 22.

If we assume for example that

$$\begin{gathered} x_\lambda(\lambda,0) = \tfrac{1}{4}e^\lambda, \quad x_{\lambda t}(\lambda,0)+x(\lambda,0) = 1+\tfrac{1}{2}e^\lambda, \\ x_{\lambda 3}(\lambda,0)+x_{\lambda t 3}(\lambda,0)+x_t(\lambda,0) = \lambda+\tfrac{3}{4}e^\lambda, \quad v(t) = \tfrac{1}{4}e^t, \end{gathered} \tag{27.6}$$

we shall have

$$sx'''+x''+s^3x'+s^2x = \tfrac{1}{4}\left(s^2+2s+3+\frac{4}{s-1}\right)e^\lambda+s+\lambda. \tag{27.7}$$

A particular solution of this equation will easily be found by splitting it into the following two:

$$sx_1'''+x_1''+s^3x_1'+s^2x_1 = \tfrac{1}{4}\left(s^2+2s+3+\frac{4}{s-1}\right)e^\lambda,$$

$$sx_2'''+x_2''+s^3x_2'+s^2x_2 = s+\lambda.$$

For the first of these equations we find a particular solution (see § 17)

$$x_1(\lambda) = \frac{\tfrac{1}{4}\left(s^2+2s+3+\dfrac{4}{s-1}\right)}{s+1+s^3+s^2}\,e^\lambda = \frac{e^\lambda}{4(s-1)},$$

and for the second (see § 16)

$$x_2(\lambda) = \lambda/s^2.$$

Consequently we may regard the function

$$x_0(\lambda) = x_1(\lambda)+x_2(\lambda) = \frac{e^\lambda}{4(s-1)}+\frac{\lambda}{s^2}$$

as a particular solution of equation (27.7).

Since the characteristic equation has only one root that is logarithmic, namely $-1/s$, the general solution of equation (27.7) has the form

$$x(\lambda) = ce^{-\lambda/s}+\frac{e^\lambda}{4(s-1)}+\frac{\lambda}{s^2}.$$

Adapting it to the condition

$$x(0) = \nu = \frac{1}{4(s-1)}$$

we easily obtain $c = 0$ and

$$x(\lambda) = \frac{e^\lambda}{4(s-1)}+\frac{\lambda}{s^2}.$$

Consequently the required solution of the partial equation (27.1) is the function

$$x(\lambda, t) = \tfrac{1}{4}e^{\lambda+t}+\lambda t;$$

this is the only solution of this equation that satisfies conditions (27.6).

§ 28. The question of the equivalence of a partial equation and an operational equation. The partial equation (27.1) with conditions (27.3) has the corresponding operational equation (27.5). Let us consider whether they are wholly equivalent.

Each solution of the partial equation (27.1) that satisfies the initial conditions (27.3) regarded as a parametric function is at the same time a solution of the operational equation (27.5). If we add to such a solution the operational equation (27.5) for example, the sum will still satisfy the operational equation (27.5) since the function $se^{-s^{-1}\lambda}$ satisfies the homogeneous equation

$$sx'''+x''+s^3x'+s^2x = 0.$$

But that sum will no longer be a parametric function and therefore it cannot be a solution of a partial equation.

The class of solutions of the operational equation (27.5) is thus wider than the class of solutions of the partial equation (27.1) with conditions (27.3).

However, if we restrict ourselves to the class of parametric functions $x(\lambda) = x(\lambda, t)$ such that the partial derivatives

$$x_{\lambda^3 t}(\lambda, t), \quad x_{\lambda t^3}(\lambda, t), \quad x_{\lambda^2}(\lambda, t), \quad \text{and} \quad x_{t^2}(\lambda, t)$$

are continuous, then each solution of the operational equation (27.5) will simultaneously be a solution of the partial equation (27.1) satisfying conditions (27.3). Thus within that class the operational equation (27.5) is equivalent to the partial equation (27.1) with conditions (27.3).

The same occurs in the general case:

Within the class of functions $x(\lambda, t)$ *whose partial derivatives* $x_{\lambda^\mu t^\nu}(\lambda, t)$ *occurring in equation* (22.1) *are all continuous in a certain domain* D,

$$\alpha \leqslant \lambda \leqslant \beta, \qquad 0 \leqslant t < \infty,$$

equation (22.1) *with the addition of initial conditions* (26.1) *is equivalent to the operational equation* (22.3) *considered in the interval* $\alpha \leqslant \lambda \leqslant \beta$.

G. Doetsch [2] points out that in numerous physical applications the class of solutions considered above is too narrow. Thus it is advisable to extend it to functions whose partial derivatives, occurring in the equation, are defined and continuous inside the domain D. Those functions must satisfy the equation inside the domain D but need not satisfy the equation on its boundary. Then the conditions on the λ axis and on the t axis should be regarded as equalities which are obtained in the limit in approaching those axes. (This is how the conditions for the equation of heat (Chapter 6, Part II) and conditions (24.4) for equation (24.1) should be understood). We shall not consider in general the question of equivalence of an operational equation and a partial one with limit conditions of this kind; it will only be observed that owing to the general character of the notion of limit in the operational calculus boundary conditions in partial equations can be taken in a very broad sense.

§ 29. Further examples of solving partial equations.

EXAMPLE 1. Solve the differential equation

$$x_{\lambda^3} + x_{t^3} = 1 + t^2\lambda \qquad (t \geqslant 0,\ \lambda \geqslant 0) \tag{29.1}$$

with the initial conditions

$$x(\lambda, 0) = x_t(\lambda, 0) = x_{t^2}(\lambda, 0) = 0, \tag{29.2}$$

$$x(0, t) = 0. \tag{29.3}$$

On the λ axis the Cauchy conditions are given, since according to the criterion of § 26 the equation is not restrictive.

The operational equation corresponding to equation (29.1) and conditions (29.2) has the form

$$x''' + s^3 x = l + 2l^3\lambda;$$

by the method of undetermined coefficients we find its polynomial solution

$$x_0(\lambda) = l^4 + 2l^6\lambda.$$

In order to find the general solution we seek the roots of the characteristic equation

$$u^3 + s^3 = 0;$$

they are the operators

$$-s, \quad \tfrac{1}{2} + i\frac{\sqrt{3}}{2}s, \quad \tfrac{1}{2} - i\frac{\sqrt{3}}{2}s,$$

of which only the first is logarithmic. Consequently the general solution will be the expression

$$x(\lambda) = ce^{-s\lambda} + l^4 + 2l^6\lambda.$$

By (29.3) we have $x(0) = 0$, *i. e.*, $c + l^4 = 0$. Hence $c = -l^4$ and the required solution is

$$x(\lambda) = -l^4 e^{-s\lambda} + l^4 + 2l^6\lambda.$$

Taking into account the translation operator $e^{-\lambda s}$ we can write

$$x(\lambda, t) = \begin{cases} \frac{1}{6}t^3 + \frac{1}{60}t^5\lambda & \text{for} \quad 0 \leqslant t \leqslant \lambda, \\ \frac{1}{2}t^2\lambda - \frac{1}{2}t\lambda^2 + \frac{1}{6}\lambda^3 + \frac{1}{60}t^5\lambda & \text{for} \quad 0 \leqslant \lambda \leqslant t. \end{cases}$$

This is the only solution of equation (29.1) that satisfies conditions (29.2) and (29.3).

Example 2. Solve the equation

$$x_{\lambda^4 t^2} + 4x_{\lambda^2 t^4} - x_{\lambda^2} - 4x_{t^2} = 0 \qquad (\lambda \geqslant 0,\ t \geqslant 0)$$

with the conditions

$$4x_{\lambda^2}(\lambda, 0) = 0,$$

$$4x_{t\lambda^2}(\lambda, 0) = 4,$$

$$x_{\lambda^4}(\lambda, 0) + 4x_{\lambda^2 t^2}(\lambda, 0) - 4x(\lambda, 0) = 0,$$

$$x_{\lambda^4 t}(\lambda, 0) + 4x_{\lambda^2 t^3}(\lambda, 0) - 4x_t(\lambda, 0) = 0,$$

(29.4) $$x(0, t) = 0, \qquad x_\lambda(0, t) = 0.$$

According to the criterion of § 26 this time the equation is restrictive; therefore the conditions on the λ axis are given in the general form.

We easily obtain the operational equation

$$s^2 x^{(4)} + (4s^4 - 1)x'' - 4s^2 x = 4s^2$$

and its particular solution

$$x_0 = -1.$$

The characteristic equation has the form

$$s^2 u^4 + 4s^4 u^2 - u^2 - 4s^2 = 0;$$

its roots are the operators

$$l, \quad -l, \quad 2is, \quad -2is,$$

of which only the first two are logarithms. Consequently the general solution is the expression

$$x(\lambda) = c_1 e^{l\lambda} + c_2 e^{-l\lambda} - 1.$$

By (29.4) we have $x(0) = x'(0) = 0$, whence $c_1 = c_2 = \frac{1}{2}$. Consequently

$$x(\lambda) = \operatorname{ch} l\lambda - 1 = \frac{l^2\lambda^2}{2!} + \frac{l^4\lambda^4}{4!} + \ldots$$

and

$$x(\lambda, t) = \frac{t\lambda^2}{1!2!} + \frac{t^3\lambda^4}{3!4!} + \ldots$$

This is the only solution that satisfies the conditions imposed.

EXAMPLE 3. Solve the equation

$$x_{\lambda^2 t^2} - 2x_{\lambda^2 t} + x_{\lambda^2} - x + 4e^{\lambda} = 0 \qquad (\lambda \geqslant 0, \ t \geqslant 0)$$

with the conditions

$$x_{\lambda^2}(\lambda, 0) = e^{\lambda},$$

$$x_{\lambda^2 t}(\lambda, 0) - 2x_{\lambda^2}(\lambda, 0) = \lambda, \tag{29.5}$$

$$x(0, t) = 1 + 2t, \quad x_{\lambda}(0, t) = 2t.$$

As in the preceding example, the equation is restrictive and the conditions on the λ axis are given in the general form.

We now have the operational equation

$$(s-1)^2 x'' - x = (s - 4l)e^{\lambda} + \lambda,$$

and the conditions resulting from (29.5)

$$x(0) = l + 2l^2, \quad x'(0) = 2l^2. \tag{29.6}$$

In order to find the particular solution $x_0(\lambda)$ let us split the equation into the following two:

$$(s-1)^2 x_1'' - x_1 = (s - 4l)e^{\lambda}, \quad (s-1)^2 x_2'' - x^2 = \lambda;$$

for these solutions we easily find the particular solution

$$x_1(\lambda) = (l+2l^2)e^\lambda \quad \text{and} \quad x_2(\lambda) = -\lambda.$$

Hence

$$x_0(\lambda) = x_1(\lambda)+x_2(\lambda) = (l+2l^2)e^\lambda - \lambda.$$

In order to find the general solution let us solve the characteristic equation

$$s^2u^2-2su^2+u^2-1 = 0;$$

its roots are the operators

$$\frac{1}{s-1} \quad \text{and} \quad \frac{-1}{s-1};$$

both are logarithmic since $1/(s-1) = \{e^t\}$. Consequently we have the general solution

$$x(\lambda) = c_1 \exp\left(\frac{\lambda}{s-1}\right) + c_2 \exp\left(-\frac{\lambda}{s-1}\right) + (l+2l^2)e^\lambda - \lambda.$$

From conditions (29.6) we obtain

$$c_1 = \tfrac{1}{2}l(s-1)^2, \qquad c_2 = -\tfrac{1}{2}l(s-1)^2.$$

Consequently

$$x(\lambda) = l(s-1)^2 \operatorname{sh}\frac{\lambda}{s-1} + (l+2l^2)e^\lambda - \lambda$$

$$= l(s-1)^2\left(\frac{\lambda}{1!(s-1)} + \frac{\lambda^3}{5!s(s-1)^3} + \ldots\right) + (l+2l^2)e^\lambda - \lambda$$

$$= \left((1-l)\lambda + \frac{\lambda^3}{3!s(s-1)} + \frac{\lambda^5}{5!s(s-1)^3} + \ldots\right) + (l+2l^2)e^\lambda - \lambda$$

$$= -l\lambda + \sum_{\nu=1}^{\infty} \frac{\lambda^{2\nu+1}}{(2\nu+1)!s(s-1)^{2\nu-1}} + (l+2l^2)e^\lambda$$

$$= (l+2l^2)e^\lambda - l\lambda - \sum_{\nu=1}^{\infty} \frac{\lambda^{2\lambda+1}}{(2\nu+1)!}\left(\frac{1}{s} - \frac{1}{s-1} + \ldots - \frac{1}{(s-1)^{2\nu-1}}\right)$$

and finally

$$x(\lambda, t) = (1+2t)e^\lambda - \lambda - \sum_{\nu=1}^{\infty} \frac{\lambda^{2\nu+1}}{(2\nu+1)!}\left(1+e^t\left[1-\frac{t}{1!}+\ldots+\frac{t^{2\nu-2}}{(2\nu-2)!}\right)\right].$$

This is the only solution satisfying the conditions imposed.

§ 30. General remarks on solving partial equations by the operational method. In the examples considered so far exponential functions of the following types have occurred:

$$e^{\lambda}, \quad e^{-\lambda s}, \quad e^{-\lambda\sqrt{s}}, \quad e^{-\lambda\sqrt{s+1}}, \quad e^{\lambda/s}, \quad e^{\lambda/(s-1)};$$

they correspond to the roots

$$(30.1) \qquad 1, \quad -s, \quad -\sqrt{s}, \quad -\sqrt{s+1}, \quad 1/s, \quad 1/(s-1)$$

of a characteristic equation. Obviously it is only in special cases that the roots of a characteristic equation are so simple in form.

The question arises whether a characteristic equation always has roots and what form they have. Now it can be proved (see Mikusiński [2]) that if the operational equation

$$a_m x^m + \ldots + a_0 x = f(\lambda)$$

has been deduced from the partial equation with constant coefficients

$$\sum_{\mu=0}^{m} \sum_{\nu=0}^{n} a_{\mu\nu} x_{\lambda^\mu t^\nu}(\lambda, t) = \varphi(\lambda, t),$$

then the characteristic equation

$$a_m u^m + \ldots + a_0 = 0$$

always has m roots and all those roots can be represented in the form of an infinite convergent series with numerical coefficients

$$(30.2) \qquad w = \beta_k s^{k/q} + \ldots + \beta_1 s^{1/q} + \beta_0 + \sum_{\varkappa=1}^{\infty} \gamma_\varkappa l^{\varkappa/q},$$

where k is a certain non-negative integer and q a natural number not greater than m. For instance

$$-\sqrt{s+1} = -\sqrt{s}\,(1+l)^{1/2} = -\sqrt{s}\left[1 + \binom{\frac{1}{2}}{1} l + \binom{\frac{1}{2}}{2} l^2 + \ldots\right]$$

$$= -\sqrt{s} - \sum_{\varkappa=1}^{\infty} \binom{\frac{1}{2}}{\varkappa} l^{\frac{2\varkappa-1}{2}};$$

$$\frac{1}{s-1} = \frac{l}{1-l} = \sum_{\varkappa=1}^{\infty} l^{\varkappa}.$$

All operators (30.1) can be regarded as particular cases of an operator of the type (30.2).

Having found all the roots of a characteristic equation, we must decide whether they are logarithms. For this determines the shape of the general solution and the number of arbitrary parameters occurring in it. Now we have the following criterion (Mikusiński [2]):

If $k/q > 1$ and $\beta_k \neq 0$ or if $k/q = 1$ and β_k is not real, then the operator w defined by equality (30.2) is not logarithmic. In the opposite case w is always a logarithm.

Hence it follows for example that the operators

$$s^2, \qquad s^3, \qquad s^2 + is, \qquad s^2 + 1/s$$

are not logarithmic and that all operators (30.1) are logarithmic.

If all the coefficients β_k are equal to zero, then the operator w is reduced to a function of class $\mathcal{K}$,

$$f = \sum_{\varkappa=1}^{\infty} \gamma_n l^{\varkappa/q} = \left\{ \sum_{\varkappa=1}^{\infty} \gamma_n \frac{t^{\frac{\varkappa}{q}-1}}{\Gamma(\varkappa/q)} \right\},$$

which is continuous for $t > 0$. In that case $e^{\lambda f}$ expands in a power series,

$$(30.3) \qquad e^{\lambda f} = 1 + \frac{\lambda f}{1!} + \frac{\lambda^2 f^2}{2!} + \dots$$

If $k = 0$, then the function $e^{\lambda w}$ may be written in the form

$$e^{\lambda w} = \exp(\beta_0 \lambda) \exp(\lambda f).$$

If $k = 1$, then

$$e^{\lambda w} = \exp(\lambda \beta_1 s^{1/q}) \exp(\lambda \beta_0) \exp(\lambda f);$$

if $k = 2$, then

$$e^{\lambda w} = \exp(\lambda \beta_2 s^{2/q}) \exp(\lambda \beta_1 s^{1/q}) \exp(\lambda \beta_0) \exp(\lambda f),$$

and so forth.

In these formulas the shape of the function $e^{\lambda f}$ is given by the series (30.3); the function $e^{\lambda \beta_0}$ is an ordinary exponential function. The remaining factors are of the form $\exp(\lambda \beta_n s^{\varkappa/q})$.

It can be proved in general that if $0 < \alpha < 1$, then for any complex β we have the expansion

$$(30.4) \qquad \exp(\lambda \beta s^\alpha) = 1 + \frac{\lambda \beta s^\alpha}{1!} + \frac{(\lambda \beta s^\alpha)^2}{2!} + \dots,$$

this series being convergent in the operational sense for any real λ (see Ryll-Nardzewski [2]).

If β is real and negative, then it is more convenient to use the formula (see Mikusiński [2]),

$$(30.5) \qquad \exp(\lambda\beta s^\alpha) = \left\{ \frac{1}{2\pi i} \int_{-i\infty}^{+i\infty} \exp(zt - z^\alpha \lambda\beta)\,dz \right\}$$

or the equivalent formula

$$(30.6) \quad \exp(\lambda\beta s^\alpha) = \left\{ \frac{1}{\pi} \int_0^\infty \exp(-xt - x^\alpha \lambda\beta \cos\alpha\pi) \cdot \sin(x^\alpha \lambda\beta \sin\alpha\pi)\,dx \right\}.$$

In the particular case of $\alpha = \frac{1}{2}$ we have a parabolic exponential function and the formulas may be reduced to the form

$$\exp(\lambda\beta\sqrt{s}) = \left\{ -\frac{\beta\lambda}{2\sqrt{\pi t^3}} \exp\left(-\frac{\beta^2\lambda^2}{4t}\right) \right\};$$

this function was discussed in detail in Part II (§ 29).

In particular formulas (30.5) and (30.6) can be applied if $\alpha = p/q < 1$. If $p/q = 1$ and β is real (for non-real β the exponential function does not exist), then the function $\exp(\lambda\beta s)$ is simply reduced to the hyperbolic exponential function $\exp(\lambda\beta s)$.

These remarks show that the operational calculus is applicable to every partial equation with constant coefficients and it is always possible to find out how many logarithmic roots there are in the corresponding characteristic equation and to obtain all the exponential functions connected with them. In many cases the shapes of the roots of the characteristic equation and the corresponding exponential functions are comparatively simple thus making the use of general formulas unnecessary.

The case where no root of the characteristic equation is logarithmic is of particular interest and importance. The operational equation is then termed *pure* (see § 6); the partial equation corresponding to it can also be termed thus but it should be remembered that the term pure is not symmetrial with respect to the variables λ and t.

It is easy to verify that in all the cases previously discussed pure equations were not restrictive. One can prove the general theorem (see Mikusiński [2]):

A pure equation is never restrictive.

Consequently in the case of pure equations conditions on the λ axis can always be given in the Cauchy form.

§ 31. Mixed problems. In the preceding sections the initial conditions for the partial equations under consideration were always given either on one axis, λ, (fig. 156a) or on two axes, λ and t (fig. 156b).

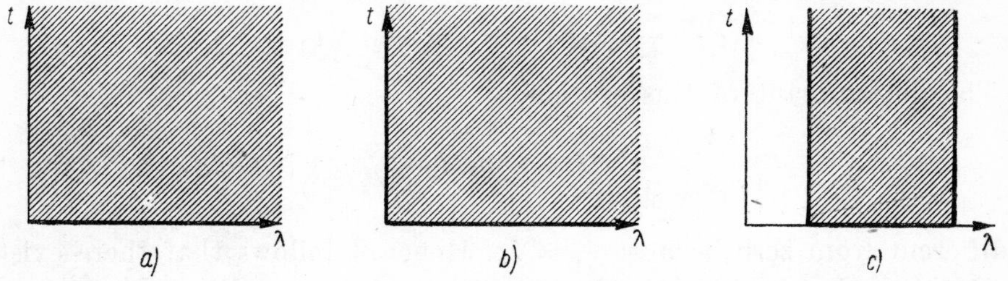

Fig. 156

In physical and technical applications conditions of another type are important (fig. 156c): they are conditions on the boundary of a half-strip D:

$$0 \leqslant t < \infty, \qquad \lambda_1 \leqslant \lambda \leqslant \lambda_2.$$

Conditions of this type occur for instance in the problem of heat propagation if we know the temperature at the ends of a heat-conducting bar, in certain problems of long lines in electricity and in many other problems where one of the variables is considered in a closed interval and the other, namely the time variable t, in the infinite interval $(0, \infty)$.

In this section we shall give the necessary and sufficient condition for the unicity of the solution of a problem of that kind.

Suppose that for equation (22.1) we are given the conditions on the λ axis (26.1) and also the following two conditions:

$$(31.1) \qquad x(\lambda_1, t) = v_1(t), \quad x(\lambda_2, t) = v_2(t) \quad (0 \leqslant t \leqslant \infty)$$

where $v_1(t)$ and $v_2(t)$ are known functions. These conditions define the behaviour of the solution on the half-lines $\lambda = \lambda_1$ and $\lambda = \lambda_2$ $(0 \leqslant t < \infty)$.

Under given conditions (26.1) equation (22.1) changes into the operational equation (22.3). The operational form of conditions (31.1) is

$$(31.2) \qquad x(\lambda_1) = v_1, \quad x(\lambda_2) = v_2.$$

Suppose that the characteristic equation

$$(31.3) \qquad a_m w^m + \ldots + a_1 w + a_0 = 0$$

of equation (22.3) has at least two logarithmic roots, w_1 and w_2.

Consider first the case where these roots are equal: $w_1 = w_2$. If $x_0(\lambda)$ is a certain solution of equation (22.3), the function

$$x(\lambda) = c_1 e^{\lambda w_1} + c_2 e^{\lambda w_2} + x_0(\lambda),$$

where c_1 and c_2 are arbitrary operators, is also a solution of that equation. In order to adapt it to conditions (31.2) we must solve the system of algebraic equations

$$c_1 e^{\lambda_1 w_1} + c_2 \lambda_1 e^{\lambda_1 w_1} = -x_0(\lambda_1) + v_1,$$
$$c_1 e^{\lambda_2 w_1} + c_2 \lambda_2 e^{\lambda_2 w_1} = -x_2(\lambda_2) + v_2.$$

The determinant of this system,

$$\begin{vmatrix} e^{\lambda_1 w_1} & \lambda_1 e^{\lambda_1 w_1} \\ e^{\lambda_2 w_1} & \lambda_2 e^{\lambda_2 w_1} \end{vmatrix} = e^{(\lambda_1+\lambda_2)w_1}(\lambda_2 - \lambda_1),$$

is different from zero because $\lambda_1 \neq \lambda_2$. Hence it follows that there exists a solution $x(\lambda)$ of equation (22.3) which satisfies conditions (31.2) and that the solution is unique.

Let us now consider the case where $w_1 \neq w_2$. Then the function

$$x(\lambda) = c_1 e^{\lambda w_1} + c_2 e^{\lambda w_2} + x_0(\lambda)$$

is the general solution of equation (22.3). In order to adapt it to conditions (31.2), we must solve the system of algebraic equations

$$c_1 e^{\lambda_1 w_1} + c_2 e^{\lambda_1 w_2} = -x_0(\lambda_1) + v_1,$$
$$c_1 e^{\lambda_2 w_1} + c_2 e^{\lambda_2 w_2} = -x_0(\lambda_2) + v_2.$$

The determinant of this system has the form

$$\begin{vmatrix} e^{\lambda_1 w_1} & e^{\lambda_1 w_2} \\ e^{\lambda_2 w_1} & e^{\lambda_2 w_2} \end{vmatrix} = e^{\lambda_2 w_1 + \lambda_1 w_2}[e^{(w_2 - w_1)(\lambda_2 - \lambda_1)} - 1]. \tag{31.4}$$

This determinant is different from zero if and only if

$$w_2 - w_1 \neq \frac{2k\pi i}{\lambda_2 - \lambda_1} \quad (k \text{ being an integer}) \tag{31.5}$$

since the only solutions of the equation $e^w = 1$ have the form $w = 2k\pi i$ (see § 9, Part III). Consequently if w_1 and w_2 are the only logarithmic roots of the characteristic equation (31.3), a solution of the operational equation (22.3) satisfying conditions (31.2) exists and is unique.

On these grounds we shall prove the following criterion for the partial equation (22.1):

If the characteristic equation (31.3) *has at least two logarithmic roots,* w_1 *and* w_2*, then the solution of the partial equation* (22.1) *satisfying conditions* (26.1) *and* (31.1) *is unique if and only if equation* (31.1) *has no logarithmic roots except* w_1 *and* w_2 *and*

$$w_2 - w_1 \neq \frac{2k\pi i}{\lambda_2 - \lambda_1} \quad (k = 1, 2, \ldots).$$

The assumption that the characteristic equation (31.3) has at least two logarithmic roots is quite natural because: 1° if this equation has only one logarithmic root, then condition (26.1) and one of the conditions (31.1) are sufficient for the unicity of the solution; 2° if equation (31.1) has no logarithmic root, then conditions (26.1) alone are sufficient.

Proof. The sufficiency of the condition follows at once from what we have proved with regard to the operational equation (22.3). In order to prove its necessity let us consider the case where the characteristic equation (31.3) has at least three logarithmic roots, w_1, w_2 and w_3. Then there exist three linearly independent solutions of the homogeneous equation

$$a_m x^{(m)} + \ldots + a_0 x = 0. \tag{31.6}$$

We can choose the three operators, c_1, c_2 and c_3 (not all of them equal to zero) in such a way that

$$c_1 x_1(\lambda_1) + c_2 x_2(\lambda_1) + c_3 x_3(\lambda_1) = 0,$$

$$c_1 x_2(\lambda_2) + c_2 x_2(\lambda_2) + c_3 x_3(\lambda_1) = 0.$$

Then the function

$$x_4(\lambda) = c_1 x_1(\lambda) + c_2 x_2(\lambda) + c_3 x_3(\lambda)$$

satisfies equation (31.6) and the conditions

$$x_4(\lambda_1) = x_4(\lambda_2) = 0. \tag{31.7}$$

This function can be represented in every interval $\lambda_1 \leqslant \lambda \leqslant \lambda_2$ in the form $x_4(\lambda) = p(\lambda)/q$, where $q \in \mathcal{C}$ $(q \neq 0)$, and $p(\lambda) = p(\lambda, t)$ is a parametric function whose derivatives

$$\frac{\partial^{\mu+\nu}}{\partial \lambda^{\mu} \partial t^{\nu}} p(\lambda, t)$$

of the orders occurring in equation (22.1) all exist and are continuous in the half-strip D. The function $p(\lambda, t)$ satisfies the homogeneous equation obtained from (22.1) by neglecting the function $\varphi(\lambda, t)$ and the homogeneous conditions obtained from (26.1) and (31.1) by replacing everywhere the functions on the right side by zero. Moreover the function $p(\lambda, t)$ is not identically equal to zero. Now if $x_0(\lambda, t)$ is a solution of equation (22.1) satisfying conditions (26.1) and (31.1), then every function

$$x(\lambda, t) = x_0(\lambda, t) + \gamma p(\lambda, t)$$

where γ is an arbitrary number, also satisfies equation (22.1) and conditions (26.1) and (31.1).

Finally, suppose that the operators w_1 and w_2 are the only logarithmic roots of equation (31.3) and that we have the equality

$$w_2 - w_1 = \frac{2k\pi i}{\lambda_2 - \lambda_1}$$

where k is an integer different from zero. Then the determinant (31.4) is equal to zero and there exist operators c_1 and c_2 for which

$$c_1 e^{w_1 \lambda_1} + c_2 e^{w_2 \lambda_1} = 0,$$
$$c_1 e^{w_1 \lambda_2} + c_2 e^{w_2 \lambda_2} = 0.$$

The function

$$x_1(\lambda) = c_1 e^{w_1 \lambda} + c_2 e^{w_2 \lambda}$$

satisfies equation (31.6) and conditions (37.7). Hence it follows, in the same way as before, that if $x_0(\lambda, t)$ is a solution of equation (22.1) satisfying conditions (26.1) and (31.1), then it is not unique.

The proof of the criterion is complete.

EXAMPLE 1. For the equation

$$\frac{\partial^2 x}{\partial \lambda^2} = \frac{\partial^2 x}{\partial t^2} \tag{31.8}$$

the conditions on the λ axis have the form

$$x(\lambda, 0) = g_0(\lambda), \quad x_t(\lambda, 0) = g_1(\lambda). \tag{31.9}$$

The characteristic equation $w^2 = s^2$ has two roots, s and $-s$. Both are logarithmic: their difference is not of the form $2k\pi i/(\lambda_2 - \lambda_1)$. In view of the criterion we have proved there exists in the half-strip D at most one solution of equation (31.8) satisfying conditions (31.9) and (31.1).

EXAMPLE 2. For the equation

$$\frac{\partial^2 x}{\partial \lambda^2} = \frac{\partial x}{\partial t} \tag{31.10}$$

the conditions on the λ axis are reduced to one equality,

$$x(\lambda, 0) = g_0(\lambda). \tag{31.11}$$

The characteristic equation $w^2 = s$ has two roots, $\sqrt{s}$ and $-\sqrt{s}$. Both are logarithms and their difference, $2\sqrt{s}$, is not of the form $2k\pi i/(\lambda_2 - \lambda_1)$. Thus there exists in the half-strip D at most one solution of equation (31.10) satisfying conditions (31.11) and (31.1).

EXAMPLE 3. We seek a solution of equation

$$(31.12)\qquad \frac{\partial^6 x}{\partial\lambda^4\partial t^2}-4\frac{\partial^6 x}{\partial\lambda^2\partial t^4}-\frac{\partial^2 x}{\partial\lambda^2}-4\frac{\partial^2 x}{\partial\lambda^2}=0 \qquad (0\leqslant\lambda\leqslant 1,\ 0\leqslant t<\infty)$$

satisfying the conditions

$$(31.13)\qquad \begin{aligned} x_{\lambda^2}(\lambda,0)&=0,\\ x_{\lambda^2 t}(\lambda,0)&=0,\\ x_{\lambda^4}(\lambda,0)+4x_{\lambda^2t^2}(\lambda,0)-4x(\lambda,0)&=0,\\ x_{\lambda^4 t}(\lambda,0)+4x_{\lambda^2t^3}(\lambda,0)-4x_t(\lambda,0)&=0 \end{aligned}$$

and

$$(31.14)\qquad x(0,t)=0,\quad x(1,t)=t.$$

Now the characteristic equation has the form

$$(31.15)\qquad s^2w^4+4s^4w^2-w^2-4s^2=0;$$

its roots are the operators

$$l,\qquad -l,\qquad 2is,\qquad -2is,$$

of which the first two are logarithmic operators and the remaining two are not. According to our criterion, conditions (31.13) and (31.14) define the solution of equation (31.12) in a unique manner.

This solution can be found effectively. The corresponding operational equation is

$$s^2x^{(4)}+(4s^4-1)x''+4s^2x=0;$$

its general solution has the form

$$x(\lambda)=c_1e^{l\lambda}+c_2e^{-l\lambda}.$$

Adapting it to the conditions $x(0)=0$ and $x(1)=l^2$, corresponding to conditions (31.14), we have the system of equations $c_1+c_2=0$, $c_1e^l+c_2e^{-l}=l^2$ to solve. Hence

$$c_1=\frac{l^2e^l}{e^{2l}-1}\qquad\text{and}\qquad c_2=-\frac{l^2e^l}{e^{2l}-1}.$$

Since the analytic function $z/(e^z-1)$ expands in the series

$$\sum_{\nu=0}^{\infty}\frac{B_\nu z^\nu}{\nu!},$$

where B_ν are *Bernoulli numbers*, we have

$$c_1=-c_2=c^l\sum_{\nu=0}^{\infty}\frac{B_\nu}{\nu!}2^{\nu-l}l^{\nu+1}.$$

The required solution can thus be written in the form

$$x(\lambda) = (e^{l(1+\lambda)} - e^{l(1-\lambda)}) \sum_{\nu=0}^{\infty} \frac{B_\nu}{\nu!} 2^{\nu-1} l^{\nu+1}$$

$$= \sum_{\mu=1}^{\infty} \frac{1}{\mu!} [(1+\lambda)^\mu - (1-\lambda)^\mu] \sum_{\nu=0}^{\infty} \frac{B_\nu}{\nu!} 2^{\nu-1} l^{\mu+\nu+1}.$$

In the ordinary, non-operational notation we have

$$x(\lambda, t) = \sum_{\mu=1}^{\infty} \sum_{\nu=0}^{\infty} \frac{2^{\nu-1} B_\nu}{\mu!\nu!(\mu+\nu)!} [(1+\lambda)^\mu - (1-\lambda)^\mu] t^{\mu+\nu}.$$

EXAMPLE 4. Consider the equation

$$\text{(31.16)} \qquad \frac{\partial^4 x}{\partial \lambda^4} + \frac{\partial^4 x}{\partial \lambda^2 \partial t^2} + \frac{\partial^2 x}{\partial \lambda^2} + \frac{\partial^2 x}{\partial t^2} = 0 \qquad (\lambda_1 \leqslant \lambda \leqslant \lambda_2,\ 0 \leqslant t < \infty).$$

We seek all the solutions of this equation that satisfy the conditions

$$\text{(31.17)} \qquad \begin{aligned} x_{\lambda^2}(\lambda, 0) + x(\lambda, 0) &= 0, \\ x_{\lambda^2 t}(\lambda, 0) + x_t(\lambda, 0) &= 0, \\ x(\lambda_1, t) &= 0, \\ x(\lambda_2, t) &= 0. \end{aligned}$$

The characteristic equation

$$w^4 + s^2 w^2 + w^2 + s^2 = 0$$

has the roots

$$i, \quad -i, \quad is, \quad -is.$$

The first two roots are logarithmic, the remaining two are not. The difference of the logarithmic roots is $2i$. According to our criterion, conditions (31.17) ensure the unicity of the solution of equation (31.1) if and only if $\lambda_2 - \lambda_1 \neq k\pi$, where $k = \pm 1, \pm 2, \ldots$ Obviously it is the function $x(\lambda, t) \equiv 0$ that constitutes this unique solution.

If $\lambda_2 - \lambda_1 = k\pi$, the solution is not unique. Namely, it is easy to verify that every function of the form

$$\text{(31.18)} \qquad x(\lambda, t) = f(t) \sin(\lambda - \lambda_1),$$

where f is an arbitrary function of the variable t (having a continuous second derivative), satisfies equation (31.16) with conditions (31.17).

The operational calculus makes it easy to prove that in the last case functions (31.18) are the only solutions of equation (31.16) satisfying conditions (31.17). In the operational form our problem is expressed by the equation

$$x^{(4)}+(s^2+1)x''+s^2x = 0 \tag{31.19}$$

and the boundary conditions

$$x(\lambda_1) = 0, \quad x(\lambda_2) = 0. \tag{31.20}$$

The operational function

$$x(\lambda) = c_1 e^{i\lambda}+c_2 e^{-i\lambda},$$

where c_1 and c_2 are arbitrary operators, is the general solution of equation (31.16). It follows that the solution satisfying conditions (31.19) has the form

$$x(\lambda) = f\sin(\lambda-\lambda_1), \tag{31.21}$$

where f is an arbitrary operator. Function (31.20) will be parametric if and only if f is an ordinary function of the variable t. Hence follows the form (31.18) for every solution of the problem in question concerning the partial equation (31.16).

PART FIVE

INTEGRAL OPERATIONAL CALCULUS

CHAPTER I

THE INTEGRAL OF AN OPERATIONAL FUNCTION AND ITS APPLICATIONS

§ 1. Operational functions of class ($\mathcal{K}$). It would be most convenient to introduce the notion of integral in the operational calculus by a suitable generalization of the Lebesgue integral. It is possible, however, to avoid the theory of the Lebesgue integral if we restrict ourselves to a certain particular class of operational functions.

To begin with we shall define a certain class of functions $f(\lambda, t)$, which will be denoted by $[\mathcal{K}]$.

A function $f(\lambda, t)$ will be said *to be a function of class* $[\mathcal{K}]$ in the domain D:

$$\alpha \leqslant \lambda \leqslant \beta, \quad 0 \leqslant t < \infty,$$

if

1° every partial domain D_0:

$$\alpha \leqslant \lambda \leqslant \beta, \quad 0 \leqslant t < t_0,$$

can be intersected by at most a finite number of straight lines parallel to the axes λ and t and containing infinitely many discontinuity points of the function $f(\lambda, t)$;

2° at the discontinuity points belonging to the domain D we have the inequality

$$|f(\lambda, t)| \leqslant \varphi(\lambda) g(t)$$

with a suitably chosen function g of class $\mathcal{K}$ and a function $\varphi(\lambda)$ having at most a finite number of discontinuity points in the interval $\alpha \leqslant \lambda \leqslant \beta$ and such that the integral $\int_\alpha^\beta |\varphi(\lambda)|\, d\lambda$ (taken in the ordinary sense) has a finite value.

For instance the function $f(\lambda, t)$ which is equal to 1 in the shaded triangles in fig. 157 and equal to zero everywhere else in the domain D

has discontinuity points along the perimeters of the triangles. Each of the straight lines

$$\lambda = \lambda_0, \quad t = t_1, \quad t = t_2, \quad \ldots \tag{1.1}$$

contains infinitely many discontinuity points, and every other straight line parallel to the λ axis or to the t axis contains at most two discontinuity points. Each bounded part of the domain D is intersected by a finite number of straight lines (1.1), *i. e.*, property 1° is satisfied.

Moreover, property 2° is obviously also satisfied. Consequently the function under consideration belongs to class $[\mathcal{K}]$.

In particular every function $f(\lambda, t)$ which is continuous in the domain D is a function of class $[\mathcal{K}]$. Also, every function of the form $\varphi(\lambda)g(t)$, where φ and g have properties 2°, is a function of class $[\mathcal{K}]$.

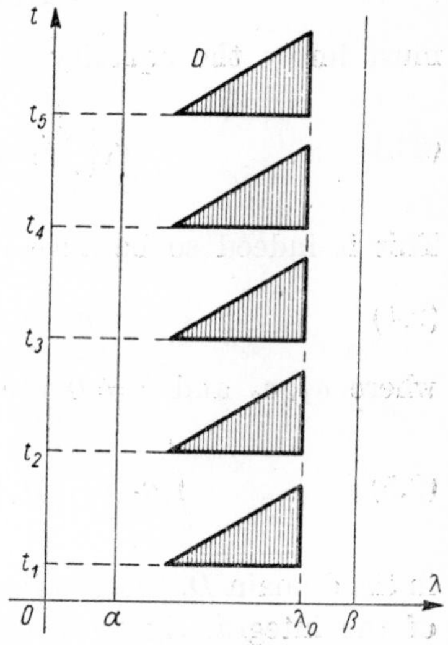

Fig. 157

An operational function $f(\lambda)$ will be said to be a *function of class* $(\mathcal{K})$ in the interval $\alpha \leqslant \lambda \leqslant \beta$ if it can be represented in the form

$$f(\lambda) = q\{f_1(\lambda, t)\} \tag{1.2}$$

where q is an operator and the function $f_1(\lambda, t)$ is a function of class $[\mathcal{K}]$ in the domain D.

In particular *every continuous operational function is a function of class* $(\mathcal{K})$.

§ 2. The definition of the integral.

By the *integral* of a function $f(\lambda)$ of class $(\mathcal{K})$ in the interval $\alpha \leqslant \lambda \leqslant \beta$ we shall understand the operator

$$\int_\alpha^\beta f(\lambda)\,d\lambda = q\Big\{\int_\alpha^\beta f_1(\lambda, t)\,d\lambda\Big\} \tag{2.1}$$

with the notation (1.2).

We accept definition (2.1) also if $\beta \leqslant \alpha$.

Every operational function of class $(\mathcal{K})$ can be represented in the form (1.2) in infinitely many ways. For if $a \in \mathcal{C}$ and $a \neq 0$, then we can always write

$$f(\lambda) = \frac{q}{a}\{f_2(\lambda, t)\},$$

where the function

$$f_2(\lambda, t) = \int_0^t a(t-\tau) f_1(\lambda, \tau)\, d\tau$$

is, like $f_1(\lambda, t)$, a function of class $[\mathcal{K}]$.

In order that the definition of the integral be unique the equality

$$q_1\{f_1(\lambda, t)\} = q_2\{f_2(\lambda, t)\} \tag{2.2}$$

must imply the equality

$$q_1\Big\{\int_\alpha^\beta f_1(\lambda, t)\, d\lambda\Big\} = q_2\Big\{\int_\alpha^\beta f_2(\lambda, \ )\, d\lambda\Big\}. \tag{2.3}$$

This is indeed so because if we write

$$q_1 = a_1/c \quad \text{and} \quad q_2 = a_2/c, \tag{2.4}$$

where a_1, a_2 and $c \neq 0$ are elements of class $\mathcal{C}$, we have by (2.2)

$$\int_0^t a_1(t-\tau) f_1(\lambda, \tau)\, d\tau = \int_0^t a_2(t-\tau) f_2(\lambda, \tau)\, d\tau \tag{2.5}$$

in the domain D. Integrating (2.5) with respect to λ and changing the order of the integral signs we obtain the equality

$$\int_0^t a_1(t-\tau)\Big[\int_\alpha^\beta f_1(\lambda, \tau)\, d\lambda\Big] d\tau = \int_0^t a_2(t-\tau)\Big[\int_\alpha^\beta f_2(\lambda, \tau)\, d\lambda\Big] d\tau,$$

whence

$$a_1\Big\{\int_\alpha^\beta f_1(\lambda, t)\, d\lambda\Big\} = a_2\Big\{\int_\alpha^\beta f_2(\lambda, t)\, d\lambda\Big\}.$$

Dividing by c we obtain equality (2.3).

We have thus ascertained the unicity of the definition of the integral.

If the function $f(\lambda)$ is numerical, then the above definition is identical with the ordinary definition of the integral. Indeed, we can then write $f(\lambda) = s\{f(\lambda)\}$ and

$$\int_\alpha^\beta f(\lambda)\, d\lambda = s\Big\{\int_\alpha^\beta f(\lambda)\, d\lambda\Big\},$$

where the integral on the left side is understood in the operational sense and that on the right side in the ordinary sense.

§ 3. Properties of the integral. An integral of an operational function has similar properties to those of an ordinary integral.

PROPERTY I. $\int_a^a f(\lambda)\,d\lambda = 0.$

Indeed, we have

$$\int_a^a f(\lambda)\,d\lambda = q\Big\{\int_a^a f_1(\lambda, t)\,d\lambda\Big\} = q\{0\} = 0.$$

PROPERTY II. $\int_a^\beta f(\lambda)\,d\lambda = -\int_\beta^a f(\lambda)\,d\lambda.$

Indeed, we have

$$\int_a^\beta f(\lambda)\,d\lambda = q\Big\{\int_a^\beta f_1(\lambda, t)\,d\lambda\Big\} = q\Big\{-\int_\beta^a f_1(\lambda, t)\,d\lambda\Big\}$$

$$= -q\Big\{\int_\beta^a f_1(\lambda, t)\,d\lambda\Big\} = -\int_\beta^a f(\lambda)\,d\lambda.$$

PROPERTY III. $\int_a^\beta f(\lambda)\,d\lambda = \int_a^\gamma f(\lambda)\,d\lambda + \int_\gamma^\beta f(\lambda)\,d\lambda.$

Indeed, we have

$$\int_a^\beta f(\lambda)\,d\lambda = q\Big\{\int_a^\beta f_1(\lambda, t)\,d\lambda\Big\} = q\Big\{\int_a^\gamma f_1(\lambda, t)\,d\lambda + \int_\gamma^\beta f_1(\lambda, t)\,d\lambda\Big\}$$

$$= \int_a^\gamma f(\lambda)\,d\lambda + \int_\gamma^\beta f(\lambda)\,d\lambda.$$

PROPERTY IV. $\int_a^\beta cf(\lambda)\,d\lambda = c\int_a^\beta f(\lambda)\,d\lambda$ *(for every operator c)*.

Indeed, representing $f(\lambda)$ in the form (1.2) we have $cf(\lambda) = cq\{f_1(\lambda, t)\}$ and, consequently, according to the definition of the integral,

$$\int_a^\beta cf(\lambda)\,d\lambda = cq\Big\{\int_a^\beta f_1(\lambda, t)\,d\lambda\Big\} = c\int_a^\beta f(\lambda)\,d\lambda.$$

PROPERTY V. $\int_a^\beta [f(\lambda) \pm g(\lambda)]\,d\lambda = \int_a^\beta f(\lambda)\,d\lambda \pm \int_a^\beta g(\lambda)\,d\lambda.$

Indeed, we can write

$$f(\lambda) = q_1\{f_1(\lambda, t)\}, \quad g(\lambda) = q_2\{g_1(\lambda, t)\}, \tag{3.1}$$

where both the function $f_1(\lambda, t)$ and the function $g_1(\lambda, t)$ are of class $[\mathcal{K}]$.

Assuming (2.4) we shall have

$$f(\lambda) = \frac{1}{c}\{f_2(\lambda, t)\} \quad \text{and} \quad g(\lambda) = \frac{1}{c}\{g_2(\lambda, t)\}$$

where

$$\{f_2(\lambda, t)\} = a_1\{f_1(\lambda, t)\} \quad \text{and} \quad \{g_2(\lambda, t)\} = a_2\{g_1(\lambda, t)\},$$

$$f(\lambda) \pm g(\lambda) = \frac{1}{c}\{f_2(\lambda, t) \pm g_2(\lambda, t)\},$$

whence

$$\int_a^\beta [f(\lambda) \pm g(\lambda)]\, d\lambda = \frac{1}{c}\left\{\int_a^\beta [f_2(\lambda, t) \pm g_2(\lambda, t)]\, d\lambda\right\}$$

$$= \frac{1}{c}\left\{\int_a^\beta f_2(\lambda, t)\, d\lambda\right\} \pm \frac{1}{c}\left\{\int_a^{\beta_2} g_2(\lambda, t)\, d\lambda\right\} = \int_a^\beta f(\lambda)\, d\lambda \pm \int_a^\beta g(\lambda)\, d\lambda.$$

PROPERTY VI. *If operational functions $f(\lambda)$ and $g(\lambda)$ have continuous derivatives in the interval $a \leqslant \lambda \leqslant \beta$, then*

$$\int_a^\beta f'(\lambda) g(\lambda)\, d\lambda = f(\beta) g(\beta) - f(a) g(a) - \int_a^\beta f(\lambda) g'(\lambda)\, d\lambda.$$

Indeed, writing (3.1) we have

$$\int_a^\beta f'(\lambda) g(\lambda)\, d\lambda = q_1 q_2 \left\{\int_a^\beta \left[\int_0^t \frac{\partial}{\partial \lambda} f_1(\lambda, t-\tau) g_1(\lambda, \tau)\, d\tau\right] d\lambda\right\}$$

$$= q_1 q_2 \left\{\int_0^t \left[\int_a^\beta \frac{\partial}{\partial \lambda} f_1(\lambda, t-\tau) g_1(\lambda, \tau)\, d\lambda\right] d\tau\right\}$$

$$= q_1 q_2 \left\{\int_0^t \left[f_1(\beta, t-\tau) g_1(\beta, \tau) - f_1(a, t-\tau) g_1(a, \tau) - \right.\right.$$

$$\left.\left. - \int_a^\beta f(\lambda, t-\tau) \cdot \frac{\partial}{\partial \lambda} g_1(\lambda, \tau)\, d\lambda\right] d\tau\right\}$$

$$= f(\beta) g(\beta) - f(a) g(a) - \int_a^\beta f(\lambda) g'(\lambda)\, d\lambda.$$

PROPERTY VII. *If $\varphi(\lambda)$ is a numerical function having a continuous derivative $\varphi'(\lambda)$ and $f(\lambda)$ an arbitrary continuous operational function, then*

$$\int_a^\beta f[\varphi(\lambda)] \varphi'(\lambda)\, d\lambda = \int_{\varphi(a)}^{\varphi(\beta)} f(\lambda)\, d\lambda.$$

Indeed, we have

$$\int_{\alpha}^{\beta} f[\varphi(\lambda)]\varphi'(\lambda)\,d\lambda = q\left\{\int_{\alpha}^{\beta} f_1[\varphi(\lambda), t]\varphi'(\lambda)\,d\lambda\right\}$$

$$= q\left\{\int_{\varphi(\alpha)}^{\varphi(\beta)} f_1(\lambda, t)\,d\lambda\right\} = \int_{\varphi(\alpha)}^{\varphi(\beta)} f(\lambda)\,d\lambda.$$

Property VIII. *If an operational function $f(\lambda)$ is* ***continuous****, then the function*

$$F(\lambda) = \int_{a}^{\lambda} f(\varkappa)\,d\varkappa$$

has a derivative $F'(\lambda) = f(\lambda)$.

Indeed

$$F'(\lambda) = q\left\{\frac{\partial}{\partial\lambda}\int_{a}^{\lambda} f_1(\varkappa, t)\,d\varkappa\right\} = q\{f_1(\lambda, t)\} = f(\lambda).$$

§ 4. Operational functions of two variables. If an operator is assigned to each point $(\lambda, \varkappa)$ of a domain, we say that *an operational function of two variables $f(\lambda, \varkappa)$ is defined in that domain.*

The function $f(\lambda, \varkappa)$ is *continuous* in the rectangle

(4.1) $$\lambda_1 \leqslant \lambda \leqslant \lambda_2, \qquad \varkappa_1 \leqslant \varkappa \leqslant \varkappa_2$$

if there exist an operator q and a function of three variables $f_1(\lambda, \varkappa, t)$ (with numerical values) continuous in the domain

(4.2) $$\lambda_1 \leqslant \lambda \leqslant \lambda_2, \qquad \varkappa_1 \leqslant \varkappa \leqslant \varkappa_2, \qquad 0 \leqslant t < \infty$$

such that

(4.3) $$f(\lambda, \varkappa) = q\{f_1(\lambda, \varkappa, t)\}.$$

If $\varkappa$ is fixed arbitrarily in the interval $\varkappa_1 \leqslant \varkappa \leqslant \varkappa_2$, then $f(\lambda, \varkappa)$ can be regarded as a function of one variable λ

$$g(\lambda) = f(\lambda, \varkappa).$$

The function $g(\lambda)$ is continuous in the interval $\lambda_1 \leqslant \lambda \leqslant \lambda_2$ if $f(\lambda, \varkappa)$ is continuous in (4.1).

Similarly, if λ is fixed arbitrarily in the interval $\lambda_1 \leqslant \lambda \leqslant \lambda_2$, then $f(\lambda, \varkappa)$ can be regarded as a function of one variable $\varkappa$,

$$h(\varkappa) = f(\lambda, \varkappa).$$

The function $h(\varkappa)$ is continuous in the interval $\varkappa_1 \leqslant \varkappa \leqslant \varkappa_2$ if $f(\lambda, \varkappa)$ is continuous in (4.1).

The definition of continuity of an operational function of two variables can be extended to an arbitrary domain by saying that the function is continuous in that domain if it is continuous in every rectangle (4.1) contained in it.

By a *partial derivative* $\frac{\partial}{\partial\lambda}f(\lambda, \varkappa)$ we understand a derivative with respect to λ, $(f(\lambda, \varkappa))'$ with an arbitrarily fixed $\varkappa$. We shall limit ourselves to the case where the derivative in question is continuous. Then there exist an operator q and a function $f_1(\lambda, \varkappa, t)$ (with numerical values) having a partial derivative (in the ordinary sense)

$$\frac{\partial}{\partial\lambda}f_1(\lambda, \varkappa, t)$$

continuous in (4.2) and such that

$$\frac{\partial}{\partial\lambda}f(\lambda, \varkappa) = q\left\{\frac{\partial}{\partial\lambda}f_1(\lambda, \varkappa, t)\right\}.$$

We shall also prove the following property of the integral:

Property IX. *If an operational function of two variables $f(\lambda, \varkappa)$ is continuous in the square*

$$\alpha \leqslant \lambda \leqslant \beta, \quad \alpha \leqslant \varkappa \leqslant \beta$$

and has a partial derivative $\frac{\partial}{\partial\lambda}f(\lambda, \varkappa)$ continuous in that square, then for an arbitrarily fixed λ_0 $(\alpha \leqslant \lambda_0 \leqslant \beta)$ we have the formula

$$\left(\int_{\lambda_0}^{\lambda} f(\lambda, \varkappa)\,d\varkappa\right)' = f(\lambda, \lambda) + \int_{\lambda_0}^{\lambda} \frac{\partial}{\partial\lambda}f(\lambda, \varkappa)\,d\varkappa \qquad (\alpha \leqslant \lambda \leqslant \beta).$$

Proof. We have

$$\begin{aligned}\left(\int_{\lambda_0}^{\lambda} f(\lambda, \varkappa)\,d\varkappa\right)' &= q\left\{\frac{\partial}{\partial\lambda}\int_{\lambda_0}^{\lambda} f_1(\lambda, \varkappa, t)\,d\varkappa\right\}\\ &= q\left\{f_1(\lambda, \lambda, t) + \int_{\lambda_0}^{\lambda}\frac{\partial}{\partial\lambda}f_1(\lambda, \varkappa, t)\,d\varkappa\right\}\\ &= f(\lambda\lambda) + \int_{\lambda_0}^{\lambda}\frac{\partial}{\partial\lambda}f(\lambda, \varkappa)\,d\varkappa.\end{aligned}$$

Property IX can be generalized to the case where the bounds of integration are arbitrary differentiable numerical functions.

§ 5. Cutting down a function. We shall prove that *if* $f(\lambda)$ *assumes numerical values in the interval* $[\lambda_1, \lambda_2]$, *then*

$$(5.1)\qquad \int_{\lambda_1}^{\lambda_2} e^{-\lambda s} f(\lambda)\, d\lambda = \left\{\begin{matrix} f(t) \text{ in the interval } \lambda_1 < t < \lambda_2 \\ 0 \text{ outside this interval} \end{matrix}\right\} \qquad (0 \leqslant \lambda_1 < \lambda_2).$$

The meaning of this formula is illustrated by figs. 158 and 159.

Thus formula (5.1) makes it possible, in a way, to *cut down* a function f outside an arbitrary interval (λ_1, λ_2).

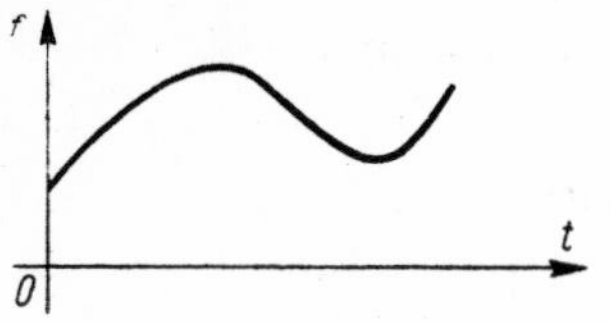

Fig. 158

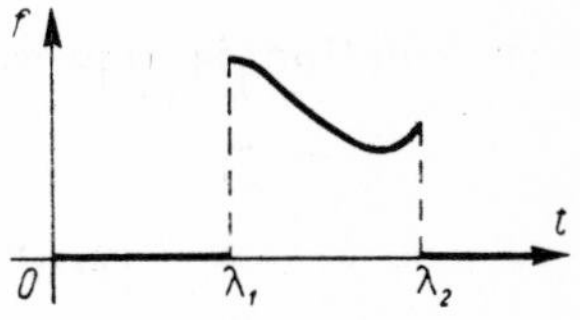

Fig. 159

In order to prove this formula we assume first that $\lambda_1 = 0$. Since $e^{-\lambda s} = s\{h(\lambda, t)\}$ where

$$h(\lambda, t) = \begin{cases} 0 & \text{for} \quad 0 \leqslant t < \lambda, \\ 1 & \text{for} \quad 0 \leqslant \lambda < , \end{cases}$$

we have

$$\int_0^{\lambda_2} e^{-\lambda s} f(\lambda)\, d\lambda = s\left\{\int_0^{\lambda_2} h(\lambda, t) f(\lambda)\, d\lambda\right\} = s\left\{\int_0^t 1 \cdot g(\lambda_2, \lambda)\, d\lambda\right\} = \{g(\lambda_2, t)\},$$

where

$$g(\lambda, t) = \begin{cases} f(t) & \text{for} \quad 0 \leqslant t < \lambda, \\ 0 & \text{for} \quad 0 \leqslant \lambda < t. \end{cases}$$

The case of $\lambda_1 > 0$ is reduced to the preceding one by splitting the integral in formula (5.1) into two integrals

$$\int_{\lambda_1}^{\lambda_2} e^{-\lambda s} f(\lambda)\, d\lambda = \int_0^{\lambda_2} e^{-\lambda s} f(\lambda)\, d\lambda - \int_0^{\lambda_1} e^{-\lambda s} f(\lambda)\, d\lambda.$$

If the function $f(t)$ is periodic with the period $2\lambda_0$, then we have the formula

$$\{f(t)\} = \frac{\int_0^{2\lambda_0} e^{-\lambda s} f(\lambda)\, d\lambda}{1 - e^{-2\lambda_0 s}}.$$

Indeed, the integral in the numerator represents the function cut down at the point $t = 2\lambda_0$, *i. e.*, one period of the function; now the denominator induces a successive repetition of that period infinitely many times at intervals $2\lambda_0$.

E. g. we have

$$\{\sin t\} = \frac{\int\limits_0^{2\pi} e^{-\lambda s} \sin \lambda \, d\lambda}{1-e^{-2\pi s}};$$

integrating twice by parts we obtain the known formula $\{\sin t\} = 1/(s^2+1)$ (this, of course, is not the simplest method of obtaining this formula).

Another function is represented by the expression

$$\{f(t)\} = \frac{\int\limits_0^{\pi} e^{-\lambda s} \sin \lambda \, d\lambda}{1-e^{-2\pi s}};$$

the graph of this function represents a sinusoid cut down at the point $t = \pi$ and then repeated infinitely many times at distances of 2π. A graph of this kind is given in fig. 117 (p. 153).

Finding the integral in the numerator according to the rules of integration we obtain

$$\int\limits_0^{\pi} e^{-\lambda s} \sin \lambda \, d\lambda = \frac{1+e^{-\pi s}}{1+s^2};$$

thus

$$\{f(t)\} = \frac{1}{1+s^2} \cdot \frac{1+e^{-\pi s}}{1-e^{-2\pi s}} = \frac{1}{(1+s^2)(1-e^{-\pi s})}$$

according to the formula found in Part II (p. 153).

The function

$$\{g(t)\} = \frac{\int\limits_0^{\beta/2} e^{-\lambda s} \, d\lambda}{1-e^{-\beta s}}$$

has the value 1 in the interval $0 < t < \beta/2$ and in every interval translated by $n\beta$, *i. e.*, in the intervals $n\beta < t < (2n+1)\beta/2$ $(n = 0, 1, \ldots)$. But we have

$$\int\limits_0^{\beta/2} e^{-\lambda s} \, d\lambda = \frac{1-e^{-\beta s/2}}{s}$$

and thus

$$\{g(t)\} = \frac{1-e^{-\beta s/2}}{s(1-e^{-\beta s})} = \frac{1}{s(1+e^{-\beta s/2})}$$

(see Example 6 on fig. 113, p. 152).

§ 6. The integral form of a certain particular solution of the logarithmic differential equation. Assume that the operational equation

$$a_m x^{(m)} + \ldots + a_0 x = 0 \tag{6.1}$$

is logarithmic, *i. e.*, that all the roots of its characteristic solution (m in number) are logarithmic. Then the general solution has the form

$$x(\lambda) = c_1 x_1(\lambda) + \ldots + c_m x_m(\lambda),$$

where $c_1, \ldots, c_m$ are arbitrary operators and the functions $x_1(\lambda), \ldots, x_m(\lambda)$ have the form $\lambda^\mu e^{\lambda w}$. Let us choose the constants $c_1, \ldots, c_m$ so that

$$x^{(\nu)}(0) = 0 \quad \text{for} \quad 0 \leqslant \nu \leqslant m-2, \qquad x^{(m-1)}(0) = 1. \tag{6.2}$$

For this purpose we solve the system of equations

$$\begin{aligned} c_1 x_1(0) + \ldots + c_m x_m(0) &= 0, \\ \cdots\cdots\cdots\cdots\cdots\cdots\cdots \\ c_1 x_1^{(m-2)}(0) + \ldots + c_m x_m^{(m-2)}(0) &= 0, \\ c_1 x_1^{(m-1)}(0) + \ldots + c_m x_m^{(m-1)}(0) &= 1. \end{aligned}$$

Introducing the determinant

$$D = \begin{vmatrix} x_1(0) & \ldots & x_m(0) \\ \cdots & \cdots & \cdots \\ x_1^{m-2}(0) & \ldots & x_m^{(m-2)}(0) \\ x_1^{(m-1)}(0) & \ldots & x_m^{(m-1)}(0) \end{vmatrix}$$

and denoting by $D_1, \ldots, D_m$ its minors corresponding to the elements of the last row, we can write

$$c_1 = \frac{D_1}{D}, \quad \ldots, \quad c_m = \frac{D_m}{D};$$

as we know from § 4 of Part IV, the determinant D is always different from zero. Consequently the required solution is of the form

$$x(\lambda) = \frac{D_1 x_1(\lambda) + \ldots + D_m x_m(\lambda)}{D};$$

it is easy to see that the numerator is an expansion of the determinant

$$E(\lambda) = \begin{vmatrix} x_1(0) & \ldots & x_m(0) \\ \cdots & \cdots & \cdots \\ x_1^{(m-2)}(0) & \ldots & x_m^{(m-2)}(0) \\ x_1(\lambda) & \ldots & x_m(\lambda) \end{vmatrix},$$

which is formed from the determinant D by replacing the last row by $x_1(\lambda), \ldots, x_m(\lambda)$.

The solution $x(\lambda)$ may thus be written as the quotient of two determinants

$$x(\lambda) = \frac{E(\lambda)}{D}.$$

Let us now consider the expression

$$x_0(\lambda) = \int_0^\lambda f(\varkappa)x(\lambda-\varkappa)\,d\varkappa \tag{6.3}$$

where $f(\varkappa)$ is an arbitrary continuous operational function. Using property IX of the integral proved in § 4 and equality (6.2), it is easy to find that

$$x_0'(\lambda) = \int_0^\lambda f(\varkappa)x'(\lambda-\varkappa)\,d\varkappa,$$

$$\cdots\cdots\cdots\cdots\cdots\cdots$$

$$x_0^{(m-1)}(\lambda) = \int_0^\lambda f(\varkappa)x^{(m-1)}(\lambda-\varkappa)\,d\varkappa,$$

$$x_0^{(m)}(\lambda) = \int_0^\lambda f(\varkappa)x^{(m)}(\lambda-\varkappa)\,d\varkappa + f(\lambda).$$

Hence

$$a_m x_0^{(m)}(\lambda) + \ldots + a_0 x_0(\lambda)$$
$$= \int_0^\lambda f(\varkappa)[a_m x^{(m)}(\lambda-\varkappa) + \ldots + a_0 x(\lambda-\varkappa)]\,d\varkappa + a_m f(\lambda).$$

The function $x(\lambda)$ satisfying equation (6.1), the expression in square brackets is identically equal to zero and obviously $x_0(\lambda)$ is a solution of the non-homogeneous equation

$$a_m x^{(m)} + \ldots + a_0 x = a_m f(\lambda);$$

introducing the determinants D and $E(\lambda)$ we can write this solution in the form

$$x_0(\lambda) = \int_0^\lambda f(\varkappa)\frac{E(\lambda-\varkappa)}{D}\,d\varkappa. \tag{6.4}$$

Thus we see that *in the case of a logarithmic equation a solution always exists provided the right side of $f(\lambda)$ is a continuous function.*

It should be noted that, as follows from formulas (6.3) and (6.4), the solution $x_0(\lambda)$ satisfies the initial conditions

$$x_0^{(\nu)}(0) = 0 \quad (\nu = 0, \ldots, m-1).$$

§ 7. Application to the equation of a vibrating string. In the case of the equation

$$x'' - a^2 s^2 x = 0 \tag{7.1}$$

we have the general solution

$$x(\lambda) = c_1 e^{-a\lambda s} + c_2 e^{a\lambda s}.$$

The determinants D and E then have the form

$$D = \begin{vmatrix} 1 & 1 \\ -as & as \end{vmatrix} = 2as, \qquad E(\lambda) = \begin{vmatrix} 1 & 1 \\ e^{-a\lambda s} & e^{a\lambda s} \end{vmatrix} = e^{a\lambda s} - e^{-a\lambda s}.$$

Hence we immediately obtain the function

$$x(\lambda) = \frac{e^{a\lambda s} - e^{-a\lambda s}}{2as} = \frac{1}{as}\,\mathrm{sh}\, a\lambda s,$$

which satisfies equation (7.1) and the conditions

$$x(0) = 0, \qquad x'(0) = 1.$$

For the non-homogeneous equation

$$x'' - a^2 s^2 x = f(\lambda) \tag{7.2}$$

we thus have the particular solution

$$x_0(\lambda) = \frac{1}{as}\int_0^\lambda f(\varkappa)\,\mathrm{sh}[a(\lambda-\varkappa)s]\,d\varkappa.$$

The general solution of equation (7.2) can be written in the form

$$x(\lambda) = c_1 e^{-a\lambda s} + c_2 e^{a\lambda s} + \frac{1}{as}\int_0^\lambda f(\varkappa)\,\mathrm{sh}[a(\lambda-\varkappa)s]\,d\varkappa. \tag{7.3}$$

In § 20 of Part III we considered the case of

$$f(\lambda) = -a^2 s\varphi(\lambda) \qquad (a > 0), \tag{7.4}$$

$$x(0) = 0 \quad \text{and} \quad x(\lambda_0) = 0, \tag{7.5}$$

where $\varphi(\lambda)$ is an arbitrary numerical function. In order to adapt the constants c_1 and c_2 in formula (7.3) to conditions (7.5) we must solve the system of equations

$$c_1 + c_2 = 0,$$

$$c_1 e^{-a\lambda_0 s} + c_2 e^{a\lambda s} - a\int_0^{\lambda_0} \varphi(\varkappa)\,\mathrm{sh}[a(\lambda_0-\varkappa)s]\,d\varkappa = 0.$$

Having calculated the values of c_1 and c_2 and substituted them in (7.3) we obtain, in view of equality (7.4),

$$x_0(\lambda) = \frac{a \operatorname{sh} a\lambda s}{\operatorname{sh} a\lambda_0 s} \int_0^{\lambda_0} \varphi(\varkappa) \operatorname{sh}[a(\lambda_0 - \varkappa)s] d\varkappa - a \int_0^{\lambda} \varphi(\varkappa) \operatorname{sh}[a(\lambda - \varkappa)s] d\varkappa. \tag{7.6}$$

But previously we found the solution of the same problem in the form

$$\frac{1}{2}\left\{\varphi\left(\lambda + \frac{t}{a}\right) + \varphi\left(\lambda - \frac{t}{a}\right)\right\}$$

where we assumed $-\varphi(-\lambda) = \varphi(\lambda) = \varphi(\lambda + 2\lambda_0)$. Since the solution is unique, we must have

$$x_0(\lambda) = \frac{1}{2}\left\{\varphi\left(\lambda + \frac{t}{a}\right) + \varphi\left(\lambda - \frac{t}{a}\right)\right\};$$

this equality may be obtained directly from equality (7.6) but the calculation is rather cumbersome.

We shall give another application of formula (7.3).

Let us solve the partial equation

$$x_{\lambda\lambda} - x_{tt} = 0 \qquad (0 \leqslant \lambda \leqslant \lambda_0,\ 0 \leqslant t < \infty) \tag{7.7}$$

with the initial conditions

$$x(\lambda, 0) = h_0(\lambda), \qquad x_t(\lambda, 0) = h_1(\lambda), \tag{7.8}$$

$$x(0, t) = v_0(t), \qquad x_\lambda(0, t) = v_1(t). \tag{7.9}$$

To this problem corresponds the operational equation

$$x'' - s^2 x = -s h_0(\lambda) - h_1(\lambda) \tag{7.10}$$

with the conditions

$$x(0) = v_0, \qquad x'(0) = v_1. \tag{7.11}$$

The general solution has the form

$$x(\lambda) = c_1 e^{-\lambda s} + c_2 e^{\lambda s} - \int_0^{\lambda} [h_0(\varkappa) + l h_1(\varkappa)] \operatorname{sh}[(\lambda - \varkappa)s] ds. \tag{7.12}$$

By conditions (7.11) we must have

$$c_1 + c_2 = v_0, \qquad -sc_1 + sc_2 = v_1,$$

whence we obtain

$$c_1 = \frac{v_0}{2} - \frac{v_1}{2s} \quad \text{and} \quad c_2 = \frac{v_0}{2} + \frac{v_1}{2s}.$$

Substituting these values in (7.12) we obtain by a simple transformation

$$x(\lambda) = \tfrac{1}{2}(v_0 - lv_1)e^{-\lambda s} + \tfrac{1}{2}\int_0^\lambda e^{-(\lambda-\varkappa)s}[h_0(\varkappa) + lh_1(\varkappa)]\,d\varkappa + \tfrac{1}{2}e^{\lambda s}y(\lambda),$$

where

$$y(\lambda) = v_0 + lv_1 - \int_0^\lambda e^{-\varkappa s}[h_0(\varkappa) + lh_1(\varkappa)]\,d\varkappa.$$

The function $x(\lambda)$ will be parametric if and only if the function $y(\lambda) = \{y(\lambda, t)\}$ is parametric and moreover

(7.13) $$y(\lambda, t) = 0 \quad \text{for} \quad 0 \leqslant t \leqslant \lambda.$$

But we have

$$\int_0^\lambda e^{-\varkappa s}[h_0(\varkappa) + lh_1(\varkappa)]\,d\varkappa = \begin{cases} h_0(t) + \int_0^t h_1(\tau)\,d\tau & \text{for} \quad 0 \leqslant t < \lambda, \\ 0 & \text{for} \quad 0 \leqslant \lambda < t, \end{cases}$$

and consequently

$$y(\lambda, t) = v_0(t) + \int_0^t v_1(\tau)\,d\tau - h_0(t) - \int_0^t h_1(\tau)\,d\tau \quad \text{for} \quad 0 \leqslant t < \lambda.$$

Since λ varies in the interval $0 \leqslant \lambda \leqslant \lambda_0$, condition (7.13) gives

(7.14) $$v_0(t) + \int_0^t v_1(\tau)\,d\tau = h_0(t) + \int_0^t h_1(\tau)\,d\tau \quad \text{for} \quad 0 \leqslant t \leqslant \lambda_0.$$

This is the necessary and sufficient condition for the solution (7.12) satisfying equalities (7.11) to be a parametric function.

Hence it follows that for the partial equation (7.7) conditions (7.8) and (7.9) cannot be given in an arbitrary manner but have to satisfy relation (7.14). Consequently it is sufficient, for instance, to give conditions (7.8) and any condition of (7.9) and to determine the other condition from (7.14).

Example. Find the function $x(\lambda, t)$ satisfying the equation

(7.15) $$x_{\lambda\lambda} - x_{tt} = 0 \quad (0 \leqslant \lambda < \infty,\ 0 \leqslant t < \infty)$$

and the conditions

(7.16) $$x(\lambda, 0) = \lambda^2, \quad x(0, t) = t^3, \quad x_\lambda(0, t) = 0.$$

From relation (7.14) we easily obtain

$$x_t(\lambda, 0) = 3\lambda^2 - 2\lambda.$$

Consequently the operational equation has the form

$$x'' - s^2 x = -s\lambda^2 - 3\lambda^2 + 2\lambda.$$

It is not worth while, however, to determine a particular solution from the general integral solution (7.6); it is better to find the polynomial solution, which has the form

$$x_0(\lambda) = 3l^2\lambda^2 + l\lambda^2 - 2l^2\lambda + 2l^3 + 6l^4.$$

Hence the general solution

$$x(\lambda) = c_1 e^{-\lambda s} + c_2 e^{\lambda s} + x_0(\lambda).$$

In order that this solution be a parametric function we must assume $c_2 = 0$. The constant c_1 is determined from the initial condition $x(0) = 6l^4$

$$c_1 + 2l^3 + 6l^4 = 6l^4.$$

We obtain hence

$$c_1 = -2l^3.$$

Consequently

$$x(\lambda) = -2l^3 e^{-\lambda s} + 3l^2\lambda^2 + l\lambda^2 - 2l^2\lambda + 2l^3 + 6l^4,$$

and on taking into account the significance of the translation operator

$$x(\lambda, t) = \begin{cases} 3\lambda^2 t + \lambda^2 - 2\lambda t + t^2 + t^3 & \text{for} \quad 0 \leqslant t \leqslant \lambda, \\ 3\lambda^2 t + t^3 & \text{for} \quad 0 \leqslant \lambda \leqslant t. \end{cases}$$

This is the only function which in the interval $0 \leqslant \lambda < \infty$, $0 \leqslant t < \infty$ satisfies equation (7.15) and also conditions (7.16).

Remark. Condition (7.14) is sufficient to make the solution of the operational equation (7.10) a parametric function but does not ensure the differentiability of that function in the ordinary sense. In the case of solving the partial equation (7.7) it is thus necessary to check in the end the differentiability of the function obtained. If it is not differentiable, then a solution of the partial equation does not exist at all under the given conditions and the problem has a mathematical significance only if it is regarded from the point of view of operators.

§ 8. Application of infinite series and definite integrals. Formula (6.4) may be applied only if the given equation is logarithmic. In other cases we can often successfully apply expansions into infinite series or the method of definite integrals.

We already dealt with expansions into trigonometric series in Part III (§§ 30-35). Here we shall give some more examples.

EXAMPLE 1. Solve the equation

$$x_{\lambda^2} + x_{t^3} = 0 \qquad (-1 < \lambda < 1,\ 0 \leqslant t < \infty) \tag{8.1}$$

with the conditions

$$x(\lambda, 0) = 0, \quad x_t(\lambda, 0) = 0, \quad x_{tt}(\lambda, 0) = 1/(1-\lambda). \tag{8.2}$$

The operational equation has the form

(8.3) $$x''+s^3x = 1/(1-\lambda).$$

The function $1/(1-\lambda)$ expands in the power series

$$1+\lambda+\lambda^2+\ldots$$

Seeking the polynomial solution $x_n(\lambda)$ of the equation

$$x''+s^3x = \lambda^n$$

we obtain

$$x_n(\lambda) = \begin{cases} \dfrac{n!}{n!} l^3\lambda^n - \dfrac{n!}{(n-2)!} l^6\lambda^{n-2} + \ldots + (-1)^{n/2}\dfrac{n!}{0!} l^{3(n+2)/2} & \text{if } n \text{ is even,} \\[2ex] \dfrac{n!}{n!} \lambda^3\lambda^n - \dfrac{n!}{(n-2)!} l^6 l^{n-2} + \ldots + (-1)^{(n-1)/2}\dfrac{n!}{1!} l^{3(n+1)/2} & \text{if } n \text{ is odd.} \end{cases}$$

The formal solution of equation (8.3) is the expression

(8.4) $$x(\lambda) = x_0(\lambda)+x_1(\lambda)+\ldots = c_0+c_1\lambda+\ldots,$$

where

$$c_n = \sum_{\nu=0}^{\infty}(-1)^\nu\frac{(n+2\nu)!}{n!}l^{3(\nu+1)} = \left\{\sum_{\nu=0}^{\infty}(-1)^\nu\frac{(n+2\nu)!}{n!(3\nu+2)!}t^{3\nu+2}\right\}.$$

Obviously the series within the braces are uniformly convergent in every interval $[0, t_0]$; it follows hence that the coefficients c_n are meaningful. It can be proved that the series $c_0+c_1\lambda+\ldots$ is (operationally) convergent for $|\lambda| < 1$. Consequently it really (and not only formally) represents the operational function satisfying equation (8.3). Therefore the solution of the partial equation (8.1) has the form

$$x(\lambda, t) = \sum_{n=0}^{\infty}\frac{\lambda^n}{n!}\sum_{\nu=0}^{\infty}(-1)^\nu(n+2\nu)!\frac{t^{3\nu+2}}{(3\nu+2)!} \qquad (-1 < \lambda < 1).$$

It can easily be proved that it is the only solution of equation (8.1) satisfying conditions (8.2). This is due to the fact that the characteristic equation

$$u^2+s^3 = 0$$

has the roots $-is^{3/2}$ and $is^{3/2}$, neither of which is a logarithm.

Remark. The constants $c_0, c_1, c_2, \ldots$ in formula (8.4) cannot be determined directly by substituting the series $c_0+c_1\lambda+c_2\lambda^2+\ldots$ in the equation

$$x''+s^3x = 1+\lambda+\lambda^2+\ldots$$

and by comparing the coefficients of the powers of λ. Doing this we should obtain a certain recursive formula but we should find it difficult to determine the initial two coefficients, c_0 and c_1, which cannot be fixed in an arbitrary manner.

EXAMPLE 2. Solve the equation

$$x_{\lambda^4}+2x_{\lambda^2 t^2}+x_{t^4}=0 \qquad (-1<\lambda<\infty,\ 0\leqslant t<\infty) \tag{8.5}$$

with the initial conditions

$$x(\lambda,0)=0,\quad x_t(\lambda,0)=0,\quad x_{t^2}(\lambda,0)=0,\quad x_{t^3}(\lambda,0)=\frac{1}{1+\lambda}e^{-1-\lambda}. \tag{8.6}$$

The operational equation has the form

$$x^{(4)}+2s^2x''+s^4x=\frac{1}{1+\lambda}e^{-1-\lambda}. \tag{8.7}$$

The right side of this equation can be represented in the form of the integral

$$\int_1^\infty e^{-(1+\lambda)a}\,da.$$

We can at once write the solution of the equation

$$x^{(4)}+2s^2x''+s^4(x)=e^{-(1+\lambda)a};$$

it is the function

$$x_a(\lambda)=\frac{e^{-(1+\lambda)a}}{(a^2+s^2)^2}=\left\{\frac{1}{2a^3}e^{-(1+\lambda)a}(\sin at-at\cos at)\right\}.$$

Integrating this function with respect to the parameter a from 1 to ∞ we shall obtain the formal solution of equation (8.5),

$$x(\lambda)=\int_1^\infty\frac{e^{-(1+\lambda)a}}{(a^2+s^2)^2}\,da \tag{8.8}$$

whence

$$x(\lambda,t)=\frac{1}{2}\int_1^\infty\frac{1}{a^3}e^{-(1+\lambda)a}\qquad(\sin at-at\cos at)\,da.$$

It is easy to observe the uniform convergence of this integral and its derivatives with respect to λ; consequently the expression obtained really, and not only formally, satisfies the given equation. It is the only solution of this equation satisfying conditions (8.6) since the characteristic equation

$$u^4+2u^2s^2+s^4=0$$

has the (double) roots $-is$, is, which are not logarithmic.

CHAPTER II

INTEGRAL TRANSFORMATIONS

§ 9. The Laplace transform. In the last example of the preceding section we dealt with an improper integral (8.8). It should be regarded as a limit,

$$\lim_{\beta\to\infty}\int_1^\beta \frac{e^{-(1+\lambda)a}}{(a^2+s^2)^2}\,da.$$

Other improper integrals should be similarly understood. Let us take in particular the integral

$$\int_0^\infty e^{-\lambda s} f(\lambda)\,d\lambda = \lim_{\beta\to\infty}\int_0^\beta e^{-\lambda s} f(\lambda)\,d\lambda$$

where f is an arbitrary function of class $\mathcal{K}$.

But by § 5 we have

$$\int_0^\beta e^{-\lambda s} f(\lambda)\,d\lambda = \begin{cases} f(t) & \text{for} \quad 0 \leqslant t < \beta, \\ 0 & \text{for} \quad \beta < t < \infty, \end{cases}$$

and, in the limit,

$$\int_0^\infty e^{-\lambda s} f(\lambda)\,d\lambda = \{f(t)\}. \tag{9.1}$$

This limit, of course, always exists, whatever function f of class $\mathcal{K}$ is taken.

Let us assume for the moment that the letter s in integral (9.1) is not the differential operator but an ordinary complex number. In that case this integral, if it remains convergent, will represent an analytic function of the variable s. In this way to every function f for which the integral in question is convergent we can assign an analytic function,

$$F(s) = \int_0^\infty e^{-st} f(t)\,dt. \tag{9.2}$$

Such a correspondence is termed the *Laplace transform*.

§ 10. The Laplace transform as a basis for the operational calculus. Let us apply the Laplace transform to the solution of the ordinary differential equation

$$x'(t)-x(t) = e^t \tag{10.1}$$

with the initial condition $x(0) = 1$.

We have of course the equality

$$\int_0^\infty e^{-ts}[x'(t)-x(t)]\,dt = \int_0^\infty e^{-ts}e^t\,dt; \tag{10.2}$$

the symbol s is regarded here as a complex variable.

Integrating by parts we obtain

$$\int_0^\infty e^{-ts}x'(t)\,dt = [e^{-ts}x(t)]_0^\infty + s\int_0^\infty e^{-ts}x(t)\,dt;$$

if we assume that the function $x(t)$ does not increase too rapidly, we shall have $[e^{-ts}x(t)]_0^\infty = -x(0) = -1$ and it will be possible to write

$$\int_0^\infty e^{-ts}x'(t)\,dt = -1+sX(s),$$

where

$$X(s) = \int_0^\infty e^{-ts}x(t)\,dt.$$

Considering that

$$\int_0^\infty e^{-ts}e^t\,dt = \frac{1}{s-1},$$

we can write equation (10.2) in the form

$$sX(s)-X(s) = 1+\frac{1}{s-1}. \tag{10.3}$$

Hence we can easily find

$$X(s) = \frac{s}{(s-1)^2}.$$

The problem is now reduced to the finding of a function $x(z)$ which satisfies the integral equation

$$\int_0^\infty e^{-ts}x(t)\,dt = \frac{s}{(s-1)^2}.$$

This can be done by applying the so called *inversion formula*

$$(10.4)\qquad x(t)=\frac{1}{2\pi i}\int_{a-i\infty}^{a+i\infty} e^{st}\frac{s}{(s-1)^2}\,ds,$$

where the integration proceeds along a straight line parallel to the imaginary axis and situated to the right of that axis. Using the method of residua we can find hence that

$$x(t)=(1+t)e^t.$$

This example shows that, apart from the performance of the transformations themselves, the calculus resembles from the formal point of view the method of solving differential equations which was given in the first part of this book.

Using the Laplace transform we can also solve partial equations. The formal calculations will be similar to those involved in the use of the methods given in the second and the third parts of this book, with the addition of the Laplace transform introduced at the beginning of the calculations and the inverse transformation performed to obtain the final form of the solution.

This method, or related methods, will be found in most contemporary textbooks on operators.

§ 11. A comparison of the direct method and the method of Laplace transform. The formal similarity of the Laplace transform method and the direct method expounded in this book can be put more precisely from the mathematical point of view by establishing a certain *isomorphism.* We shall not give the definition of this rather abstract term, contenting ourselves with giving an example. Having performed the Laplace transform upon the function e^t we obtained the function $1/(s-1)$. The function $1/(s-1)$ is said to be a *transform of the function* e^t; this is usually written in the form

$$(11.1)\qquad \mathcal{L}\{e^t\}=\frac{1}{s-1}.$$

On the other hand, in the direct method we have the formula

$$(11.2)\qquad \{e^t\}=\frac{1}{s-1}.$$

In formula (11.1) the letter s stands for a complex variable and in formula (11.2) for the differential operator. To the analytic function $1/(s-1)$ of formula (11.1) corresponds the operator $1/(s-1)$ of formula (11.2). In formal calculations the symbol $1/(s-1)$ is treated in the same way in both cases, whether it denotes an analytic function or an operator. And this, roughly speaking, is what an isomorphism consists in.

In spite of the formal resemblance of the Laplace transform method and the direct method, the two methods are not equivalent. If the function e^t on the right side of equation (10.1) is replaced by the function $(2t-1)e^{t^2}$ for example (see p. 42), then it will be impossible to apply the Laplace transform because of the divergence of the integral

$$\int_0^\infty e^{-ts}(2t-1)e^{t^2}\,dt.$$

This method restricts the range of applicability of the operational calculus to a class of functions for which the integral

$$\int_0^\infty e^{-ts}f(t)\,dt$$

is convergent.

But even in the case where the function e^t is retained on the right side of equation (10.1), the Laplace transform method does not provide the full solution of the problem since it is necessary to assume during the calculation that the function sought does not increase too fast, *i. e.*, to be more exact, that it is *transformable*. Consequently we do not know if the solution obtained is unique.

§ 12. Other related methods. There exist numerous textbooks of the operational calculus in which the exposition is based on the transformation

$$F(p) = p\int_0^\infty e^{-pt}f(t)\,dt, \tag{12.1}$$

where p is a complex variable. This transformation differs from the Laplace transform (9.2) in the introduction of the factor p before the integral. The introduction of the letter p instead of s has of course no mathematical significance and is only a question of usage. The tables for transform (12.1) can be obtained form the tables for the Laplace transform by replacing the letter s by p and introducing before each formula the factor p.

In some textbooks the starting point is the transformation inverse to (12.1),

$$f(t) = \frac{1}{2\pi i}\int_{a-i\infty}^{a+i\infty} e^{pt}\frac{F(p)}{p}\,dp;$$

in this formula the integration should be performed along a straight line parallel to an imaginary axis suitably chosen for every function $F(p)$.

Besides, there exist numerous variants of these methods. Some authors for instance introduce, beside the set of functions of the real variable t and the set of analytic functions of the complex variable p, a set of operators which is defined by an isomorphism with the set of analytic functions under consideration. We shall not discuss those methods, referring the reader to the bibliography given at the end of the book.

PART SIX

APPENDIX

CHAPTER I

DEFINITION OF OPERATORS IN TERMS OF ABSTRACT ALGEBRA

(Appendix to Chapter I of Part I)

§1. Commutative ring. For a reader acquainted with abstract algebra, operators can be defined in a shorter and more exact way by means of the notions of a commutative ring and a field.

A set A of arbitrary elements $a, b, \ldots$ is called a *commutative ring*, if two operations, addition $a+b$ and multiplication ab, are defined in A with the following properties:

(i) $a+b = b+a$ (commutativity of addition);

(ii) $(a+b)+c = a+(b+c)$ (associativity of addition);

(iii) For any pair of elements a, b there is a third element x, satisfying the equation $a+x = b$;

(iv) $ab = ba$ (commutativity of multiplication);

(v) $(ab)c = a(bc)$ (associativity of multiplication);

(vi) $a(b+c) = ab+ac$ (distributivity of multiplication with respect to addition).

Property (iii) requires some explanations. This property ensures the existence of an element x, such that $a+x = b$ holds. It follows from (iii), by aid of (i) and (ii), that this element x is unique.

First we prove that there is an element in A, say 0, such that $b+0 = b$ for any b. In fact, let a be an arbitrarily fixed element of A. In view of (iii), there is an element 0 such that $a+0 = a$. We shall prove that the same element 0 satisfies the equation $b+0 = b$ for any b. For this purpose, put $a+x = b$ (the existence of such an element x is ensured by (iii)). Then we have, in view of (i) and (ii),

$$b+0 = (a+x)+0 = a+(x+0) = a+(0+x) = (a+0)+x = a+x = b.$$

Thus the existence of the element 0 with the required properties is proved. Now, let a and b be two given elements of A. Suppose that x_1 and x_2 are two solutions of the same equation $a+x = b$. Then we have $a+x_1 = a+x_2$ and, by (i), $x_1+a = x_2+a$. Consequently

$$(x_1+a)+y = (x_2+a)+y$$

and by (ii)

$$x_1+(a+y) = x_2+(a+y).$$

By (iii), the element y can be chosen so as to satisfy the equation $a+y = 0$. Then, the last equality implies $x_1 = x_2$. In this way it is proved that the element x satisfying the equation $a+x = b$ is unique.

Thus, for every pair of elements a, b there exists *one and only one* element x satisfying the equation $a+x = b$. This element x is called the *difference* of a and b and written as $b-a$. Property (iii) is often called *feasibility of subtraction.* We have proved that the feasibility of subtraction, together with properties (i) and (ii) ensures the uniqueness of subtraction.

Properties (i)-(vi) are called *axioms of the commutative ring.*

The element $a-a$ (not depending on choice of a) is denoted by 0 and called *zero* of the considered ring.

We say that *a ring has no divisors of zero* if:

(vii) $ab = 0$ implies $a = 0$ or $b = 0$.

§ 2. Quotient field. Any ring without divisors of zero can be extended to a quotient field, i. e. to a set of fractions b/a $(a \neq 0)$ with the following properties:

(1) $\dfrac{b}{a} = \dfrac{d}{c}$ if and only if $bc = ad$;

(2) $a = \dfrac{ak}{k}$ for any $k \neq 0$.

The following is, from the logical point of view, the correct construction of a quotient field. We consider pairs (a, b) of elements of A whose first element is different from zero. Two pairs (a, b) and (c, d) are called *equivalent* if and only if $bc = ad$. By the relation of this equivalency the set of pairs is decomposed into abstraction classes so that all the pairs of the same class are equivalent to each other and the pairs belonging to different classes are not equivalent. The class of all the elements which are equivalent to a given pair (a, b) is denoted by b/a. This construction explains the sense of condition (1).

Relation (2) identifies the elements of the given ring with some elements of the constructed quotient field. It is easy to see that this identification does not depend on the choice of $k \neq 0$. In fact, we have steadily $ak_1/k_1 = ak_2/k_2$ $(k_1, k_2 \neq 0)$ in view of (1).

In the quotient field we define addition and multiplication as follows:

$$\frac{b}{a} + \frac{d}{c} = \frac{bc+ad}{ac}, \qquad \frac{b}{a}\,\frac{d}{c} = \frac{bd}{ac}.$$

These definitions are possible owing to axiom (vii). For the supposition that the denominators a and c are different from zero implies that the denominators ac in the sum and in the product are different from zero.

Obviously the construction of a quotient field with addition and multiplication would be impossible by starting from a ring with a divisor of zero.

It is easy to prove that the elements (fractions) of a quotient field with introduced addition and multiplication satisfy also axioms (i)-(vii). Thus the quotient field is a commutative ring without divisors of zero. Moreover the following condition is satisfied:

(viii) For any pair of elements a, b, provided $a \neq 0$, there is a third element x satisfying the equation $ax = b$.

In fact, this element is just the fraction b/a, for

$$a\frac{b}{a} = \frac{ak}{k}\,\frac{b}{a} = \frac{akb}{ka} = \frac{b(ak)}{ak} = b \qquad (a, k \neq 0).$$

It can be proved that the element x in (viii) is unique for any given pair a, b. The proof is analoguous to that concerning addition and is based on axioms (iv), (v) ans (viii). The only element x with the property $ax = a$ for every a is called *unit* and written as 1.

Any set of arbitrary elements with addition and multiplication satisfying axioms (i)-(vi) and (viii) is called a *field*. Thus a field is a ring. Moreover it is a ring without divisors of zero. In fact, if $ab = 0$ and $a \neq 0$, then multiplying this equality by the element a^{-1}, defined as the solution of $ax = 1$, we get $b = 0$. Thus (ii) holds.

The quotient field is a particular case of a field: it is a field whose elements are fractions constructed by the method described above.

In a field, calculations are easier than in a ring, for we have no restrictions regarding division, which is always feasible except by zero.

§ 3. Operators. Let us consider now the set C of the complex functions of a real variable t, defined continuous in the interval $0 \leqslant t < \infty$. This set is a commutative ring with respect to addition and multiplication defined as follows:

Addition: $$a+b = \{a(t)\}+\{b(t)\} = \{a(t)+b(t)\};$$

Multiplication: $$ab = \{a(t)\}\{b(t)\} = \left\{\int_0^t a(t-\tau)b(\tau)\,d\tau\right\}.$$

Thus addition is taken in the ordinary sense, while multiplication is taken in the sense of convolution.

By Titchmarsh's theorem on convolution the considered ring C has no divisors of zero. Therefore it can be extended to a quotient field. The elements of this quotient field are called *operators*.

CHAPTER II

LOCALLY INTEGRABLE FUNCTIONS

(Appendix to Chapter VII of Part I)

§ 1. The convolution of integrable functions. A function $f(t)$ is said to be *locally integrable* in the interval $0 \leqslant t < \infty$ if it is integrable (in the sense of Lebesgue) in any bounded interval $0 \leqslant t \leqslant T$.

If f and g are locally integrable complex valued functions in the interval $0 \leqslant t < \infty$, then so is their convolution.

Proof. Suppose first that f and g are real and non-negative. Then it is true that

$$(1) \qquad \int_0^T dt \int_0^t f(t-\tau)g(\tau)\,d\tau = \int_0^T g(\tau)\,d\tau \int_\tau^T f(t-\tau)\,d\tau \qquad (0 \leqslant T < \infty),$$

provided that the infinite values of integrals are admitted. Now the integral

$$\int_\tau^T f(t-\tau)\,dt = \int_0^{T-\tau} f(t)\,dt$$

is a continuous function of τ. This implies that the right side of (1) and consequently also the left side are bounded for any fixed T. Thus the function $\int_0^t f(t-\tau)g(\tau)\,d\tau$ is finite almost everywhere and integrable in the interval $0 \leqslant t \leqslant T$.

To prove the theorem generally it suffices to remark that any integrable complex valued function can be represented in the form $f_1 - f_2 + if_3 - if_4$, where f_1, f_2, f_3 and f_4 are locally integrable and, moreover, real and non-negative.

§ 2. Properties of this convolution. Similarly to the case of continuous functions, also the convolution of locally integrable functions is commutative, associative and distributive with respect to addition. The proofs are the same as in case of continuous functions. Moreover, Titchmarsh's theorem on convolution holds:

If the function of two locally integrable functions f and g vanishes almost everywhere in the interval $0 \leqslant t < \infty$, then at least one of these functions vanishes almost everywhere in this interval.

The proof is easily reduced to the case of continuous functions. Indeed, if $fg = 0$, then also $l^2 fg = 0$, i. e. $(lf)(lg) = 0$, where $l = \{1\}$. But lf and lg are continuous functions, at least one of them must vanish, i. e.

$$\int_0^t f(\tau)\,d\tau = 0 \quad \text{or} \quad \int_0^t g(\tau)\,d\tau = 0 \quad \text{for} \quad 0 \leqslant t < \infty,$$

whence $f = 0$ or $g = 0$ almost everywhere in the interval $0 \leqslant t < \infty$.

§ 3. Locally integrable functions as operators. If f is a locally integrable function, then

$$lf = \left\{\int_0^t f(\tau)\,d\tau\right\}$$

is a continuous function. It is natural to identify the function f with the operator lf/l. By this identification, two functions f_1 and f_2 which differ from each other on a set of measure 0 only, must be considered as the same function. For we then have $lf_1 = lf_2$ and the same operator $lf_1/l = lf_2/l$ corresponds to f_1 and f_2.

To the convolution fg of two locally integrable functions f and g corresponds the operator lfg/l, which is evidently equal to the product $(lf/l)(lg/l)$ of the operators corresponding to f and g. If this argument is to be correct, we must base ourselves upon the theorems of existence, and upon the commutativity and associativity of convolution in the domain of locally integrable functions.

Similarly, to the sum $f+g$ of two locally integrable functions f and g corresponds the operator $l(f+g)/l$, which is equal to the sum $lf/l+lg/l$ of operators corresponding to f and g.

When the correspondence between the locally integrable functions f and the operators of the form lf/l is already established, we can deal with these functions as with any other operators and no knowledge of the Lebesgue theory of integrals is further necessary. That is one of the advantages of the operational calculus.

§ 4. Functions of class $\mathcal{K}$. We can now give the proof of the fact that the convolution of two functions of class $\mathcal{K}$ is again a function of class $\mathcal{K}$. This follows from the following theorem:

If the functions f and g are integrable in the interval $[0, T]$ and their convolution is discontinuous at some point t_0 $(0 < t_0 < T)$, then there exist *two points $t_1 \geqslant 0$ and $t_2 \geqslant 0$ such that $t_1+t_2 = t_0$ and the functions f and g are unbounded in the neighbourhoods of t_1 and t_2.*

Proof. Suppose, conversely, that there are no points with this property. By the Borel-Lebesgue theorem it is then possible to cover the interval $[0, t_0]$ with a finite number of open intervals Δ so that in each of these intervals at least one of the factors of the product $f(t_0-t)g(t)$ is bounded. Thus, there exist $n+1$ points

$$u_0 < u_1 < \ldots < u_{n-1} < u_n \qquad (u_0 = 0,\ u_n = t_0)$$

and a positive number δ such that each of the intervals

$$(u_{i-1}-\delta,\ u_i+\delta) \tag{2}$$

is contained in some of the intervals Δ. If we put identically $f(t) = g(t) = 0$ outside the interval $[0, T]$, then in each of the intervals (2) at least one of the functions f and g is bounded. Moreover, one can chose the points 0 and t_0 so as to obtain

$$\Big|\int_{u_{n-1}}^{t} f(t-\tau)g(\tau)\,d\tau\Big| < \varepsilon \tag{3}$$

for $0 \leqslant t_0-t < u_1$, $u_{n-1} < t \leqslant t_0$, where ε is a given positive number.

If h denotes the convolution of f and g, then we can write

$$h(t_0)-h(t) = \sum_{i=0}^{n-1} \int_{u_{i-1}}^{u_i} [f(t_0-\tau)-f(t-\tau)]g(\tau)\,d\tau + \tag{4}$$

$$+ \int_{u_{n-1}}^{t_0} f(t_0-\tau)g(\tau)\,d\tau - \int_{u_{n-1}}^{t} f(t-\tau)g(\tau)\,d\tau.$$

If the function $g(t)$ is bounded in $(u_{i-1}-\delta,\ u_i+\delta)$, $|g(t)| < M$, the integral

$$J_i = \int_{u_{i-1}}^{u_i} [f(t_0-\tau)-f(t-\tau)]g(\tau)\,d\tau$$

satisfies the inequality

$$|J_i| \leqslant M \int_{u_{i-1}}^{u_i} |f(t_0-\tau)-f(t-\tau)|\,d\tau,$$

which implies

$$\lim_{t\to t_0-} J_i = 0. \tag{5}$$

We shall show that (5) holds also when instead of $g(t)$ the function $a(t_0-t)$ is bounded in $(u_{i-1}-\delta, u_i+\delta)$: $|f(t_0-t)| < M$. In that case we write

$$J_i = \int_{u_{i-1}}^{u_i} f(t_0-\tau)[g(\tau)-g(\tau-\theta)]d\tau -$$

$$- \int_{u_{i-1}-\theta}^{u_{i-1}} f(t-\tau)g(\tau)d\tau + \int_{u_i-\theta}^{u_i} f(t-\tau)g(\tau)d\tau,$$

where $\theta = t_0-t$. Hence we have, for $0 \leqslant t_0-t < \delta$,

$$|J_i| \leqslant M \int_{u_{i-1}}^{u_i} |g(\tau)-g(\tau-\theta)|d\tau + M \int_{u_{i-1}-\theta}^{u_{i-1}} |g(\tau)|d\tau + M \int_{u_i-\theta}^{u_i} |g(\tau)|d\tau,$$

which implies (5).

It follows from (5) that the first number on the right side of (4) becomes smaller than ε as $t \to t_0-$. Consequently

$$|h(t_0)-h(t)| < 3\varepsilon.$$

Since ε can be as small as we wish, we have

$$\lim_{t \to t_0-} h(t) = h(t_0).$$

Thus we have proved that the convolution $h(t)$ is at t_0 continuous on the left.

When $t_0 < T$, we can prove in the same way that the convolution $h(t)$ is at t_0 continuous on the right. Thus, the supposition that, in some neighbourhood of each point t of $[0, T]$, at least one of the functions $f(t-t_0)$ and $g(t)$ is bounded implies the continuity of the convolution $h(t)$. This proves the theorem.

Now, the functions of class $\mathcal{K}$ are characterized by the following two properties:

(I) The function has, in any bounded interval $[0, T]$, at most a finite number of points of discontinuity;

(II) The function is integrable in any bounded interval $[0, T]$.

If f and g satisfy condition (II), then so does their convolution, in view of the theorem proved in § 1. If, moreover, f and g satisfy condition (I), then their convolution does so, in view of the theorem we have just proved.

Thus, the convolution of two functions of class $\mathcal{K}$ belongs to the same class.

§ 5. Absolutely continuous functions. As in § 21 of part I we can prove the following theorem:

If a function a of class $\mathcal{C}$ is absolutely continuous, then

$$sa = a' + a(0),$$

where $a(0)$ is the value of a at $t = 0$.

More generally:

If a function a of class $\mathcal{C}$ has its $(n-1)$-th derivative absolutely continuous, then

$$a^{(n)} = s^n a - s^{n-1} a(0) - \ldots - a^{(n-1)}(0). \tag{6}$$

These theorems allow us to solve the differential equations

$$a_n x^{(n)} + a_{n-1} x^{(n-1)} + \ldots + a_0 x = f, \tag{7}$$

where a_i are constant coefficients and f is an arbitrary function of class $\mathcal{K}$. The function x is considered as a solution of (7), if it has its $(n-1)$-th derivative absolutely continuous and if equation (7) is satisfied almost everywhere in the interval $0 \leqslant t < \infty$.

Formula (6), applied to the unknown function x, reduces (7) to an algebraical equation, exactly as described in § 28 of part I. This method ensures the existence and the uniqueness of the solution of (7) with any locally integrable function f on the right side of the equation.

§ 6. The ring of locally integrable functions. Let $\mathcal{L}$ be the set of the complex-valued locally integrable functions in $0 \leqslant t < \infty$. This set can be considered as a ring without divisors of zero, whenever addition is taken in the ordinary sense and multiplication in the sense of convolution. The ring $\mathcal{C}$ of continuous functions is evidently a *partial ring* or *subring* of the ring $\mathcal{L}$ of locally integrable functions.

Starting from $\mathcal{L}$, it is possible to construct a quotient field. The elements of this quotient field are fractions b/a whose numerator and denominator belong to $\mathcal{L}$.

It might appear at first that this ring yields some new kind operators. But it can easily be seen that every quotient of elements of $\mathcal{L}$ is equal to a quotient of elements cf $\mathcal{C}$. In fact,

$$\frac{b}{a} = \frac{lb}{la};$$

if b and a belong to $\mathcal{L}$, then lb and la belong to $\mathcal{C}$. Thus the extensions of both rings $\mathcal{C}$ and $\mathcal{L}$ to quotient fields are equivalent.

Practically, it is more advantageous to start from the ring of continuous functions than from the ring of locally integrable functions, for then the proofs in the theory to be developed become easier.

CHAPTER III

DISTRIBUTIONS

(Appendix to Chapter VII of Part I)

§ 1. Introduction. The theory of distributions, created by L. Soboleff and widely developped by L. Schwartz [1], has many aspects common with the theory of operators. Moreover, some distributions can be considered as operators and vice versa. There exist, at present, a lot of different but equivalent definitions of distributions. The definition we are going to give here is a new one. It is not our aim to present fully the theory of distributions; we only attempt to show the most natural approach to it from the part of operators. We restrict ourselves to the distributions of a single variable, i. e. to the one-dimensional distributions. Our definition is equivalent to other definitions, which may easily be proved thanks to the proposition that every distribution is, in every bounded interval, a derivative of some order of a continuous function.

§ 2. Distributional operators. We start from the operators of the form

(1) $$h^{-\lambda}\frac{f}{l^k},$$

where: h = translation operator, $l = \{1\}$, f = function of class $\mathcal{C}$, λ = real number, k = non-negative integer.

The operators which can be represented in form (1) will be called *distributional operators*. The name *operational distribution* would also be adequate.

The sum and product of distributional operators are again distributional operators.

Any distributional operator can be represented in form (1) in different manners, because

$$h^{-\lambda}\frac{f}{l^k} = h^{-\lambda-\mu}\frac{l^n h^\mu f}{l^{k+n}} \quad (\mu > 0,\ n \text{ positive integer}),$$

where $l^n h^\mu f$ is again a function of class $\mathcal{C}$. Moreover, it will be seen that the numbers λ and k can be made arbitrarily large.

Particular cases of distributional operators are those which can be represented in the form f/l^k. Suppose that, in this representation, the function f is reduced, in some interval (α, β) where $\alpha \geqslant 0$, to a polynomial of degree $< k$. Since division by l^k is a generalization of k-tuple derivation, it is natural to say that the operator f/l^k *vanishes* in the interval (α, β).

More generally, we adopt the following definition:

A distributional operator *vanishes* in a given interval (α, β) where $\alpha > -\infty$ if, written in form (1), the function f is reduced in the interval $(\alpha+\lambda, \beta+\lambda)$ to a polynomial of degree $< k$.

E. g. the operator 1 (corresponding to the function delta of Dirac) vanishes in every interval (α, β) which does not contain the point $t = 0$. In fact, we can write

$$1 = h^{-\alpha}\frac{\{H_\alpha(t)\}}{l},$$

where H_α is the function of Heaviside. The function H_α is equal in the interval (α, β), to a polynomial of degree 0, for its values are 1 in this interval.

For any distributional operator, the sum of all open intervals in which it vanishes is an open set. The complement of this set is called the *support* of a. Thus the support of a is a closed set which is bounded from below. E. g. the support of the operator 1 consists of the only point $t = 0$. The support of the Heaviside function H_α is the interval $\alpha \leqslant t < \infty$.

If $f \in \mathcal{C}$, then the support of (1) is bounded from below by the number $-\lambda$. Conversely, if the support of a distributional operator is bounded from below by the number $-\lambda$, then the considered operator can be represented in form (1) with the given $-\lambda$.

§3. Distributions. Let us consider the sequence

(1) $$H_{-1}, H_{-2}, H_{-3}, \ldots$$

Since the values of H_{-n} are 0 for $t < -n$ and 1 for $-n < t$, the sequence converges almost uniformly in the interval $-\infty < t < \infty$ to the constant function whose values are 1 everywhere.

More generally, we consider sequence of functions

(2) $$f_1, f_2, f_3, \ldots$$

of class $\mathcal{V}$ which contains all locally integrable functions f in $(-\infty, \infty)$ vanishing in an interval $(-\infty, a)$ (a may be different for different f). Class $\mathcal{V}$ evidently embraces class $\mathcal{U}$, considered in § 66 of Part I. Every function of $\mathcal{V}$ can be interpreted as an operator in the same way as the functions of class $\mathcal{U}$.

Suppose that the functions $f_n, f_{n+1}, \ldots$ of sequence (2) coincide with each other in the interval $(-n, \infty)$. Then this sequence converges almost uniformly in the interval $(-\infty, \infty)$ to a function which is locally integrable in $(-\infty, \infty)$, but is not necessarily of class $\mathcal{V}$. Instead of $(-n, \infty)$ one can take the interval $(-n, n)$. E. g. if f_n has the values $\cos t$ in the interval $(-n, n)$ and the values 0 outside of this interval, then the considered sequence converges to $\cos t$ in the whole interval $(-\infty, \infty)$.

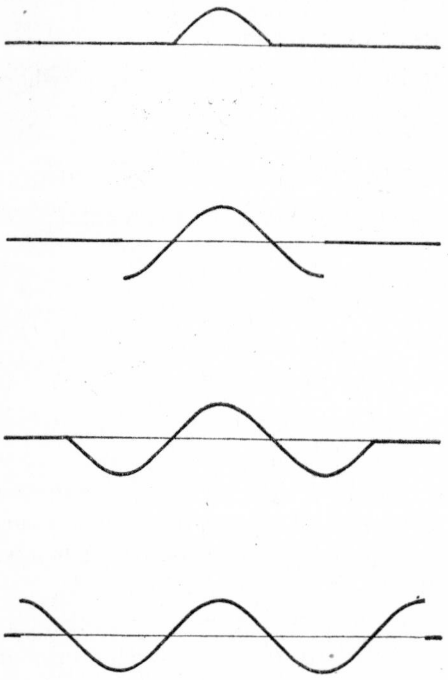

Fig. 160

The same process can be applied to the distributional operators. Two such operators are said *to coincide* or *to be equal* in an open interval if their difference vanishes in that interval. Now let (2) be a sequence of distributional operators such that the operators $f_n, f_{n+1}, \ldots$ coincide in the interval $(-n, n)$.

The limit of this sequence is per definitione a *distribution*. Of course, every distributional operator is a distribution. Thus a distribution can be considered as a generalization of a distributional operator.

In the particular case where f_n are functions of class $\mathcal{V}$ the limit is a function in $(-\infty, \infty)$. Every function which is locally integrable in $(-\infty, \infty)$ is the limit of a sequence of functions of $\mathcal{V}$ with the considered property. Thus every locally integrable function is a distribution.

The function f which is constant in $(-\infty, \infty)$, its values being a, can be interpreted as the distribution which is the limit of the sequence of distributional operators alh^{-n}.

In general, when the operators f_n are not functions, the limit of the sequence can be considered neither in the classical nor in the operational sense. In this case we have to consider the sequence $f_1, f_2, \ldots$ itself as a distribution.

Denote generally by $[f_n]$ the distribution given by the sequence $f_1, f_2, \ldots$ Two distributions $[f_n]$ and $[g_n]$ are *equal* if and only if the operators f_n and g_n $(n = 1, 2, \ldots)$ coincide in the interval $(-n, n)$.

The last definition of equality shows that, from the logical point of view, a distribution should be considered as a class of sequences of distributional operators such that operators with the same index n coincide in the interval $(-n, n)$.

§ 3. Derivation of distributions. Observe that *if two distributional operators a and b coincide in some interval, then also the operators sa and sb coincide in that interval.*

In fact, suppose that a and b coincide in an interval (α, β). Then the difference $a-b$ vanishes in (α, β). Thus, if we represent this difference in the form

$$a-b = h^{-\alpha}\frac{f}{l^k},$$

where f is a function of class $\mathcal{C}$, then f coincides with a polynomial of degree $<k$ in the interval $(0, \beta-\alpha)$. Also in the difference

$$sa-sb = h^{-\alpha}\frac{f}{l^{k+1}},$$

the function f appears in the numerator. Hence the difference $sa-sb$ vanishes in (α, β) and, consequently, the operators sa and sb coincide in (α, β). Thus multiplication by the differential operator s does not disturb the coincidence of distributional operators in intervals.

In the distribution $[f_n]$ the distributional operators $f_n, f_{n+1}, \ldots$ coincide with each other in $(-n, n)$. Therefore so do the distributional operators $sf_n, sf_{n+1}, \ldots$ This argument allows us to define the derivative of the distribution $[f_n]$ as the distribution $[sf_n]$. In symbols

$$s[f_n] = [sf_n]. \tag{3}$$

By this definition: *every distribution is derivable.*

Formula (3) generalizes to distributions multiplication by the operator s. An analoguous generalization is impossible for the operator l. Indeed, let f be a constant function with value 1. Then $f = [h^{-n}l]$ and, multiplying the right side by l, we should obtain $[h^{-n}l^2]$. But the operators $h^{-n}l^2$ are functions whose values are 0 for $t<-n$ and $t+n$ for $t>n$. Thus the sequence of these functions diverges everywhere and does not represent any distribution.

If f is an absolutely continuous function in $(-\infty, \infty)$, then its derivative (in the ordinary sense) f' is a locally integrable function in $(-\infty, \infty)$. Let f_n $(n = 1, 2, \ldots)$ be a function which coincides with f in the interval $(-n, n)$ and vanishes outside this interval. Then f can be considered as the distribution

$$f = [f_n]. \tag{4}$$

Moreover, we have

$$sf_n = f'_n + h^{-n} f(-n) - h^n(n),$$

where f'_n is the ordinary derivative of f_n. Hence the distributional operator sf_n coincides with f' in $(-n, n)$ and, consequently, we may write $f' = [sf_n] = s[f_n]$, and, by (4), $f' = sf$.

Thus, *if a distribution is an absolutely continuous function, then its derivative in the distributional sense is the derivative of the function in the ordinary sense.* In other words, distributional derivation generalizes ordinary derivation.

In particular, if f is a constant function, then $sf = 0$. Thus the ordinary algebra of operators is no longer valid for distributions. If it were so, the equality $sf = 0$ would imply $f = 0$, which is not true.

§ 4. Equivalency of the theory here presented with other theories of distributions. We say that two distributions $f = [f_n]$ and $g = [g_n]$ *coincide* or *are equal* in a given bounded interval (α, β) if the distributional operators coincide in it for sufficiently great values of n. Then we write $f = g$ in (α, β).

By this definition, every distribution $f = [f_n]$ coincides in $(-n, n)$ with f_n, i. e. $f = f_n$ in $(-n, n)$.

Let $f = [f_n]$ be a given distribution and (α, β) a given bounded interval. We can fix n so as to have $-n < \alpha$ and $\beta < n$. For n chosen thus, let us write

$$f_n = h^{-n} \frac{\bar{f}}{l^k},$$

where $\bar{f}$ is a function continuous for $t \geqslant 0$. Let $\tilde{f}$ be a function which is continuous in $(-\infty, \infty)$ and coincides with the function $h^{-n}\bar{f}$ for $t \geqslant -n$. Then we can write $f = f_n = s^k \tilde{f}$ in (α, β).

Thus, *every distribution f is in every bounded interval (α, β) a derivative (of some order k) of a continuous function $\tilde{f}$.*

If there are, for a given distribution f, an integer $k \geqslant 0$ and a function F, continuous in $(-\infty, \infty)$, such that f is the k-th derivative of F, then f is called a *distribution of finite order*. All other distributions are of infinite order.

Every distributional operator is evidently a distribution of finite order. The distribution $f = [f_n]$, where

$$f_n = 1 + sh + \ldots + s^n h^n, \tag{5}$$

is an example of a distribution of infinite order.

The last theorem leads to an alternative definition of distributions as derivatives of continuous functions and shows the equivalence of those definitions. Thus the theory of distributions developed here is equivalent, in the domain of a single variable, to other known theories of distributions. Of course, we must still define, in an adequate manner, some operations on distributions, such as addition, subtraction, multiplication and the limit of a sequence of distributions.

We adopt the following definitions:

$$[f_n] + [g_n] = [f_n + g_n],$$

$$[f_n] - [g_n] = [f_n - g_n],$$

$$a[f_n] = [af_n] \quad (a \text{ number}).$$

The distributions cannot in general be multiplied by one another. Under some restrictions, a distribution f can be multiplied by a function φ. But the symbol $f\varphi$ denotes, in the operational calculus, a kind of multiplication which is based on the concept of convolution and is different from usual multiplication. The ordinary product of functions or of a function by a distribution is foreign to the theory of operators and we shall not introduce it here.

Also there are difficulties in determining the convolution of distributions. In the case of functions of class $\mathcal{U}$ or $\mathcal{V}$, the convolution is given by the expression

$$f(t-\tau)g(\tau)d\tau$$

and it is easily seen that this expression loses its sense, e. g. when f and g are constant functions with values different from 0 in the interval $(-\infty, \infty)$. Thus convolution cannot be generalized to every pair of distributions. Convolution can be defined under certain hypotheses only, e. g. when the support of both distributions is bounded from below, in particular, when those distributions are distributional operators.

§ 5. Sequences of distributions. We say that a sequence of distributions f_n *converges to the distribution* f, if, for any bounded interval (α, β) there are a sequence of continuous functions F_n in $(-\infty, \infty)$ which converges uniformly to F and non negative integer k such that

$$f_n = s^k F_n \quad \text{in} \quad (\alpha, \beta),$$

$$f = s^k F \quad \text{in} \quad (\alpha, \beta).$$

This definition of convergence of distributions is different from the definition of convergence of operators. Distributional operators are both: distributions and operators. Thefore one can consider their distributional and operational convergence. For instance, the sequence lh^{-n} converges distributionally but not operationally.

It is more difficult to give an example of a sequence which converges operationally but not distributionally. Probably the sequence of functions

$$e^{-\sqrt[3]{s}/n+\sqrt{s}}$$

(vanishing for $t \leqslant 0$) has this property. This sequence evidently converges operationally, but no proof is known that it diverges distributionally(1).

Every distribution is a distributional limit of distributional operators and every operator is an operational limit of distributional operators.

§ 6. Operators and distributions. Operators and distributions are different concepts, but there are many similarities between them. Both are generalizations of functions such that derivation, in a certain sense, is always feasible. The question arises which of the two theories, of operators and of distributions, is more general. Before answering this question, we must formulate it more exactly.

The notion of distribution generalizes arbitrary locally integrable functions in $(-\infty, \infty)$. On the other hand, those functions which vanish in an interval $(-\infty, a)$ may be considered as operators. By means of those functions a correspondence is established between some distributions and some operators, which, from the logical point of view are different concepts, for they have been constructed in different ways. The correspondence can be extended to a larger class of distributions and operators by means of distributional operators. Namely every distributional operator f is an operator and can be identified with the distribution $[f_n]$, where $f_n = f$.

Now there are distributions and operators which are not distributional operators. No correspondence is established between them. From this points of view, neither of the two theories considered is embraced by the other.

It is easily seen that the set of distributions and also the set of operators are of power equal to the cardinal number $\mathfrak{f}$. Therefore a one-to-one correspondence can be established between the distributions and the operators. But such an artificial correspondence would be of no advantage. Rather it is necessary to establish some additional conditions which have to be fullfilled after introducing the correspondence. These conditions can be chosen in a lot of different ways and this point must be settled before the question, which of the two theories is more general, can be answered.

Let us remark that sequence (5) converges in the operational sense. It is thus natural to identify the operational limit of this sequence with the distribution which it represents. But, on the other hand, the sequence

---

(1) The proof was found recently. It follows from a theorem given in the paper: J. Mikusiński, *Sur les notions de distribution et d'opérateur,* Bull. Ac. Pol. Sci. (in print).

converges not only in the operational sense, but also in the distributional sense to the same distribution which it represents.

This remark suggest the following condition:

A distribution and an operator are to be identified if there is a sequence of distributional operators which converges distributionally to the distribution and operationally to the operator.

If all operators could be identified with distributions in this way then we could say that theory of distribution embraced, potencially, the theory of operators, and vice versa. Now the question which of the two theories is more general, is formulated precisely (in one of the possible ways).

It is easy to prove that the constant function with the value 1 in $(-\infty, \infty)$, i. e. the distribution $[h^{-n} l]$ is not an operator.

In fact, every function f of class $\mathcal{C}$ can be represented in one and only one way in the form $h^a f_0$, where a is a non-negative number and f_0 a continuous function which does not vanish identically in any right-hand neighbourhood of $t = 0$. The number a is the lower bound of the support of f. If we represent the distributional operator $h^{-n} l$ in the form

$$h^{-n} l = \frac{h^{a_n} f_n}{h^{\beta_n} g_n}, \tag{6}$$

where a_n, β_n are non-negative numbers and f_n, g_n are continuous functions which do not vanish in any neighbourhood of $t = 0$, then we see that $-n = a_n - \beta_n$ and hence $\beta_n \geqslant n$. This proves that the denominator in (6) cannot be fixed independently of n and, consequently, that the sequence $h^{-n} l$ does not converge operationally.

It is much more difficult to prove the existence of operators which are not distributions. Probably $e^{\sqrt{s}}$ is such an operator (¹). To prove it, we must show that any sequence of distributional operators which converges operationally to $e^{\sqrt{s}}$ does not converge distributionally to any limit.

In view of the above considerations we can say that the theory of operators does not embrace the theory of distributions and, *vice versa*, the theory of distributions does not embrace the theory of operators.

(¹) This is a particular case of a more general theorem proved recently (see footnote on p. 356).

CHAPTER IV

ABSTRACT SPACES WITH CONVERGENCE

(Appendix to Chapter I of Part II)

§ 1. Uniform and almost uniform convergence. Let $\mathcal{B}$ denote the set of continuous and bounded functions in a given interval I.

DEFINITION (I). A sequence f_n of functions of $\mathcal{B}$ is said *to converge to f uniformly in I*, if there is a sequence of positive numbers ε_n converging to 0, such that

$$|f_n(t)-f(t)| < \varepsilon_n \tag{1}$$

for $n = 1, 2, \ldots$ and for every $t \in I$.

This definition is equivalent to the following one:

DEFINITION (I′). A sequence f_n of functions of $\mathcal{B}$ is said *to converge to f uniformly in I*, if for any positive number ε there is an index n_0 such that

$$|f_n(t)-f(t)| < \varepsilon \tag{2}$$

for every $n \geqslant n_0$ and every $t \in I$.

If f_n converges in sense (I), then for every $\varepsilon > 0$ there is an index n_0 such that $\varepsilon_n < \varepsilon$ for $n \geqslant n_0$. Then (2) holds for every $n \geqslant n_0$ and every $t \in I$. If, conversely, f_n converges in sense (I′), then for every positive integer k there is an index n_k such that

$$|f_n(t)-f(t)| < 1/k$$

for every $n \geqslant n_k$ and every $t \in I$. Put $\varepsilon_n = 1/k$ for $n_k \leqslant n < n_{k+1}$. Then the sequence ε_n is defined for $n \geqslant n_0$ so that $\varepsilon_n \to 0$ and (1) holds for $n = n_1, n_1+1, \ldots$ and for every $t \in I$. To complete the sequence $\varepsilon_1, \varepsilon_2, \ldots$ it suffices to take, at its first $n_1 - 1$ elements, $\varepsilon_n = M$, where M is the upper bound of $|f_n(t)-f(t)|$ in I.

Now let $\mathcal{C}$ be the set of continuous (not necessarily bounded) functions in the interval I.

DEFINITION (II). A sequence f_n of functions of $\mathcal{C}$ is said *to converge almost uniformly in I to f*, if it converges uniformly to f in every bounded and closed interval contained in I.

Thus, almost uniform convergence is, in the case of a bounded and closed interval I, equivalent to uniform convergence. An equivalent definition of almost uniform convergence is

DEFINITION (II′). A sequence f_n of functions of $\mathcal{C}$ is said *to converge to f almost uniformly in I*, if there is a positive function $b \in \mathcal{B}$ such that the functions $b(t)f_n(t)$ belong to $\mathcal{B}$ and converge uniformly to the function $b(t)f(t)$.

We shall prove the equivalence of definitions (II) and (II′).

Suppose that f_n converges in sense (II′). Then $b(t)|f_n(t)-f(t)| < \varepsilon_n$, where $\varepsilon_n \to 0$. For any interval $[\alpha, \beta]$ contained in I, there is a number $\eta > 0$ such that $b(t) > \eta$ in $[\alpha, \beta]$. Hence

$$|f_n(t)-f(t)| < \varepsilon_n/\eta,$$

where $\varepsilon_n/\eta \to 0$. Thus f_n converges in sense (II).

Suppose, conversely, that f_n converges in sense (II). Then there exists a function $q \in \mathcal{C}$ such that

$$|f_n(t)-f(t)| < q(t)$$

and $q(t) > 1$ in I $(n = 1, 2, \ldots)$. Let $r \in \mathcal{B}$ be a function such that $0 < r(t) < 1$. Moreover, if the interval I is open at its left end A, then we assume that $\lim_{t\to A} r(t) = 0$. Similarly, if the interval I is open at its right end B, then we assume that $\lim_{t\to B} r(t) = 0$. Let ε be an arbitrary positive number. If I is open on the left, there exists a number α such that $|r(t)| < \varepsilon$ in (A, α). Similarly, if I is open on the right, there is a number β such that $|r(t)| < \varepsilon$ in (β, B). If A or B is finite and belongs to I, we put $\alpha = A$ or $\beta = B$ respectively. Now in the interval $[\alpha, \beta]$ the sequence f_n converges uniformly; thus there is an index n_0 such that (2) holds in $[\alpha, \beta]$ for $n \geqslant n_0$. Put $b(t) = r(t)/q(t)$ in I. Then evidently $0 < b(t) < 1$ and

$$|b(t)f_n(t)-b(t)f(t)| < \varepsilon$$

for $n \geqslant n_0$ in the whole interval I. This proves the uniform convergence of $b(t)f_n(t)$ to $b(t)f(t)$ in I, which completes the proof.

Let the factor $b(t)$ appearing in definition (II′) be termed the *factor of regularisation.*

If two sequences f_n and g_n converge almost uniformly in a given interval I, then we can choose for both sequences a common factor of regularisation.

In fact, if $b_1(t)$ and $b_2(t)$ are factors of regularisation for the f_n and g_n respectively, then their product $b_1(t)b_2(t)$ is their common factor of regularisation.

§ 2. Extensions of convergence in abstract spaces. Let $\mathfrak{B}$ be a set of arbitrary elements. Consider sequences f_n ($n = 1, 2, \ldots$) of elements of $\mathfrak{B}$. Some of these sequences are called *convergent.* To any convergent sequence f_n an element $f \in \mathfrak{B}$ is assigned. We call f the *limit* of f_n and we write $f_n \rightrightarrows f$. Nothing being assumed at first as to the nature of the convergent sequences, their limits can be assigned arbitrarily. We suppose only that the limit of any convergent sequence is unique.

Let $\mathfrak{M}$ be a family of one-to-one mappings b of $\mathfrak{B}$ into a set $\mathfrak{C}$ which embraces $\mathfrak{B}$. The element assigned by the mapping b to the element f will be denoted by bf. The set of all the elements bf, where $f \in \mathfrak{B}$, will be denoted by $b\mathfrak{B}$. We assume that $\mathfrak{C}$ is the union of all the sets $b\mathfrak{B}$, where $b \in \mathfrak{M}$.

Let b^{-1} denote the inverse of the mapping b: thus $b^{-1}bf = f$. We adopt, in the sequel, the following convention: if we write $b^{-1}f_n \rightrightarrows b^{-1}f$, then it means that 1° the elements $b^{-1}f_n$ and $b^{-1}f$ exist, i. e. f_n and f belong to the set $b\mathfrak{B}$ and 2° the sequence $b^{-1}f_n$ converges to the limit f. Similarly, if we write $f_n \rightrightarrows f$, then it means that 1° the elements f_n and f belong to $\mathfrak{B}$ and 2° $b^{-1}f_n$ converges to f.

If $b^{-1}f_n \rightrightarrows b^{-1}f$ implies $c^{-1}f \rightrightarrows c^{-1}f$, then we write $b \leqslant c$. The relation $\leqslant$ is evidently transitive, i. e. it follows from $b_1 \leqslant b_2$ and $b_2 \leqslant b_3$ that $b_1 \leqslant b_3$. We assume that the family has the following properties:

(i) For any b_1 and b_2 there is a b_3 such that $b_1 \leqslant b_3$ and $b_2 \leqslant b_3$.

(ii) $\mathfrak{M}$ contains the identical mapping of $\mathfrak{C}$ on $\mathfrak{C}$.

One can say that b maps the convergence $\rightrightarrows$ from $\mathfrak{B}$ to $b\mathfrak{B}$; by means of all the mappings of the family $\mathfrak{M}$, one maps the convergence $\rightrightarrows$ on the whole set $\mathfrak{C}$. We say that a *sequence f_n of elements of $\mathfrak{C}$ converges to an element f of $\mathfrak{C}$* and we write $f_n \to f$, if there is a $b \in \mathfrak{M}$ such that $b^{-1}f_n \rightrightarrows b^{-1}f$. The limit f is unique. In fact, it follows from $f_n \to f$ and $f_n \to g$ that $b_1^{-1}f_n \rightrightarrows b_1^{-1}f$ and $b_2^{-1}f_n \rightrightarrows b_2^{-1}g$ for some b_1 and b_2. By (i), there is a b_3 such that $b_3^{-1}f_n \rightrightarrows b_3^{-1}f$ and $b_3^{-1}f_n \rightrightarrows b_3^{-1}g$. Since the limit in $\mathfrak{B}$ is unique, we have $b_3^{-1}f = b_3^{-1}g$ and, consequently, $f = g$. Thus the uniqueness of the limit is proved for the introduced convergence. Moreover, this convergence is compatible with the original convergence in $\mathfrak{B}$, i. e. if $f_n \to f$ and $f_n \rightrightarrows g$, then $f = g$. This fact follows from (ii) and from the uniqueness we have just proved.

§ 3. Application to the operational calculus. Let $\mathfrak{B}$ be the set of continuous and bounded functions in the interval $0 \leqslant t < \infty$ and let $\mathfrak{C}$ be the set of continuous (but not necessarily bounded) functions in that interval.

Let the mapping b consist in multiplying (in the ordinary sense) by a continuous and positive function $b(t)$. Then b maps $\mathfrak{B}$ into $\mathfrak{C}$.

Moreover, it is easily seen that the family $\mathfrak{M}$ of all these mappings b satisfies conditions (i) and (ii).

If the convergence in $\mathcal{B}$ is understood as uniform convergence, then the convergence in $\mathcal{C}$, obtained by means of $\mathfrak{M}$, is the almost uniform convergence.

Now, let A be the set of operators. Consider the mappings which consist in multiplying (in the operational sense) by an operator $c \neq 0$; let the mapping be denoted by the same letter c. Then c maps $\mathcal{C}$ into A. The family Q of all these mappings satisfies conditions (i) and (ii) (in this case $\mathcal{C}$ must be replaced in (ii) by A).

If the convergence in $\mathcal{C}$ is almost uniform, then the convergence in A, obtained by means of the family Q, is the operational convergence.

It is possible to obtain operational convergence in A directly from uniform convergence in $\mathcal{B}$. Let cb denote a mapping which consists in multiplying (in the usual sense) by a continuous and positive function b and in the operational multiplication of the result by the operator c. Then cb maps $\mathcal{B}$ into A. The family $\mathfrak{P}$ of these mappings satisfies conditions (i) and (ii) (in (ii) the letter $\mathcal{C}$ must then be replaced by A). It is clear for (ii) and will be proved in the next paragraph for (i).

If the convergence in $\mathcal{B}$ is uniform, then the convergence in A, obtained by means of the family $\mathfrak{P}$, is the operational convergence.

§ 4. Iterated extension of convergence. Let B, C and A be three arbitrary sets such that $B \in C \in D$. Suppose that a convergence $\rightrightarrows$ is defined in B. Let $\mathfrak{M}$ be a family of mappings of B into C, satisfying conditions (i) and (ii). This family extends the convergence $\rightrightarrows$ in B to a convergence $\to$ in C. Moreover, let Q be family of mappings of C into A, satisfying conditions (i) and (ii). This family extends the convergence $\to$ in C to a convergence $\rightrightarrows$ in A.

Let $\mathfrak{P}$ be the family of all mappings (cb) which consist in the successive performance of two mappings, $b \in M$ and $c \in Q$. Since the families M and Q contain identical mappings, so does the family $\mathfrak{P}$. Thus $\mathfrak{P}$ satisfies (ii). We are going to prove that $\mathfrak{P}$ satisfies also condition (i).

Suppose that $(c_1 b_1)^{-1} f_n \rightrightarrows (c_1 b_1)^{-1} f$ and $(c_2 b_2)^{-1} g_n \rightrightarrows (c_2 b_2)^{-1} g$. Since we have generally $(cb)^{-1} f = b^{-1}(c^{-1} f)$, it follows that $b_1^{-1}(c_1^{-1} f_n) \rightrightarrows b_1^{-1}(c_1^{-1} f)$ and $b_2^{-1}(c_2^{-1} g_n) \rightrightarrows b_2^{-1}(c_2^{-1} g)$. Hence $c_1^{-1} f_n \to c_1^{-1} f$ and $c_2^{-1} g_n \to c_2^{\,1} g$. Since the family Q satisfies the condition (i) with respect to the convergence $\to$ there is a mapping $c_3 \in Q$ such that $c_3^{-1} f_n \to c_3^{-1} f$ and $c_3^{-1} g_n \to c_3^{-1} g$. In view of the definition of the convergence $\to$ there are mappings $\beta_1 \in M$ and $\beta_2 \in M$ such that $\beta_1^{-1}(c^{-1} f_n) \rightrightarrows \beta_1^{-1}(c_3^{-1} f)$ and $\beta_2^{-1}(c_3^{-1} g_n) \rightrightarrows \beta_2^{-1}(c_3^{-1} g)$. By (i) there is a mapping $b_3 \in M$ such that $b_3^{-1}(c_3^{-1} f_n) \rightrightarrows b_3^{-1}(c_3^{-1} f)$ and $b_3^{-1}(c_3^{-1} g_n) \rightrightarrows b_3^{-1}(c_3^{-1} g)$. But we generally have $b^{-1}(c^{-1} f) = (cb)^{-1} f$, thus we can write $(c_3b_3)^{-1}f_n \rightrightarrows (c_3b_3)^{-1}f$ and $(c_3b_3)^{-1}g_n \rightrightarrows (c_3b_3)^{-1}g$. This proves that the family $\mathfrak{P}$ satisfies the condition (i).

It follows from the preceeding argument that any iterated extension of convergence can be replaced by a simple extension.

§5. The set of continuous and bounded functions as a Banach space. Let $\mathfrak{B}$ be the set of continuous and bounded functions in a given interval I. The elements of $\mathfrak{B}$ will be denoted by latin letters $a, b, \ldots, x, \ldots$, Greek letters will denote complex numbers. The set $\mathfrak{B}$ is a linear space, i. e. it has the following properties:

(i) $a+b = b+a$;

(ii) $(a+b)+c = a+(b+c)$;

(iii) For any pair of elements a, b there is a third element x satisfying the equation $a+x = b$;

(iv) $\alpha(\beta a) = (\alpha\beta)a$;

(v) $\alpha(a+b) = \alpha a+\alpha b$;

(vi) $(\alpha+\beta)a = \alpha a+\beta a$;

(vii) $1a = a$.

By the norm $|a|$ of a $\mathfrak{B}$ we understand the number

$$|a| = \sup_{t\in I}|a(t)|.$$

The norm has the following properties:

$|a| = 0$ if and only if $a = 0$;

$|\alpha a| = |\alpha|\cdot|a|$ ($|\alpha|$ absolute value of the number α);

$|a+b| \leqslant |a|+|b|$.

Any linear space where a norm satisfying those three conditions is introduced is called a *normed linear space.*

By means of the norm, uniform convergence in $\mathfrak{B}$ can be expressed as follows: a sequence a_n of $\mathfrak{B}$ converges uniformly to an element a of $\mathfrak{B}$ if and only if the sequence of numbers $|a_n - a|$ tends (in the usual sense) to 0.

The set $\mathfrak{B}$ is *complete*, i. e. the following condition implies the uniform convergence of a_n to some element a:

CAUCHY'S CONDITION. *For every positive number ε there is an index n_0 such that $m, n \geqslant n_0$ implies $|a_m - a_n| < \varepsilon$.*

Any normed linear space which is complete is said to be a *Banach space.* Thus the set $\mathfrak{B}$ is a Banach space.

§6. The set of operators as a union of a partially ordered set of Banach spaces. Let $\mathfrak{B}$ be the set of continuous and bounded functions in the interval $0 \leqslant t < \infty$ and let $\mathfrak{P}$ be the family of mappings defined as in § 4. Every mapping $a \in \mathfrak{P}$ maps the set $\mathfrak{B}$ on the set of operators $a\mathfrak{B}$. The set $a\mathfrak{B}$ can itself be considered as a Banach space, provided we assign to any elements af ($f \in \mathfrak{B}$) of $a\mathfrak{B}$ the same norm as that assigned to f in the space $\mathfrak{B}$: $|af| = |f|$.

The family of mappings $\mathfrak{P}$ is partially ordered. We can assign to the set of all Banach spaces $a\mathfrak{B}$ the partial ordering induced by $\mathfrak{P}$: $a\mathfrak{B} \leqslant b\mathfrak{B}$ if and only if $a \leqslant b$.

If $a\mathfrak{B} \leqslant b\mathfrak{B}$, then $a\mathfrak{B} \subset b\mathfrak{B}$. Moreover, if f_n is a sequence of elements of $a\mathfrak{B}$ which converges with respect to the norm in $a\mathfrak{B}$, then, for every space $b\mathfrak{B}$ such that $a\mathfrak{B} \leqslant b\mathfrak{B}$, the sequence f_n converges with respect to the norm in $b\mathfrak{B}$ to the same limit. Roughly speaking, if $a\mathfrak{B} \leqslant b\mathfrak{B}$, then convergence in $a\mathfrak{B}$ is compatible with converges in $b\mathfrak{B}$.

The set of operators A is the union of all Banach spaces where $a \in \mathfrak{P}$. A sequence of operators f_n converges if and only if all its elements f_n belong to one of the Banach spaces $a\mathfrak{B}$ and if it converges with respect to the norm of that space.

The construction of the set of operators as the union of some partially ordered set of Banach spaces allows us to transfer different concepts, such as the derivative or integral of a vector function, from the Banach space to the space of operators. We shall discuss this matter in detail in § 10. Before doing so, we intend to discuss some theoretical questions.

§ 7. The set of operators is not a Banach space. The question arises whether, in the space of operators, a norm can be introduced so as to give a Banach space in which convergence is equivalent to operational convergence. The answer is negative.

First we prove the following property of any Banach space:

(K) *Let* $\lim f_{mn} = f_m$ *and* $\lim f_m = f$; *then there are sequences of positive integers* m_ν *and* n_ν *such that* $\lim f_{m_\nu n_\nu} = f$.

In fact, for any positive number ε, there are positive integers N_m ($m = 1, 2, \ldots$) and M such that

$$|f_{mn} - f_m| < \varepsilon/2 \text{ for } n \geqslant N_m \text{ and } |f_m - f| < \varepsilon/2 \text{ for } m \geqslant M.$$

Hence

$$|f_{mn} - f| < \varepsilon \quad \text{for} \quad m \geqslant M \quad \text{and} \quad n \geqslant N_m.$$

Put $m_\nu = \nu$ and $n_\nu = N_\nu$. Then

$$|f_{m_\nu n_\nu} - f| < \varepsilon \quad \text{for} \quad \nu \geqslant M,$$

which proves the theorem.

Now, it suffices to show that, in the space of operators, condition (K) does not hold for operational convergence.

Let $f_{mn} = 1/m + h^{-m}/n$. We evidently have $\lim_{n\to\infty} f_{mn} = 1/m$ and $\lim_{m\to\infty} 1/m = 0$. Suppose that m_ν and n_ν are positive integers such that

$$\lim f_{m_\nu n_\nu} = 0. \tag{3}$$

If the sequences m_ν and n_ν are bounded, then we can select from $f_{m_\nu n_\nu}$ a constant subsequence which evidently does not converge to 0. If the sequence m_ν is bounded and n_ν is unbounded, then we can choose from $f_{m_\nu n_\nu}$ a subsequence whose initial indices m_ν are constant, $m_\nu = m_0$, and the final indices n_ν increase. This subsequence evidently tends to $1/m_0 \neq 0$. It follows from this argument that the sequence m_ν must be unbounded. In view of (3) there is an operator c such that the sequence $cf_{m_\nu n_\nu}$ consists only of functions of class $\mathcal{C}$ (continuous in $0 \leqslant t < \infty$) and converges almost uniformly to 0. We can write

$$c = h^a \frac{a}{b} \quad \text{and} \quad f_{m_\nu n_\nu} = h^{-m_\nu} \frac{p_\nu}{l^2},$$

where a, b and $p_\nu = h^{m_\nu} l^2/m_\nu + l^2/n_\nu$ are functions of class $\mathcal{C}$ which do not vanish identically in any right-hand neighbourhood of $t = 0$. Since a is constant and m_ν unbounded, the operators

$$cf_{m_\nu n_\nu} = h^{a-m} \frac{ap_\nu}{l^2}$$

cannot all be functions of class $\mathcal{C}$. This contradiction proves that (3) does not hold.

We have proved that every Banach space satisfies condition (K) and that the set of operators does not. Thus the set of operators is not a Banach space.

§ 8. Different remarks. Consider the set $\mathcal{C}$ of continuous functions in $0 \leqslant t < \infty$. This is evidently a linear space. By the *k-th pseudonorm* of $a \in \mathcal{C}$ we understand the number

$$|a|_k = \max_{0 \leqslant t \leqslant k} |a(t)|.$$

The pseudonorms have the following properties:

$|a|_k = 0$ $(k = 1, 2, \ldots)$ if and only if $a = 0$;

$|\alpha a|_k = |\alpha| \cdot |a|_k$;

$|a+b|_k \leqslant |a|_k + |b|_k$.

Any linear space where pseudonorms with the above properties are defined is called a *pseudonormed space*. That is a generalization of a normed space and can be reduced to it if, for instance, the sequence of pseudonorms $|a|_1, |a|_2, \ldots$ is bounded for any element a of the considered space.

Pseudonormed spaces have been investigated first by S. Mazur and W. Orlicz [1] and later by [1] Dieudonné and L. Schwartz.

We say that a sequence of elements a_n of a pseudonormed space converges to a, if for every fixed k the sequence of numbers $|a_n - a|_k$ tends (in the usual sense) to 0. (In the case of the space $\mathcal{C}$ this convergence is equivalent to almost uniform convergence.) In every pseudonormed space condition (K) is satisfied. This implies that the set of operators cannot be pseudonormed in such a way that convergence with respect to the introduced pseudonorms should be equivalent to operational convergence.

If a_n are operators and the considered convergence is operational convergence, then:

(I) The sequence $a, a, \ldots$ converges to a;

(J) Every subsequence of a convergent sequence converges to the same limit.

Generally, if in a set there is a convergence which satisfies conditions (I), (J) and (K) (§ 7), then the convergence will be called *topological in the sense of Kuratowski*. That denomination is justified by the fact that, by defining the notion of closure by means of such a convergence, one obtains the *closure topology in the sense of Kuratowski.*

Evidently, in any normed or pseudonormed space (and, more generally, in any metric space) convergence is topological in the sense of Kuratowski. But this does not apply to the operational convergence of operators.

Similarly, the distributional convergence of distributions (see § 5, Chapter III) is not topological in the sense of Kuratowski. One can easily prove, analogously to the case of operators, that the distributions $f_{mn} = 1/m + \delta^{(m)}/n$, where $\delta^{(m)}$ is the m-th derivative of the distribution delta of Dirac, does not satisfy condition (K).

It is an open question whether the set of distributions can be considered as a union of a partially ordered set of Banach spaces.

§ 9. Regular operations. Let us return to the notation of § 2.

Suppose that an addition is defined in $\mathcal{C}$ such that $f, g \in b\mathcal{B}$ implies $f+g \in b\mathcal{B}$ and that

$$b(f+g) = bf + bg$$

for $b \in M$ and $f, g \in \mathcal{B}$. Then also $b^{-1}(f+g) = b^{-1}f + b^{-1}g$ holds for $b \in M$ and $f, g \in b\mathcal{B}$. If the addition is continuous in $\mathcal{B}$ with respect to the convergence $\rightrightarrows$, i. e. if

$$f_n \rightrightarrows f \quad \text{and} \quad g_n \rightrightarrows g \quad \text{implies} \quad f_n + g_n \rightrightarrows f + g,$$

then the addition is also continuous in $\mathcal{C}$ with respect to the convergence $\rightarrow$, i. e.

$$f_n \rightrightarrows f \quad \text{and} \quad g_n \rightrightarrows g \quad \text{implies} \quad f_n + g_n \rightrightarrows f + g.$$

In fact, there are mappings b_1 and b_2 such that $b_1^{-1}f_n \rightrightarrows b_1^{-1}f$ and $b_2^{-1}g_n \rightrightarrows b_2^{-1}g$. By (i) there is a third mapping b_3 such that $b_3^{-1}f_n \rightrightarrows b_3^{-1}f$ and $b_3^{-1}g_n \rightrightarrows b_3^{-1}g$. Hence $b_3^{-1}(f_n+g_n) \rightrightarrows b_3^{-1}(f+g)$ which implies $f_n+g_n \to f+g$.

Suppose now that a multiplication is defined in $\mathcal{C}$ such that $f, g \in b\mathcal{B}$ implies $fg \in b^2\mathcal{B}$, and that

$$b^2(fg) = bf \cdot bg,$$

where $b \in M$ and $f, g \in \mathcal{B}$. Then also $b^{-2}(fg) = b^{-1}f \cdot b^{-1}g$ holds for $b \in M$ and $f, g \in b\mathcal{B}$. If the multiplication is a continuous operation in B with respect to the convergence $\rightrightarrows$, i. e. if

$$f_n \rightrightarrows f \quad \text{and} \quad g_n \rightrightarrows g \quad \text{implies} \quad f_n+g_n \rightrightarrows f+g,$$

then the multiplication is also continuous in $\mathcal{C}$ with respect to the convergence $\to$, i. e.

$$f_n \to f \quad \text{and} \quad g_n \to g \text{ implies } f_n g_n \to fg.$$

The proof is similar.

Suppose, more generally, that there is an operation R in $\mathcal{C}$ defined on a finite number of elements $f, \ldots, k$ with the following property: Given any $b \in M$, there is a $c \in M$ such that $f, \ldots, k \in b\mathcal{B}$ implies $R(f, \ldots, k) \in c\mathcal{B}$ and that

$$cR(f, \ldots, k) = R(bf, \ldots, bk)$$

holds for $f, \ldots, k \in \mathcal{B}$. Then also

$$c^{-1}R(f, \ldots, k) = R(b^{-1}f, \ldots, b^{-1}k)$$

holds for $f, \ldots, k \in b\mathcal{B}$. Operation R with that property will be called *regular*. Addition and multiplication are examples of regular operations.

If a regular operation R is continuous in $\mathcal{B}$ with respect to the convergence $\rightrightarrows$, i. e. if

$$f_n \rightrightarrows f, \ldots, k_n \rightrightarrows k \quad \textit{implies} \quad R(f_n, \ldots, k_n) \rightrightarrows R(f, \ldots, k),$$

then the operation R is also continuous in $\mathcal{C}$ with respect to the convergence $\to$, i. e.

$$f_n \to f, \ldots, k_n \to k \quad \textit{implies} \quad R(f_n, \ldots, k_n) \to R(f, \ldots, k).$$

In fact, from $f_n \to f, \ldots, k_n \to k$ it follows that there are mappings $b_1, \ldots, b_q$ such that $b_1^{-1}f_n \rightrightarrows b_1^{-1}f, \ldots, b_q^{-1}k_n \rightrightarrows b_q^{-1}k$. From property (i) it follows by induction that there is a mapping $b \in M$ such that $b_1 \leqslant b, \ldots, b_q \leqslant b$. Thus $b^{-1}f_n \rightrightarrows b^{-1}f, \ldots, b^{-1}k_n \rightrightarrows b^{-1}k$ and $c^{-1}R(f_n, \ldots, k_n) = R(b^{-1}f_n, \ldots, b^{-1}k_n) \rightrightarrows R(b^{-1}f, \ldots, b^{-1}k) = c^{-1}R(f, \ldots, k)$. Hence the assertion follows.

§ 10. Limit, derivative and integral of an operational function. These concepts are well known in the theory of Banach spaces. We recall them shortly.

Let $f(\lambda)$ be a function of a real variable λ whose values are elements of a given Banach space $\mathcal{B}$.

We say that $f(\lambda)$ *tends to the limit* $a \in \mathcal{B}$, *as* $\lambda \to \lambda_0$, if for every given $\varepsilon > 0$ there is an $\eta > 0$ such that $|\lambda - \lambda_0| < \eta$ implies $|f(\lambda) - a| < \varepsilon$.

This definition may be be called *Cauchy's definition of limit.* We may have an alternative definition (*Heine's definition*) which runs as follows:

We say that $f(\lambda)$ *tends to the limit* $a \in B$, *as* $\lambda \to \lambda_0$, if for every sequence of numbers λ_n such that $\lambda_n \to \lambda_0$ the sequence $f(\lambda_n)$ tends to a in the sense of convergence in $\mathcal{B}$.

The function $f(\lambda)$ is *continuous* in λ_0, if $f(\lambda)$ tends to $f(\lambda_0)$, as $\lambda \to \lambda_0$.

Both definitions of limit are equivalent, which can be proved as for ordinary functions.

The derivative $f'(\lambda)$ is defined as the limit

$$f'(\lambda) = \lim_{a\to 0} \frac{f(\lambda + a) - f(\lambda)}{a}. \tag{4}$$

All these definition are formally the same as in classical analysis. Also the Riemann integral can be defined for Banach spaces in the usual way. But for the Lebesgue integral the classical definition cannot be transferred directly to Banach spaces, for that definition is based on the inequalities between values of functions, and the concept of inequality has no meaning in relation to elements of Banach spaces. Therefore we have to employ an alternative definition, due to Bochner [1]:

Suppose first that $f(\lambda)$ assumes a finite number of values $f_1, \ldots, f_n \in \mathcal{B}$ in a given interval $[\alpha, \beta]$ and let m^i denote the Lebesgue measure of the set in which $f(\lambda)$ assumes the value f_i. Put

$$\int_\alpha^\beta f(\lambda)\,d\lambda = \sum_{i=1}^n f_i m_i.$$

Now let $f_n(\lambda)$ be a sequence of finite-valued functions in $[\alpha, \beta]$ which converges almost everywhere to a function $f(\lambda)$ such that $|f_n(\lambda)| \leqslant \varphi(\lambda)$ $(n = 1, 2, \ldots)$ where $\varphi(\lambda)$ is a real positive function, integrable (Lebesgue) in $[\alpha, \beta]$. Then the function $f(\lambda)$ is called *integrable* and we write

$$\int_\alpha^\beta f(\lambda)\,d\lambda = \lim_{n\to\infty} \int_\alpha^\beta f_n(\lambda)\,d\lambda.$$

If, in particular, $\mathcal{B}$ is the space of real numbers, then the last integral coincides with the Lebesgue integral. Thus Bochner's integral is an extension of the Lebesgue integral to Banach spaces.

Since the set of operators is a union of a partially ordered set of Banach spaces $c\mathfrak{B}$, all these definitions can easily be extended to operational functions.

We say that *the operational function* $f(\lambda)$ *tends to the limit* a, *as* $\lambda \to \lambda_0$, if the values of $f(\lambda)$ belong to some of the spaces $a\mathfrak{B}$ and the limit is understood in $a\mathfrak{B}$ in the sense of the norm of that space. By means of the limit of an operational function the derivative of an operational function can simply be defined by formula (4). It can easily be seen that this definition coincides with that given in § 7, part II. Finally, an operational function $f(\lambda)$ is said to be *integrable in the interval* $[\alpha, \beta]$ if its values belong to some of the spaces $a\mathfrak{B}$ and its Bochner integral exists. This definition is slightly more general than that given in § 2, Part V.

In applications continuous operational functions are particularly important. An operational function $f(\lambda)$ is said to be *continuously d ffe-rentiable* in a given interval $[\alpha, \beta]$ if its values belong to some of the spaces $c\mathfrak{B}$ and the derivative $f'(\lambda)$ exists and is continuous in $[\alpha, \beta]$ with respect to the norm of $c\mathfrak{B}$. This definition coincides with that given in § 3, Part II.

Generally, we say that an operational function $f(\lambda)$ is *continuous* in $[\alpha, \beta]$ if its values in $[\alpha, \beta]$ belong to some of the spaces $c\mathfrak{B}$ and if it is continuous in $[\alpha, \beta]$ with respect to the norm of $c\mathfrak{B}$. In the case of an infinite interval I, we say that a function $f(\lambda)$ is continuous in it, if it is continuous in every partial bounded interval $[\alpha, \beta]$.

Let $[\alpha_n, \beta_n]$ be an increasing sequence of intervals whose union is I. For different intervals $[\alpha_n, \beta_n]$ the values of $f(\lambda)$ may belong to different spaces $c_n\mathfrak{B}$. There may be a space cB such that $c_nB \in cB$. In that case the function $f(\lambda)$ is continuous in I with respect to the norm in cB. But it is not so in general. E. g. the function $f(\lambda) = h^\lambda$ is continuous operationally in $(-\infty, \infty)$, but there is no space cB to which all values h^λ belong.

It is also possible to give another definition of continuity. To begin with, we say that an operational function $f(\lambda)$ is continuous at some point λ_0 if, in some neighbourhood of this point, the values of $f(\lambda)$ belong to one of the spaces cB and $f(\lambda)$ is continuous in λ_0 with respect to the norm of that space. The question arises whether a function which is continuous at every point of a given bounded and closed interval $[\alpha, \beta]$ is also continuous in the preceeding sense. The answer is unknown.

Finally, two definitions of the limit can be given: one in the sense of Cauchy and one in the sense of Heine. Both definitions are equivalent when the values of $f(\lambda)$ belong to the same Banach space. But we do not know how the matter stands in the case of an arbitrary operational function.

CHAPTER V

POWER SERIES OF OPERATORS

(Appendix to Chapter I of Part II)

§ 1. Power series of integrable functions. We have proved in § 15 of Part II that if the series

$$(1) \qquad \Phi(\lambda) = a_0 + a_1\lambda + a_2\lambda^2 + \ldots,$$

with numerical coefficients a_n, has a positive radius ϱ of convergence, then the series

$$\Phi(f) = a_0 + a_1 f + a_2 f^2 + \ldots,$$

where $f \in \mathcal{C}$ (the class of continuous functions in $0 \leqslant t < \infty$), converges operationally. Here we are going to prove the same theorem for arbitrary function f of the class $\mathcal{L}$ of locally integrable functions in $0 \leqslant t < \infty$.

Let us introduce generally the notation

$$[f](t) = \int_0^t |f(\tau)|\, d\tau \quad \text{and} \quad [f] = \left\{\int_0^t |f(\tau)|\, d\tau\right\}.$$

We have

$$[fg](t) \leqslant [f](t)\cdot[g](t),$$

because

$$\int_0^t d\omega \left|\int_0^\omega f(t-\tau)g(\tau)\, d\tau\right| \leqslant \int_0^t |f(\tau)|\, d\tau \cdot \int_0^t |g(\tau)|\, d\tau.$$

Moreover, if $|f(t)| \leqslant g(t)$ in $0 \leqslant t < \infty$ and g is a non-decreasing function, then

$$(2) \qquad [f^\nu](t) \leqslant \frac{1}{\nu!}\big(tg(t)\big)^\nu \qquad (\nu = 1, 2, \ldots).$$

In fact, we have

$$\int_0^t |f(\tau)|\, d\tau \leqslant \int_0^t g(\tau)\, d\tau \leqslant \int_0^t g(t)\, d\tau = tg(t),$$

thus formula (2) holds for $\nu = 1$. Assuming that (2) holds for some $\nu \geqslant 1$, we have

$$[f^{\nu+1}](t) \leqslant [gg^{\nu}](t)$$

and

$$[f^{\nu+1}](t) \leqslant \int_0^t g(t-\tau)\frac{1}{\nu!}\big(\tau g(\tau)\big)^{\nu} d\tau$$

$$\leqslant \int_0^t g(t)\frac{1}{\nu!}\tau^{\nu}\big(g(t)\big)^{\nu} d\tau = \frac{1}{(\nu+1)!}\big(tg(t)\big)^{\nu+1}.$$

Thus formula (2) is proved by induction.

Any integrable function $f \in \mathfrak{L}$ can be decomposed into two functions of class $\mathfrak{L}$, $f = f_1 + f_2$, so that $|f_1(t)| \leqslant g(t)$, where $g(t)$ is a non-decreasing function, and $[f_2](t) \leqslant \varrho/3$. Since

$$f^n = \sum_{\nu=0}^{n} \binom{n}{\nu} f_1^{\nu} f_2^{n-\nu},$$

we have

$$[f^n](t) \leqslant \sum_{\nu=0}^{n} \binom{n}{\nu} \frac{1}{\nu!}\big(tg(t)\big)^{\nu}\left(\frac{\varrho}{3}\right)^{n-\nu}$$

$$< \sum_{\nu=0}^{n} 2^{\nu}\frac{1}{\nu!}\left(\frac{3tg(t)}{\varrho}\right)^{\nu}\left(\frac{\varrho}{3}\right)^{n} < \left(\frac{2\varrho}{3}\right)^{n} e^{3tg(t)/\varrho}.$$

Since the modulus of the function lf^n is less than $[f^n]$, it follows from the last inequality that the series

$$(3) \qquad l\Phi(f) = a_0 l + a_1 lf + a_2 lf^2 + \ldots$$

converges almost uniformly in $0 \leqslant t < \infty$, which proves the assertion.

The operational convergence of $\Phi(\lambda)$ must be formulated more exactly. If we neglect the first of this series, then it converges in mean. Therefore its limit is of the form $a_0 + g$, where $g \in \mathfrak{L}$.

As an immediate corollary we find that *if $\Phi(\lambda)$ has a positive radius of convergence, then the series*

$$(4) \qquad \Phi(\lambda f) = a_0 + a_1\lambda f + a_2\lambda^2 f^2 + \ldots,$$

where $f \in \mathfrak{L}$, converges operationally for every complex value of λ.

§2. A more general case. We assume now that the operator f is of the form $f = \mu + g$, where μ is a number different from 0 and g is a function of class $\mathfrak{L}$.

Let ε be an arbitrarily fixed positive number and let T be a positive number such that

$$\int_0^T |g(t)|\,dt \leqslant \frac{\varepsilon}{2}.$$

Put

$$g = g_1 + g_2,$$

where

$$g_1(t) = \begin{cases} g(t) & \text{for} \quad 0 \leqslant t < T, \\ 0 & \text{for} \quad T \leqslant t < \infty. \end{cases}$$

Write generally

$$[\mu + g](t) = |\mu| + [g](t).$$

Then

$$[(\mu + g_1)^n](t) \leqslant \left(|\mu| + \frac{\varepsilon}{2}\right)^n$$

for $0 \leqslant t < \infty$.

From the equality we get

$$[f^n](t) \leqslant \sum_{\nu=0}^{n} \binom{n}{\nu} \left(|\mu| + \frac{\varepsilon}{2}\right)^{n-\nu} [g_2^\nu](t).$$

Since $g_2(t) = 0$ for $0 \leqslant t < T$, we have $g_2^n(t) = 0$ for $0 \leqslant t < nT$, and, as $n \geqslant n_0 > t/T$,

$$[f^n](t) \leqslant \sum_{\nu=0}^{n} \binom{n}{\nu} \left(|\mu| + \frac{\varepsilon}{2}\right)^{n-\nu} [g_2^\nu](t) < n^{n_0} \left(|\mu| + \frac{\varepsilon}{2}\right)^{n-n_0} \sum_{\nu=1}^{n_0} [g_2^\nu](t).$$

This inequality proves that the sequence

$$\frac{1}{(|\mu| + \varepsilon)^n} l f^n$$

converges to 0 almost uniformly in $0 \leqslant t < \infty$.

We are now in a position to prove the following theorem:

If the radius of convergence of (1) *is* $\varrho > 0$, *then the radius of operational convergence of* (4), *where* $f = \mu + g$ (μ *number*, $g \in \mathcal{L}$), *is* ϱ/μ.

In fact, if $|\lambda| < \varrho/\mu$, we can choose $\varepsilon > 0$ so that $|\lambda| < \varrho/(|\mu| + \varepsilon)$. Since $lf^n/(|\mu| + \varepsilon)^n$ converges to 0 almost uniformly in $0 \leqslant t < \infty$, series (4) multiplied by l also converges almost uniformly. Thus the radius of convergence of (4) is $\geqslant \varrho/\mu$. It remains to show that (4) diverges whenever $|\lambda| > \varrho/\mu$. We have

$$\frac{1}{f} = \frac{1}{\mu + g} = \frac{1}{\mu} - \frac{g}{\mu^2} + \frac{g^2}{\mu^3} - \ldots \tag{5}$$

Since the series

$$\frac{1}{\mu} - \frac{\lambda}{\mu^2} + \frac{\lambda^2}{\mu^3} - \ldots$$

has a positive radius of convergence, series (5) converges operationally to a limit of the form $1/\mu + g_1$, where $g_1 \in \mathcal{L}$. In view of the result just obtained, the sequence

$$\frac{1}{(|1/\mu|+\varepsilon)^n} \frac{1}{f^n} \qquad (\varepsilon > 0)$$

converges to 0 as $n \to \infty$. Let $|\lambda| > \varrho/|\mu|$; we can choose an $\varepsilon > 0$ so that

$$\lambda_0 = \frac{|\lambda|}{|1/\mu|+\varepsilon} > \varrho .$$

Then

(6) $$\left(\frac{\lambda_0}{\lambda}\right)^n \frac{1}{f^n} \to 0 .$$

Assuming that series (4) converges for the chosen λ, we have $a_n \lambda^n f_n \to 0$; this implies, together with (6), that $a_n \lambda_0^n \to 0$. But this is impossible for $\lambda_0 > \varrho$.

Observe that the result of the preceeding paragraph can be considered as a limit case (as $\mu \to 0$) of the theorem proved here. Moreover, putting in the last proof $\mu = 0$ we obtain an alternative proof of this result.

§ 3. Some particular power series. The question arises whether series (4) has a positive radius of convergence for every operator f whenever the radius ϱ of (1) is positive. The answer is negative. E. g. the series

$$a_0 + a_1 \lambda h^{-1} + a_2 \lambda^2 h^{-2} + \ldots,$$

where $a_n \neq 0$ $(n = 0, 1, \ldots)$, diverges for every $\lambda \neq 0$, since the sequence of its terms $a_n \lambda^n h^{-n}$ does not converge to 0 as $n \to \infty$. Also the series

(7) $$a_0 + a_1 \lambda s + a_2 \lambda^2 s^2 + \ldots,$$

where $a_n \geqslant 1/n!$ $(n = 0, 1, \ldots)$, diverges for every $\lambda \neq 0$, but the proof of this fact is not trivial. Assume for a moment that (7) converges for some λ_0. Thus there is a function $q \in \mathcal{C}$ such that the terms of the series

$$a_0 q + a_1 \lambda_0 s q + a_2 \lambda_0^2 s^2 q + \ldots$$

are functions of class $\mathcal{C}$. Hence the function q must be indefinitely differentiable with $q(0) = q'(0) = \ldots = 0$. The last series can also be written in the form

$$a_0 q(t) + a_1 \lambda_0 q'(t) + a_2 \lambda_0^2 q''(t) + \ldots;$$

since this series converges almost uniformly in $0 \leqslant t < \infty$, so does the series

$$q(t+\lambda) = q(t) + \frac{\lambda}{1!} q'(t) + \frac{\lambda^2}{2!} q''(t) + \ldots$$

for every fixed $|\lambda| \leqslant \lambda_0$. Therefore q must be an analytical function in $0 \leqslant t < \infty$. Since $q^{(\nu)}(0) = 0$ $(\nu = 0, 1, \ldots)$, we get for $t = 0$

$$q(\lambda) = 0 \quad \text{for} \quad |\lambda| < \lambda_0,$$

which is not true.

In particular, the series

$$1 - \frac{\lambda}{1!} s + \frac{\lambda^2}{2!} s^2 - \ldots$$

diverges. Thus the operational function $e^{-\lambda s}$ cannot be defined by its Taylor series. However it is interesting to remark that

$$e^{-\lambda s} = \lim_{n\to\infty} \left(1 + \frac{s\lambda}{n}\right)^{-n}. \tag{8}$$

In fact

$$\left(1 + \frac{\lambda s}{n}\right)^{-n} = \left(\frac{n}{\lambda}\right)^n \left(s + \frac{n}{\lambda}\right)^{-n} = \{f_n(\lambda, t)\},$$

where

$$f_n(\lambda, t) = \left(\frac{n}{\lambda}\right)^n \frac{t^{n-1}}{(n-1)!} \exp\left(-\frac{nt}{\lambda}\right).$$

In view of Stirling's formula, the sequence $f_n(\lambda, t)$ tends, for $0 < t \neq \lambda > 0$ and $n \to \infty$, to the same limit as

$$\frac{1}{t} \sqrt{\frac{n}{2\pi}} \left[\frac{t}{\lambda} \exp\left(1 - \frac{t}{\lambda}\right)\right]^n,$$

i. e., to 0, because

$$\exp\left(1 - \frac{t}{\lambda}\right) < \frac{\lambda}{t}.$$

If λ and n are fixed, then $f_n(\lambda, t)$ has its maximum at $t = (n-1)\lambda/n$; hence $f_n(\lambda, t)$ converges uniformly to 0 in every interval $0 \leqslant t_1 \leqslant t \leqslant t_2$ that does not contain the point $t = \lambda$.

But we have

$$f_n(\lambda, t) > 0 \quad \text{and} \quad \int_0^\infty f_n(\lambda, t)\, dt = 1;$$

thus the sequence

$$\int_0^t f_n(\lambda, \tau)\, d\tau$$

tends to $H_\lambda(t)$ for any fixed λ (see § 62, Part I), and the sequence

$$\int_0^t d\tau_1 \int_0^{\tau_1} f_n(\lambda, \tau)\, d\tau$$

converges, for any fixed λ, to $\int_0^t H_\lambda(\tau)\, d\tau$ uniformly in every interval $0 \leqslant t \leqslant t_0$ (which does or does not contain the point $t = \lambda$).

This means that the sequence $l^2(1+\lambda s/n)^{-n}$ converges to lK_λ almost uniformly in $0 \leqslant t < \infty$. This implies (8).

For the sequences of form (7), the following general criterion of convergence has been given by Ryll-Nardzewski [1]:

If

$$\limsup_{n\to\infty} n^{\delta n} |a_n| < \infty \tag{9}$$

for some $\delta > 1$, then series (7) converges for every complex λ.

If

$$\limsup_{n\to\infty} n^n |a_n| > 0, \tag{10}$$

then series (7) diverges for every complex $\lambda \neq 0$.

Proof. Let $1 < 1/a < \beta < \delta$ and let

$$f(t) = \int_J \exp(zt - z^a)\, dz, \tag{11}$$

where t is real and the integral is taken along the imaginary axis J. Then

$$f^{(n)}(t) = \int_J z^n \exp(zt - z^a)\, dz \qquad (n = 0, 1, \ldots); \tag{12}$$

integral (11) converges uniformly in $0 \leqslant t < \infty$, because

$$|z^n| \exp(zt - z^a) \leqslant |z|^n \exp\left(-|z|^a \cos\frac{a\pi}{2}\right) \tag{13}$$

whenever $\mathrm{Im}\, z = 0$. It follows from (12) and (13) that

$$|f^{(n)}(t)| \leqslant 2 \int_0^\infty r^n \exp\left(-r^a \cos\frac{a\pi}{2}\right) dr.$$

Putting $r^a \cos(a\pi/2) = x$, we find

$$|f^{(n)}(t)| \leqslant \frac{2}{a}\left(\cos\frac{a\pi}{2}\right)^{-\frac{n+1}{a}} \int_0^\infty x^{\frac{n+1}{a}-1} e^{-x}\, dx$$

$$\leqslant \frac{2}{a}\left(\cos\frac{a\pi}{2}\right)^{-\frac{n+1}{a}} \Gamma\left(\frac{n+1}{a}\right).$$

Moreover, we have $f^{(n)}(0) = 0$ $(n = 0, 1, \ldots)$. In fact, by (13), the integral

$$\int_{C(R,\varrho)} z^n \exp(-z^a \lambda)\, dz,$$

taken along the contour represented in the enclosed figure, is equal to 0. Now, inequality (13) holds also for $\operatorname{Im} z = 0$ whenever $t = 0$. Hence the integrals along the semi-circles tend to 0, as $R \to \infty$ and $\varrho \to 0$. Thus we obtain in the limit

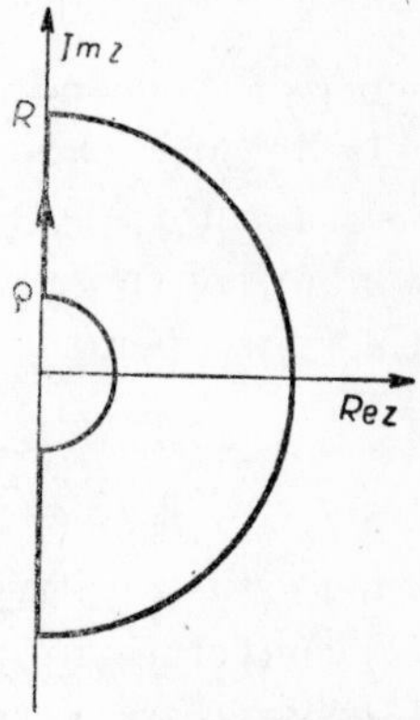

Fig. 161

$$\int_J z^n \exp(-z^a)\, dz = 0 \qquad (n = 0, 1, \ldots).$$

Multiplying series (7) by $f = \{f(t)\}$, we get

$$\{a_0 f(t) + a_1 f'(t)\lambda + \ldots\}.$$

If (9) holds, the last series converges uniformly in $0 \leqslant t < \infty$ for every fixed λ because we have

$$|a_n f^{(n)}(t)| \leqslant A_n = \frac{2}{a}\left(\cos\frac{a\pi}{2}\right)^{-\frac{n+1}{a}} \Gamma\left(\frac{n+1}{a}\right)(n^n)^{-\beta}$$

for great values of n, and the series $A_1\lambda + A_2\lambda^2 + \ldots$ converges for every λ. Hence follows the first part of the theorem.

Assume now that (10) holds and that there is a function $f \in \mathcal{C}$ which does not vanish identically in any neighbourhood of $t = 0$ and which is such that the series $\sum_{n=0}^{\infty} a_n s^n \lambda^n f$ consists of functions of class $\mathcal{C}$ and converges almost uniformly for a certain value $\lambda \neq 0$. Then f is indefinitely differentiable and $f^{(n)}(0) = 0$ for $n = 0, 1, \ldots$ Moreover

$$\lim_{n\to\infty} a_n \lambda^n f^{(n)}(t) = 0$$

uniformly in every bounded interval.

In view of the Taylor formula we have

$$f(t) = \frac{t^n}{n!} f^{(n)}(\theta n) = a_n \lambda^n f^{(n)}(\theta t)\left(\frac{3t}{\lambda}\right)^n \frac{n^n}{3^n n!}\,\frac{1}{3n^n a_n}$$

for all values of indexes n such that $a_n \neq 0$. The right side is divided here into four factors. If $0 \leqslant t \leqslant |\lambda|/3$, the first three of them converge to 0 as $n \to \infty$. On the other hand, if (10) holds, then the last factor also converges to 0, provided n assumes the values of a suitably chosen increasing sequence of positive integers. Thus, we obtain in the limit

$$f(t) = 0 \quad \text{for} \quad 0 \leqslant t \leqslant |\lambda|/3.$$

This contradicts the hypothesis regarding the function f. Hence follows the second part of the theorem.

There is an essential difference between the series of h^{-1} and those of s. The first converge if and only if $a_n = 0$ for $n \geqslant n_0$, i. e. if the series is reduced to a polynomial. On the other hand, series (7) converges provided a_n approaches 0 rapidly enough. It could be asked what is the property of operators f for which there exist convergent power series (4), with numerical coefficients $a_n \neq 0$. One can exclude at once all the operators

$$f = h^{-\beta} \frac{p}{q},$$

where $\beta > 0$ and p and q are functions of class $\mathcal{C}$, not vanishing identically in any right-hand neighbourhood of $t = 0$. For such operators the n-th term $a_n h^{-\beta n}(p/q)^n$ does not converge to 0 as $n \to \infty$. Thus the series cannot converge whatever are the coefficients $a_n = 0$. It can also be seen that for operators of the form

$$f = h^{\beta} \frac{p}{q},$$

where β is positive and p and q are such as in the preceding case, series (4) converges for any sequence of numerical coefficients a_n, even when they increase very rapidly.

Thus the only class of operators that is of interest is the class

$$f = \frac{p}{q},$$

where p and q are functions of class $\mathcal{C}$ not vanishing identically in any right-hand neighbourhood of $t = 0$. It is probable that there always exist numerical coefficients a_n, all different from 0, such that series (4) converges for some values of $\lambda \neq 0$. However, no proof is known. Neither do we know whether there exists a function $g \in \mathcal{C}$ such that $gf^n \in \mathcal{C}$ for $n = 1, 2, \ldots$

CHAPTER VI

LAPLACE TRANSFORM

(Appendix to Chapter II of Part V)

§ 1. Fundamental properties of the Laplace transform. In § 9 of Part V we have found the formula

$$\int_0^\infty e^{-s\lambda} f(\lambda)\, d\lambda = \{f(t)\}.$$

This formula has been proved for the function of class $\mathcal{K}$, but it also holds for every locally integrable function $f(\lambda)$. The proof is the same.

The integral

$$\int_0^\infty e^{-s\lambda} f(\lambda)\, d\lambda \tag{1}$$

always converges in the operational sense. If the letter s in (1) in interpreted as a complex variable (and not as the differential operator), then (1) is an integral of a complex-valued function and can either converge or not. Moreover, the convergence can be understood in the ordinary sense or as absolute convergence. We restrict ourselves in the sequel to the case of absolute convergence, which is the most important in applications.

Let $\mathcal{T}$ be the class of locally integrable functions f for which integral (1) *converges absolutely* for a certain complex s_0. Then this integral converges also for every s such that $\operatorname{Re} s > \operatorname{Re} s_0$; this follows from the inequality

$$|e^{-s\lambda} f(\lambda)| \leqslant |e^{-s_0\lambda} f(\lambda)| \qquad (\operatorname{Re} s > \operatorname{Re} s_0). \tag{2}$$

Thus integral (1) represents a function $F(s)$ of the complex variable s, defined in the half-plane $\operatorname{Re} s > \operatorname{Re} s_0$.

The correspondence between the functions $f(t)$ of class $\mathcal{T}$ and the functions $F(s)$ in termed the *Laplace transform* and is usually written as:

$$F(s) = \int_0^\infty e^{-st} f(t)\, dt.$$

The theory of the Laplace transform is widely developed and there are many books on that subject. Therefore it seems sufficient to mention here a few of the most important properties of the Laplace transform, which will be needed in the sequel.

It follows from (2) that the integral converges not only absolutely but also uniformly in the half-plane $\operatorname{Re} s \geqslant \operatorname{Re} s_0$, if it converges for $s = s_0$. Therefore $F(s)$ is an analytic function in that half-plane.

The correspondence between the functions of class $\mathcal{T}$ and the analytic functions is one-to-one, provided the functions whose values coincide almost everywhere are considered as equal.

In fact, suppose that the transforms of f_1 and f_2 are equal. Then we have, for $\operatorname{Re} s > \operatorname{Re} s_0$,

$$\int_0^\infty e^{-st} g(t)\,dt = 0,$$

where $g = f_1 - f_2$. Integrating per parts we have, on cancelling the factor $-s$,

$$\int_0^\infty e^{-st} G(t)\,dt = 0,$$

where $G(t) = \int_0^t g(\tau)\,d\tau$ is a continuous function in $0 \leqslant t < \infty$. Put $e^{-t} = x$ and $s = \operatorname{Re} s_0 + n$ $(n = 1, 2, \ldots)$; then

$$x^{n-1} G_0(x)\,dx = 0 \qquad (n = 1, 2, \ldots),$$

where $G_0(x) = x^{s_0} G(\ln(1/x))$. Hence, by Lerch's theorem on moments (see § 11 of Part I), we find $G_0(x) = 0$ for $0 \leqslant x \leqslant 1$, which implies $G(t) = 0$ for $0 \leqslant t < \infty$ and $g(t) = 0$ almost everywhere. This proves the theorem.

§ 2. Complex inversion formula. When $F(s)$ is a given analytic function in a half-plane $\operatorname{Re} s \geqslant x_0$, it may be asked whether it can be considered as the Laplace transform of some function $f(t)$ of class $\mathcal{T}$. If it can be considered thus, then our problem is to find the proper function $f(t)$, i.e. to give a formula which express $f(t)$ by means of $F(s)$. This problem is solved by the formula

$$f(t) = \frac{1}{2\pi i} \int_{x_0 - i\infty}^{x_0 + i\infty} e^{zt} F(z)\,dz, \tag{3}$$

provided some supplementary conditions on $F(s)$ are imposed; the integration in (3) is understood along the boundary $\operatorname{Re} s = x_0$ of the considered half-plane.

We shall suppose that:

1° $F(s)$ is analytic in the half-plane $\mathrm{Re}\, s > x_0$ and continuous on its boundary $\mathrm{Re}\, s = x_0$;

2° $F(s)$ tends uniformly to 0, as $|s| \to \infty$;

3° Integral (3) converges absolutely.

Under these conditions we shall prove that the Laplace transform of the function $f(t)$ given by (3) is $F(s)$, i. e. that

$$(4) \qquad \int_0^\infty e^{-st}\, dt \frac{1}{2\pi i} \int_{x_0-i\infty}^{x_0+i\infty} e^{zt} F(z)\, dz = F(s) \quad \text{for} \quad \mathrm{Re}\, s > x_0.$$

Conditions 1°-3° could be relaxed a little, but our aim is to give here a possibly simple and useful theorem for further applications. Formula (3) is termed the *complex inversion formula for the Laplace transform.* There exist also other inversion formulas. One of them will be given in the next paragraph.

By 3° we have

$$|f(t)| \leqslant \frac{1}{2\pi i} e^{x_0 t} \int_{-\infty}^{\infty} |F(iy)|\, dy = A e^{x_0 t} \qquad (0 < A < \infty);$$

hence integral (4) converges for $\mathrm{Re}\, s > x_0$. Since the convergence of both integrals in (4) is absolute, we can interchange the order of integration, which gives

$$\frac{1}{2\pi i} \int_{x_0-i\infty}^{x_0+i\infty} F(z)\, dz \int_0^\infty e^{-st} e^{zt}\, dt = \frac{1}{2\pi i} \int_{x_0-i\infty}^{x_0+i\infty} \frac{F(z)}{s-z}\, dz \qquad (\mathrm{Re}\, s > x_0).$$

The last integral is the limit of the integral

$$(5) \qquad \frac{1}{2\pi i} \int_\Gamma \frac{F(z)}{s-z}\, dz$$

along the contour Γ consisting of the segment $\mathrm{Re}\, z = x_0$, $|\mathrm{Im}\, z| \leqslant R$ and the semi-circle $|z - x_0| = R$, $\mathrm{Re}\, z > x_0$. To see this it is sufficient to remark that the part of the integral corresponding to the semi-circle is, for $R > 2|s - x_0|$, majorated by

$$\frac{1}{2\pi} \int_{-\pi/2}^{\pi/2} \frac{M(R)}{R/2} R\, d\theta = M(R),$$

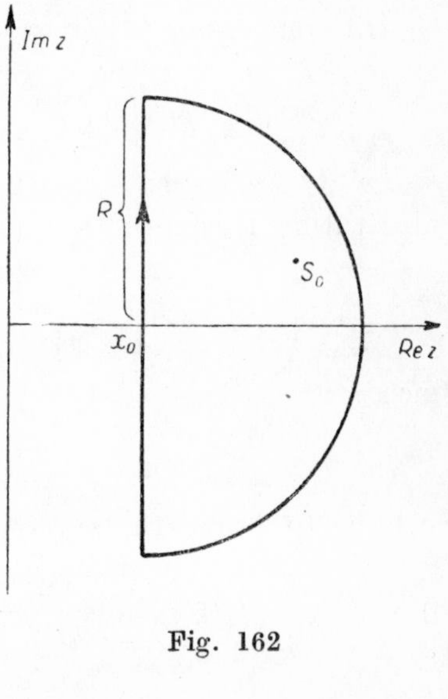

Fig. 162

where $M(R)$ is the upper bound of $|F(z)|$ along the semi-circle with the radius R. By 2°, $M(R)$ tends to 0, as $R \to \infty$. Thus we have proved that integral (4) is the limit of (5) as $R \to \infty$. But every fixed point s ($\operatorname{Re} s > x_0$) lies, for sufficiently large values of R, inside the path of integration and integral (5) is then, by Cauchy's integral theorem, equal to $F(s)$. This proves formula (4).

§ 3. Post's inversion formula. If the integral

$$F(x) = \int_0^\infty e^{-x\tau} f(\tau)\,d\tau \tag{6}$$

converges for $x > x_0$, then

$$f(t) = \lim_{n\to\infty} \frac{(-1)^n}{n!}\left(\frac{n}{t}\right)^{n+1} F^{(n)}\left(\frac{n}{t}\right) \tag{7}$$

for every point $t > 0$ of continuity of $f(t)$.

Otherwise than in theorem of the preceeding paragraph, we suppose here that F is the Laplace transform of some function f. On the other hand, the advantage of formula (7) is that f is expressed by means of the values of F (and its derivatives) on the real axis only.

Formula (7) is valid not only when integral (6) converges absolutely, but also when it converges in the ordinary sense. We shall assume absolute convergence, for it simplifies the proof and is entirely sufficient for our further purposes. However, we shall finally add some remarks as to what should be changed in order to be the proof valid also in the case of the ordinary convergence of the integral.

Differentiating (6) n times, we find, for $x = n/t$,

$$F^{(n)}\left(\frac{n}{t}\right) = (-1)^n \int_0^\infty \tau^n \exp\left(-\frac{n\tau}{t}\right) f(\tau)\,d\tau.$$

Substituting this into the right side of (7), we get

$$\lim_{n\to\infty} \frac{n^{n+1}}{e^n n!}\,\frac{1}{t}\int_0^\infty \left[\frac{\tau}{t}\exp\left(1-\frac{\tau}{t}\right)\right]^n f(\tau)\,d\tau.$$

Since

$$\lim_{n\to\infty} \frac{n^n}{\sqrt{2\pi n}\, e^n\, n!} = 1,$$

we have to prove that

$$f(t) = \lim_{n\to\infty} \frac{\sqrt{2\pi}}{t} \int_0^\infty n^{3/2}\left[\frac{\tau}{t}\exp\left(1-\frac{\tau}{t}\right)\right]^n f(\tau)\,d\tau. \tag{8}$$

Let t and η be two fixed positive numbers such that $\eta < t$. We can expand the last integral into three integrals,

$$\int_0^\infty = \int_0^{t-\eta} + \int_{t-\eta}^{t+\eta} + \int_{t+\eta}^\infty = J_1 + J_2 + J_3.$$

Since the function

$$x \exp(1-x) \tag{9}$$

increases monotonically in $0 \leqslant x \leqslant 1$ from 0 to 1, we have

$$\frac{t-\eta}{t} \exp\left(1 - \frac{t-\eta}{t}\right) = \alpha < 1$$

and

$$|J_1| \leqslant n^{3/2} \alpha^n \int_0^{t-\eta} |f(\tau)|\, d\tau.$$

This implies that J_1 approaches 0 as $n \to \infty$. Since function (9) decreases monotonically in $1 \leqslant x < \infty$ from 1 to 0, we have

$$\frac{t+\eta}{t} \exp\left(1 - \frac{t+\eta}{t}\right) = \beta < 1$$

and

$$|J_3| \leqslant n^{3/2} \alpha^{n-n_0} \int_{t+\eta}^\infty \left(\frac{\tau}{t}\right)^{n_0} \exp\left(-\frac{n_0}{t}\tau\right) |f(\tau)|\, d\tau$$

$$\leqslant n^{3/2} \alpha^n \left(\frac{t+\eta}{t} e\right)^{n_0} \int_{t+\eta}^\infty \exp\left(-\frac{n_0}{t}\tau\right) |f(\tau)|\, d\tau$$

for $n_0/t > x_0$. This inequality proves that J_3 approaches 0 as $n \to \infty$.

Given any positive number ε and a fixed point t of continuity of f we can choose η so that

$$f(t) - \varepsilon < f(\tau) < f(t) + \varepsilon \quad \text{for} \quad t - \eta < t < t + \eta.$$

Then

$$\big(f(t) - \varepsilon\big) J_0 < J_2 < \big(f(t) + \varepsilon\big) J_0, \tag{10}$$

where

$$J_0 = \int_{t-\eta}^{t+\eta} n^{3/2} \left[\frac{\tau}{t} \exp\left(1 - \frac{\tau}{t}\right)\right]^n dt.$$

The whole preceeding argument is true in particular when $f(t) = 1$ in $0 \leqslant t < \infty$. But in that case we have $F(x) = 1/x$, $F^{(n)} = (-1)^n n! x^{-n-1}$ and $F^{(n)}(n/t) = (-1)^n n!(t/n)^{n+1}$. Substituting this in (7) we find that (7) holds. Since formulae (7) and (8) are equivalent, also (8) must hold for $f(t) = 1$. Thus

$$1 = \lim_{n\to\infty} \frac{\sqrt{2\pi}}{t}(J_1 + J_2 + J_3) \quad \text{for} \quad f(t) = 1.$$

Since J_1 and J_3, as we have just proved generally, tend to 0, and J_2 is equal to J_0 for $f(t) = 1$, we get

$$1 = \lim \frac{\sqrt{2\pi}}{t} J_0. \tag{11}$$

Let us return to the general case. Since J_1 and J_3 tend to 0, we find by (10) that the inferior limit and the superior limit of the integral in (8) lie between the numbers $f(t) - \varepsilon$ and $f(t) + \varepsilon$. This implies that both limits are equal to $f(t)$, for ε can be chosen arbitrarily small. Thus formula (8) and the equivalent formula (7) are proved.

If the absolute convergence of integral (6) is not assumed, but only the ordinary convergence exists, the proof is the same, but the estimation of J_3 becomes slightly more involved and requires the use of the second mean value theorem.

§ 4. Laplace transform of convolution. Let the integrals

$$F(s) = \int_0^\infty e^{-st} f(t)\,dt \quad \text{and} \quad G(s) = \int_0^\infty e^{-st} g(t)\,dt$$

be absolutely convergent for $\operatorname{Re} s \geqslant x_0$ and let

$$h(t) = \int_0^t f(t-\tau) g(\tau)\,d\tau.$$

Then also the integral

$$H(s) = \int_0^\infty e^{-st} h(t)\,dt$$

converges absolutely and

$$F(s)G(s) = H(s).$$

Roughly speaking, the Laplace transform changes convolution into ordinary multiplication.

As a matter of fact, in view of the absolute convergence of the considered integrals, we can write

$$F(s)G(s) = \iint_{\Omega} e^{-su} f(u) e^{-sv} g(v)\,du\,dv,$$

where $\operatorname{Re} s > x_0$ and the double integral stretched on the quadrant $0 < u$, $v < \infty$. By substituting $u+v = t$, $v = \tau$, the integral becomes

$$\iint_{T} e^{-st} f(t-\tau) g(\tau)\,dt\,d\tau,$$

where the region of integration T is $0 \leqslant \tau \leqslant t < \infty$. The last integral is equal to $H(s)$ for $\operatorname{Re} s > x_0$.

§ 5. Finite Laplace transform. In the case of the finite Laplace transform

$$F(s) = \int_0^T e^{-st} f(t)\,dt$$

an analogous theorem is not true. However we can modify it as follows:

If f and g are integrable functions over $[0, T]$, *then*

$$\int_0^T e^{-st}\,dt \int_0^t f(t-\tau) g(\tau)\,d\tau = \int_0^T e^{-st} f(t)\,dt \int_0^T e^{-st} g(t)\,dt + e^{-sT} R(s) \tag{12}$$

for $\operatorname{Re} s > 0$, *where*

$$|R(s)| \leqslant M = \int_0^T |f(t)|\,dt \int_0^T |g(t)|\,dt.$$

Proof. The integral on the left side of (12) is equal to the double integral

$$\iint_{A} e^{-st} f(t-\tau) g(\tau)\,dt\,d\tau,$$

stretched on the triangle A: $0 \leqslant \tau \leqslant t < T$. Substituting $t = u+v$, $\tau = v$, we obtain

$$\iint_{B} e^{-s(u+v)} f(u) g(v)\,du\,dv,$$

where the region of integration B is the triangle: $0 \leqslant u$, $0 \leqslant v$, $u+v \leqslant T$. The last integral can be decomposed into two integrals

$$\iint_{B} = \iint_{C} - \iint_{D},$$

where C is the square $0 \leqslant u \leqslant T, 0 \leqslant v \leqslant T$ and D is the triangle $T \leqslant u+v$, $u \leqslant T$, $v \leqslant T$. The integral over the square C is equal to the product of integrals

$$\int_0^T e^{su} f(u)\,du \int_0^T e^{-sv} g(v)\,dv.$$

The integral over the triangle D can be represented in the form $e^{-sT} R(s)$, where the absolute value of $R(s)$ is not larger than

$$\iint_D |f(u) g(v)|\,du\,dv \leqslant \iint_C |f(u) g(v)|\,du\,dv = \int_0^T |f(u)|\,du \int_0^T |g(v)|\,dv.$$

Hence follows the theorem.

CHAPTER VII

A CLASS OF DIRICHLET SERIES

(Appendix to Chapter II of Part I)

§ 1. Introduction. Let $\beta_1, \beta_2, \ldots$ be a given indefinitely increasing sequence of positive numbers. Consider the Dirichlet series

$$1+a_1 e^{-\beta_1 t}+a_2 e^{-\beta_2 t}+\ldots, \tag{1}$$

where the coefficients $a_1, a_2, \ldots$ and the variable t are real. Our purpose is to determine the coefficients $a_1, a_2, \ldots$ so that series (1) should represent, in the interval $-\infty < t < \infty$, a positive function which increases from 0 to 1.

As an example we have the series

$$1-\frac{1}{1!}e^{-t}+\frac{1}{2!}e^{-2t}-\ldots, \tag{2}$$

which converges to the function $\exp(-e^{-t})$. Series (2) has played a fundamental role in the proof of Phragmén's formula (10.1) from § 9, Part I. The construction of an analogous series for a more general class of exponents $\beta_1, \beta_2, \ldots$ will allow us to generalize this formula, which is important for applications.

The inverse of series (2) is

$$1+\frac{1}{1!}e^{-t}+\frac{1}{2!}e^{-2t}+\ldots$$

and this series evidently represents a positive function which decreases in $(-\infty, \infty)$ from 1 to 0. Hence follow the required properties of (2). This is the usual process of finding the properties of the exponential function, employed in the elementary course of analysis. But this process cannot be extended to more general series of form (1), for their inverse is not, in general, a series with exponents $\beta_1, \beta_2, \ldots$ Therefore we shall use another method.

The idea is the following. We construct a sequence of functions

$$\varphi_k(t) = 1 + a_{k1}e^{-\beta_1 t} + \ldots + a_{kk}e^{-\beta_k t}$$

which increase in the interval $0 \leqslant t < \infty$ from 0 to 1. Then we choose a sequence of positive numbers $c_1, c_2, \ldots$, increasing to ∞, such that the sequence

$$\varphi_k(t+c_k) = 1 + \gamma_{k1}e^{-\beta_1 t} + \ldots + \gamma_{kk}e^{-\beta_k t} \qquad (\gamma_{kn} = a_{kn}e^{\beta_n c_k})$$

converges in $(-\infty, \infty)$. The limit will be obtained in form (1), where $a_n = \lim\limits_{k\to\infty} \gamma_{kn}$, and will have the required properties.

§ 2. Hirschman-Widder functions. Let us determine the numbers $a_{k0}, \ldots, a_{kk}$ by the identity

$$\frac{1}{s}\,\frac{\beta_1}{s+\beta_1}\cdots\frac{\beta_k}{s+\beta_k} = a_{k0}\frac{1}{s} + a_{k1}\frac{\beta_1}{s+\beta_1} + \ldots + a_{kk}\frac{\beta_k}{s+\beta_k}, \tag{3}$$

where s is a variable. If we multiply (3) by s and put $s = 0$, we obtain $a_{k0} = 1$. Similarly, if we multiply (3) by $s+\beta_n$ $(n = 1, 2, \ldots, k)$ and put $s = -\beta_n$, we obtain

$$a_{kn} = -\prod_{\nu=1}^{k}{}' \frac{\beta_\nu}{\beta_\nu - \beta_n} \tag{4}$$

where the sign $'$ means that the factor with $\nu = n$ drops out from the product.

Of course, equality (3) holds also when s is understood as the differential operator. Then its left side represents the convolution of the functions $1, \beta_1 e^{-\beta_1 t}, \ldots, \beta_k e^{-\beta_k t}$ and its right side is a linear aggregate of them. Both sides represent the same function; we shall denote it by φ_k. Thus we can write

$$\varphi_k(t) = 1 + a_{k1}e^{-\beta_1 t} + \ldots + a_{kk}e^{-\beta_k t}. \tag{5}$$

Functions (5) with the coefficients of form (4) have been introduced by Hirschman and Widder [1].

Since $\varphi_k(t)$ is the convolution of $k+1$ positive functions, it is itself positive for $t < 0$ and vanishes at $t = 0$. Moreover, the derivate $\varphi_k'(t)$ is the convolution of k positive functions

$$\beta_1 e^{-\beta_1 t}, \ldots, \beta_k e^{-\beta_k t}$$

and is also positive for $t > 0$. Thus $\varphi_k(t)$ is increasing in the interva $0 \leqslant t < \infty$. By (4) it is easily seen that $\varphi_k(\infty) = 1$. Thus each of Hirschman-Widder functions $\varphi_k(t)$ increases in the interval $0 \leqslant t < \infty$ from 0 to 1.

§ 3. A sequence of translated Hirschman-Widder functions. We have

$$\varphi_k(t+c_k) = 1+\gamma_{k1}e^{-\beta_1 t}+\ldots+\gamma_{kk}e^{-\beta_k t},$$

where

$$\gamma_{kn} = -\prod_{\nu=1}^{k}{}' \frac{\beta_\nu}{\beta_\nu-\beta_n} e^{-\beta_n c_k} \qquad (n = 0, \ldots. k).$$

To ensure the existence of the limit

$$a_n = \lim_{k\to\infty} \gamma_{kn} \qquad (n = 1, 2, \ldots)$$

we shall suppose that

(6) $$\sum_{\nu=1}^{\infty} \frac{1}{\beta_\nu^2} < \infty$$

and

$$c_k = \frac{1}{\beta_1}+\ldots+\frac{1}{\beta_k}.$$

Then we can write

$$\gamma_{kn} = \frac{1}{e}\prod_{\nu=1}^{k}{}' \frac{\beta_\nu}{\beta_\nu-\beta_n} \exp\left(-\frac{\beta_n}{\beta_\nu}\right)$$

and

(7) $$a_n = -\frac{1}{e}\prod_{\nu=1}^{\infty} \frac{\beta_\nu}{\beta_\nu-\beta_n} \exp\left(-\frac{\beta_n}{\beta_\nu}\right).$$

By the well-known inequalities for exponential function we have

$$\frac{\beta_\nu-\beta_n}{\beta_\nu} < \exp\left(-\frac{\beta_n}{\beta_\nu}\right) < \frac{\beta_\nu}{\beta_\nu+\beta_n}.$$

If $\nu > n$, then

$$1 < \frac{\beta_\nu}{\beta_\nu-\beta_n} \exp\left(-\frac{\beta_n}{\beta_\nu}\right) < 1+\frac{\beta_n^2}{\beta_\nu^2-\beta_n^2}$$

and by hypothesis (6) it follows that product (7) converges absolutely.

Since the sequence β_n is increasing, it is easily seen that product (7) has exactly n negative factors. Thus a_n is negative for odd n and positive for even n.

§ 4. Entire function generated by a given sequence of exponents. Now we suppose that

$$\sum_{\nu=1}^{\infty} \frac{1}{\beta_\nu} = \infty, \tag{8}$$

$$\beta_{\nu+1} - \beta_\nu > \delta > 0 \quad (\nu = 1, 2, \ldots). \tag{9}$$

Condition (8) means that $c_k \to \infty$. Condition (9) is a stronger one than (6); obviously (9) implies (6), but not conversely.

If (8) *and* (9) *hold, the series*

$$\varphi(z) = 1 + a_1 e^{-\beta_1 z} + a_2 e^{-\beta_2 z} + \ldots, \tag{10}$$

whose coefficients are determined by (7), *converges absolutely for every complex* z *and uniformly in each half-plane* $\operatorname{Re} z \geqslant x_0$.

Proof. First, we are going to show that

$$\frac{\ln|a_n|}{\beta_n} < \frac{1+\ln 2}{\delta} - \sum_{\nu=1}^{\infty} \frac{1}{\beta_\nu}. \tag{11}$$

We evidently have

$$\frac{\ln|a_n|}{\beta_n} = -\sum_{\nu=1}^{\infty} \frac{1}{\beta_\nu} + \frac{1}{\beta_n} \sum_{\nu=1}^{n-1} \ln \frac{\beta_\nu}{\beta_\nu - \beta_n} + \frac{1}{\beta_n} \sum_{\nu=n+1}^{\infty} \left(\ln \frac{\beta_\nu}{\beta_\nu - \beta_n} - \frac{\beta_n}{\beta_\nu} \right)$$

$$= S_1 + S_2 + S_3$$

(if $n = 1$, one assumes that $S_2 = 0$). Since the function $x/(\beta_n - x)$ increases in the interval $0 < x < \beta_n$, we can write, in view of (9),

$$S_2 < \frac{1}{\beta_\nu} \sum_{\nu=1}^{n-1} \ln \frac{\beta_n - \delta(n-\nu)}{\delta(n-\nu)} = \frac{1}{\beta_\nu} \sum_{\nu=1}^{n-1} \ln \frac{\beta_n - \delta\nu}{\delta\nu}$$

$$< \frac{1}{\beta_\nu} \int_0^{n-1} \ln \frac{\beta_n - \delta x}{\delta x}\, dx = \frac{1}{\delta} \int_0^{\delta(n-1)/\beta_n} \ln\left(\frac{1}{t} - 1\right) dt;$$

the last integral is obtained by substituting $t = dx/\beta_n$. The function $\ln(1/t - 1)$ being positive for $0 < t < 1/2$ and negative for $t > 1/2$, we have a fortiori

$$S_2 < \frac{1}{\delta} \int_0^{1/2} \ln\left(\frac{1}{t} - 1\right) dt = \frac{\ln 2}{\delta}.$$

Now the function

$$\ln \frac{x}{x-\beta_n} - \frac{\beta_n}{x}$$

decreases in the interval $\beta_n < x < \infty$, because its derivative

$$\frac{\beta_n}{x^2} - \frac{\beta_n}{x(x-\beta_n)}$$

is negative. Hence

$$S_3 < \frac{1}{\beta} \sum_{\nu=n+1}^{\infty} \left(\ln \frac{\beta_n + \delta(\nu - n)}{\delta(\nu - n)} - \frac{\beta_n}{\beta_n + \delta(\nu - n)}\right)$$

$$= \frac{1}{\beta_n} \sum_{\nu=1}^{\infty} \left(\ln \frac{\beta_n + \delta\nu}{\delta\nu} - \frac{\beta\nu}{\beta_n + \delta\nu}\right)$$

$$< \frac{1}{\beta_n} \int_0^{\infty} \left(\ln \frac{\beta_n + \delta x}{\delta x} - \frac{\beta_n}{\beta_n + \delta x}\right) dx$$

$$< \frac{1}{\delta} \int_0^{\infty} \left(\ln \frac{1+t}{t} - \frac{1}{1+t}\right) dt = \frac{1}{\delta}.$$

The obtained inequalities for S_1 and S_3 imply (11).

It follows from (11) that

$$\lim_{n\to\infty} |a_n|^{1/\beta_n} = 0.$$

Now let x_0 be an arbitrary real number. We have

$$|a_n e^{-\beta_n z}| \leqslant |a_n| e^{-\beta_n x_0} = (|a_n|^{1/\beta_n} e^{-x_0})^{\beta_n}$$

and, for large values of n,

$$|a_n e^{-\beta_n z}| < \left(\frac{1}{2}\right)^{\beta_n} = n^{-\frac{\beta_n}{\ln n}\ln 2}.$$

But it follows from (9) that

$$\lim_{n\to\infty} \frac{\beta_n}{\ln n} = \infty;$$

thus we have, for large values of n,

(12) $$|a_n e^{-\beta_n z}| < n^{-2}.$$

The last inequality implies the absolute and uniform convergence of the Dirichlet series (10) in the half-plane $\operatorname{Re} z \geqslant x_0$. It follows from this theorem that the function $\varphi(t)$ is analytic in the whole plane of z, and thus an entire function. We shall call it the *entire function generated by the sequence* $\beta_1, \beta_2, \ldots$ We know very little about the behaviour of this function. We know neither its zeros nor its Taylor series.

For real values of t, the function $\varphi(t)$ is real and non-decreasing in the interval $-\infty < t < \infty$ and such that $0 < \varphi(t) < 1$. Because $\varphi(t)$ is the limit of the sequence of functions $\varphi_k(t+c_k)$ which increase in the interval $-c_k \leqslant t < \infty$ from 0 to 1.

We shall prove moreover, that

$$\lim_{t\to\infty} \varphi(t) = 1 \tag{13}$$

and

$$\lim_{t\to-\infty} \varphi(t) = 0. \tag{14}$$

Since the convergence of series (10) is absolute, we can write, for $t > t_0$,

$$|\varphi(t)-1| \leqslant e^{-\beta_1(t-t_0)} \sum_{n=1}^{\infty} |a_n| e^{-\beta_n t_0}.$$

This implies (13).

The proof of (14) requires a little more finesse. We shall give it in the next paragraph.

Observe also that series (10) can be differentiated term by term, i. e. that the series

$$\varphi^{(m)}(z) = a_1(-\beta_1)^m e^{-\beta_1 z} + a_2(-\beta_2)^m e^{-\beta_2 z} + \ldots \tag{15}$$

converges uniformly in each half-plane $\operatorname{Re} z \geqslant x_0$.

In fact, it follows from (12) that

$$|a_n(-\beta_n)^m e^{-\beta_n z}| < \frac{\beta_n^m}{n^2} = \left(\frac{\beta_n}{\ln n}\right)^m \frac{(\ln n)^m}{n^2} < \frac{(\ln n)^m}{n^2}$$

for large values of n. Since the series

$$\sum_{n=1}^{\infty} \frac{(\ln n)^m}{n^2}$$

converges, the uniform convergence of (15) follows.

§ 5. Generalized Euler's gamma function. Let s be any fixed positive number. Then we have, by (8) and (9),

$$\sum_{\nu=1}^{\infty} \frac{1}{s+\beta_n} = \infty \quad \text{and} \quad (s+\beta_{\nu+1})-(s+\beta_\nu) > \delta > 0 \quad (\nu = 1, 2, \ldots).$$

Thus the sequence $s+\beta_1, s+\beta_2, \ldots$ satisfies conditions analogous to (8), (9), and we can therefore write down the entire function generated by this sequence:

$$\Phi(z) = 1+A_1 e^{-(s+\beta_1)z}+A_2 e^{-(s+\beta_2)z}+\ldots$$

The coefficients A_n are given as convergent infinite products:

$$A_n = -\frac{1}{e}\prod_{\nu=1}^{\infty}{}' \frac{s+\beta_\nu}{\beta_\nu-\beta_n} \exp\left(-\frac{s+\beta_n}{s+\beta_\nu}\right).$$

Hence, by (7),

$$\frac{A_n}{a_n} = \frac{\beta_n}{s+\beta_n}\prod_{\nu=1}^{\infty} \frac{s+\beta_\nu}{\beta_\nu} \exp\left(-\frac{s}{s+\beta_\nu}+\frac{\beta_n s}{\beta_\nu(s+\beta_\nu)}\right).$$

Here the factor $\beta_n/(s+\beta_n)$ is added before the sign Π in order to cancel the factor which corresponds to $\nu = n$. Putting

$$Q = \prod_{\nu=1}^{\infty} \frac{s+\beta_\nu}{\beta_\nu} \exp\left(-\frac{s}{s+\beta_\nu}\right) \quad \text{and} \quad q = \sum_{\nu=1}^{\infty} \frac{s}{\beta_\nu(s+\beta_\nu)},$$

we can write

$$\frac{A_n}{a_n} = \frac{\beta_n}{s+\beta_n} Q e^{q\beta_n}. \tag{16}$$

The convergence of the series q follows from (9). The convergence of the infinite product Q follows, in view of (16), from the convergence of the products representing A_n and a_n; the convergence of Q may also be easily proved directly.

From (10) we find, integrating per parts,

$$\int_u^\infty e^{-st}\varphi(t)\,dt - \frac{1}{s}e^{-su}\varphi(u) = \frac{1}{s}\int_u^\infty e^{-st}\varphi'(t)\,dt = -\frac{1}{s}\left(\frac{a_1\beta_1}{s+\beta_1}e^{-(s+\beta_1)u}+\ldots\right)$$

$$= -\frac{e^{qs}}{sQ}\left(A_1 e^{-(s+\beta_1)(u+q)}+\ldots\right)$$

by (16).

Hence

$$(17)\qquad \int_u^\infty e^{-st}\varphi(t)\,dt = \frac{1}{s}e^{-su}\varphi(u) - \frac{e^{qs}}{Q}\Phi(u+q) + \frac{e^{qs}}{sQ}.$$

Now the functions φ and Φ are monotonic and bounded in the interval $(-\infty, \infty)$. Thus the right side of (17) tends to a limit as $u \to -\infty$, and so does the left side. This proves that the integral

$$(18)\qquad \int_{-\infty}^{+\infty} e^{-st}\varphi(t)\,dt$$

is convergent. Since φ is monotonic and positive, this implies that

$$\lim_{t\to-\infty}\varphi(t) = 0.$$

That is the property of every entire function φ generated by a sequence satisfying conditions (8) and (9). But Φ is also such a function. Thus

$$\lim_{t\to-\infty}\Phi(t) = 0.$$

Now we are in a position to determine the exact value of integral (18). Letting u tend to $-\infty$, we find from (17) that this integral is equal to e^{qs}/sQ. On account of the expressions for q and Q we obtain the formula

$$(19)\qquad \int_{-\infty}^{+\infty} e^{-st}\varphi(t)\,dt = \frac{1}{s}\prod_{\nu=1}^{\infty}\frac{\beta_\nu}{s+\beta_\nu}\exp\left(\frac{s}{\beta_\nu}\right).$$

This formula is proved for every positive number s. However, it is valid for every complex number s whose real part is positive. In fact, the integral on the left side of (19) converges uniformly in any half-plane $\operatorname{Re} s \geqslant x_0 > 0$; thus it represents an analytical function in the half-plane $\operatorname{Re} s > 0$. (It can also easily be seen that the integral diverges for $\operatorname{Re} s < 0$.)

On the other hand, let $\Psi(s)$ denote the inverse of the product on the right side of (19):

$$\Psi(s) = s\prod_{\nu=1}^{\infty}\left(1+\frac{s}{\beta_\nu}\right)\exp\left(-\frac{s}{\beta_\nu}\right).$$

This product is, by (9), the Weierstrass expansion of an entire function whose only zeros are $-\beta_1, -\beta_2, \ldots$ Thus both sides of (19) are analytical functions for $\operatorname{Re} s > 0$. Since they coincide on the positive part of the real axis, formula (19) must hold in the whole half-plane $\operatorname{Re} s > 0$.

In the particular case of $\beta_n = n$ we have

$$a_n = -\frac{1}{e}\prod_{\nu=1}^{\infty}{}' \frac{\nu}{\nu - n}\exp\left(-\frac{n}{\nu}\right)$$

$$= (-1)^n \lim \frac{k!}{n!(k-n)!}\exp\left(-n\left(\frac{1}{1}+\ldots+\frac{1}{k}\right)\right)$$

$$= (-1)^n \frac{1}{n!}\lim_{k\to\infty}\frac{(k-n+1)\ldots k}{k^n}\exp\left(n\left(\ln k - \frac{1}{1} - \ldots - \frac{1}{k}\right)\right)$$

$$= \frac{(-1)^n}{n!}e^{-\gamma n},$$

where γ is the Euler constant. Thus, the entire function generated by the sequence $1, 2, \ldots$ is

$$\varphi(t) = \exp(-e^{-t-\gamma}).$$

Substituting $x = e^{-t-\gamma}$, we get from (19) the well-known formula for Euler's gamma function:

$$\int_0^\infty x^{s-1}e^{-x}\,dx = e^{-\gamma s}\frac{1}{s}\prod_{\nu=1}^{\infty}\frac{\nu}{s+\nu}\exp\left(\frac{s}{\nu}\right).$$

Hence the function appearing in (19) can be considered as a generalization of Euler's gamma function; on the left side we have its integral representation and on the right side its expansion into an infinite product.

§ 6. Generalized Phragmén's discontinuity factor. As *Phragmén's discontinuity factor* we understand the sequence

$$\psi_m(t) = \exp(-e^{-mt}) = 1 - \frac{1}{1!}e^{-mt} + \frac{1}{2!}e^{-2mt} - \ldots;$$

that is a sequence of continuous and monotonic functions which give, as $m \to \infty$, a discontinuity at $t = 0$. For we evidently have

$$\text{(20)} \qquad \lim_{n\to\infty}\psi_m(t) = \begin{cases} 0 & \text{as} \quad -\infty < t < 0, \\ 1 & \text{as} \quad 0 < t < \infty. \end{cases}$$

We are going to give a large class of analogous discontinuity factors.

Let $\beta_1, \beta_2, \ldots$ be a sequence of positive numbers satisfying conditions (8) and (9):

$$\sum_{\nu=1}^{\infty}\frac{1}{\beta_\nu} = \infty, \qquad \beta_{\nu+1} - \beta_\nu > \delta > 0 \quad (\nu = 1, 2, \ldots).$$

Then each of the sequence

$$\beta_m, \beta_{2m}, \ldots \qquad (m = 1, 2, \ldots) \tag{21}$$

satisfies analogous conditions. Let $\psi_m(t)$ denote the entire function generated by sequence (20). We shall show that the sequence of functions

$$\psi_1(t), \psi_2(t), \ldots$$

represents a discontinuity factor with property (10).

Write

$$\psi_m(t) = 1 + a_1^{(m)} e^{-\beta_m t} + a_2^{(m)} e^{-\beta_{2m} t} + \ldots,$$

where

$$a_n^{(m)} = -\frac{1}{e} \prod_{\nu=1}^{\infty}{}' \frac{\beta_{m\nu}}{\beta_{m\nu} - \beta_{mn}} \exp\left(-\frac{\beta_{mn}}{\beta_{m\nu}}\right).$$

Let $t > 0$. Since $|a_n^{(m)}| < \exp 2\beta_{mn}/m\delta$, we have for sufficiently large values of m:

$$|1 - \psi_m(t)| \leqslant \sum_{n=1}^{\infty} |a_n^{(m)}| e^{-\beta_{mn} t} < \sum_{n=1}^{\infty} e^{-\beta_{mn} t/2} < \sum_{n=1}^{\infty} e^{-(mn-1)\delta t/2} = \frac{e^{-(m-1)\delta t/2}}{1 - e^{-m\delta t/2}}.$$

This proves that $\lim\limits_{m\to\infty} \psi_m(t) = 1$ as $0 < t < \infty$. Hence

$$\lim_{m\to\infty} \int_0^{\infty} e^{-st} \psi_m(t)\, dt = 1.$$

To prove that $\lim\limits_{m\to\infty} \psi_m(t) = 0$, as $-\infty < t < 0$, it sufficies to show that

$$\lim_{m\to\infty} \int_{-\infty}^{+\infty} e^{-st} \psi_m(t)\, dt = 1,$$

for the functions $\psi_m(t)$ are positive and increasing. By (19) we have

$$\int_{-\infty}^{+\infty} e^{-t} \psi_m(t)\, dt = \prod_{\nu=1}^{\infty} \frac{\beta_{m\nu}}{1 + \beta_{m\nu}} \exp\left(\frac{1}{\beta_{m\nu}}\right). \tag{23}$$

Since the infinite product

$$\prod_{\nu=1}^{\infty} \frac{\beta_\nu}{1 + \beta_\nu} \exp\left(\frac{1}{\beta_\nu}\right)$$

is convergent, the product on the right side of (23) must tend to 1, as $m \to \infty$.

This proves that (20) holds.

§7. A theorem on bounded moments. The following theorem will be useful later:

(I) *If a sequence of positive numbers $\beta_1, \beta_2, \ldots$ satisfies conditions* (8) *and* (9):

$$\sum_{\nu=1}^{\infty} \frac{1}{\beta_\nu} = \infty, \qquad \beta_{\nu+1} - \beta_\nu > \delta > 0,$$

and $f(t)$ is a function integrable in $[0, T]$ such that

$$\left| \int_0^T e^{\beta_n t} f(t)\, dt \right| < M,$$

then $f(t) = 0$ almost everywhere in $[0, T]$.

Proof. Let $0 < \theta < T$. Using the notation of the foregoing paragraph, we can write

$$\int_0^T \big(1 - \psi_m(\theta - t)\big) f(t)\, dt = - \sum_{n=1}^{\infty} a_n^{(m)} e^{-\beta_{mn}\theta} \int_0^T e^{\beta_{mn}} f(t)\, dt.$$

If $m \to \infty$, the left-hand member approaches the limit $\int_0^T f(t)\, dt$. On the other hand, the right-hand member tends to 0, since its absolute value is less than

$$M \sum_{n=1}^{\infty} |a_n^{(m)}|\, e^{-\beta_{mn}\theta}$$

and tends to 0, by (22). Thus we have

$$\int_0^T f(t)\, dt = 0,$$

and, since t can be fixed arbitrarily in $(0, T)$, $f(t) = 0$ almost everywhere in $[0, T]$.

The last theorem may be put in the following equivalent form:

(II) *If $\beta_1, \beta_2, \ldots$ is a sequence of positive numbers satisfying conditions* (8) *and* (9), *and $g(x)$ is a function integrable in $[1, b]$ such that*

$$\left| \int_1^b x^{\beta_n} g(x)\, dx \right| < M \qquad (n = 1, 2, \ldots),$$

then $g(x) = 0$ almost everywhere in $[1, b]$.

The equivalency of the two theorems follows by the substitution

$$e^t = x, \qquad b = e^T, \qquad f(t) = g(x).$$

This form is similar to the well-known theorem of Müntz on vanishing moments:

(III) *If* $\beta_1, \beta_2, \ldots$ *is an increasing sequence such that*

$$\sum_{\nu=1}^{\infty} \frac{1}{\beta_\nu} = \infty$$

and $g(x)$ *is a function integrable in* $[0, b]$ *such that*

$$\left| \int_0^b x^{\beta_n} g(x)\,dx \right| = 0 \qquad (n = 1, 2, \ldots),$$

then $g(x) = 0$ *almost everywhere in* $[0, b]$.

In the particular case of $\beta_n = n$, this theorem is reduced to Lerch's theorem (§ 11, Part I).

In (III) the conditions imposed on the sequence $\beta_1, \beta_2, \ldots$ are relaxed, for hypothesis (9) drops. Moreover, the lower bound of the considered interval is 0. On the other hand, the condition imposed on the integrals is such stronger than in (II).

It is easy to see that the lower bound of the considered interval in (II) cannot by diminished. Indeed, all moment of any function which vanishes for $x > 1$ are always commonly bounded. One can also prove that, if condition (9) is neglected, theorem (II) loses validity.

Theorem (I) can be formulated also in the following, slightly stronger form:

(IV) *If* $\beta_1, \beta_2, \ldots$ *and* f *satisfy the hypotheses of* (I) *and*

$$\lim_{n\to\infty} \int_0^T e^{\beta_n(t-\varepsilon)} f(t)\,dt = 0 \tag{24}$$

for every $\varepsilon > 0$, *then* $f(t) = 0$ *almost everywhere in* $[0, T]$.

Proof. It follows from (24) that

$$\left| \int_0^T e^{\beta_n(t-\varepsilon)} f(t)\,dt \right| < M.$$

Putting $u = t - \varepsilon$, we have

$$\left| \int_{-\varepsilon}^{T-\varepsilon} e^{\beta_n u} f(u+\varepsilon)\,du \right| < M.$$

Since

$$\left| \int_{-\varepsilon}^{0} e^{\beta_n u} f(u+\varepsilon)\,du \right| < \int_{-\varepsilon}^{0} |f(u+\varepsilon)|\,du = N,$$

it follows that

$$\left| \int_{-\varepsilon}^{T-\varepsilon} e^{\beta_n u} f(u+\varepsilon)\, du \right| < M$$

and, by (I), $f(u+\varepsilon) = 0$ almost everywhere in $[0, T-\varepsilon]$, i. e. $f(t) = 0$ almost everywhere in $[\varepsilon, T]$. Since ε is arbitrary, (IV) follows.

§ 8. Titchmarsh's theorem on convolution. In Chapter II, Part I, we have proved the following theorem of Titchmarsh:

If the convolution of two functions f and g vanishes in $0 \leqslant t < \infty$, then at least one of these functions vanishes.

By means of the theorem on bounded moments, that theorem can be strengthen as follows:

(T) *If the convolution of two functions f and g, integrable over the interval $[0, T]$ $(T < \infty)$, vanishes almost everywhere in that interval, than there are two numbers $t_1 \geqslant 0$ and $t_2 \geqslant 0$ such that f and g vanish almost everywhere in $[0, t_1]$ and $[0, t_2]$ respectively.*

This theorem can be expressed also in the equivalent form:

(T′) *If the functions f and g satisfy the hypothesis of* (T), *then at least one of them vanishes almost everywhere in* $[0, T/2]$.

It is evident that (T′) follows from (T). To prove the converse, denote respectively by $[0, t_1]$ and $[0, t_2]$ the largest intervals in which f and g vanish. Then

$$h(t) = \int_0^t f(t-\tau) g(\tau)\, d\tau = \int_{t_2}^{t-t_1} f(t-\tau) g(\tau)\, d\tau = \int_0^{\mu} f(t_1+u-\tau) g(t_2+\tau)\, d\tau$$

for $t = t_1 + t_2 + u$. If (T′) holds, then h cannot vanish in any right-hand neighbourhood of $t_1 + t_2$. Thus we have $t_1 + t_2 \geqslant T$.

We shall prove Titchmarsh's theorem in the form (T′). If

$$\int_0^t f(t-\tau) g(\tau)\, d\tau = 0,$$

we also have

$$\int_0^T e^{-nt} dt \int_0^t f(t-\tau) g(\tau)\, d\tau = 0 \qquad (n = 1, 2, \ldots)$$

and by the theorem on convolution (see § 5, Chapter IV)

$$(25) \qquad \left| \int_0^T e^{-nt} f(t)\, dt \int_0^T e^{-nt} g(t)\, dt \right| \leqslant e^{-nT} M.$$

Let $\alpha_1, \alpha_2, \ldots$ be the sequence of all positive integers n such that

$$\left| \int_0^T e^{-nt} f(t)\, dt \right| \leqslant e^{-nT/2}\sqrt{M}$$

and $\beta_1, \beta_2, \ldots$ the sequence of all positive integers n such that

$$\left| \int_0^T e^{-nt} g(t)\, dt \right| \leqslant e^{-nT/2}\sqrt{M}.$$

By (25), at least one of the relations

$$\sum_{n=1}^{\infty} \frac{1}{\alpha_n} = \infty \quad \text{or} \quad \sum_{n=1}^{\infty} \frac{1}{\beta_n} = \infty$$

must hold. Suppose that the first does.

Since

$$\int_{T/2}^{T} e^{\alpha_n(T/2-t)} f(t)\, dt \leqslant \sqrt{M} + \int_0^{T/2} |f(t)|\, dt = N,$$

i. e., by substituting $T/2 - t = \tau$,

$$\left| \int_0^{T/2} e^{\alpha_n \tau} f(T/2 - \tau)\, d\tau \right| \leqslant N,$$

we have, by theorem (I), $f(T/2-\tau) = 0$ almost everywhere in $[0, T/2)$, i. e. $f(t) = 0$ almost everywhere in $[0, T/2]$. Thus the theorem is proved.

CHAPTER VIII

THE EXPONENTIAL FUNCTION $\exp(-\lambda s)$

(Appendix to Chapter I of Part IV)

§ 1. Introduction. The exponential function $x(\lambda) = e^{w\lambda}$ is defined for real values of λ as the unique solution of the differential equation

$$x'(\lambda) = wx(\lambda),$$

satisfying the initial condition $x(0) = 1$. If the variable λ is complex, we can always replace it by the product $e^{i\omega}\lambda$, where λ is real. In this manner the definition of $e^{w\lambda}$ is extended to complex values of λ.

The main purpose of this chapter is to investigate the function

$$e^{-\lambda s^a} = \exp(-\lambda s^a),$$

where λ is real and

$$s^{-a} = \left\{\frac{t^{a-1}}{\Gamma(a)}\right\} \quad \text{for} \quad a < 0, \quad s^{-a} = \frac{1}{s^a} \quad \text{for} \quad a > 0 \quad \text{and} \quad s^0 = 1.$$

The variable λ may assume complex values.

The function $\exp(-e^{i\omega}\lambda s^a)$ is the solution of the differential equation

$$y'(\lambda) = -e^{i\omega}s^a y(\lambda) \tag{1}$$

whose value at $\lambda = 0$ is 1.

§ 2. Case $a < 0$. In this case the required solution can be given in the form of the power series

$$\exp(-e^{i\omega}\lambda s^a) = 1 - \frac{\lambda}{1!}e^{i\omega}s^a + \frac{\lambda^2}{2!}e^{2i\omega}s^{2a} - \ldots;$$

this series assumes the value 1 for $\lambda = 1$ and formally satisfies equation (1). Its operational convergence follows for every λ from the fact that s^a is, for $a < 0$, a locally integrable function (see § 1, Chapter V).

We can write

$$\exp(-e^{i\omega}\lambda s^{\alpha}) = 1 + \left\{\frac{-e^{i\omega}\lambda}{1!}\,\frac{t^{-\alpha-1}}{\Gamma(-\alpha)} + \frac{(-e^{i\omega}\lambda)^2}{2!}\,\frac{t^{-2\alpha-1}}{\Gamma(-2\alpha)} + \dots\right\}$$

$$= 1 + \left\{\frac{1}{t}F(-\alpha, -e^{i\omega}\lambda t^{-\alpha})\right\},$$

where

$$F(\beta, x) = \frac{x}{1!\Gamma(\beta)} + \frac{x^2}{2!\Gamma(2\beta)} + \dots$$

Thus, the investigation of $\exp(-e^{i\omega}\lambda s^{\alpha})$ is reduced, for $\alpha < 0$, to the analysis of the function $F(\beta, x)$. We can easily see that $F(\beta, x)$ is positive for $x > 0$ and tends monotonically to infinity, as $x \to \infty$, faster than any power of x. If $\beta = 1$, we have $F(1, x) = -i\sqrt{x}J_1(2i\sqrt{x})$ for $x \geqslant 0$, and $F(1, x) = \sqrt{-x}J_1(2\sqrt{-x})$ for $x \leqslant 0$, where J_1 is the Bessel function of order 1 (see § 20 of Part II). From the last equality it follows that $F(1, x)$ oscilates (changes its sign an infinite number of times) as x tend to $-\infty$. But if $\beta \neq 1$, we do not know how $F(\beta, x)$ behaves for negative values of x.

§ 3. Case $\alpha = 0$. In this case the function $\exp(-\lambda s^{\alpha})$ is reduced to the ordinary numerical exponential function e^{λ}.

§ 4. Case $0 < \alpha < 1$. For the particular value $\alpha = 1/2$ we have the formula

$$\exp(-\lambda s^{t}) = \left\{\frac{\lambda}{2\sqrt{\pi t^3}}\exp\left(-\frac{\lambda^2}{4t}\right)\right\} \qquad (0 < \lambda < \infty),$$

as we have seen in § 23 of Part II. The function in braces is, for fixed λ, a continuous and positive function of t in the interval $0 < t < \infty$, which tends to 0 at both extremities of this interval.

Similarly, for every $0 < \alpha < 1$ and positive λ the operational function $\exp(-\lambda s\ )$ can be expressed as a function of t, but we do not know its explicit expression by means of known functions. However, it is possible to express it by means of a complex integral To find this integral we shall use the Laplace transform.

Assume that

$$\exp(-e^{i\omega}\lambda s^{\alpha}) = \{f(\lambda, t)\}.$$

Then we find by (1)

$$\int_0^1 \frac{(t-\tau)^{\alpha-1}}{\Gamma(\alpha)} f_{\lambda}(\lambda, \tau)\,d\tau = -e^{i\omega}f(\lambda, t).$$

Taking the Laplace transform of both sides, we get, in view of the formula of convolution (§ 4, Chapter VI),

(2) $$\frac{1}{s^a} F_\lambda(\lambda, s) = -e^{i\omega} F(\lambda, s),$$

where s denotes, for a moment, a complex variable, and $F(\lambda, s)$ is the Laplace transform of $f(\lambda, t)$. From (2) we get

$$F(\lambda, s) = \exp(-e^{i\omega} s^a \lambda)$$

as a solution which assumes the value 1 at $\lambda = 0$. By means of the inversion formula, we finally find

$$f(\lambda, t) = \frac{1}{2\pi i} \int\limits_{-i\infty}^{+i\infty} \exp(zt - e^{i\omega} z^a \lambda)\, dz.$$

But this argument is only heuristic, for 1° we know nothing beforehand about the convergence of the found complex integral, 2° we do not know whether the differentiation under the sign of integral is correct and 3° it is not quite clear whether the operational value at $\lambda = 0$ is 1.

We are going to show that the operational formula

(3) $$\exp(-e^{i\omega} s^a \lambda) = \left\{ \frac{1}{2\pi i} \int\limits_{-i\infty}^{+i\infty} \exp(zt - e^{i\omega} z^a \lambda)\, dz \right\},$$

where s again denotes the differential operator, holds under the following conditions:

1° $|\omega| \leqslant \omega_0 < \frac{\pi}{2}(1 - a)$;

2° $0 < \lambda < \infty$;

3° The values of z^a on the imaginary axis are taken so that z^a represents an analytic function in the region $|z| > 0$, $|\arg z| < \pi$ and assumes real values on the positive part of the real axis.

Let us consider a more general integral

(4) $$f(\lambda, \mu, t) = \frac{1}{2\pi i} \int\limits_{\Omega} z^\mu \exp(zt - e^{i\omega} z^a \lambda)\, dz,$$

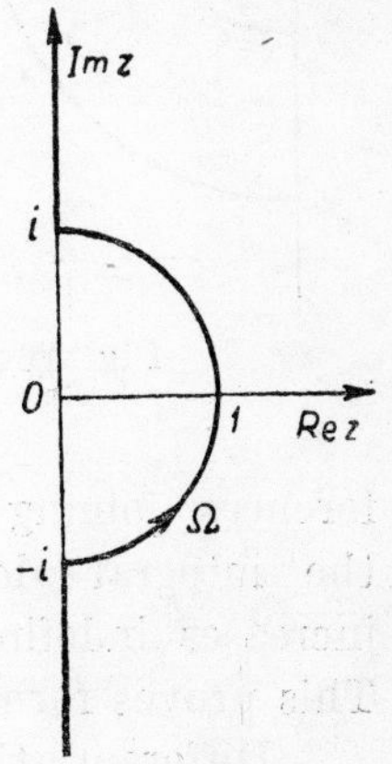

Fig. 163

where μ is real and z^μ is understood in the same way as z^a; the path of integration Ω is here the imaginary axis with the exception of its segment between $-i$ and i, which is replaced by the semi-circumference of radius 1 lying on the right of the imaginary axis. Such a path of integration is chosen in order to admit also negative values of μ. Otherwise the integral, stetched along the whole imaginary axis, would be divergent at $z = 0$. However, when μ is non-negative, the path of integration can be replaced simply by the imaginary axis, for the integrand is analytic inside the region limited by the semi-circumference and the imaginary axis and is continuous on the boundary of that region.

The integral (4) is absolutely and uniform convergent for

$$0 \leqslant \mu \leqslant \mu_0, \quad 0 < \lambda_0 \leqslant \lambda,$$

$$|\omega| \leqslant \omega_0, \quad 0 \leqslant t < \infty,$$

because the absolute value of the integrand is, on the imaginary axis, less than

$$(1+r)^{\mu_0}\exp(-r^a\lambda_0\cos\omega_0) \qquad (r = |z|).$$

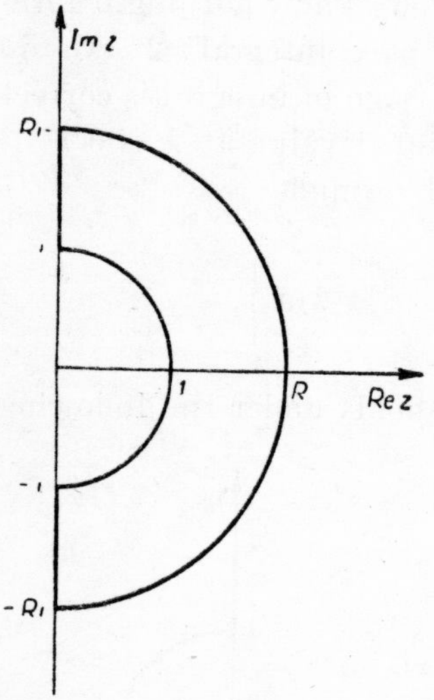

Fig. 164

Moreover, if μ, λ and ω are fixed, $f(\mu, \lambda, t)$ is a function of t, continuous in $0 \leqslant t < \infty$ and, when $\mu \geqslant 0$, bounded.

We have

$$f(\lambda, \mu, 0) = 0. \tag{5}$$

In fact, if $t = 0$, we get from (4)

$$f(\lambda, \mu, 0) = \frac{1}{2\pi i}\int_{\Omega} z^{\mu}\exp(-e^{i\omega}z^a\lambda)\,dz.$$

The integral of the last integrand, when taken along the contour consisting of the segments $(-Ri, -i)$, (i, Ri) and the semi-circumferences joining the points $-Ri$, Ri and $-i$, i, is equal to 0. Since the integral along the larger semi-circumference tends to 0 as R increases indefinitely, also the integral along the path Ω must vanish. This proves formula (5).

Differentiating (4) with respect to λ, we get

$$\frac{\partial}{\partial\lambda}f(\lambda, \mu, t) = -e^{i\omega}f(\lambda, \mu+a, t). \tag{6}$$

We also have

$$(7) \qquad \int_0^t \frac{(t-\tau)^{\alpha-1}}{\Gamma(\alpha)} f(\lambda, \mu+\alpha, \tau)\,d\tau = f(\lambda, \mu, t).$$

In fact, for $\operatorname{Re} z > 0$ we have

$$\int_0^\infty e^{-zt}\frac{t^{\alpha-1}}{\Gamma(\alpha)}\,dt = z^{-\alpha} \quad \text{and} \quad \int_0^\infty e^{-zt} f(\lambda, \mu, t)\,dt = z^{\mu}\exp(-e^{i\omega}z^{\alpha}\lambda),$$

for the right side of (4) is obtained by applying the inverse formula of the Laplace transform to the function $z\exp(-e^{i\omega}z^{\alpha}\lambda)$. Similarly

$$\int_0^\infty e^{-zt} f(\lambda, \mu+\alpha, t)\,dt = z^{\mu+\alpha}\exp(-e^{i\omega}z^{\alpha}\lambda).$$

Thus, the last integral is the product of both foregoing integrals. Hence, by theorem on the transform of a convolution, we obtain (7).

Using the operational notation

$$f(\lambda, \mu) = \{f(\lambda, \mu, t)\},$$

we get from (6) and (7)

$$f_\lambda(\lambda, \mu) = -e^{i\omega}s^{\alpha}f(\lambda, \mu).$$

In particular we have for $\mu = 0$

$$f_\lambda(\lambda, 0) = -e^{\omega}s^{\alpha}f(\lambda, 0).$$

We shall prove that $f(\lambda, 0)$ is the required exponential function. For this purpose we still have to show that

$$(8) \qquad \lim_{\lambda\to 0+} f(\lambda, 0) = 1.$$

Differentiating (4) twice with respect to t, we find for $\mu = 0$

$$\frac{\partial^2}{\partial t^2} f(\lambda, -2, t) = f(\lambda, 0, t).$$

This implies, by (5),

$$(9) \qquad s^2 f(\lambda, -2) = f(\lambda, 0).$$

But the integral

$$f(\lambda, -2, t) = \frac{1}{2\pi i}\int_{\Omega} \frac{1}{z^2}\exp(zt - e^{i\omega}z^{\alpha}\lambda)\,dz$$

converges absolutely and uniformly for $0 \leqslant \lambda < \infty$ and $0 \leqslant t < \infty$; thus it represents a continuous function of λ and t. This implies that $f(\lambda, -2)$ is operationally continuous in $0 \leqslant \lambda < \infty$ and in particular

$$\lim_{\lambda \to 0+} f(\lambda, -2) = f(0, -2).$$

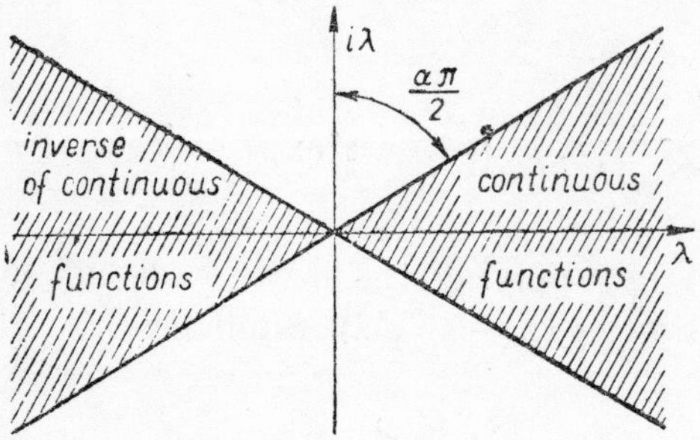

Fig. 165

Hence (8) follows by (9).

This completes the proof of formula (3) under conditions 1°, 2° and 3°.

This is at once a proof of the existence of the exponential function $\exp(-e^{i\omega}\lambda s^{a})$ in the region $0 \leqslant \lambda < \infty$, $|\omega| < \pi(1-a)/2$.

If we put

$$\exp(-e^{i\omega}\lambda s^{a}) = \frac{1}{\exp(e^{-i\omega}\lambda s^{a})},$$

the function is extended to every real λ and still satisfies equation (1) and the condition $y(0) = 1$. Thus the existence of the exponential function is proved for the shaded region on the enclosed diagram.

Now, given an arbitrary ω ($|\omega| < \pi$) we can choose real numbers ε_1, ε_2 and ω_1 such that

$$0 < |\omega_1| < \frac{\pi}{2}(1-a) \quad \text{and} \quad e^{i\omega} = \varepsilon_1 + e^{i\omega_1}\varepsilon_2.$$

Putting

$$\exp(-e^{i\omega}\lambda s^{a}) = \exp(-\varepsilon_1 \lambda s^{a})\exp(-e^{i\omega}\varepsilon_2 s^{a}),$$

we can prove again that equation (1) and the condition $y(0) = 1$ are fulfilled.

In this way, the existence of $\exp(-\lambda s^{a})$ is proved for every complex λ. In particular, taking

$$\omega_1 = \frac{\pi}{4}(1-a), \quad \varepsilon_1 = -\cos\omega_1 \quad \text{and} \quad \varepsilon_2 = \sin\omega_1,$$

we have $\omega = i$ and

$$\exp(-i\lambda s^{a}) = \frac{\exp(-e^{i\omega_1} - \sin\omega_1 \cdot s^{a})}{\exp(-\lambda\cos\omega_1 \cdot s^{a})},$$

where the numerator and the denominator are functions of class $\mathcal{C}$. Probably the fraction itself cannot be simplified so as to give a function of class $\mathcal{C}$, but we do not know the proof [1].

§ 5. Expansion into Taylor's series. We are going to prove that the function $\exp(-\lambda s^\alpha)$ can be expanded, for $0 < \alpha < 1$ and every complex λ, into a convergent Taylor series

$$\exp(-\lambda s^\alpha) = 1 - \frac{s^\alpha}{1!}\lambda + \frac{s^{2\alpha}}{2!}\lambda^2 - \ldots \tag{10}$$

Suppose first that $\alpha = p/q$, where p and q are positive integers, $p < q$. Then series (10) is equal to the sum of q series with integral coefficients

$$\sum_{\nu=0}^{q-1} s^{\nu p/q} \lambda^\nu \left(\frac{1}{\nu!} + \frac{s}{(q+\nu)!}(-\lambda)^q + \frac{s}{(2q+\nu)!}(-\lambda)^{2q} + \ldots \right) \tag{11}$$

Applying the criterion of convergence of § 3, Chapter V, we find

$$\lim_{n\to\infty} \frac{n^{\delta n}}{(nq+\nu)!} = \lim_{n\to\infty} \frac{n^{\delta n}}{(nq+\nu)!} \frac{\sqrt{2\pi}\, e^{nq+\nu}(nq+\nu)!}{(nq+\nu)^{nq+\nu-1/2}}$$

$$= \lim_{n\to\infty} \frac{\sqrt{2\pi}\, e^{nq+\nu}}{q^{\delta n}(1+\nu/nq)^{\delta n}(nq+\nu)^{n(q-\delta)+\nu-1/2}}$$

$$= \lim_{n\to\infty} \frac{\sqrt{2\pi}\, e^{nq+\nu}}{q^{\delta n} e^{\delta q/\nu}(nq+\nu)^{n(q-\delta)+\nu-1/2}};$$

since $q \geqslant 2$, we can take such a δ that $1 < \delta < q$; then the limit is ∞. Hence the series in (11) converges and so does (10) for every complex λ.

If α is irrational, we choose an α_0 such that $0 < \alpha < \alpha_0 < 1$. There is a function $f \epsilon \mathcal{C}$ such that the terms of the series

$$f + \frac{1}{1!} s^{\alpha_0} f\lambda + \frac{1}{2!} s^{2\alpha_0} f\lambda^2 + \ldots$$

are again functions of class $\mathcal{C}$ and that the series converges almost uniformly with respect to t, no matter what the complex number λ is like.

We have for $n = 1, 2, \ldots$

$$|s^{n\alpha} f| = |s^{n\beta_0} f s^{-n(\beta_0-\alpha)}| \leqslant |s^{n\beta_0} f|\, l^{n(\beta_0-\alpha)} \leqslant |s^{n\beta_0} f|\,(l^{\beta_0-\alpha} + l^{2(\beta_0-\alpha)} + \ldots),$$

---

[1] The proof was found recently. It follows from a theorem given by J. Mikusiński (see footnote on p. 356).

where, generally, $|f|$ denotes the absolute value of the function f. Since the last series in parentheses represents a continuous function in $(0, \infty)$, integrable in the neighbourhood of $t = 0$, the series

$$f + \frac{1}{1!} s^a f \lambda + \frac{1}{2!} s^{2a} f \lambda^2 + \ldots$$

must converge almost uniformly with respect to t. This implies the operational convergence of series (10) for every complex λ.

Series (10) evidently satisfies equation (1) and the condition $y(0) = 1$. Thus the above argument gives an alternative proof of the existence of the exponential function $\exp(-\lambda s^a)$ for every complex λ. However, we do not find in this way that the values of $\exp(-e^{i\omega}\lambda s^a)$ are, for $0 < \omega < \pi(1-a)/2$, functions of class $\mathcal{C}$. It is even somewhat difficult to imagine that the sum of a power series of the differential operator could be an ordinary continuous function.

§ 6. Function $U_a(t)$. We have proved that the integral (3) converges uniformly in each region $|\omega| \leqslant \omega_0 < \pi(1-a)/2$, $0 < \lambda_0 < \lambda$. One can also say that, for complex λ, the integral

(12) $$\frac{1}{2\pi i} \int_{-i\infty}^{+i\infty} \exp(zt - z^a \lambda)\, dz$$

converges uniformly in each region $|\arg \lambda| < \omega_0 < \pi(1-a)/2$, $|\lambda| > \lambda_0 > 0$. This implies that (12) represents an analytic function in the angle $|\arg \lambda| < \omega_0 < \pi(1-a)/2$.

Substituting in (12) $z = u\lambda^{-1/a}$, we find

$$\frac{1}{\lambda^{1/a}} \frac{1}{2\pi i} \int_{-i\infty}^{+i\infty} \exp\left(u \frac{t}{\lambda^{1/a}} - u^a\right) du.$$

Put

(13) $$U_a(t) = \frac{1}{2\pi \mathrm{i}} \int_{-i\infty}^{+i\infty} \exp(zt - z^a)\, dz.$$

Then function (12) can be written in the form

$$\frac{1}{\lambda^{1/a}} U\left(\frac{t}{\lambda^{1/a}}\right)$$

and we have

$$\exp(-s^a \lambda) = \left\{\frac{1}{\lambda^{1/a}} U_a\left(\frac{t}{\lambda^{1/a}}\right)\right\} \quad \text{for} \quad |\arg \lambda| < \pi a/2.$$

Our purpose is, in the sequel, to investigate the function $U_a(t)$ on the positive part of the real axis, but we shall make use of the fact that it is analytic there.

Differentiating (13) m times, we find

$$U_a^{(m)}(t) = \frac{1}{2\pi i} \int_{-i\infty}^{+i\infty} z^m \exp(zt - z^a)\, dz.$$

It is irrelevant whether we integrate here along the imaginary axis or along the path Ω defined in § 4. Thus, putting $\omega = 0$ and $\lambda = 1$, we get from (4) $f(1, mt) = U_a^{(m)}(t)$. On account of (5) we have

$$U_a^{(m)}(0) = 0 \qquad (m = 0, 1, \ldots).$$

Thus the function $U_a(t)$ vanishes at $t = 0$ with all its derivatives. We shall prove that it does so at $t = +\infty$, i.e.

(14) $U_a^{(m)}(+\infty) = 0 \qquad (m = 0, 1, \ldots).$

This easily follows from a well-known theorem on the Fourier integral, but can also be deduced conveniently from a real formula of U_a which we are going to establish in the nex paragraph.

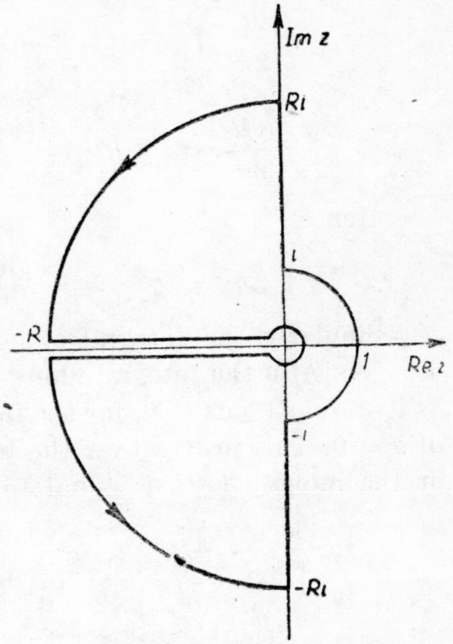

Fig. 166

§ 7. Real formula of $U_a(t)$. The formula to be proved is

(15) $U_a(t) =$

$$\frac{1}{\pi} \int_0^\infty \exp(-tr - r^a \cos \pi a) \sin(r^a \sin \pi a)\, dr.$$

We can modify formula (13) by replacing the imaginary axis by the negative part of the real axis. For this purpose consider the integral

$$\frac{1}{2\pi i} \int_\Xi \exp(zt - z^a)\, dz$$

along the contour represented on the enclosed diagram. This integral is equal to 0, for the integrand is analytic on the contour and inside it. The integral I_R along the upper arc $(-R, Ri)$ of circumference,

$$I_R = \frac{1}{2\pi} \int_{\pi/2}^{\pi} \exp(tRe^{i\theta} - Re^{ia\theta}) Re^{i\theta}\, d\theta,$$

satisfies the inequalities

$$|I_R| \leqslant \frac{R}{2\pi} \int\limits_{\pi/2}^{\pi} \exp(tR\cos\theta - R^a \cos a\theta)\, d\theta$$

$$\leqslant \frac{R}{2\pi} \int\limits_{\pi/2}^{\pi/2+\varepsilon} \exp(-R^a \cos a\theta)\, d\theta + \frac{R}{2\pi} \int\limits_{\pi/2+\varepsilon}^{\pi} \exp(tR\cos\theta - R^a \cos a\theta)\, d\theta.$$

We choose $\varepsilon > 0$ so that $\cos a\theta > \eta > 0$ for $\pi/2 < \theta < \pi/2+\varepsilon$. Then, for sufficiently large values of R, we have

$$|I_R| \leqslant \frac{R}{2\pi} \int\limits_{\pi/2}^{\pi/2+\varepsilon} \exp(-R^a \eta)\, d\theta + \frac{R}{2\pi} \int\limits_{\pi/2+\varepsilon}^{\pi} \exp\left(\frac{1}{2} tR \cos\left(\frac{\pi}{2} - \varepsilon\right)\right) d\theta$$

$$= \frac{\varepsilon R}{2\pi} \exp(-R^a \eta) + \frac{1}{4} R \exp\left(-\frac{1}{2} tR \sin\varepsilon\right).$$

Hence

$$\lim_{R\to\infty} I_R = 0.$$

Similarly the integral along the lower arc $(-R, -Ri)$ tends to 0 as $R \to \infty$. Also the integral along the smallest circumference approaches 0 as its radius tends to 0, for the integrand is bounded in the neighbourhood of $z = 0$. This proves that the integral along the curve Ω defined in § 4, or the integral (12), is equal to the sum of the integrals

$$\frac{1}{2\pi i} \int\limits_{\infty}^{0} \exp(tre^{i\pi} - r^a e^{i\pi a}) e^{i\pi}\, dr + \frac{1}{2\pi i} \int\limits_{0}^{\infty} \exp(tre^{-i\pi} - r^a e^{-i\pi a}) e^{-i\pi}\, dr$$

$$= \frac{1}{2\pi i} \int\limits_{0}^{\infty} \exp(-tr - r^a e^{i\pi a})\, dr - \frac{1}{2\pi i} \int\limits_{0}^{\infty} \exp(-tr - r^a e^{-i\pi a})\, dr.$$

But the integrands in the last two integrals are conjugate, and thus their difference is equal to the doubled imaginary part of the first integrand, i. e. to

$$2i \exp(-tr - r^a \cos\pi a) \sin(r^a \sin\pi a)\, dr.$$

Hence follows (15).

Differentiating m times, we obtain from (15)

$$U_a^{(m)}(t) = \frac{1}{\pi} \int\limits_{0}^{\infty} (-r)^m \exp(-tr - r^a \cos\pi a) \sin(r^a \sin\pi a)\, dr. \tag{16}$$

§ 8. Properties of $U_a(t)$ on the real axis. Let ε be an arbitrary positive number. Since integral (16) is absolutely convergent for $t \geqslant 0$, we can find a positive number ϱ such that the integral

$$\left|\frac{1}{\pi}\int_0^{\varrho} u(1, r)\,dr\right| < \varepsilon,$$

where $u(t, r)$ denotes the integrand of (16). Then a fortiori

$$\left|\frac{1}{\pi}\int_0^{\varrho} u(t, r)\,dr\right| < \varepsilon \quad \text{for} \quad t > 1. \tag{17}$$

Now, there is a number $T > 1$ such that $\frac{1}{2}T\varphi > \varrho^a|\cos\pi a|$; therefore $-tr - r^a\cos\pi a < -\frac{1}{2}tr$ for $t > T$ and $r \geqslant \varrho$. Hence

$$\left|\frac{1}{\pi}\int_{\varrho}^{\infty} u(t, r)\,dr\right| \leqslant \frac{1}{\pi}\int_0^{\infty} r^m \exp(-\tfrac{1}{2}tr)\,dr = \frac{1}{\pi}\,\frac{m!\,2^m}{t^{m+1}}. \tag{18}$$

Inequalities (17) and (18) prove that $|U_a^{(m)}(t)| < 2\varepsilon$ for large values of t. Since ε is arbitrary, this gives the required equality (14).

Formula (15) shows explicitly that $U_a(t)$ is a real function for real and non-negative values of t. But it would be difficult to show by the use either of formula (12) or of (15) that

$$U_a(t) > 0 \quad \text{for} \quad 0 < t < \infty. \tag{19}$$

This inequality can be obtained by means of Post's inversion formula (7) of § 3 of Chapter VI [1]:

$$U_a(t) = \lim_{n\to\infty} \frac{(-1)^n}{n!}\left(\frac{n}{t}\right)^{n+1} F^{(n)}\left(\frac{n}{t}\right),$$

where

$$F(x) = \int_0^{\infty} e^{-xt}\,U_a(t)\,dt = e^{-x^a} > 0 \quad \text{for} \quad x > 0.$$

In fact

$$-F'(x) = x^{a-1}F(x) > 0$$

[1] An alternative proof was given recently in the paper: J. Mikusiński, *Sur la fonction dont la transformée de Laplace est* e^{-s^a}, Bull. Ac. Pol. Sci. VI, 11 (1958), p. 691-693.

and generally, for $x > 0$ and $n = 0, 1, \ldots$,

$$(-1)^n F^{(n)}(x) = x \sum_{\nu=1}^{n} \binom{n}{\nu} (1-a)(2-a)\ldots(n-\nu-a) x^{a+n-\nu-2} (-1)^\nu F^{(\nu)}(x) > 0,$$

where the symbol

$$(1-a)(2-a)\ldots(n-\nu-a)$$

must be replaced by 1 whenever $\nu = n$. Hence $U_a(t) \geqslant 0$.

Now, it follows from

$$e^{-s} = e^{-s/2} e^{-s/2}$$

that

$$U_a(t) = 2^{2/a} \int_0^t U_a\big(2^{1/a}(t-\tau)\big) U_a(2^{1/a}\tau)\, d\tau .$$

Since the function U_a is analytic, it can vanish at most at isolated points. The convolution of two non-negative functions which vanish at most at isolated points is positive. Thus inequality (19) is proved.

§ 9. The case of $a > 1$ and real λ. In this case the exponential function $e^{-s^a\lambda}$ does not exist. To prove this, it suffices to prove that the operational differential equation

$$x'(\lambda) = -s^a x(\lambda) \tag{20}$$

considered in an arbitrary interval $\lambda_1 \leqslant \lambda \leqslant \lambda_2$ has the only solution $x(\lambda) = 0$.

Suppose that $x(\lambda)$ is a solution of (20). Then $x(\lambda)$ can be represented in the form

$$x(\lambda) = \frac{y(\lambda)}{q} = \frac{\{y(\lambda, t)\}}{\{q(t)\}},$$

where $q = \{q(t)\} \in \mathcal{C}$ and $\{y(\lambda, t)\}$ is a continuous function with a continuous partial derivative $y_\lambda(\lambda, t)$ in the region

$$\lambda_1 \leqslant \lambda \leqslant \lambda_2, \quad 0 \leqslant t < \infty$$

such that

$$\frac{\{y_\lambda(\lambda, t)\}}{q} = -s^a \frac{\{y(\lambda, t)\}}{q}.$$

Hence, multiplying by $l^a q$, we obtain

$$\int_0^t \frac{(t-\tau)^{a-1}}{\Gamma(a)} y_\lambda(\lambda, \tau)\, d\tau + y(\lambda, t) = 0.$$

Let $T(\lambda)$ be a non-negative numerical function, continuously derivable in $[\lambda_1, \lambda_2]$ and vanishing at the extremities of this interval.

Put

$$Y(\lambda, \sigma) = \int_0^{T(\lambda)} e^{-\sigma[T(\lambda)-t]} y(\lambda, t)\, dt$$

and

$$A(\lambda, \sigma) = \int_0^{T(\lambda)} e^{-\sigma t} \frac{t^{a-1}}{\Gamma(a)}\, dt.$$

Then, by the theorem on convolution (see § 5, Chapter VI), we have

$$A(\lambda, \sigma) \int_0^{T(\lambda)} e^{[T(\lambda)-t]} y_\lambda(\lambda, t)\, dt + Y(\lambda, \sigma) = R(\lambda, \sigma), \tag{21}$$

where

$$|R(\lambda, \sigma)| \leqslant \int_0^{T(\lambda)} \frac{t^{a-1}}{\Gamma(a)}\, dt \int_0^{T(\lambda)} |y_\lambda(\lambda, t)|\, dt.$$

It is easy to verify that

$$Y_\lambda(\lambda, \sigma) = T'(\lambda) y\big(\lambda, T(\lambda)\big) + \sigma T'(\lambda)\, Y(\lambda, \sigma) + \int_0^{T(\lambda)} e^{\sigma[T(\lambda)-t]} y_\lambda(\lambda, t)\, dt.$$

Hence, in view of (21),

$$A(\lambda, \sigma)\, Y_\lambda(\lambda, \sigma) + [1 - \sigma A(\lambda, \sigma) T'(\lambda)]\, Y(\lambda, \sigma) = R(\lambda, \sigma) - A(\lambda, \sigma) T'(\lambda) y\big(\lambda, T(\lambda)\big).$$

Since

$$0 \leqslant A(\lambda, \sigma) < \int_0^{\infty} e^{-\sigma t} \frac{t^{a-1}}{\Gamma(a)}\, dt = \frac{1}{\sigma^a},$$

there is a number S such that

$$1 - \sigma A(\lambda, \sigma) T'(\lambda) > \tfrac{1}{2} \quad \text{for} \quad \sigma > S. \tag{22}$$

Fix arbitrarily $\sigma > S$ and denote by λ_σ the interval $[\lambda_1, \lambda_2]$ at which the modulus of $Y(\lambda, \sigma)$ has its maximum. The existence of this maximum is ensured by $Y(\lambda_1, \sigma) = Y(\lambda_2, \sigma) = 0$. Hence $Y_\lambda(\lambda_\sigma, \sigma) = 0$ and, on account of (21) and (22),

$$|Y(\lambda, \sigma)| \leqslant |Y(\lambda_\sigma, \sigma)| \leqslant 2 |R(\lambda_\sigma, \sigma) - T'(\lambda_\sigma) y\big(\lambda_\sigma, T(\lambda_\sigma)\big)| \leqslant M,$$

where the number M depends, for given $y(\lambda)$, on the choice of function $T(\lambda)$ and is independent on λ and σ. Writing this inequality in the form

$$\left|\int_0^{T(\lambda)} e^{\sigma[T(\lambda)-t]} y(\lambda, t)\,dt\right| = \left|\int_0^{T(\lambda)} e^{\sigma t} y(\lambda, T(\lambda)-t)\,dt\right| \leqslant M \qquad (\sigma > S)$$

we find, by the moment theorem (see § 11, Chapter II, Part I), $y(\lambda, t) = 0$ for $\lambda_1 \leqslant \lambda \leqslant \lambda_2$, $0 \leqslant t \leqslant T(\lambda)$.

Now, the function $T(\lambda)$ can be chosen arbitrarily, thus the equality $y(\lambda, t)$ must hold in the whole region $\lambda_1 \leqslant \lambda \leqslant \lambda_2$, $0 \leqslant t < \infty$.

This implies $x(\lambda) = 0$ in $\lambda_1 \leqslant \lambda \leqslant \lambda_2$ and proves that the exponential function $e^{-s\alpha\lambda}$ does not exist for $\alpha > 1$ and real λ.

This result can easily be extended to complex, but not imaginary, values of λ. In order to do it, we first add some remarks on real and complex operators.

§ 10. Real and imaginary part of an operator. An operator a is said to be *real* if it can be represented in the form p/q, where p and q are real functions of class $\mathcal{C}$. For instance the operators 1, s^{α} (α real), e^{-s} are real. The sum, the difference, the product and the quotient of real operators are again real.

Every operator a can be represented in the form

$$a = a_1 + ia_2, \tag{23}$$

where a_1 and a_2 are real operators. This representation is unique.

In fact, let $a = p/q$, where $p \in \mathcal{C}$ and $\tau \in \mathcal{C}$, $q \neq 0$. The functions p and q can be represented in the form

$$p = p_1 + ip_2, \qquad q = q_1 + iq_2,$$

where p_1, p_2, q_1 and q_2 are real functions of class $\mathcal{C}$, $q_1 \neq 0$ or $q_2 \neq 0$. We can write

$$a = \frac{p_1 q_1 - p_2 q_2}{q_1^2 + q_2^2} + i\,\frac{p_1 q_2 + p_2 q_1}{q_1^2 + q_2^2}. \tag{24}$$

The denominator $q_1^2 + q_2^2$ is not identically 0, for it is the convolution of two non-vanishing functions $q_1 + iq_2$ and $q_1 - iq_2$. Thus representation (23) exists.

To prove its uniqueness, suppose that

$$a_1 + ia_2 = b_1 + ib_2,$$

where a_1, a_2, b_1 and b_2 are real operators. Then

$$c_1 + ic_2 = 0,$$

where $c_1 = a_1 - b_1$ and $c_2 = a_2 - b_2$ are real operators. We must show that $c_1 = 0$ and $c_2 = 0$. Let $c = p/q$, where $p \in \mathcal{C}$, and $q \in \mathcal{C}$, $q \neq 0$. Then it follows from $c_1 + ic_2 = 0$ that

$$(p_1 q_1 - p_2 q_2) - i(p_1 q_2 + p_2 q_1) = 0.$$

But here we deal with ordinary functions, and thus both equalities

$$p_1 q_1 - p_2 q_2 = 0 \quad \text{and} \quad p_1 q_2 + p_2 q_1 = 0$$

must hold. By multiplying the first of these equalities by q_1, we find, taking into account the second equality,

$$p_1 (q_1^2 + q_2^2) = 0,$$

which implies $p_1 = 0$, $p_2 = 0$ and $c_1 = 0$, $c_2 = 0$. This proves the uniqueness of decomposition (23).

If (23), denote by $\bar{a} = a_1 - ia_2$ the conjugated operator to a; we have, just as for complex numbers,

$$\overline{ab} = \bar{a}\bar{b},$$

i. e. the conjugated operator to a product ab is equal to the product of operators conjugated to a and b.

§ 11. The case of $a > 0$ and a complex, but not imaginary λ. Suppose that the function $x(\lambda) = \exp(-e^{\omega i} \lambda s^a)$ exists for $\omega \neq \pm \pi/2$. Then

$$x'(\lambda) = -e^{i\omega} s^a x(\lambda) \quad \text{and} \quad x(0) = 1. \tag{25}$$

If $\bar{x}(\lambda)$ is the operational function whose values are conjugated to $x(\lambda)$, then of course

$$\bar{x}'(\lambda) = \overline{x'(\lambda)},$$

i. e. the derivative of the conjugated function is the conjugated function to the derivative. It follows from (25) that

$$\bar{x}'(\lambda) = -e^{-i\omega} s^a \bar{x}(\lambda) \quad \text{and} \quad \bar{x}(0) = 1.$$

Thus $\bar{x}(\lambda)$ is the exponential function:

$$\bar{x}(\lambda) = \exp(-e^{-i\omega} \lambda s^a).$$

From the existence of $x(\lambda)$ and $\bar{x}(\lambda)$ it follows, for $\omega \neq \pm \pi/2$, the existence of the exponential function

$$x\left(\frac{\lambda}{2\cos\omega}\right) \bar{x}\left(\frac{\lambda}{2\cos\omega}\right) = \exp\left(-\frac{e^{i\omega}}{2\cos\omega} \lambda s^a\right) \exp\left(-\frac{e^{-i\omega}}{2\cos\omega} \lambda s^a\right) = \exp(-\lambda s^a)$$

which contradicts the result of § 8.

Thus the exponential function $\exp(-e^{i\omega}\lambda s^a)$ does not exist when $a > 1$ and $\omega \neq \pm\pi/2$.

§ 12. The case of $a \geqslant 1$ and imaginary λ. Also in this case the exponential function does not exist but the proof cannot be deduced from the preceeding results. We shall use a different method.

Suppose that there is a function $x(\lambda) = \exp(-i\lambda s^a)$ such that

$$x'(\lambda) = -is^a x(\lambda) \quad \text{and} \quad x(0) = 1. \tag{26}$$

Let λ_1 and λ_2 be two arbitrary real numbers, $\lambda_1 < \lambda_2$, and let $\omega = 2\pi/(\lambda_2 - \lambda_1)$. By multiplying the first equality in (26) by $e^{in\omega}$ and integrating it afterwards from λ_1 to λ_2, we get

$$\int_{\lambda_1}^{\lambda_2} e^{in\omega\lambda} x'(\lambda)\,d\lambda = -is^a \int_{\lambda_1}^{\lambda_2} e^{in\omega\lambda} x(\lambda)\,d\lambda.$$

Integrating per parts we find

$$\int_{\lambda_1}^{\lambda_2} e^{in\omega\lambda} x'(\lambda)\,d\lambda = e^{-in\omega\lambda_2} x(\lambda_2) - e^{in\omega\lambda_1} x(\lambda_1) - in\omega \int_{\lambda_1}^{\lambda_2} e^{in\omega\lambda} x(\lambda)\,d\lambda.$$

But $e^{in\omega\lambda_1} = e^{in\omega\lambda_2}$ $(n = 1, 2, \ldots)$, thus

$$e^{in\omega\lambda_2}[x(\lambda_2) - x(\lambda_1)] = -i(s^a - n\omega) \int_{\lambda_1}^{\lambda_2} e^{in\omega\lambda} x(\lambda)\,d\lambda$$

and hence

$$\frac{x(\lambda_2) - x(\lambda_1)}{s^a - n\omega} = -ie^{-in\omega\lambda_2} \int_{\lambda_1}^{\lambda_2} e^{in\omega\lambda} x(\lambda)\,d\lambda. \tag{27}$$

Let $x(\lambda) = y(\lambda)/q$, where $q = \{q(t)\} \in \mathcal{C}$ and $y(\lambda) = \{y(\lambda, t)\}$ is a continuous function in the region $\lambda_1 \leqslant \lambda \leqslant \lambda_2$, $0 \leqslant t < \infty$. Multiplying (27) by q, we get

$$\frac{y(\lambda_2) - y(\lambda_1)}{s^a - n\omega} = ie^{-iu\omega\lambda_2} \int_{\lambda_1}^{\lambda_2} e^{in\omega\lambda} y(\lambda)\,d\lambda. \tag{28}$$

Since

$$\frac{1}{s^a - n\omega} = \frac{1}{1 - n\omega l^a} = l^a\left(1 + n\omega l^a + (n\omega)^2 l^{2a} + \ldots\right) \in \mathcal{C},$$

both sides of (28) are functions of class $\mathcal{C}$ and we have

$$\frac{y(\lambda_2) - y(\lambda_1)}{s^a - n\omega} \leqslant \int_{\lambda_1}^{\lambda_2} |y(\lambda)|\,d\lambda.$$

Generally, we write $a < b$ if and only if the operators a and b are continuous or locally integrable functions $a = \{a(t)\}$, $b = \{b(t)\}$ and $a(t) < b(t)$ almost everywhere in $0 \leqslant t < \infty$. We can also write $b > a$ instead of $a < b$.

Now we have

$$\text{(29)} \qquad \frac{y(\lambda_2) - y(\lambda_1)}{s^a[s - (n\omega)^{1/a}]} = \frac{s^a - n\omega}{s^a[s - (n\omega)^{1/a}]} \frac{y(\lambda_2) - y(\lambda_1)}{s^a - n\omega}.$$

It is easy to verify that

$$\frac{s^a - n\omega}{s^a[s - (n\omega)^{1/a}]} = \left\{\frac{n\omega}{\Gamma(a)} \int_t^\infty e^{-(n\omega)^{1/a}(\tau - t)} \tau^{a-1} d\tau\right\}.$$

Hence

$$0 < \frac{s^a - n\omega}{s^a[s - (n\omega)^{1/a}]} < n\left\{\frac{\omega}{\Gamma(a)} \int_t^\infty e^{-\omega^{1/a}(\tau - t)} \tau^{a-1} d\tau\right\} = \frac{n}{s - \omega^{1/a}}$$

and, by (29),

$$\left|\frac{y(\lambda_2) - y(\lambda_1)}{s^a[s - (n\omega)^{1/a}]}\right| = \frac{n}{s - \omega^{1/a}} \int_{\lambda_1}^{\lambda_2} |y(\lambda)|\, d\lambda.$$

Put

$$\text{(30)} \quad f = \{f(t)\} = \frac{y(\lambda_2) - y(\lambda_1)}{s^a} \quad \text{and} \quad g = \{g(t)\} = \frac{1}{s - \omega^{1/a}} \int_{\lambda_1}^{\lambda_2} |y(\lambda)|\, d\lambda.$$

Then we can write

$$\int_0^t e^{(n\omega)^{1/a}} f(t - \tau)\, d\tau \leqslant n g(t) \qquad (0 \leqslant t < \infty).$$

Hence, multiplying by $e^{-(n\omega)^{1/a}}$, where $\varepsilon > 0$,

$$\lim_{n \to \infty} \int_0^t e^{(n\omega)^{1/a}(\tau - \varepsilon)} (\tau - \varepsilon) f(t - \tau)\, d\tau = 0.$$

Since $a \geqslant 1$, we can select from $\omega^{1/a}, (2\omega)^{1/a}, \ldots$ a subsequence $\beta_1, \beta_2, \ldots$ such that

$$\sum_{n=1}^{\infty} \frac{1}{\beta_n} = \infty \qquad \text{and} \qquad \beta_{n+1} - \beta_n \geqslant \infty.$$

Of course, we also have

$$\lim_{n\to\infty}\int_0^t e^{\beta n(\tau-\varepsilon)} f(t-\tau)\,d\tau = 0$$

and, by the theorem on moments (see IV, § 7, Chapter VII), we obtain $f(t-\tau)=0$ for $0 \leqslant \tau \leqslant t$. Since t is arbitrary, we have $f(t) = 0$ in $0 \leqslant t < \infty$. This implies, by (30), $y(\lambda_2) = y(\lambda_1)$ and $x(\lambda_2) = x(\lambda_1)$.

Since λ_1 and λ_2 are arbitrary, the function $x(\lambda)$ is constant and its derivative vanishes. But this is not compatible with (26). Thus the exponential function $e^{-i\lambda s^\alpha}$ does not exist for $\alpha > 1$.

§ 13. The case of $\alpha = 1$. If λ is real, the function $e^{-s\lambda}$ represents the known translation operator. If λ is imaginary, this function does not exist, as we have seen in the preceeding paragraph. To complete our discussion, it remains to consider the case of $\lambda = \lambda_1 + i\lambda_2$, where λ_1 and λ_2 are real and different from 0. However, in this case function does not exist. In fact, if it existed, then also the function

$$e^{-is\lambda_2} = \frac{e^{s\lambda_1}}{e^{s(\lambda_1+\lambda_2)}}$$

would exist, which is not true.

§ 14. Table of existence. The main result of this Chapter may be put into the following table:

$e^{-s^\alpha\lambda}$	λ real	λ non real
$\alpha < 1$	Region of	
$\alpha = 0$	existence	Region
$\alpha > 1$	of non-existence	

CHAPTER IX

GENERAL THEORY OF LINEAR DIFFERENTIAL EQUATIONS WITH OPERATIONAL COEFFICIENTS

(Appendix to Chapters I and II of Part IV)

§ 1. Notation. We shall consider the differential equations

$$a_n x^{(n)}(\lambda)+\ldots+a_1 x'(\lambda)+a_0 x(\lambda) = f(\lambda) \qquad (a_n \neq 0),$$

where the coefficients a_i are arbitrary operators and $f(\lambda)$ a given operational function. We shall write these equations in the form

$$a_n D^n x+\ldots+a_1 Dx+a_0 x = f \qquad (a_n \neq 0)$$

or

$$P(D)x = f,$$

where

$$P(D) = a_n D^n+\ldots+a_1 D+a_0$$

is a formal polynomial of D with operational coefficients. First we shall deal with homogeneous equations, i. e. such that $f = 0$.

Given two polynomials of D with operational coefficients $P(D)$ and $Q(D)$, we can interpret the equation

(1) $$P(D)Q(D)x = 0$$

in two different ways: either as $P(D)\big(Q(D)x\big) = 0$ or as $\big(P(D)Q(D)\big)x = 0$. It is easy to verify that both ways lead to the same equation, so that the outer parentheses are superfluous. This implies that if x_0 is a solution of $P(D)x = 0$ or of $Q(D)x = 0$, then it is also a solution of (1).

§ 2. The space of solutions. Let X be the space of all the operational functions $x(\lambda)$ in a given interval I such that $x(\lambda)$ is a solution of some equation $P(D)x = 0$. The equations $P(D)x = 0$ can be different for different $x(\lambda)$. In other words X is the space of the solutions of the equations $P(D)x = 0$.

If the function $x(\lambda)$ is a solution of $P(D)x = 0$, its product $cx(\lambda)$ by an arbitrary operator is again a solution of the same equation. Thus the product cx of an element x of X by an arbitrary operator c is an element of X. Similarly the sum $x+y$ and the difference $x-y$ of two elements of X are elements of X. For, if $P(D)x = 0$ and $Q(D)y = 0$, then $P(D)Q(D)(x+y) = 0$ and $P(D)Q(D)(x-y) = 0$.

It is easy to verify that X is a linear space over the field of operators, i. e. that conditions (i)-(vii) (§ 5, Chapter IV) are satisfied provided the letters a, b, c denote, at present, elements of X, and α, β denote operators.

§ 3. Linearly independent solutions. Since every element $x \in X$ is a solution of some differential equation $P(D)x = 0$, it is differentiable, i. e. $x \in X$ implies $Dx \in X$. (Also in the particular case when $P(D)$ is a polynomial of degree 0: $P(D) = a = 0$, the solution is differentiable, for it is identically 0 and satisfies every other equation.) Thus D is a mapping of X into X. Moreover we have

$$D(ax) = a(Dx) \quad \text{and} \quad D(x+y) = Dx + Dy,$$

i. e. the mapping D is linear. Every linear mapping of a linear space into itself is called an *endomorphism*. The differentiation D is endomorphism defined on X.

The elements $x_1, \ldots, x_n$ of X are linearly independent, if

$$c_1 x_1 + \ldots + c_n x_n = 0 \quad (c_i \text{ operators}) \tag{2}$$

implies $c_1 = \ldots = c_n = 0$; they are *linearly dependent* if, conversely, there exist operators $c_1, \ldots, c_n$, not all null, such that (2) holds.

The number of linearly independent solutions of the equation $P(D)x = 0$ is less than or equal to the order of this equation (i. e. to the degree of the polynomial P).

Proof. Let $x_1, \ldots, x_{n+1}$ be solution of $P(D)x = 0$, where the degree of P is n, and let λ_0 be an arbitrary point of the considered interval I. It is always possible to choose $n+1$ operators $c_1, \ldots, c_{n+1}$, not all null, such that

$$c_1 x_1^{(i)}(\lambda_0) + \ldots + c_{n+1} x_{n+1}^{(i)}(\lambda_0) = 0 \quad \text{for} \quad i = 0, \ldots, n-1.$$

Then the function

$$x(\lambda) = c_1 x_1(\lambda) + \ldots + c_{n+1} x_{n+1}(\lambda)$$

also satisfies the equation $P(D)x = 0$, and the initial conditions are

$$x^{(i)}(\lambda_0) = 0 \quad \text{for} \quad i = 0, \ldots, n-1.$$

By the unicity theorem of § 7 of Part IV, we have $x(\lambda) = 0$ identically in I. Thus the solutions $x_1, \ldots, x_{n+1}$ are linearly dependent, which proves the theorem.

§ 4. A set of solutions. Let P^m denote the m-th power of the polynomial P.

THEOREM. *If the function* $x_0 = x_0(\lambda)$ *is a solution of* $P(D)x = 0$, *and* m *is a positive integer, then each of the functions*

$$\lambda^i D^j x_0 \quad (i = 0, \ldots, m-1; j = 0, 1, \ldots) \tag{3}$$

is a solution of $P^m(D)x = 0$.

Proof. From $P(D)x = 0$ it follows that $P^m(D)D^j x = 0$ for $j = 0, 1, \ldots$ Thus the theorem holds for $i = 0$. Since for $m = 0$ the index i can assume the value 0 only, the theorem is proved for $m = 1$. Suppose in the sequel that $m \geqslant 2$.

We have

$$D^j(\lambda x) = \lambda D^j x + jD^{j-1} x \quad (j = 1, 2, \ldots)$$

and hence

$$\sum_{j=0}^{n} a_j D^j(\lambda x) = \sum_{j=0}^{n} a_j D^j x + \sum_{j=0}^{n} j a_j D^{j-1} x.$$

Since $P(D) = a_n D^n + \ldots + a_0$, we can write

$$P(D)(\lambda x) = \lambda P(D)x + P'(D)x, \tag{4}$$

where P' is the ordinary derivative of the polynomial P. Formula (4) holds for every polynomial P and every function x, differentiable n times (n degree of P). It holds also when P is replaced by the m-th power P^m of P and the function x by $\lambda^i x$. Then we obtain

$$P^m(D)(\lambda^{i+1}x) = P^m(\lambda^i x) + mP^{m-1}P'(\lambda^i x). \tag{5}$$

If $m \geqslant 2$ and $j = 0$, we find by (5) that $P^m(\lambda D^j x) = 0$ $(j = 0, 1, \ldots)$. If $m \geqslant 3$ and $j = 1$, we find by (5) that $P^m(\lambda^2 D^j x) = 0$ $(j = 0, 1, \ldots)$. Generally the theorem follows by induction.

§ 5. Common solution of two equations.

If $Q(D)x = 0$ *is an equation of the lowest possible degree* ($\geqslant 0$) *which is satisfied by a given function* $x_0 \neq 0$ *of class* X, *and* $P(D)x = 0$ *is any of the equations satisfied by* x_0, *then* Q *is a divisor of* P.

In fact, write $P = P_0 Q + R$, where P_0 and R are polynomials such that the degree of R is less than the degree of Q. Then

$$P(D)x_0 = P_0(D)Q(D)x_0 + R(D)x_0,$$

i. e. $0 = R(D)x_0$. Since the degree of R is less that that of Q, this implies $R = 0$ and $P = P_0 Q$.

As an immediate corollary we have:

If two equations $P_1(D)x = 0$ *and* $P_2(D)x = 0$ *have a common solution* $x_0 \neq 0$, *the polynomials* P_1 *and* P_2 *have a common divisor.*

§ 6. Powers of irreducible polynomials. We say that a polynomial is *irreducible* if it cannot be decomposed into the product of two polynomials of degree $\geqslant 1$. If $P(a)=0$ for an operator a, and the degree of P is $\geqslant 2$, then P is not irreducible, because it can be represented in the form $P(D)=(D-a)P_0(D)$, where P_0 is a polynomial of degree $\geqslant 1$.

THEOREM. *If a polynomial P of degree $n>1$ is irreducible and $x_0 \neq 0$ is a solution of the equation $P(D)x=0$, then the functions*

$$\lambda^i D^j x_0 \quad (i=0,1,\ldots;\ j=0,\ldots,n-1) \tag{6}$$

are linearly independent (i. e. every finite number of them is linearly independent.)

Proof. We shall first prove that the functions

$$x_0,\ Dx_0,\ \ldots,\ D^{n-1}x_0$$

are linearly independent. If the converse were true, then there would exist operators $c_0,\ldots,c_{n-1}$, not all null, such that

$$c_0x_0+c_1x_0+\ldots+c_{n-1}D^{n-1}x_0=0.$$

Thus x_0 would be a non-vanishing solution of an equation of order less than n. By § 5, this is impossible, for x_0 is a solution of $P(D)x=0$, where the polynomial P is irreducible of degree n.

Assume that the functions (6) are linearly dependent. Let i_0 be the least integer such that those of functions (6) whose index i is $\leqslant i_0$ are lineraly independent. From the preceding argument it follows that $i_0 \geqslant 1$. The linear dependence means that

$$\sum_{j=0}^{n-1} b_j \lambda^{i_0} D^j x_0 = \sum_{i=0}^{i_0-1}\sum_{j=0}^{n-1} b_{ij}\lambda^i D^j x_0 \tag{7}$$

for some operators b_j and b_{ij} such that at least one of b_j is different from 0.

For brevity, let us denote the right side of (7) by y_1. Since y_1 is a sum of solutions of the equation

$$P^{i_0}(D)x=0, \tag{8}$$

it is itself a solution. Denote the left side of (7) by λy_0. Then the function

$$y_0=\sum_{j=0}^{n-1} b_j \lambda^{i_0-1} D^j x_0$$

is again a solution of (8). We have $\lambda y_0 = y_1$. Hence, differentiating j times, we obtain

$$\lambda D^j y_0 + jD^{j-1}y_0 = D^j y_1 \quad (j=0,1,\ldots). \tag{9}$$

Suppose that

$$P^{i_0}(D) = c_k D^k + \ldots + c_1 D + c_0.$$

Multiplying (9) by c_j and summing over $j = 0, \ldots, k$, we obtain

$$\lambda P^{i_0}(D) y_0 + i_0 P^{i_0-1}(D) P'(D) y_0 = P^{i_0}(D) y_1, \tag{10}$$

where

$$P^{i_0-1}(D) P'(D) = k c_k D^{k-1} + \ldots + c_1$$

and $P'(D)$ is the derivative, in the ordinary sense, of the polynomial P. Since y_0 and y_1 are solutions of (8) we obtain from (10)

$$P^{i_0-1}(D) P'(D) y_0 = 0. \tag{11}$$

Now the functions $\lambda^i D^j x_0$ ($i = 0, \ldots, i_0-1$; $j = 0, \ldots, n-1$), whose number is $i_0 n$, are by hypothesis linearly independent. Those of them whose index i is $\leqslant i_0-2$ satisfy the equation

$$P^{i_0-1}(D) x = 0; \tag{12}$$

but the other functions $\lambda^{i-1} D^j x_0$ do not, for the equation is of order $(i_0-1)n$ and therefore cannot have more than $(i_0-1)n$ linearly independent solutions by § 2. Similarly y_0 does not satisfy (12). Let $Q(D)x = 0$ be the equation of the lowest degree which is satisfied by y_0. By § 5, Q must be a divisor of P^{i_0}. Since P is irreducible, the greater divisor of P^{i_0} whose degree is less than the degree of P^{i_0} is P^{i_0-1}. This contradicts (11).

The contradiction follows from the assumption that functions (6) are linearly dependent. Thus the theorem is proved.

§ 7. Factorization of operational polynomials. In order to study the equation $P(D)x = 0$, where $P(D)$ is an arbitrary polynomial of D with operational coefficients, we must factorize $P(D)$ into irreducible polynomials. Assume that

$$P(D) = a_n D^n + \ldots + a_1 D + a_0 \quad (a_n \neq 0);$$

then we represented $P(D)$ in the form

$$P(D) = a_n P_1^{k_1}(D) \ldots P_m^{k_m}(D), \tag{13}$$

where $P_i(D)$ are irreducible polynomials whose coefficients at the highest power of D is 1. The factorization (13) is unique.

The theorem of unique factorization is well known in the case of polynomials with numerical coefficients. It is also proved, in Abstract Algebra, for polynomials with coefficients from an arbitrary commutative field. Thus is it also true in our case of operational polynomials. However, it seems convenient for the reader, not acquainted with Abstract Algebra, to have the proof reproduced here.

The proof will be given in a few stages. First we prove that:

(I) *If the polynomials P and Q are relatively prime (i. e. have no common divisor of positive degree), then there are polynomials A and B such that*

$$AP + BQ = 1. \tag{14}$$

Proof. There exist polynomials Q_1 and R_1 such that

$$P = QQ_1 + R_1, \tag{15}$$

where the degree of R_1 is less than the degree of Q. The coefficients of Q_1 can be found stepwise by dividing, in the usual sense, 0 by Q. Then R_1 is obtained as the remainder. Since P and Q have no common divisor, we have $R_1 \neq 0$. (If the degree of Q is higher than that of P, we obtain $Q_1 = 0$ and $R_1 = Q$.) Similarly we find polynomials $Q_2, R_2, Q_3, R_3, \ldots$ such that

$$\begin{aligned} Q &= R_1 Q_2 + R_2, \\ R_1 &= R_2 Q_3 + R_3, \\ &\cdots\cdots\cdots \end{aligned} \tag{16}$$

Since the degrees of $R_1, R_2, \ldots$ decrease, we must obtain, after a finite number of steps, $R_k \neq 0$ and $R_{k+1} = 0$. Thus the last two equations will be of the form

$$R_{k-2} = R_{k-1} Q_k + R_k, \qquad R_{k-1} = R_k Q_{k+1}.$$

From the last equation we see that R_k is a divisor of R_{k-1}. From the preceding equation we see that R_k is also a divisor of R_{k-2}. We find in succesion that R_k is a divisor of all the polynomials $R_{k-1}, \ldots, R_1, Q$ and P. Since P and Q have no common divisor of positive degree, R_k must be of degree 0. Thus R is an operator, different from 0. Now we find from (15) and (16)

$$R_1 = 1P - Q_1 Q, \qquad R_2 = -Q_2 P + (Q_1 Q_2 + 1) Q.$$

We see that R_1 and R_2 are of the form

$$R_i = A_i P + B_i Q, \tag{17}$$

where A_i and B_i are polynomials.

Assume that (17) holds for a certain i and also that $R_{i-1} = A_{i-1} P + B_{i-1} Q$. Since $R_{i-1} = R_i Q_{i+1} + R_{i+1}$, we find

$$R_{i+1} = (A_{i-1} - Q_{i+1} A_i) P + (B_{i-1} - Q_{i+1} B_i) Q.$$

Thus R_{i+1} is also of form (17) and so are by induction all the $R_1, \ldots, R_k$. In particular we have

$$R_k = A_k P + B_k Q.$$

Dividing by R_k we obtain

$$1 = \frac{A_k}{R_k} P + \frac{B_k}{R_k} Q.$$

Since A_k and B_k are polynomials, and R_k is an operator different from 0, theorem (I) is proved.

(II) *If P is a divisor of QR, but has no common divisor with Q, then P is a divisor of R.*

Proof. Multiplying (14) by R we obtain $APR+BQR = R$. Since P is a divisor of QR, it is a divisor of the entire left-hand member, and therefore of R.

(III) *If an irreducible polynomial P is a divisor of the product of polynomials $P_1, \ldots, P_k$, then it is a divisor of one of the factors.*

Proof. If P is not a divisor of P_1, it has no common divisor with P_1 so that P must be a divisor of $P_2, \ldots, P_k$. By induction, if P is not a divisor of $P_1, \ldots, P_{k-1}$, it must be a divisor of P_k.

Now we are in a position to prove the unique factorization theorem. Suppose that there are two representations

$$P = a_n P_1, \ldots, P_h \quad \text{and} \quad P = a_n Q_1, \ldots, Q_k,$$

where P_i and Q_i are irreducible polynomials of positive degree, whose coefficients of the highest power are 1. Then

$$P_1 \ldots P_h = Q_1 \ldots Q_k.$$

Since P_1 is a divisor of $Q_1 \ldots Q_k$, it must be a divisor of a certain Q_i. Since P_1 and Q_i are irreducible, we have $P_1 = Q_i$. By a rearrangement, if necessary, of the order of the polynomials we may assume that $P_1 = Q_1$. Then

$$P_2 \ldots P_h = Q_2 \ldots Q_k.$$

As before, P_2 is a divisor of one of the remaining polynomials Q_i, say Q_2, and hence $P_2 = Q_2$. We proceed until all the polynomials P_i and Q_i are exhausted. It is now evident that $h = k$ for otherwise one at least of P_i or Q_i would be equal to 1.

In § 16 of Part II we have seen that there is no operator w satisfying the equation $w^2-f = 0$, where $f = \{t \sin \ln t\}$. This implies that the polynomial D^2-f is irreducible. For if we had a representation $D^2-f = (D-w_1)(D-w_2)$, the operators w_1 and w_2 would be roots of the equation $w^2-f = 0$.

We do not know whether there exist irreducible operational polynomials of degree greater than 2.

§ 8. Logarithmic equations.

Consider the equation

$$P(D)x = 0, \tag{18}$$

where $P(D)$ is an arbitrary polynomial whose coefficients are operators. Let us represent $P(D)$ in the form (13). If the equation $P_1(D)x = 0$, of order d_1, has a non-vanishing solution x_1, then the equation $P_1^{k_1}(D)x = 0$ has exactly $d_1 k_1$ linearly independent solutions

$$\lambda^i D^j x_1 \quad (i = 0, \ldots, k_1-1;\ j = 0, \ldots, d_1-1). \tag{19}$$

Similarly, if another equation $P_2(D)x = 0$, of order d_2, has a non-vanishing solution x_2, then the equation $P_2^{k_2}(D)x = 0$ has exactly $d_2 k_2$ (d_2 degree of P_2) linearly independent solutions

$$\lambda^i D^j x_2 \quad (i = 0, \ldots, k_2-1;\ j = 0, \ldots, d_2-1). \tag{20}$$

Functions (19) and (20) are also solutions of (18). They are all linearly independent. In fact, in the converse case we should have

$$\sum_{i,j} b_{ij} \lambda^i D^j x_1 = \sum_{i,j} c_{ij} \lambda^i D^j x_2 \tag{21}$$

for some operators b_{ij}, c_{ij}, one at least of b_{ij} being different from 0. But the left side of (21) is a non-vanishing solution of $P_1^{k_1}(D)x = 0$ and the right side of (21) is a solution of $P_2^{k_2}(D)x = 0$. Hence, both equations have a common non-vanishing solution *ad*, by § 5, the polynomials $P_1^{k_1}$ and $P_2^{k_2}$ must have a common divisor. But this is impossible, for P_1 and P_2 are irreducible and different polynomials. Hence functions (19) and (20) are linearly independent. Similarly, if each of the equations $P_\mu(D)x = 0$ $(\mu = 1, \ldots, m)$ has a non-vanishing solution x_μ, all the functions

$$\lambda^i D^j x_\mu \quad (i = 0, \ldots, k_\mu - 1;\ j = 0, \ldots, d_\mu - 1;\ \mu = 1, \ldots, m),$$

where d_μ is the degree of P_μ, are linearly independent solutions of (18). The number of these solutions is equal to the order n of equations (18). There exist no other linearly independent solutions, for the number of them is limited by the order of the equation, by § 3.

If the number of linearly independent solutions of an equation $P(D)x = 0$ is equal to its order, then that equation is called *logarithmic*. This is an extension of the concept introduced in § 6 of Part IV, because here the irreducible factors of $P(D)$ are admitted. It is also convenient to call the polynomial $P(D)$ *logarithmic*, if the equation $P(D)x = 0$ is logarithmic.

Let $f = \{t \sin \ln t\}$; then

$$(D^2 - f)x = 0 \tag{22}$$

is an example of an irreducible logarithmic equation. In fact, the function

$$x(\lambda) = 1 + \frac{\lambda^2}{2!} f + \frac{\lambda^4}{4!} f^2 + \ldots$$

is evidently a non-vanishing solution of (22). Similarly

$$(D^2 + f)x = 0$$

is an irreducible logarithmic equation with a non-vanishing solution

$$x(\lambda) = 1 - \frac{\lambda^2}{2!} f + \frac{\lambda^4}{4!} f^2 - \ldots$$

This is an analogue of the cosine function, but the expression $\cos(\lambda\sqrt{f})$ can be employed symbolically only, for the operator $\sqrt{f}$ does not exist.

We meet here an interesting case namely that an analogue of trigonometrical functions exists although the corresponding exponential function does not.

Probably there exist irreducible logarithmic equations of order higher than 2, but we do not know any examples of them.

§ 9. Pure equations. If an equation $P(D)x = 0$ has no solution different from 0, it is called *pure*. This is an extension of the concept introduced in § 6 of Part IV. The polynomial $P(D)$ of a pure equation will also be called *pure*.

As an example of a pure polynomial we can give $P(D) = D - s^2$ (s being a differential operator); the equation $(D - s^2)x = 0$ has no solution different from 0, by § 8, Chapter VIII. We do not know any example of an irreducible pure polynomial of degree $\geqslant 2$.

If we decompose a pure polynomial $P(D)$ into factors $P_1(D)\ldots P_k(D)$, then every factor P_i is pure, for every solution of $P_i(D)x = 0$ satisfies also the equation $P(D)x = 0$. Conversely, the product of pure polynomials is again a pure polynomial. This results from the following lemma:

If the equations $P(D)x = 0$ and $Q(D)x = 0$ have exactly m and n linearly independent solutions, then the equation $P(D)Q(D)x = 0$ has at most $m+n$ linearly independent solutions.

Proof. Assume that there exist $m+n+1$ linearly independent solutions. Let $x_1, \ldots, x_m$ be linearly independent solutions of $P(D)x = 0$. Each of these solutions satisfies also the equation $P(D)Q(D)x = 0$. Let $y_1, \ldots, y_{n+1}$ be solutions of the last equation such that all the functions $x_1, \ldots, x_m, y_1, \ldots, y_{n+1}$ are linearly independent. Then also the functions $P(D)y_1, \ldots, P(D)y_{n+1}$ are linearly independent. For, if

$$\sum_{i=1}^{n+1} c_i P(D) y_i = 0,$$

then the sum $\sum c_i y_i$ satisfies the equation $P(D)x = 0$ and therefore is a linear combination of $x_1, \ldots, x_m$. This is impossible. On the other hand, the elements $P(D)y_1, \ldots, P(D)y_{n+1}$ satisfy the equation $Q(D)x = 0$, which contradicts the hypothesis that $Q(D) = 0$ has n linearly independent solutions only.

§ 10. Miscellaneous equations. The last result can be strengthened as follows:

If the equations $P(D)x = 0$ and $Q(D)x = 0$ have exactly m and n linearly independent solutions, then the equation $P(D)Q(D)x = 0$ has exactly $m+n$ linear independent solutions.

By decomposition into irreducible polynomials we can see that it suffices to prove the following theorem:

If the polynomial $P(D)$ is logarithmic and of degree m and the polynomial $Q(D)$ is pure, then the equation $P(D)Q(D)x = 0$ has exactly m linearly independent solutions.

Proof. Since the polynomial P is logarithmic, the equation $P(D)x = 0$ has exactly m linearly independent solutions. On the other hand, the equation $Q(D)x = 0$ has 0 linearly independent solutions (i. e. its only solution is 0). By the lemma of the foregoing paragraph, the equation $P(D)Q(D)x = 0$ has at most m linearly independent solutions. But every solution of $P(D)x = 0$ is also a solution of $P(D)Q(D)x = 0$. Thus this equation has at m linearly independent solutions, which proves the theorem.

If the number of linearly independent solutions is positive but less than the order of the equation, then this equation is called *miscellaneous*. The corresponding polynomial can also be called *miscellaneous*. Every miscellaneous polynomial can be decomposed into the product of a logarithmic and a pure polynomial (both of positive degree).

§ 11. Unhomogeneous logarithmic equations. As have we seen in § 15 of part IV, if $y_1(\lambda)$ is a solution of the unhomogeneous equation

$$P(D)x = f, \tag{23}$$

where $f = f(\lambda)$ is a given operational function, then every solution of (23) can be represented as the sum

$$x(\lambda) = y(\lambda) + y_1(\lambda),$$

where $y(\lambda)$ is a solution of the homogeneous equation $P(D)x = 0$. Thus, if we know all the solutions of the homogeneous equation, we shall also know all the solutions (23) whenever we find any of the particular solutions of (23).

That particular solution always exist if the function $f(\lambda)$ is continuous and the polynomial P logarithmic. Suppose that $P(D)x = 0$ is of order n and let $x_1, \ldots, x_n$ be a set of its linearly independent solutions. Write

$$y_0 = c_1 x_1 + \ldots + c_n x_n$$

and choose the operators $c_1, \ldots, c_n$ so as to have

$$y_0(0) = \ldots = y_0^{(n-2)}(0) = 0 \quad \text{and} \quad y_0^{(n-1)}(0) = 1, \tag{24}$$

where $y^{(\nu)}(\lambda) = D^\nu y(\lambda)$ $(\nu = 1, \ldots, n-1)$.

In order to determine $c_1, \ldots, c_n$ we have to solve the system of n equations (24). This is always possible. In fact, suppose the converse. Then the determinant of the considered system vanishes, and we can find a set of c_i such that $y^{(\nu)}(0) = 0$ for $\nu = 0, \ldots, n-1$. By the unicity theorem we then have identically $y_0(\lambda) = 0$, which contradicts the hypothesis that $x_1, \ldots, x_n$ are lineraly independent. Thus we have proved that there is a solution $y_0(\lambda)$ of $P(D)x = 0$, satisfying conditions (24).

Now we can easily verify that

$$y_1(\lambda) = \int_0^\lambda y_0(\lambda - \varkappa) f(\varkappa) d\varkappa$$

is the required solution of (23). In fact, in view of (24) we find

$$D^\nu y_1(\lambda) = y_1^{(\nu)}(\lambda) = \int_0^\lambda y_0^{(\nu)}(\lambda - \varkappa) f(\varkappa) d\varkappa \quad \text{for} \quad \nu = 1, \ldots, n-1,$$

and

$$D^n y_1(\lambda) = y_1^{(n)}(\lambda) = \int_0^\lambda y_0^{(n)}(\lambda - \varkappa) f(\varkappa) d\varkappa + f(\lambda).$$

Assuming that $P(D) = a_n D^n + \ldots + a_0$, we have

$$P(D) y_1(\lambda) = \int_0^\lambda [a_n y_0^{(n)}(\lambda - \varkappa) + \ldots + a_0 y_0(\lambda - \varkappa)] f(\varkappa) d\varkappa + f(\lambda).$$

Since $y_0(\lambda)$ is a solution of the homogeneous equation, the expression in brackets vanishes and we obtain $P(D) y_1(\lambda) = f(\lambda)$.

§ 12. Unhomogeneous pure equations. If $Q(D)$ is a pure polynomial, it may happen that the equation

$$Q(D)x = f \tag{25}$$

has no solution at all, even when $f(\lambda)$ is continuous. For instance, if $Q(D) = D^2 + s^2$ and

$$f(\lambda) = \begin{cases} 0 & \text{for} \quad -1 \leqslant \lambda \leqslant 0, \\ \lambda^2 & \text{for} \quad 0 \leqslant \lambda \leqslant 1, \end{cases}$$

no solution of (25) exist in $[-1, 1]$. In fact, there exist solutions of (25) in the partial intervals

$$x(\lambda) = 0 \quad \text{in} \quad [-1, 0] \quad \text{and} \quad x(\lambda) = l^2\lambda^2 - 2l^4\lambda + 2l^6 \quad \text{in} \quad [0, 1]. \tag{26}$$

This is easy to verify by substitution. Those solutions are unique, for equation (25) is pure. But the function $x(\lambda)$ defined by (26) and considered in the whole interval $[-1, 1]$ is discontinuous at $\lambda = 0$. Thus it is not differentiable at $\lambda \neq 0$, and therefore cannot be a solution of the differential equation (25).

If $Q(D)$ is pure and f is a function of class X, i. e. a solution of some equation $P(D)x = 0$, then equation (25) is solvable and its solution is unique.

Proof. Let $P(D)x = 0$ be the equation of the lowest possible order such that f is its solution. Let m be its order. Then the functions $f, Df, \ldots, D^{m-1}f$ are linearly independent solutions of $P(D)x = 0$. The functions

(27) $$Q(D)f,\ Q(D)Df,\ \ldots,\ Q(D)D^{m-1}f$$

are also linearly independent. In fact, assuming that

$$c_0 Q(D)f + \ldots + c_{m-1}Q(D)D^{m-1}f = 0,$$

not all operators c_i being 0, we have

$$Q(D)(c_0 f + c_1 Df + \ldots + c_{m-1}D^{m-1})f = 0,$$

which contradicts the hypothesis that Q is pure. Thus the functions (27) are linearly independent. Moreover, they satisfy the equation $P(D)x = 0$, for $f, Df, \ldots, D^{m-1}f$ satisfy $P(D)Q(D)x = 0$. This implies that f is a linear combination of (27), i. e. that

(28) $$Q(D)(b_{m-1}D^{m-1}f + \ldots + b_0 f) = f$$

for properly chosen operators $b_{n-1}, \ldots, b_0$. Thus

$$x(\lambda) = (b_{n-1}D^{n-1} + \ldots + b_0)f(\lambda)$$

is the required solution.

In practice, the solution $x(\lambda)$ can be found from (28) by comparison of the coefficients of both sides. Before doing it, we must carry out the multiplication of the polynomials on the left side of (28), and then to eliminate the powers of D of degree $> n$ by means of the equality

$$a_n D^n f = -(a_{n-1}D^{n-1} + \ldots + a_0)f,$$

where the operators a_i are supposed to be the coefficients of the polynomial $P(D) = a^n D_n + \ldots + a_0$.

§ 13. Unhomogeneous miscellaneous equations. Such an equation may be written in the form

(29) $$P(D)Q(D)x = f,$$

where P is logarithmic and Q is pure. This equation is solvable if and only if the equation

(30) $$Q(D)x = f$$

is solvable. In fact, if x_0 is a solution of (29), then $P(D)x_0$ is a solution of (30). Conversely, if x_0 is a solution of (30), then finding a solution x_1 of $P(D)x = x_0$ by the method given in § 11, we see that x_1 satisfies also equation (29).

CHAPTER X

A CLASS OF OPERATIONAL POLYNOMIALS

(Appendix to Chapter I of Part IV)

§ 1. Introduction. Particularly important for applications is the class of differential equations

$$(a_m D^m + \ldots + a_0)x = f,$$

where a_μ are polynomials of the differential operators s with numerical coefficients

$$a_\mu = \sum_{\nu=0}^{d_n} a_{\mu\nu} s^\nu \qquad (\mu = 0, \ldots, m).$$

In that case the polynomial

$$P(D) = a_m D^m + \ldots + a_0 \qquad (a_m \neq 0)$$

can always be decomposed into linear factors

$$P(D) = a_m \prod_{\mu=1}^{m} (D - w_\mu).$$

This decomposition can be carried out in two steps: *rational factorization* and *irrational factorization*. Although, rational factorization can be applied to polynomials with arbitrary coefficients, we shall discuss it briefly, for it is an introductory step to irrational factorization.

§ 2. Rational factorization. Suppose that a polynomial $P(D)$ can be factorized so that one of the factors appears in a power higher than 1:

(1) $$P = Q^k R \qquad (k \geqslant 2).$$

Then the derivative of $P(D)$

$$P' = Q^{k-1}(kQ'R + QR')$$

has a common divisor with P. To find it we can apply to P and P' the Euclidean algorithm or any other method.

For any polynomial $P(D)$ it is always advantageous in carrying out the factorization to seek the greatest divisor of $P(D)$ and $P'(D)$. If that divisor does not exist (i. e. is of degree 0), then all irreducible factors of $P(D)$ are different from each other. On the other hand, if that divisor is of positive degree, we can represent $P(D)$ in form (1) and apply the same method as before to each of the polynomials Q and R. This process can be continued until we obtain the decomposition

$$P = P_1^{k_1} \dots P_2^{k_r},$$

each of the polynomials P_i being such that all its irreducible factors are different from each other. No further factorization is possible by the method in question.

This method of factorization will be called *rational*. It is based on the four arithmetical operations (addition, subtraction, multiplication and division). It reduces the problem of factorization to polynomials whose all irreducible factors are different from each other. In order to find the explicit form of all those irreducible factors we must apply another method.

To give an example to rational factorization, consider the polynomial

$$P(D) = D^{15} + (s-1)D^{10} - (s^2+2s)D^5 - (s^3+s^2).$$

Here we have

$$P'(D) = 5D^4 Q(D), \quad \text{where} \quad Q(D) = 3D^{10} + 2(s-1)D^5 - (s^2+2s)$$

The greatest common divisor of P and Q can be found by the Euclidean algorithm: first we divide P by Q,

$$P(D) = \left(\frac{1}{3}D^5 + \frac{1}{9}(s-1)\right)Q(D) + R(D),$$

where

$$R(D) = \frac{1}{3}(s-1)D^{10} - \frac{2}{3}(s^2+2s)D^5 - (s^3+s^2).$$

Further, we divide Q by R and obtain

$$Q(D) = -\frac{2}{9}(s^2+4s+2)(D^5+s)R(D).$$

Hence D^5+s is the greatest common divisor of $P(D)$ and $P'(D)$. We can now verify directly that $P(D)$ is twice divisible by D^5+s and find in this way the required representation

(2) $$P(D) = (D^5+s)^2(D^5-s-1).$$

We could further try to factorize the polynomials D^5+s and D^5-s-1 in a similar manner. But the derivative of both polynomials is $5D^4$ and evidently has no common factor with them. Thus representation (2) is definitive.

§ 3. Irrational factorization. Thanks to the result of the foregoing paragraph we can restrict ourselves to the case where all the irreducible factors of a given polynomial are different from one another. If all the factors are of the first degree, we can write

$$P(D) = a_m \prod_{\mu=1}^{m} (D - w_\mu) \qquad (w_\mu = w_\nu \text{ for } \mu = \nu),$$

where $a_m \neq 0$ is the coefficient of the highest (m-th) power of $P(D)$. Of course $P(w_\mu) = 0$ for $\mu = 1, \ldots, m$. Thus the decomposition of $P(D)$ in linear factors is equivalent to the solving the equation $P(w) = 0$.

We shall begin with examples.

Example 1. Factorize D^5+s. Here we must solve the equation $w^5+s = 0$. Letting $w = \omega\sqrt[5]{s}$, where $\sqrt[5]{s} = \{t^{-1/5}/\Gamma(1/5)\}$ we obtain an equation with numerical coefficients $\omega^5+1 = 0$, whose roots are

$$\omega_\nu = -a^\nu \qquad (\nu = 0, \ldots, 4)$$

with

$$\text{(3)} \qquad a = \cos\frac{\pi}{5} + i\sin\frac{\pi}{5}.$$

Hence the roots of $w^5+s = 0$ are $w_\mu = a^\mu\sqrt[5]{s}$ ($\mu = 0, \ldots, 4$) and the required representation

$$D^5+s = \prod_{\mu=0}^{4} (D - a^\mu \sqrt[5]{s}).$$

Example 2. Factorize D^5-s-1. Here we must solve the equation $w^5 = s+1$. We can write

$$s+1 = \sqrt[5]{s}\,(1+l)^{1/5} = \sqrt[5]{s} \sum_{\nu=0}^{\infty} \binom{1/5}{\nu} l^\nu = \sqrt[5]{s} + f,$$

where

$$f = \left\{\sum_{\nu=1}^{\infty} \binom{1/5}{\nu} \frac{t^{\nu-1}}{(\nu-1)!}\right\}.$$

Letting $w = a(\sqrt[5]{s}+f)$, we obtain, as in example 1,

$$D^5-s-1 = \prod_{\mu=0}^{4} \left(D + a^\mu(\sqrt[5]{s}+f)\right),$$

where a is the complex number (3).

EXAMPLE 3. Factorize $P(D) = D^5+D-s-1$. We seek a solution of $w^5+w-s-1 = 0$ in the form of a series:

$$w = \beta_0 s^{1/5}+\beta_1+\beta_2 s^{-1/5}+\beta_3 s^{-2/5}+\dots \tag{4}$$

Substituting this series into the equation we can determine the coefficients β_n. It is easy to see that β_0 must satisfy the equation $\beta_0^5 = 1$. Thus β_0 must be of the form a^ν, where a is given by (3) and $\nu = 0, 1, 2, 3$, or 4. All the remaining β_n can be found successively, by solving mere linear equations. In this way we obtain exactly 5 expansions of form (4). The reader will verify that the initial terms are

$$w_\mu = a^\mu s^{1/5} - \tfrac{1}{5} a^{2\mu} s^{-3/5} + \tfrac{1}{5} a^\mu s^{-4/5} - \tfrac{1}{25} a^{3\mu} s^{-7/5} +$$
$$+ \tfrac{1}{25} a^{2\mu} s^{-8/5} - \tfrac{2}{25} a^\mu s^{-9/5} + \dots \qquad (\mu = 0, \dots, 4).$$

We can also write

$$w_\mu = a^\mu \sqrt[5]{s} + f_\mu,$$

where

$$f_\mu = \left\{-\frac{a^{2\mu} t^{-2/5}}{5\Gamma(3/5)} + \frac{a^\mu t^{-1/5}}{5\Gamma(4/5)} - \frac{a^{3\mu} t^{2/5}}{25\Gamma(7/5)} + \frac{a^{2\mu} t^{3/5}}{25\Gamma(8/5)} - \frac{2a^\mu t^{4/5}}{25\Gamma(9/5)} + \dots\right\}.$$

The required representation of $P(D)$ is

$$D^5+D-s-1 = \prod_{\mu=0}^{4} (D - a^\mu \sqrt[5]{s} - f_\mu).$$

EXAMPLE 4. Factorize $D^5 - sD^2+1$. On the grounds of the preceding examples we might suppose at first that again a series (4) with properly chosen coefficients will satisfy the equation

$$w^5 - sw^2+1 = 0. \tag{5}$$

But then the highest power of s in w^5 would be s and the highest power in sw^2 would be $s^{7/5}$. In this situation no series of that form can satisfy equation (5).

Suppose that there exists a proper power series satisfying (5) and let $\beta_0 s^k$ be its first term (with the highest power of s). All the remaining terms are powers with exponents less than k. Substituting this in (5) we obtain

$$(\beta_0^5 s^{5k}+\dots) - (\beta_0^2 s^{2k+1}+\dots+1) = 0.$$

In order to cancel the highest power we must have either $5k = 2k+1$, or $2k+1 = 0$, or $5k = 0$. From these equations we find three possible values of k: $2/3$, $-1/2$ or 0. The last value does not fit, for then the first term in sw^2 would be of higher degree than both the remaining terms. Thus we adopt successively the other two values, $k = 1/3$ and $k = 1/2$.

The series corresponding to $k = 1/3$ is

$$\beta_0 s^{1/3} + \beta_1 + \beta_2 s^{-1/3} + \beta_3 s^{-2/3} + \beta_4 s^{-3/3} + \dots \qquad (\beta_0 \neq 0).$$

Substituting this into (5) we determine the coefficients β_n. The first of them must satisfy the equation

$$\beta_0^5 - \beta_0^2 = 0.$$

Since $\beta_0 \neq 0$, we find that β_0 must be equal to one of the numbers 1, β and β^2, where

$$\beta = \cos\frac{\pi}{3} + i \sin\frac{\pi}{3}.$$

All the remaining coefficients β_n can be determined by solving linear equations and are thus determined uniquely whenever β_0 is fixed. In this way we find three of the solutions of (5). Expanded into power series they have the initial terms:

$$w_\mu = \beta^\mu s^{1/3} + \tfrac{1}{3}\beta^{2\mu} s^{-4/3} - \tfrac{1}{3} s^{-9/3} + \tfrac{44}{81}\beta^\mu s^{-14/3} + \dots \qquad (\mu = 0, 1, 2).$$

We can also write

$$w_\mu = \beta^\mu \sqrt[3]{s} + f_\mu \qquad (\mu = 0, 1, 2),$$

where

$$f_\mu = \left\{ \frac{\beta^{2\mu} t^{1/3}}{3\Gamma(4/3)} - \frac{t^{6/3}}{3\Gamma(9/3)} + \frac{44\beta^\mu t^{11/3}}{81\Gamma(14/3)} + \dots \right\} \qquad (\mu = 0, 1, 2).$$

Now the series corresponding to $k = -1/2$ is

$$\beta_0 s^{-1/2} + \beta_1 s^{-2/2} + \beta_3 s^{-3/2} + \dots$$

Substituting it into (5) we see that

$$-\beta_0^2 + 1 = 0.$$

Hence $\beta_0 = \pm 1$. Proceeding as before we obtain the remaining two solutions of (5):

$$w_\mu = (-1)^\mu s^{-1/2} + \tfrac{1}{2} s^{-6/2} + (-1)^\mu \tfrac{9}{8} s^{-11/2} + \tfrac{7}{2} s^{-16/2} + \dots \qquad (\mu = 3, 4),$$

i. e.

$$w_\mu = f_\mu = \left\{ \frac{(-1)^\mu t^{-1/2}}{\Gamma(1/2)} + \frac{t^{4/2}}{2\Gamma(6/2)} + \frac{(-1)^\mu t^{9/2}}{\Gamma(11/2)} + \frac{7t^{14/2}}{\Gamma(16/2)} + \dots \right\}$$

$$(\mu = 3, 4).$$

The required representation is

$$D^5-sD^2+1=(D-\sqrt[3]{s}+f_0)(D-\beta\sqrt[3]{s}+f_1)(D-\beta^2\sqrt[3]{s}+f)(D-f_3)(D-f_4),$$

where $f_0, \ldots, f_4$ are continuous in $(0, \infty)$ and integrable at $t=0$.

§ 4. General method. Suppose that the polynomial

$$P(D)=a_m D^m+\ldots+a_0 \quad (a_m \neq 0),$$

where

(6) $$a_\mu=\sum_{\nu=0}^{d_\mu} \alpha_{\mu\nu} s^\nu \quad (\mu=0, \ldots, m)$$

has no multiple factors. We intend to expand the solutions of the equation

(7) $$a_m w^m+\ldots+a_0 \neq 0$$

into power series

(8) $$w=\beta_0 s^k+\beta_1 s^{k-r}+\beta_2 s^{k-2r}+\ldots$$

The first question is to find the numbers k and r so that the coefficients β_n can be determined successively after substituting (8) into (7).

By (6), d_μ is the degree of a_μ (if $a_\mu=0$, we adopt $d_\mu=-\infty$). Hence $a_\mu w^\mu$ can be expanded into a power series whose highest exponent is $\mu k+d_\mu$. In order that (7) might hold, the highest of the powers $s^{\mu k+d_\mu}$ must be cancelled together with another term. Therefore, for two different values μ_1 and μ_2, the following relations must hold:

(9) $$\mu_1 k+d_{\mu_1}=\mu_2 k+d_{\mu_2} \geqslant \mu k+d_\mu \quad (\mu=0, \ldots, m).$$

All the values of k satisfying conditions (9) can be conveniently found by a geometrical method. We draw in Cartesian coordinates k and y the straight lines

$$y=\mu k+d_\mu \quad (\mu=0, \ldots, m)$$

and their upper envelope $y=\max\limits_{\mu}(\mu k+d_\mu)$. This envelope is a polygonal line. The abscissae of its vertices are the required values of k.

For example, in case of (5) we have to deal with three straight lines

$$y=5k, \quad y=2k+1 \quad \text{and} \quad y=0.$$

The abscissae of the vertices of their upper envelope are $-1/2$ and $1/3$ (fig. 167), accordingly to § 3.

The geometrical method is especially advantageous in more complicated cases.

Let $k_1, \ldots, k_\sigma$ be the required values of k. We can assume that k_1 is the greatest of these values. If we substitute (8) with $k = k_1$, i. e.

$$w = \beta_0 s^{k_1} + \beta_1 s^{k_1 - r} + \beta_2 s^{k_1 - 2r} + \ldots, \tag{10}$$

into (7), the greatest exponent of the powers of s will be $e_1 = mk_1 + d_m$. The coefficient of s^{e_1} is a polynomial $Q_1(\beta_0)$ of β_0. From the definition of k_1 it follows that the degree of this polynomial is m and its first coefficient is $a_m d_m \neq 0$. We must choose $\beta_0 \neq 0$ so that

$$Q_1(\beta_0) = 0. \tag{11}$$

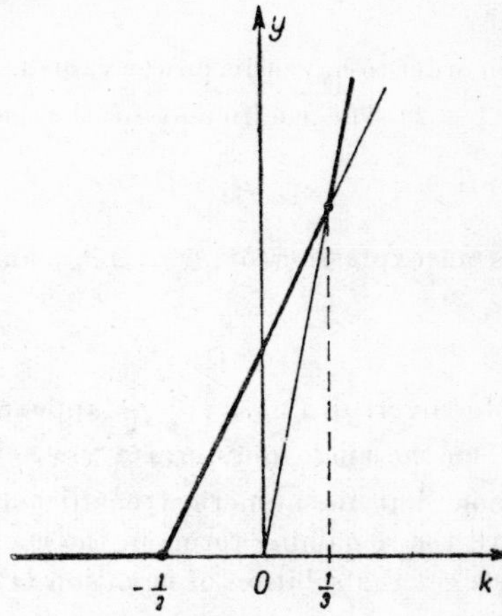

Fig. 167

This equation is of the m-th degree and has numerical coefficients. Suppose that $\beta_0 = 0$ is a $\varkappa$-tuple root of (11). Suppose moreover that $k_1 = p/q$, where p and q are relatively prime, $q \geqslant 1$. Then we put $r = 1/\varkappa q$, and determine the coefficients $\beta_2, \beta_3, \ldots,$ on substituting (10) into (7) and comparing the coefficients of equal powers of s. We proceed similarly with all the roots, different from 0, of (11). We apply successively the same method to find the expansions (8) with $k = k_2, \ldots, k_\sigma$.

§ 5. General method (continuation). The above method requires some more detailed explanations. Suppose first that $\beta_0 = 0$ is a simple root of (11); then $Q'(\beta_0) = 0$, $r = 1/q$. After substituting (10) in (7) we determine β_1, assuming that the coefficient of $s^{e_1 - r}$ vanishes. The expression representing this coefficient contains some of the numbers $a_{\mu\nu}$ and moreover β_0 and β_1. The unknown quantity β_1 appears in this expression linearly with the coefficient $Q'(\beta_0) \neq 0$. Thus β_1 is determined uniquely. Now, we determine β_2, letting the coefficient of $s^{e_1 - 2r}$ vanish. The expression representing this coefficient contains some of the numbers $a_{\mu\nu}$ and moreover β_0, β_1 and β_2. The unknown quantity β_2 appears again linearly with the same coefficient $Q_1'(\beta_0) = 0$ and is therefore determined uniquely. We determine in succession all the coefficients $\beta_1, \beta_2, \beta_3, \ldots$ We have proved that for every simple root $\beta_0 \neq 0$ of (11) series (10) is determined uniquely.

In order to prove the convergence of the obtained series, put

$$\delta = \frac{1}{m} \beta_0^{-m+1} Q_1'(\beta_0) \quad \text{and} \quad A = \delta + \max_{\mu,\nu} a_{\mu\nu}.$$

Consider the equation

$$\begin{aligned} &\delta s^{dm} (w^m - \beta_0^m s^{k_1 m}) - \\ &- A s^{dm - k_1 - r} (w^2 + |\beta_0|^2 s^{2k_1}) (w^{m-1} + s^{k_1} |\beta_0| w^{m-2} + \ldots + s^{(m-1)k_1} |\beta_0|^{m-1}) \frac{1}{1 - s^{-r}} = 0. \end{aligned} \tag{12}$$

This equation is formed so that:

1° On substituting in it

$$w = \bar{\beta}_0 s^{k_1} + \bar{\beta}_1 s^{k_1 - r} + \dots, \qquad \frac{1}{1 - s^{-r}} = 1 + s^{-r} + s^{-2r} + \dots \tag{13}$$

we obtain a power series of s (with decreasing exponents) whose highest power is

$$\delta(\bar{\beta}_0^{-m} - |\beta_0|^m)\, s^{mk_1 + d_1}.$$

In order to have this power vanish, we assume $\bar{\beta}_0 = |\beta_0|$.

2° The coefficient of the power

$$s^{mk_1 + d_1 - nr} \tag{14}$$

is an expression of $\bar{\beta}_0, \dots, \bar{\beta}_n$, and $\bar{\beta}_n$ appears in it linearly with the coefficient

$$\delta m \bar{\beta}_0^{-m} = |Q'(\beta_0)|.$$

Moreover, if $\beta_0^{i_1}, \dots, \beta_{n-1}^{i_{n-1}}$ appears in the coefficient of (14) in the previous expansion, then the analogous term $\bar{\beta}_0^{i}, \dots, \bar{\beta}_{n-1}^{i}$ appears at the same place in the present expansion, but its numerical coefficient is negative and absolutely greater than before. All the remaining terms in the coefficient of (14) are, at present, also negative. Hence we get the solution of equation (12) similarly to the solution of (7), and we shall have

$$|\beta_0| = \bar{\beta}_0, \qquad |\beta_n| \leqslant \bar{\beta}_n \qquad (n = 1, 2, \dots).$$

Thus, if expansion (13) is convergent, then also expansion (10) is convergent. But the required solution of (12) can be obtained by cancelling in (13) the factor

$$s^{d_m}(w^{m-1} + s^{k_1}|\beta_0|\, w^{m-1} + \dots + s^{(m-1)}|\beta_0|^{m-1}).$$

In this way we obtain

$$\delta s^{d_m}(w - |\beta_0| s^{k_1}) - A s^{d_m - k_1 - r}(w^2 + |\beta_0|^2 s^{2k_1}) \frac{1}{1 - s^{-r}} = 0,$$

i. e.

$$w^2 - \frac{\delta}{A}|s^{k_1 + r} - s^{k_1}|\, w + |\beta_0|^2 s^{2k_1} + \frac{\delta}{A}(s^{2k_1 + r} - s^{k_1}) = 0. \tag{15}$$

Since $k_1 = pr$, the problem is reduced to the consideration of the solution of an equation of the form

$$w^2 - 2M(s^r)\, w + N(s^r) = 0,$$

where M and N are polynomials of degree $p+1$ and $2p+1$ respectively. First observe that the expression

$$F(s) = \sqrt{1 + R(s^{-r})},$$

where R is a polynomial, can be expanded into a convergent power series of s^{-r}. In fact, there is a geometrical series

$$G(s) = 1 + \beta s^{-r} + \beta^2 s^{-2r} + \dots \qquad (\beta > 0)$$

whose coefficients are greater than the corresponding coefficients of $1+R(s^{-r})$. The coefficients of the square

$$G^2(s) = 1+2\beta s^{-r}+3\beta^2 s^{-2r}+\ldots$$

are a fortiori greater than those of $1+R(s^{-r})$. Now we have

$$\sqrt{G^2(s)} = 1+\beta s^{-r}+\beta^2 s^{-2r}+\ldots$$

and we see that the expansion of $F(s)$ must be convergent, for the moduli of its coefficients are respectively less than the coefficients of the convergent expansion of $G(s)$. Now the solution of the equation

$$w^2-2M(s^r)w+N(s^r) = 0$$

can be writen in the form

$$w = M(s^r)\pm a s^{(p+1)r}\sqrt{1+R(s^{-r})},$$

where

$$a^2 s^{2(p+1)r}(1+R(s^{-r})) = M^2(s^r)-N(s^r).$$

This proves that the solution of (15) can be expanded into a convergent power series of s^{-r}. This implies the convergence of series (13) and (10).

Now suppose that β_0 is a $\varkappa$-tuple root of (11). Since $Q_1^{(\nu)}(\beta_0) = 0$ for $\nu = 0, \ldots, \ldots, \varkappa-1$, the $\varkappa$ initial coefficients in the series obtained after the substitution of (10) in (7) vanish whenever the first of them vanishes. The next coefficient does not vanish, and involves the quantities $a_{\mu\nu}$ and β_0, β_1. The unknown quantity β_1 appears, at present, not linearly, but in a polynomial of degree $\varkappa$. To determine β_1 we must solve the equation of degree $\varkappa$:

$$\binom{m}{\varkappa} a_{md_m}\beta_0^{m-\varkappa}\beta_1^{\varkappa}+\ldots = 0.$$

If β_1 is a simple root of this equation, we can determine successively $\beta_2, \beta_3, \ldots$, by solving mere linear equations. Thus for fixed β_1, the series is determined uniquely. If β_1 is a multiple root, say of order $\varkappa_1$, then β_2 must satisfy an equation of degree $\varkappa_1$ and so on. Finally we must find an index n such that all the numbers $\beta_n, \beta_{n+1}, \ldots$ can be determined by solving linear equations. For otherwise the polynomial $P(D)$ would have multiple roots. In this way we obtain exactly as many solutions of (7) as in the number of non-vanishing roots of (11). All these solution have form (10).

Similarly we obtain solutions (8) with $k = k_2, \ldots, k_\sigma$. The number of all those solutions is exactly m, provided the polynomial $P(D)$ has no multiple divisors. The convergence of the obtained series can be proved as before.

§ 6. Remarks. The problem of expanding the solutions of (7) in power series (8) is equivalent to the expanding of algebraical functions. Suppose, for a moment, that s is a complex variable. Then every analytic function $w = w(s)$, satisfying (7), is called an *algebraical function.* It is known that, for every equation (7), there exist solutions $w = w(s)$ which are analytic in a half-plane $\operatorname{Re} s > x_0$ and can be developed there in a power series (8) (where s^{k-nr} is assumed to be real on the part of the real axis lying in the half-plane). If the polynomial P has no multiple factors, there then are m distinct functions with this property. (However these functions are distinct when considered in the half-plane: they can be branches of the same analytical function considered on the proper Riemann surface.)

Since the addition and the multiplication of series of the form (8) is carried out in the same way, irrespective of the meaning of s, the theory of algebraical functions yields an alternative proof of existence for solutions of the *operational* equation (7).

In applications to partial equations, it is very important to know all the admissible values of k in expansion (8). The numerical method of finding these values is of course the same in the case of algebraical functions as in the operational calculus. If we wish to know these values only, we may apply the geometrical method described in § 4 even in the case when the polynomial P has multiple factors. If we wish to know also the coefficients $\beta_0, \beta_1, \ldots$, then it is advantageous to carry out first the rational factorization in order to obtain polynomials without multiple factors. The knowledge of initial coefficients $\beta_0, \beta_1, \ldots$ can be useful when seeking approximate solutions (e. g. for partial equations), because series (8) converges as fast as the expansion of the ordinary exponential function e^x. In fact, the coefficients β^n in (8) increase at most as fast as a geometrical series, for the radius of convergence of the series $\beta_0+\beta_1 z+\beta_2 z^2+\ldots$ is positive (this follows from the theory of algebraical functions). On the other hand the operator s^{k-nr} is, for negative $k-nr$, equal to the function

$$\frac{t^{nr-k-1}}{\Gamma(nr-k)}$$

and the denominator $\Gamma(nr-k)$ increases very fast with $n\to\infty$. For equations of high order, the evaluation of the coefficients β_n may be complicated, but here a field of application opens up for electronic computers.

CHAPTER XI

A CLASS OF DIFFERENTIAL EQUATIONS

(Appendix to Chapter I of Part IV)

§ 1. The number of linearly independent solutions. We shall deal here with the equations

(1) $$P(D)x = 0,$$

where

$$P(D) = a_m D^m + \dots + a_0 \quad (a_m \neq 0)$$

is a polynomial with numerical coefficients

$$a_\mu = \sum_{\nu=0}^{d_\mu} a_{\mu\nu} s^\nu \quad (\mu = 0, \dots, m).$$

The number if linearly independent solutions of (1) *can be determined exactly by using rational methods, i. e. in a finite number of steps, involving merely the four arithmetical operations on number.*

We intend first to describe the method in detail. We shall justify it in the next paragraph.

We determine all the numbers k with the following property:

(I) There exist two integers μ_1 and μ_2 ($0 \leqslant \mu_1 < \mu_2 \leqslant m$) such that

(2) $$\mu_1 k + d_{\mu_1} = \mu_2 k + d_{\mu_2} \geqslant \mu k + d_\mu \quad (\mu = 0, \dots, m).$$

To find these numbers, we may apply the geometrical method, given in § 4 of Chapter X.

Now we have theorem:

If each of the numbers k with property (I) *is greater than* 1, *equation* (1) *has the only solution* $x = 0$.

If there exist numbers $k \leqslant 1$ with property (I), *denote by $\bar{k}$ the greatest of them. If $\bar{k} < 1$, denote by $\bar{\mu}$ the greatest of numbers μ_2 such that* (2) *hold-for $k = \bar{k}$ and for some $\mu_1 < \bar{\mu}$. Then $\bar{\mu}$ is the number of linearly indepens dent solutions of* (1).

If $\bar{k} = 1$, we select from the polynomial $P(\xi s)$ the coefficient at the highest power of s. This coefficient is a polynomial $M(\xi)$ of ξ with numerical coefficients. The number of linearly independent solutions of (1) is equal to the number of real roots (counted with their multiplicity) of the equation $M(\xi) = 0$.

To determine, in the last case, the number of real roots, we can apply any of the classical methods, e. g., Sturm's method (which involves a finite number of arithmetical operations on number).

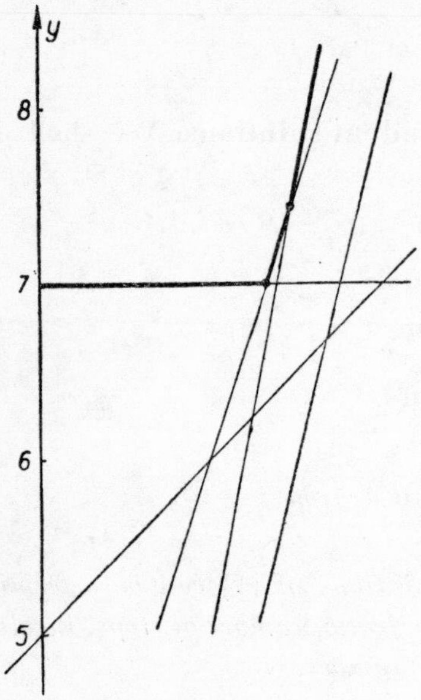

Fig. 168

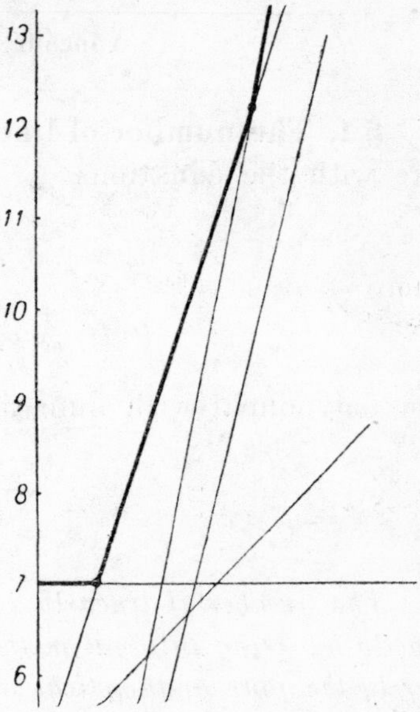

Fig. 169

EXAMPLE 1. Determine the number of linearly independent solutions of the following equation:

$$(D^5 + D^4 + s^3 D^3 + s^5 D + s^7)x = 0.$$

We draw the straight lines (fig. 168)

$$y = 5k, \quad y = 4k, \quad y = 3k+3, \quad y = k+5, \quad y = 7.$$

The upper envelope of them has two vertices, whose abscissae are $3/2$ and $4/3$. Thus the admissible values of k are $3/2$ and $4/3$, both greater than 1. This implies that the considered equation has no linearly independent solution, i. e. that its only solution is $x = 0$.

EXAMPLE 2. Determine the number of linearly independent solutions of the equation

(3) $$(D^5 + D^4 + s^5 D^3 + s^5 D + s^7)x = 0.$$

We draw the straight lines (fig. 169)

$$y = 5k, \quad y = 4k, \quad y = 3k+5, \quad y = k+5, \quad y = 7.$$

Their upper envelope has two vertices with the abscissae 5/2 and 2/3. Only the second one is less than 1. It corresponds to the lines

$$y = 3k+5 \quad \text{and} \quad y = 7.$$

The coefficients of k in the last two equations are 3 and 0; the greatest of them is 3. Thus equation (3) has exactly 3 linearly independent solutions.

EXAMPLE 3. Determine the number of linearly independent solutions of the equation

$$(4) \qquad (D^5 + D^4 + s^4 D^3 + s^5 D + s^7)x = 0.$$

We draw the straight lines (fig. 170)

$$y = 5k, \quad y = 4k,$$

$$y = 3k+4, \quad y = k+5, \quad y = 7.$$

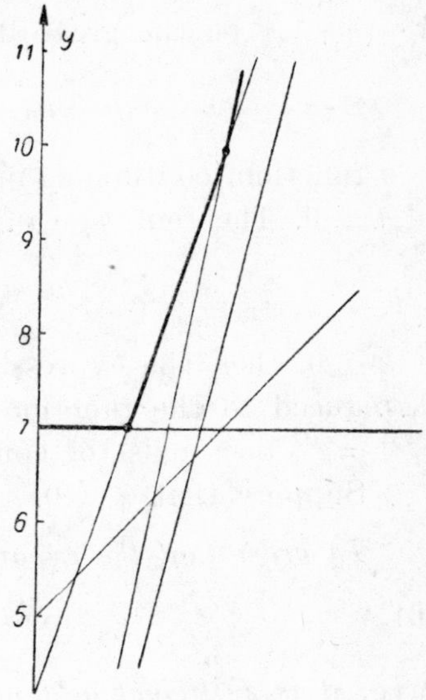

Fig. 170

Their upper envelope has two vertices with the abscissae 2 and 1. Replacing D by ξs on the left side of (4), we obtain

$$\xi^5 s^5 + \xi^4 s^4 + \xi^3 s^7 + \xi s^6 + s^7.$$

Letting the coefficients of s^7 (highest power of s) equal to 0, we obtain the equation

$$\xi^3 + 1 = 0.$$

This equation has exactly one real root. Therefore the differential equation (4) has exactly one linearly independent solution.

§ 2. A theorem on exponential functions. As we have seen in Chapter X, the polynomial $P(D)$ can be decomposed into m linear factors

$$P(D) = a_m \prod_{\mu=1}^{m} (D - w_\mu).$$

By § 10 of Chapter IX, the number of linearly independent solutions of $P(D)x = 0$ is equal to the number of logarithmic factors $D - w_\mu$; the factor is logarithmic if and only if there is a non-vanishing solution of the equation

$$Dx = w_\mu x.$$

Such a solution exists if and only if there exists the exponential function $e^{w_\mu \lambda}$.

Now, we know (§ 4 of Chapter X) that w_μ is of the form

$$\beta_0 s^k + \beta_1 s^{k-r} + \beta_2 s^{k-2r} + \ldots,$$

where k, r are rational numbers, $r > 0$, and β_ν complex numbers. Let $k-(n+1)r$ be the greatest of the negative exponents. Then

$$f = \beta_{n+1} s^{k-(n+1)r} + \beta_{n+2} s^{k-(n+2)r} + \ldots$$

is a function, continuous in $(0, \infty)$ and integrable in the neighbourhood of $t = 0$. The root w_μ can be written in the form

(5) $$\beta_0 s^k + \ldots + \beta_n s^{k-nr} + f;$$

if $k < 0$, then the expression in (5) of f vanishes and the operator w_μ is reduced to the function f. In the last case the exponential function $e^{w_\mu \lambda} = e^{f\lambda}$ does exist of course.

Suppose that $k > 0$.

In order that the exponential function

(6) $$\exp(\beta_0 s^k + \ldots + \beta_n s^{k-nr} + f)\lambda$$

exist, it is sufficient and necessary that $\exp(\beta_0 s^k \lambda)$ *exist.*

Proof. If $\exp(\beta_0 s^k \lambda)$ exists, there exists also each of the functions

$$\exp(\beta_1 s^{k-r}\lambda),\ \ldots,\ \exp(\beta_n s^{k-nr}\lambda),\ \exp(f\lambda).$$

Their product is the required exponential function (6). Thus the sufficiency of the condition is proved.

To prove its necessity, suppose that the exponential function (6) exists. Then there exists also the function

(7) $$\exp(\beta_0 s^k + \ldots + \beta_n s^{k-nr})$$

and is equal to the product of (6) and $\exp(-f\lambda)$. Denoting function (7) by $x(\lambda)$, we have

(8) $$l^{k+1} x'(\lambda) = (\beta_0 l + \ldots + \beta_n l^{1+nr}) x(\lambda).$$

The function $x(\lambda)$ can be represented, in the interval $(-1, 1)$, in the form

$$x(\lambda) = \frac{P(\lambda)}{q} = \frac{\{p(\lambda, t)\}}{\{q(t)\}}.$$

On multiplying (8) by q, we obtain

$$\frac{1}{\Gamma(k+1)}\int_0^t (t-\tau)^k p_\lambda(\lambda, \tau)\,d\tau = \sum_{\nu=0}^n \beta_\nu \int_0^t \frac{(t-\tau)^{\nu r}}{\Gamma(1+\nu r)}\, p(\lambda, t)\,d\tau$$

for $-1 < \lambda < 1$, $0 \leqslant t < \infty$.

Let δ be an arbitrarily fixed positive number. Putting

$$p(\lambda, t/\delta) = (\lambda, t),$$

we have

$$\frac{1}{\Gamma(k+1)}\int_0^t (t-\tau)^k y_\lambda(\lambda, \tau)\,d\tau = \sum_{\nu=0}^n \beta_\nu \delta^{\nu r} \int_0^t \frac{(t-\tau)^{\nu r}}{\Gamma(1+\nu r)}\, y(\lambda, t)\,d\tau.$$

Thus the function $y(\lambda) = \{y(\lambda, t)\}$ satisfies the equation

$$l^k y'(\lambda) = (\beta_0 l + \beta_1 \delta^r l^{1+r} + \ldots + \beta_n \delta^{rn} l^{1+nr}) y(\lambda).$$

The function $y(\lambda)$ can be extended to the whole interval $(-\infty, \infty)$, by § 13 of Part III. Hence

$$\frac{y(\lambda)}{y(0)} = \exp(\beta_0 s^k + \beta_1 \delta^r s^{k-r} + \ldots + \beta_n \delta^{rn} s^{k-nr})\lambda.$$

For $n+1$ positive numbers $\delta_0, \ldots, \delta_n$, different from each other, there exists also the exponential function

(9) $$\exp \sum_{\nu=0}^n \gamma_\nu (\beta_0 s^k + \beta_1 \delta^r s^{k-r} + \ldots + \beta_n \delta^{rn} s^{k-rn})\lambda,$$

no matter what the real numbers $\gamma_0, \ldots, \gamma_n$ are like. We can choose these numbers so that

$$\sum_{\nu=0}^n \gamma_\nu = 1 \quad \text{and} \quad \sum_{\nu=0}^n \gamma_\nu \delta^{\nu r} = 0 \quad \text{for} \quad \varkappa = 1, \ldots, n,$$

because the determinant

$$\begin{vmatrix} 1 & \ldots & 1 \\ \delta_0^r & \ldots & \delta_n^r \\ \cdot & \cdot\ \cdot & \cdot \\ \delta_0^{nr} & \ldots & \delta_n^{nr} \end{vmatrix}$$

is different from 0. Then expression (9) becomes

(10) $$\exp(\beta_0 s^k \lambda),$$

which proves the necessity of the condition.

We know that the exponential function (10) exists if $k < 1$, and does not exist if $k > 1$ (§ 13 of Chapter VIII). In case $k = 1$, the exponential function (10) exists if and only if β_0 is real. Exactly the same conditions of existence hold of course for (6). This yields the promised justification of the method of the foregoing paragraph.

§ 3. Determining the solution. Since our discussion of the exponential functions $\exp(\varepsilon s^{\alpha}\lambda)$ is complete (see Chapter VIII), we are in a position to determine all the linearly independent solutions of (1).

Consider for instance equation (4). Its solution corresponds to the values $k = 1$ and $\beta_0 = -1$. Using the method of Chapter XI, we find

$$w = -s + \tfrac{1}{3} + f,$$

where

$$f = \tfrac{1}{3}s^{-1} - \tfrac{7}{9}s^{-2} - \tfrac{52}{27}s^{-3} + \ldots = \left\{\tfrac{1}{3} - \tfrac{7}{9}t - \tfrac{26}{27}t^2 + \ldots\right\}.$$

Hence the required solution is

$$e^{w\lambda} = e^{-s\lambda} e^{\lambda/3} e^{f\lambda}. \tag{11}$$

This is the only linearly independent solution of (4), i. e. every solution of (4) is of the form

$$x(\lambda) = c e^{w\lambda},$$

where c is an arbitrary operator, and $e^{w\lambda}$ is of form (11).

We can expand e^f into the power series of λ by writing

$$e^f = 1 + \frac{\lambda}{1!} f + \frac{\lambda}{2!} f^2 + \ldots$$

and substituting

$$f = \tfrac{1}{3}l - \tfrac{7}{9}l^2 - \tfrac{52}{27}l^3 + \ldots$$

In this way we obtain

$$e^f = 1 + \left\{\left(\tfrac{1}{3} - \tfrac{7}{9}t - \tfrac{26}{27}t^2 + \ldots\right)\lambda + \left(\tfrac{1}{18} - \tfrac{7}{27}t - \tfrac{1}{54}t^2 + \ldots\right)\lambda^2 + \ldots\right\}.$$

Neglecting the terms which do not appear explicitly on the right side of this formula, we obtain an approximation which is satisfactory for small values of λ and t.

CHAPTER XII

A HOMOGENEOUS PROBLEM IN PARTIAL EQUATIONS

(Appendix to Chapter III of Part IV)

§ 1. Introduction to the problem. The results of Chapter XI can be useful in establishing the form of solutions of the partial equation

$$\sum_{\mu=0}^{m}\sum_{\nu=0}^{n} a_{\mu\nu} x_{\lambda^\mu t^\nu}(\lambda, t) = \varphi(\lambda, t) \tag{1}$$

in the region $\lambda_1 \leqslant \lambda \leqslant \lambda_2$, $0 \leqslant t \leqslant \infty$.

It follows from paragraphs 22 and 26 of Part IV that the corresponding operational equation is

$$(a_m D^m + \ldots + a_0)x = f(\lambda), \tag{2}$$

where

$$\left\{\begin{aligned} &a_\mu = a_{\mu\nu} s^n + \ldots + a_{\mu 0} \qquad (\mu = 0, \ldots, m),\\ &f(\lambda) = \{\varphi(\lambda, t)\} + \sum_{\varkappa=0}^{n-1} s^{n-\varkappa-1} g_\varkappa(\lambda),\\ &g_\varkappa(\lambda) = \sum_{\mu=0}^{m}\sum_{\nu=0}^{n} a_{\mu, n-\varkappa-\nu} x_{\lambda^\mu t^\nu}(\lambda, 0) \qquad (\varkappa = 0, \ldots, n-1). \end{aligned}\right. \tag{3}$$

When the functions $g_\nu(\lambda)$ are given, (3) are *initial conditions* on the λ axis. If two solutions of (1), say $y(\lambda)$ and $\overline{y}(\lambda)$, satisfy the same initial conditions (3), their difference $x(\lambda) = y(\lambda) - \overline{y}(\lambda)$ satisfies the homogeneous equation

$$\sum_{\mu=0}^{m}\sum_{\nu=0}^{n} a_{\mu\nu} x_{\lambda^\mu t^\nu}(\lambda, t) = 0 \tag{4}$$

with homogeneous initial conditions on the λ axis

$$\sum_{\mu=0}^{m}\sum_{\nu=0}^{n} a_{\mu, n-\varkappa-\nu} x_{\lambda^\mu t^\nu}(\lambda, 0) \qquad (\varkappa = 0, \ldots, n-1). \tag{5}$$

The homogeneous problem consisting of equation (4) and conditions (5) may be obtained by putting $\varphi(\lambda, t) = 0$ and $g(\lambda, t) = 0$ in the unhomogeneous problem consisting of equation (1) and conditions (3).

To have the general solution of the unhomogeneous problem it suffices to find any of the particular solutions and then add the general solution of the homogeneous problem.

The unhomogeneous problem, expressed operationally has the form of the single equation (2); the initial conditions of the λ axis enter into that equation. Similarly, the homogeneous problem is represented operationally by the homogeneous equation

$$(6) \qquad (a_m D^m + \ldots + a_0) x = 0 .$$

To have the general solution of (2), it suffices to find any of its particular solutions and then add the general solution of (6).

It is possible to find particular solution of (2) for several forms of $f(\lambda)$ (see Chapter II of Part IV), but we do not know any general method. (However, as we have seen in § 12 of Chapter IX, it may happen that no solution of (2) exists.) On the other hand, we can always find the general solution of (6); the method of finding it was widely discussed in Chapter XI. We intend to apply this method to the corresponding homogeneous problem in the domain of partial equations. Of course, every solution of the problem of partial equation is a solution of the corresponding operational problem. But not conversely. For the solution of the operational problem is, in general, an operational function, whose values have no sense in classical analysis. Thus, the general operational solution *contains* all the solutions of the problem of partial equations, but it embraces moreover a great many other solutions, which are worthless for the case of partial equations.

Suppose that

$$(7) \qquad x(\lambda) = c_1 x_1(\lambda) + \ldots + c_q x_q(\lambda)$$

is the general solution of (6). The coefficients $c_1, \ldots, c_q$ are arbitrary operators. In order that (7) be a solution of (4) and (5), we have to impose some conditions on the coefficients $c_1, \ldots, c_q$. Those conditions should be sufficiently sharp to ensure that (7) be a parametric function (i. e. a function whose values are functions of t), differentiable as far as equation (4) requires. On the other hand, the conditions should be loose enough to make (7) the general solution of equation (4) with conditions (5).

We can establish such conditions in several cases by applying the lemmas of the next paragraphs. However, we do not know the general solution of the problem.

§ 2. First lemma. As we know, the polynomial $P(D) = a_m D^m + \ldots + a_0$ can be factorized into linear factors:

$$P(D) = a_\mu \prod_{\mu=1}^{m} (D - w_\mu),$$

where the operators w_μ are of the form

$$\beta_0 s^k + \beta_1 s^{k-r} + \beta_2 s^{k-2r} + \ldots \tag{8}$$

Suppose that

(I) For $\mu = 1, \ldots, q$ $(q \leqslant m)$, the first term $\beta_0 s^k$ of the series representing w_μ is of degree $k \leqslant 1$, and different for different indices μ. For $\mu = q+1, \ldots, m$ (if $q \leqslant m$), the number k is greater than 1.

In this case the general solution (7) of (6) has the form

$$x(\lambda) = c_1 e^{w_1 \lambda} + \ldots + c_q e^{w_q \lambda}, \tag{9}$$

where $c_1, \ldots, c_q$ are arbitrary operators. In order that (9) be a solution of (4), $x(\lambda)$ must be a parametric function: $x(\lambda) = \{x(\lambda, t)\}$, and its derivatives as well: $x^{(\mu)}(\lambda) = \{x_{\lambda^\mu}(\lambda, t)\}$ $(\mu = 1, \ldots, m)$.

Lemma 1. *If* (9) *is a solution of the partial equation* (4), *each of the terms* $c_\mu e^{w_\mu \lambda}$ $(\mu = 1, \ldots, q)$ *on the right side of* (9) *must be a parametric function.*

Proof. We have

$$x^{(\mu)}(\lambda) = c_1 w_1^\mu e^{w_1 \lambda} + \ldots + c_q w_q^\mu e^{w_q \lambda} \qquad (\mu = 0, \ldots, m-1).$$

Since the determinant

$$W = \begin{vmatrix} 1 & \ldots & 1 \\ w_1 & \ldots & w_q \\ \cdot & \cdot & \cdot \\ w_1^{q-1} & \ldots & w_q^{q-1} \end{vmatrix}$$

is different from 0, it follows that

$$c_\mu e^{w_\mu \lambda} = \frac{A_{1\mu}}{W} x(\lambda) + \ldots + \frac{A_{q\mu}}{W} x^{(\mu-1)}(\lambda), \tag{10}$$

where $A_{\varkappa\mu}$ is the minor of W, corresponding to the element $w_\mu^{(\varkappa-1)}$.

Since the operators w_μ are of form (8), is the determinant W with proper k and coefficients β_ν. Let k_μ be the greatest exponent corresponding to w_μ. Without loss of generality we can assume that $k_1 \leqslant \ldots \leqslant k_q$.

In view of (I), the representation

$$W = \prod_{1\leqslant \nu-\mu\leqslant q} (w_\mu - w_\nu)$$

implies that in the development (8) of exponent k is equal to

$$K = k_2+2k_3+\ldots+(q-1)k_q.$$

Thus we can write

$$W = Bs^K(1+f),$$

where B is a number different from 0, and f a function of t, continuous in $(0, \infty)$ and integrable in the neighbourhood of $t = 0$. Similarly, each of the minors $A_{\varkappa\mu}$ can be written in the form

$$A_{\varkappa\mu} = B_{\varkappa\mu} s^{K_{\varkappa\mu}}(1+f_{\varkappa\mu});$$

here we have $K_{\varkappa\mu} \leqslant K$. Hence

$$\frac{A_{\varkappa\mu}}{W} = \frac{B_{\varkappa\mu}}{B} s^{K_{\varkappa\mu}-K}\frac{1+f_{\varkappa\mu}}{1+f} = \frac{B_{\varkappa\mu}}{B} t^{K-K_{\varkappa\mu}} + g_{\varkappa\mu},$$

where $g_{\varkappa\mu}$ is a function of t, continuous in $(0, \infty)$ and integrable in the neighbourhood of $t = 0$.

If $x(\lambda), \ldots, x^{(\mu-1)}(\lambda)$ are supposed to be parametric functions, each of the terms on the right side of (10) must be a parametric function.

§ 3. Second lemma. Consider the expression

(11) $$u(\lambda) = ce^{w\lambda},$$

where

(12) $$w = \beta_0 s^k + \beta_1 s^{k-r} + \beta_2 s^{k-2r} + \ldots$$

$(k, r$ rational, $r > 0)$.

LEMMA 2. 1° *Assume that $k \leqslant 0$. If $u(\lambda)$ is parametric in $\lambda_1 \leqslant \lambda \leqslant \lambda_2$, then $c \in \mathcal{C}$. If $c \in \mathcal{C}$, then $u(\lambda)$ and all its derivatives $u^{(\mu)}(\lambda)$ are parametric in $\lambda_1 \leqslant \lambda \leqslant \lambda_2$.*

2° *Assume that $0 < k < 1$ and $\beta_0 < 0$. If $u(\lambda)$ is parametric in $\lambda_1 \leqslant \lambda \leqslant \lambda_2$, then*

(13) $$c = e^{-w\lambda_1} f \quad (f \in \mathcal{C}).$$

If (13) holds, then $u(\lambda)$ is parametric in $\lambda_1 \leqslant \lambda \leqslant \lambda_2$, and all its derivatives $u^{(\mu)}(\lambda)$ are parametric in $\lambda_1 \leqslant \lambda \leqslant \lambda_2$.

3° *Assume that $0 < k < 1$ and $\beta_0 > 0$. If $u(\lambda)$ is parametric in $\lambda_1 \leqslant \lambda \leqslant \lambda_2$, then*

(14) $$c = e^{-w\lambda_2} f \quad (f \in \mathcal{C}).$$

If (14) *holds, then* $u(\lambda)$ *is parametric in* $\lambda_1 \leqslant \lambda \leqslant \lambda_2$, *and all its derivatives* $u^{(\mu)}(\lambda)$ *are parametric in* $\lambda_1 \leqslant \lambda \leqslant \lambda_2$.

Remark. This lemma does not embrace all the possible w. Nevertheless, when each of the operators w_μ in (9) satisfies one of the conditions 1° or 2° or 3°, then lemmas 1 and 2 allow us to establish the general solution of the partial equation (4) with conditions (5). Examples will be given in § 4.

Proof of lemma 2. If $k < 0$, then

$$e^{w\lambda} = 1+f(\lambda),$$

where $f(\lambda)$ is a parametric function. Hence

$$e^{-w\lambda} = \frac{1}{1+f(\lambda)} = 1+g(\lambda),$$

where $g(\lambda)$ is again parametric function. From (11) we find

$$c = \big(1+g(\lambda)\big)u(\lambda).$$

Hence it follows that if $u(\lambda)$ is a parametric function, the coefficient c must be a function of class $\mathcal{C}$. On the other hand, if $c \in \mathcal{C}$, the equality $u(\lambda) = c\big(1+f(\lambda)\big)$ implies that $u(\lambda)$ parametric. Since in the considered case w is a function of class $\mathcal{C}$, every derivative

$$u^{(\mu)}(\lambda) = w^\mu e^{w\lambda} \tag{15}$$

is also parametric.

Now assume that $k = 0$. Then

$$e^{w\lambda} = e^{\beta_0\lambda}e^{(w-\beta_0)\lambda} = e^{\beta_0\lambda}\big(1+f(\lambda)\big),$$

where $f(\lambda)$ is parametric. As before we find

$$c = e^{-\beta_0\lambda}\big(1+g(\lambda)\big)u(\lambda),$$

where $g(\lambda)$ is parametric. The conclusion is the same: $u(\lambda)$ is parametric if and only if $c \in \mathcal{C}$. Moreover, if $c \in \mathcal{C}$, all the derivatives $u^{(\mu)}(\lambda)$ are parametric. All this argument is concerned with the interval $\lambda_1 \leqslant \lambda \leqslant \lambda_2$. Thus part 1° of lemma is proved.

Now assume that $0 < k < 1$, and let $k-pr$ be the lowest positive exponent in (12). Then

$$e^{w\lambda} = \exp(\beta_0 s^k + \ldots + \beta_r s^{k-pr})\, e^{w_0\lambda}, \tag{16}$$

where w_0 again has the form of series (12), but its highest exponent is $\leqslant 0$.

Suppose that β_0 is negative. Then

$$(17)\qquad \exp(\beta_0 s^k + \ldots + \beta_r s^{k-pr})\lambda = \left\{\frac{1}{2\pi i}\int_{-i\infty}^{+i\infty} \exp[zt + (\beta_0 z^k + \ldots + \beta_r z^{k-pr})\lambda]\,dz\right\} \quad (\lambda > 0);$$

the function in braces is continuous for $\lambda > 0$, $0 \leqslant t < \infty$; moreover it vanishes at $t = 0$ together with all its derivatives with respect to t. The proof is analogous to that in § 4 of Chapter VIII. This implies that also function (16) is parametric for $\lambda \geqslant 0$ and vanishes together with all its derivatives with respect to t for $t = 0$. It follows from (11) that $c = e^{-w\lambda_1}\mu(\lambda_1)$. Thus c must be of form (13). Conversely, if c is of form (13), then $u(\lambda) = e^{(\lambda-\lambda_1)w}f$ is parametric for $\lambda_1 \leqslant \lambda \leqslant \lambda_2$. We still have to prove that all the derivatives $u^{(\mu)}(\lambda)$ are parametric in $\lambda_1 < \lambda < \lambda_2$. These derivatives can be written in the form

$$u^{(\mu)}(\lambda) = (lw)^{\mu} s^{\mu} e^{w(\lambda-\lambda_1)} f.$$

Here $lw \in \mathcal{C}$, and the values of $s^{\mu} e^{w(\lambda-\lambda_1)}$ belong to $\mathcal{C}$, as $\lambda_1 < \lambda \leqslant \lambda_2$, for all the derivatives with respect to t of $e^{w(\lambda-\lambda_1)}$ vanish at $t = 0$. This completes the proof of part 2° of lemma.

The proof of part 3° is analogous.

§ 4. Examples. Example 1. Find the general solution of the homogeneous problem of the partial equation

$$(18)\qquad x_{\lambda^5} + x_{\lambda^4} + x_{\lambda^3 t^3} + x_{\lambda t^5} + x_{t^7} = 0.$$

In view of the criterion given in § 26 of Part IV this equation is not restrictive, and therefore the homogeneous conditions on the λ axis can be given in Cauchy's form

$$(19)\qquad x(\lambda, 0) = x_t(\lambda, 0) = \ldots = x_{t^6}(\lambda, 0) = 0,$$

The operational form of problem (18), (19) is

$$(D^5 + D^4 + s^3 D^3 + s^5 D + s^7)x = 0.$$

As we have seen in Example 1 of § 1 of Chapter XI, the only solution of the last equation is $x(\lambda) = 0$. This implies that the function $x(\lambda, t) = 0$ is the only solution of the considered problem (18), (19).

Example 2. Determine the general form of the solution of the homogeneous problem concerning the partial equation

$$(20)\qquad x_{\lambda^4} - x_{\lambda^2 t^3} + x_{\lambda^2 t^2} + x_{\lambda t^3} + x_{t^3} = 0.$$

Here the homogeneous conditions on the λ axis are

$$x_\lambda(\lambda, 0)+x(\lambda, 0) = 0,$$

(21) $$-x_{\lambda 3}(\lambda, 0)+x_{\lambda 2}(\lambda, 0)+x_{\lambda t}(\lambda, 0)+x_t(\lambda, 0) = 0,$$

$$-x_{\lambda 3t}(\lambda, 0)+x_{\lambda 2t}(\lambda, 0)+x_{\lambda t2}(\lambda, 0)+x_{t2}(\lambda, 0) = 0.$$

The operational proper equation is

(22) $$(D^4 - s^2 D^3 + s^2 D^2 + s^3 D + s^3)x = 0.$$

In order to determine the number of linearly independent solutions of (22), we apply the method from Chapter XI. We draw the straight lines

$$y = 4k, \quad y = 3k+2, \quad y = 2k+2, \quad y = k+3, \quad y = 3.$$

Their upper envelope has three vertices with abscissae: 0, 1/2 and 2. The greatest abscissa, not exceeding 1, is 1/2. It corresponds to the vertex at which concur the lines

$$y = 3k+2 \quad \text{and} \quad y = k+3.$$

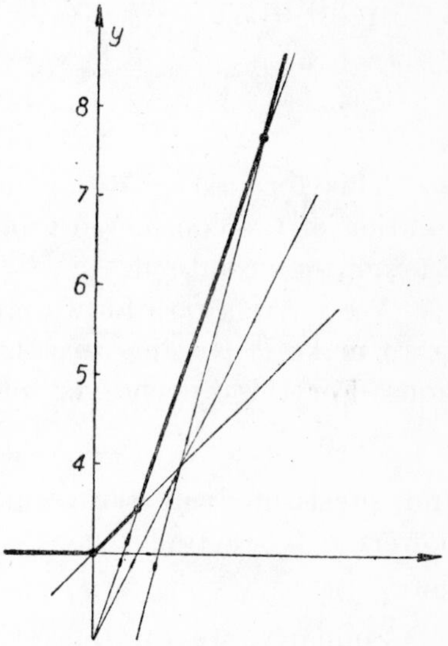

Fig. 171

The greatest of the coefficients of k is 3. Thus the number of linearly independent solutions of (22) is 3. The general solution has the form

(23) $$x(\lambda) = c_1 e^{w_1 \lambda} + c_2 e^{w_2 \lambda} + c_3 e^{w_3 \lambda}.$$

The operator w_1 corresponding to the value $k = 0$ satisfies assumption 1° of lemma 2. Thus the first term on the right side of (23) is a parametric function if and only if $c_1 \in \mathcal{C}$. Now the operators w_2 and w_3 corresponding to the value $k = 1/2$ have the form $\beta_0 s^{1/2} + \ldots$ ($\beta_0 \neq 0$). On substituting this into the equation

(24) $$w^4 - s^2 w^3 + s^2 w^2 + s^3 w + s^3 = 0,$$

we find that $-\beta_0^3 + \beta_0$ is the coefficient of $s^{7/2}$. Since this coefficient must vanish, we have $\beta_0 = \pm 1$. Thus the operators w_2 and w_3 satisfy the conditions 2° and 3° of lemma 2. Hence the second and the last term in (23) are parametric functions in $\lambda_1 \leqslant \lambda \leqslant \lambda_2$ if and only if $c_2 = e^{-w_2 \lambda_1} f_2$, $c_3 = e^{-w_3 \lambda_1} f_3$ ($f_2, f_3 \in \mathcal{C}$). The form of the general solution of (20), (21) follows from lemma 1.

Changing suitably the meaning of symbols c_2 and c_3 we can write this solution in the form

(25) $\{x(\lambda, t)\} = x(\lambda) = c_1 e^{w_1\lambda} + c_2 e^{w_2(\lambda-\lambda_1)} + c_3 e^{w_3(\lambda-\lambda_2)} \quad (\lambda_1 \leqslant \lambda \leqslant \lambda_2),$

where c_1, c_2 and c_3 are arbitrary elements of class $\mathcal{C}$. More precisely: expression (25), where $c_1, c_2, c_3 \in \mathcal{C}$, represents a continuous function in the region $\lambda_1 \leqslant \lambda \leqslant \lambda_2$, $0 \leqslant t < \infty$, which satisfies equation (20) in $\lambda_1 < \lambda < \lambda_2$, $0 \leqslant t < \infty$ and conditions (21) for $\lambda_1 < \lambda < \lambda_2$. Conversely, every function which is continuous in $\lambda_1 \leqslant \lambda \leqslant \lambda_2$, $0 \leqslant t < \infty$, and satisfies (2) in $\lambda_1 < \lambda < \lambda_2$, $0 \leqslant t < \infty$, and conditions (21) in $\lambda_1 < \lambda < \lambda_2$ is of form (25), where $c_1, c_2, c_3 \in \mathcal{C}$.

Solution (25) is given in the operational form. However, we can write

$$e^{w_1\lambda} = e^{\lambda} + \{f_1(\lambda, t)\},$$
$$e^{w_2\lambda} = \{f_2(\lambda, t)\} \qquad (\lambda > 0),$$
$$e^{w_3\lambda} = \{f_3(\lambda, t)\} \qquad (\lambda > 0)$$

with properly chosen functions f_1, f_2 and f_3. Thus we can write instead of (25)

$$x(\lambda, t) = c_1(t)e^{-\lambda} + \int_0^t c_1(t-\tau)f_1(\lambda, \tau)\,d\tau + \int_0^t c_2(t-\tau)f_2(\lambda, \tau)\,d\tau +$$
$$+ \int_0^t c_3(t-\tau)f_3(\lambda, \tau)\,d\tau \qquad (\lambda_1 \leqslant \lambda \leqslant \lambda_2;\ 0 \leqslant t < \infty).$$

This formula gives us information about the form of the general solution of the considered problem, and shows how the arbitrary functions c_1, c_2, c_3 enter into it.

We are in a position to present the functions f_1, f_2, f_3 in a such a way as to make it possible to carry out the approximate, numerical calculations. For this purpose we put

$$w_1 = \beta_0 + \beta_1 s^{-1} + \beta_2 s^{-2} + \ldots$$

and substitute this series in (24). On comparing the coefficients of powers of s we find

(26) $$w_1 = -1 - s^{-3} - 5s^{-4} + \ldots$$

Similarly, we find

(27)
$$w_2 = -s^{1/2} + 1 + \tfrac{1}{2}s^{-1/2} + 2s^{-1} + \tfrac{47}{8}s^{-3/2} + \ldots,$$
$$w_3 = s^{1/2} + 1 - \tfrac{1}{2}s^{-1/2} + 2s^{-1} - \tfrac{47}{8}s^{-3/2} + \ldots$$

From (26) we obtain

$$e^{w_1\lambda} = e^{-\lambda}[1 - (l^3 + 5l^4 + \ldots)\lambda + \ldots]$$

and

$$f_1(\lambda, t) = -\lambda e^{-\lambda}(\tfrac{1}{2}t^2 + \tfrac{5}{6}t^3) + \ldots$$

It is little more difficult to find the approximation of f_2 and f_3. From (27) we find

$$e^{w_2\lambda} = e^{-\sqrt{s}\lambda}e^{\lambda}\left[1+\frac{3}{2}s^{-1/2}+\left(2\lambda-\frac{\lambda^2}{8}\right)s^{-1}+\left(\frac{47}{8}\lambda+\lambda^2+\frac{1}{48}\lambda^3\right)s^{-3/2}+\ldots\right]$$

and

$$e^{w_3\lambda} = e^{-\sqrt{s}\lambda}e^{-\lambda}\left[1+\frac{\lambda}{2}s^{-1/2}+\left(-2\lambda-\frac{\lambda^2}{8}\right)s^{-1}+\left(\frac{47}{8}\lambda-\lambda^2+\frac{1}{48}\lambda^3\right)s^{-3/2}+\ldots\right].$$

On applying the formulae

$$e^{-\sqrt{s}\lambda} = \left\{\frac{\lambda}{2\sqrt{\pi t}}\exp\left(-\frac{\lambda^2}{4t}\right)\right\}, \qquad s^{-1/2}e^{-\sqrt{s}\lambda} = \left\{\frac{1}{\sqrt{\pi t}}\exp\left(-\frac{\lambda^2}{4t}\right)\right\},$$

$$s^{-1}e^{-\sqrt{s}\lambda} = \left\{\operatorname{cerf}\frac{\lambda}{2\sqrt{t}}\right\}, \qquad s^{-1/2}e^{-\sqrt{s}\lambda} = \left\{2\sqrt{\frac{t}{\pi}}\exp\left(-\frac{\lambda^2}{4t}\right)-\lambda\operatorname{cerf}\frac{\lambda}{2\sqrt{t}}\right\},$$

we obtain

$$f_2(\lambda, t) = \frac{e^{\lambda}}{\sqrt{\pi}}\left(\frac{\lambda}{2\sqrt{t^3}}+\frac{\lambda}{2\sqrt{t}}+\frac{47}{4}\lambda\sqrt{t}+2\lambda^2\sqrt{t}+\frac{1}{24}\lambda^3\sqrt{t}\right)\exp\left(-\frac{\lambda^2}{4t}\right)+$$

$$+e^{\lambda}\left(2\lambda-6\lambda^2-\lambda^3+\frac{1}{48}\lambda^4\right)\operatorname{cerf}\frac{\lambda}{2\sqrt{t}}+\ldots,$$

$$f_3(\lambda, t) = \frac{e^{-\lambda}}{\sqrt{\pi}}\left(\frac{\lambda}{2\sqrt{t^3}}+\frac{\lambda}{2\sqrt{t}}+\frac{47}{4}\lambda\sqrt{t}+2\lambda^2\sqrt{t}+\frac{1}{24}\lambda^3\sqrt{t}\right)\exp\left(-\frac{\lambda^2}{4t}\right)-$$

$$-e^{-\lambda}\left(2\lambda+6\lambda^2+\lambda^3-\frac{1}{48}\lambda^4\right)\operatorname{cerf}\frac{\lambda}{2\sqrt{t}}+\ldots$$

Of course, the approximations obtained here are rough, and may be satisfactory for small values of λ and t. In order to obtain better approximations, we must determine further terms in developments (26) and (27). However, in numerical calculation we always restrict ourselves to a finite number of terms. The error commited may be estimated, e. g. by replacing the considered series by their majorants, to which it is possible to assign an explicit sum, as we have done in § 5 of Chapter X. An asymptotic estimation can be obtained by means of the radius of convergence of series (26) and (27), s being considered as a complex variable. It is not our aim to enter into details. It can already be seen from these few remarks that the method given in Chapter XII is not only theoretical but also can lead to effective numerical results.

PART SEVEN

FORMULAE AND TABLES

I. Special functions

1. Gamma function of Euler:

$$\Gamma(\lambda) = \int_0^\infty t^{\lambda-1} e^{-t} dt \qquad (\lambda > 0) \qquad \text{(I, § 54)}$$

$$\Gamma(\lambda+1) = \lambda\Gamma(\lambda), \qquad \Gamma(n) = (n-1)! \qquad (n = 1, 2, \ldots)$$

$$\frac{\Gamma(\lambda)\Gamma(\mu)}{\Gamma(\lambda+\mu)} = \int_0^1 t^{\lambda-1}(1-t)^{\mu-1} dt \qquad (\lambda > 0, \ \mu > 0)$$

$$\Gamma(\tfrac{1}{2}) = 2\int_0^\infty e^{-\tau^2} d\tau = \sqrt{\pi}$$

2. Error function:

$$\operatorname{erf} t = \frac{2}{\sqrt{\pi}} \int_0^t e^{-\tau^2} d\tau \qquad \text{(I, § 55)}$$

$$\operatorname{cerf} t = 1 - \operatorname{erf} t$$

3. Bessel functions:

$$J_0(\lambda) = \sum_{\nu=0}^\infty (-1)^\nu \frac{\lambda^{2\nu}}{2^{2\nu}(\nu!)^2}, \qquad J_1(\lambda) = \sum_{\nu=0}^\infty (-1)^\nu \frac{\lambda^{1+2\nu}}{2^{1+2\nu}\nu!(1+\nu)!} \qquad \text{(II, § 51)}$$

$$J_0'(t) = -J_1(t)$$

$$J_0(i\lambda) = \sum_{\nu=1}^\infty \frac{\lambda^{2\nu}}{2^{2\nu}(\nu!)^2}, \qquad J_1(i\lambda) = i\sum_{\nu=0}^\infty \frac{\lambda^{1+2\nu}}{2^{1+2\nu}\nu!(1+\nu)!}$$

$$J_n(\lambda) = \sum_{\nu=0}^\infty (-1)^\nu \frac{\lambda^{n+2\nu}}{2^{n+2\nu}\nu!(n+\nu)!} \qquad (n = 0, 1, 2, \ldots) \qquad \text{(II, § 53)}$$

$$J_n(i\lambda) = i^n \sum_{\nu=0}^\infty \frac{\lambda^{n+2\nu}}{2^{n+2\nu}\nu!(n+\nu)!} \qquad (n = 0, 1, 2, \ldots)$$

II. Formulas of the operational calculus

1. $\{a(t)\}+\{b(t)\} = \{a(t)+b(t)\}$ (I, § 7)

$\{a(t)\}\cdot\{b(t)\} = \{\int_0^t a(t-\tau)\,b(\tau)\,d\tau\}$

$a\{f(t)\} = \{af(t)\}$ (a a number) (I, § 19)

2. $s\{a(t)\} = \{a'(t)\}+a(0)$ (I, § 21)

$\{a^{(n)}(t)\} = s^n\{a(t)\}-s^{n-1}a(0)-\ldots-s\,a^{(n-2)}(0)-a^{(n-1)}(0)$ (I, § 22)

3. $T^a\{a(t)\} = \{e^{at}a(t)\}, \quad T^aR(s) = R(s-a)$ (II, § 48)

4. $\frac{d}{ds}\{a(t)\} = \{-t\,a(t)\}$ (II, § 62)

5. $e^{-\lambda s}\{f(t)\} = \begin{Bmatrix} 0 & \text{for } 0\leqslant t<\lambda \\ f(t-\lambda) & \text{for } 0\leqslant\lambda<t \end{Bmatrix}$ (II, § 10)

$\int_{\lambda_1}^{\lambda_2} e^{-\lambda s}f(\lambda)\,d\lambda = \begin{Bmatrix} f(t) \text{ in the interval } 0\leqslant\lambda_1<t<\lambda_2 \\ 0 \text{ outside this interval} \end{Bmatrix}$ (IV, § 5)

$\int_0^\infty e^{-\lambda s}f(\lambda)\,d\lambda = \{f(t)\}$

6. $\frac{1}{s} = \{1\}$ (I, § 21)

$\frac{1}{s^n} = \left\{\frac{t^{n-1}}{(n-1)!}\right\}$ $(n = 1, 2, \ldots)$ (I, § 8)

$\frac{1}{s^\lambda} = \left\{\frac{t^{\lambda-1}}{\Gamma(\lambda)}\right\}$ $(\lambda>0)$ (I, § 55)

$\frac{1}{\sqrt{s}} = \left\{\frac{1}{\sqrt{\pi t}}\right\}$

$\frac{1}{s-a} = \{e^{at}\}$ (I, § 24)

$\frac{1}{(s-a)^\lambda} = \left\{\frac{t^{\lambda-1}}{\Gamma(\lambda)}e^{at}\right\}$ (I, § 55)

$\frac{1}{\sqrt{s+a}} = \left\{\frac{1}{\sqrt{\pi t}}e^{-at}\right\}$ (I, § 55)

$\frac{1}{s\sqrt{s+a}} = \left\{\frac{1}{\sqrt{a}}\operatorname{erf}\sqrt{at}\right\}$ $(a>0)$

$\frac{1}{s^2+\beta^2} = \left\{\frac{1}{\beta}\sin\beta t\right\}$ $(\beta>0)$ (I, § 25)

$\frac{s}{s^2+\beta^2} = \{\cos\beta t\}$

6. (continued)

$$\frac{1}{s^2-\beta^2} = \left\{\frac{1}{\beta}\,\mathrm{sh}\,\beta t\right\} \qquad (\beta > 0)$$

$$\frac{s}{s^2-\beta^2} = \{\mathrm{ch}\,\beta t\}$$

$$\frac{1}{(s-\alpha)^2+\beta^2} = \left\{\frac{1}{\beta}\,e^{\alpha t}\sin\beta t\right\} \qquad (\alpha > 0)$$

$$\frac{s-\alpha}{(s-\alpha)^2+\beta^2} = \{e^{\alpha t}\cos\beta t\}$$

$$\frac{1}{(s-\alpha)^2-\beta^2} = \left\{\frac{1}{\beta}\,e^{\alpha t}\mathrm{sh}\,\beta t\right\} \qquad (\beta > 0)$$

$$\frac{s-\alpha}{(s-\alpha)^2-\beta^2} = \{e^{\alpha t}\mathrm{ch}\,\beta t\}$$

$$\frac{1}{[(s-\alpha)^2+\beta^2]^2} = \left\{\frac{e^{\alpha t}}{2\beta^2}\left[\frac{1}{\beta}\sin\beta t - t\cos\beta t\right]\right\} \qquad (\beta > 0)$$

$$\frac{1}{[(s-\alpha)^2+\beta^2]^3} = \left\{\frac{e^{\alpha t}}{4\beta^4}\left\{\left(\frac{3}{2}-\frac{\beta^2 t^2}{2}\right)\frac{1}{\beta}\sin\beta t - \frac{3}{2}\,t\cos\beta t\right\}\right\}$$

$$\frac{s}{[(s-\alpha)^2+\beta^2]^2} = \left\{\frac{e^{\alpha t}}{2\beta^2}\left[(\alpha+\beta^2 t)\frac{1}{\beta}\sin\beta t - \alpha t\cos\beta t\right]\right\} \qquad \text{(I, § 26)}$$

$$\frac{1}{\sqrt{s^2+\lambda^2}} = \{\mathrm{J}_0(\lambda t)\} \qquad \text{(II, § 51)}$$

$$\frac{1}{\sqrt{s^2-\lambda^2}} = \{\mathrm{J}_0(i\lambda t)\}$$

$$\frac{\sqrt{s^2+\lambda^2}-s}{\sqrt{s^2+\lambda^2}} = \{\lambda\mathrm{J}_1(\lambda t)\}$$

$$\frac{\sqrt{s^2-\lambda^2}-s}{\sqrt{s^2-\lambda^2}} = \{i\lambda\mathrm{J}_1(i\lambda t)\}$$

$$(\sqrt{s^2+\lambda^2}-s)^n = \left\{\frac{n\lambda}{t}\,\mathrm{J}_n(\lambda t)\right\} \qquad (n = 1, 2, \ldots) \qquad \text{(II, § 53)}$$

$$\frac{(\sqrt{s^2+\lambda^2}-s)^n}{\sqrt{s^2+\lambda^2}} = \{\lambda^n\mathrm{J}_n(\lambda t)\} \qquad (n = 0, 1, 2, \ldots)$$

$$\frac{1}{s}\exp\left(-\frac{\lambda}{s}\right) = \{\mathrm{J}_0(2\sqrt{\lambda t})\}$$

6. (continued)

$$\frac{1}{s^2}\exp\left(-\frac{\lambda}{s}\right) = \left\{\sqrt{\frac{1}{\lambda}}\,J_1(2\sqrt{\lambda t})\right\}$$

$$\frac{1}{\sqrt{s}}\exp\left(-\frac{\lambda}{s}\right) = \left\{\frac{1}{\sqrt{\pi t}}\cos 2\sqrt{\lambda t}\right\}$$

$$\frac{1}{\sqrt{s}}\exp\frac{\lambda}{s} = \left\{\frac{1}{\sqrt{\pi t}}\operatorname{ch} 2\sqrt{\lambda t}\right\}$$

$$\exp(-\lambda\sqrt{s}) = \left\{\frac{\lambda}{2\sqrt{\pi t^3}}\exp\left(-\frac{\lambda^2}{4t}\right)\right\} \quad (\lambda > 0)$$

$$\frac{1}{\sqrt{s}}\exp(-\lambda\sqrt{s}) = \left\{\frac{1}{\sqrt{\pi t}}\exp\left(-\frac{\lambda^2}{4t}\right)\right\} \quad (\lambda > 0) \qquad \text{(II, § 53)}$$

$$\frac{1}{s}\exp(-\lambda\sqrt{s}) = \left\{\operatorname{cerf}\frac{\lambda}{2\sqrt{t}}\right\} \quad (\lambda > 0)$$

$$\exp\lambda(s-\sqrt{s^2+a^2}) = 1 - \left\{\frac{\lambda}{\sqrt{t^2+2\lambda t}}\,aJ_1(a\sqrt{t^2+2\lambda t})\right\} \qquad \text{(II, § 54)}$$

$$\frac{\exp\lambda(s-\sqrt{s^2+a^2})}{\sqrt{s^2+a^2}} = \{J_0(a\sqrt{t^2+2\lambda t})\}$$

$$\exp\lambda(s-\sqrt{s^2+a^2}) = 1 - \left\{\frac{\lambda}{\sqrt{t^2+2t\lambda}}\,iaJ_1(ia\sqrt{t^2+2t\lambda})\right\}$$

$$\frac{\exp\lambda(s-\sqrt{s^2-a^2})}{\sqrt{s^2-a^2}} = \{J_0(ia\sqrt{t^2+2\lambda t})\}$$

$$\exp\lambda(s-\sqrt{s^2+2\lambda s}) = e^{-a\lambda} - \left\{\frac{\lambda}{\sqrt{t^2+2\lambda t}}\,e^{-a(\lambda+t)}iaJ_1(ia\sqrt{t^2+2\lambda t})\right\}$$

$$\frac{\exp\lambda(s-\sqrt{s^2+2as})}{\sqrt{s^2+2as}} = \{e^{-a(\lambda+t)}J_0(ia\sqrt{t^2+2\lambda t})\}$$

$$\exp(-\lambda\sqrt{s^2+a^2}) = e^{-\lambda s} - \left\{\begin{array}{lll} 0 & \text{for} & 0 \leqslant t < \lambda \\ \dfrac{\lambda}{\sqrt{t^2-\lambda^2}}\,aJ_1(a\sqrt{z^2-\lambda^2}) & \text{for} & 0 \leqslant \lambda < t \end{array}\right\}$$

$$\frac{\exp(-\lambda\sqrt{s^2+a^2})}{\sqrt{s^2+a^2}} = \left\{\begin{array}{lll} 0 & \text{for} & 0 \leqslant t < \lambda \\ J_0(a\sqrt{t^2-\lambda^2} & \text{for} & 0 \leqslant \lambda < t \end{array}\right\}$$

$$\exp(-\lambda\sqrt{s^2-a^2}) = e^{-\lambda s} - \left\{\begin{array}{lll} 0 & \text{for} & 0 \leqslant t < \lambda \\ \dfrac{\lambda}{\sqrt{t^2-\lambda^2}}\,iaJ_1(ia\sqrt{t^2-\lambda^2}) & \text{for} & 0 \leqslant \lambda < t \end{array}\right\}$$

$$\frac{\exp(-\lambda\sqrt{s^2-a^2})}{\sqrt{s^2+a^2}} = \begin{Bmatrix} 0 & \text{for} & 0 \leqslant t < \lambda \\ J_0(ia\sqrt{t^2-\lambda^2}) & \text{for} & 0 \leqslant \lambda < t \end{Bmatrix}$$

$$\exp(-\lambda\sqrt{s^2+2as}) = e^{-a\lambda}e^{-\lambda s} - \begin{Bmatrix} 0 & \text{for} & 0 \leqslant t < \lambda \\ \frac{\lambda}{\sqrt{t^2-\lambda^2}} e^{-at} ia J_1(ia\sqrt{t^2-\lambda^2}) & \text{for} & 0 \leqslant \lambda < t \end{Bmatrix}$$

$$\frac{\exp(-\lambda\sqrt{s^2+2as}}{\sqrt{s^2+2as}} = \begin{Bmatrix} 0 & \text{for} & 0 \leqslant t < \lambda \\ e^{-at} J_0(ia\sqrt{t^2-\lambda^2}) & \text{for} & 0 \leqslant \lambda < t \end{Bmatrix}$$

$$\exp\lambda(s - \sqrt{(s-\alpha)^2+\beta^2}) = e^{\alpha\lambda} - \left\{ \frac{\lambda}{\sqrt{t^2+2\lambda t}} e^{\alpha(\lambda+t)} \beta J_1(\beta\sqrt{t^2+2\lambda t}) \right\}$$

$$\frac{\exp\lambda(s - \sqrt{(s-\alpha)^2+\beta^2})}{\sqrt{(s-\alpha)^2+\beta^2}} = \{e^{\alpha(\lambda+t)} J_0(\beta\sqrt{t^2+2\lambda t})\}$$

$$\exp(-\lambda\sqrt{(s-\alpha)^2+\beta^2}) = e^{\alpha\lambda}\cdot e^{-\lambda s} - \begin{Bmatrix} 0 & \text{for} & 0 \leqslant t < \lambda \\ \frac{\lambda}{\sqrt{t^2-\lambda^2}} e^{\alpha t}\cdot \beta J_1(\beta\sqrt{t^2-\lambda^2}) & \text{for} & 0 \leqslant \lambda < t \end{Bmatrix}$$

$$\frac{\exp(-\lambda\sqrt{(s-\alpha)^2+\beta^2})}{\sqrt{(s-\alpha)^2+\beta^2}} = \begin{Bmatrix} 0 & \text{for} & 0 \leqslant t < \lambda \\ e^{\alpha t} J_0(\beta\sqrt{t^2-\lambda^2}) & \text{for} & 0 \leqslant \lambda < t \end{Bmatrix}$$

7. $$\left.\begin{aligned} e^{-\lambda\sqrt{s}} &\leqslant 3\sqrt{\frac{6}{\pi e^3}\cdot\frac{1}{\lambda^2 s}} \\ \frac{1}{\sqrt{s}} e^{-\lambda\sqrt{s}} &\leqslant \sqrt{\frac{2}{\pi e}\cdot\frac{1}{\lambda s}} \end{aligned}\right\} \quad (\lambda > 0)$$ (II, § 36)

8. $$\frac{1}{[(s-\alpha)^2+\beta^2]^n} = \left\{ \frac{e^{\alpha t}}{(2\beta^2)^{n-2}} \left[A_n(\beta^2 t^2)\,\frac{1}{\beta}\sin\beta t - B_n(\beta^2 t^2)\cdot t\cos\beta t \right] \right\} \quad (n = 1, 2, \ldots)$$

(II, § 63)

$$\frac{s}{[(s-\alpha)^2+\beta^2]^n} = \left\{ \frac{e^{\alpha t}}{2(n-1)(2\beta^2)^{n-1}} \left[A_{n-1}(\beta^2 t^2)\cdot\frac{t}{\beta}\sin\beta t - B_{n-1}(\beta^2 t^2)\cdot t^2\cos\beta t \right] \right\}$$

$(n = 2, 3, \ldots)$

$A_1(x) = 1, \quad A_2(x) = 1$

$$A_{n+1}(x) = \frac{2n-1}{n}(A_n(x) - \frac{x}{n(n-1)} A_{n-1}(x) \qquad (n = 2, 3, \ldots)$$

$B_1(x) = 0, \quad B_2(x) = 1$

$$B_{n+1}(x) = \frac{2n-1}{n} B_n(x) - \frac{x}{n(n-1)} B_{n-1}(x) \qquad (n = 2, 3, \ldots)$$

	$A_n(x)$	$B_n(x)$
$n = 1$	1	0
$n = 2$	1	1
$n = 3$	$\frac{1}{2}(3-x)$	$\frac{3}{2}$
$n = 4$	$\frac{5}{2}-x$	$\frac{1}{2}(5-\frac{1}{3}x)$
$n = 5$	$\frac{5}{8}(7-3x+\frac{1}{15}x^2)$	$\frac{5}{8}(7-\frac{2}{3}x)$
$n = 6$	$\frac{7}{8}(9-4x+\frac{1}{7}x^2)$	$\frac{7}{8}(9-x+\frac{1}{105}x^2)$
$n = 7$	$\frac{7}{16}((33-15x+\frac{2}{3}x^2-\frac{1}{315}x^3)$	$\frac{7}{16}(33-4x+\frac{1}{15}x^2)$
$n = 8$	$\frac{1}{8}(\frac{429}{2}-99x+5x^2-\frac{2}{45}x^3)$	$\frac{1}{8}(\frac{429}{2}-\frac{55}{2}x+\frac{3}{5}x^2-\frac{1}{630}x^3)$
$n = 9$	$\frac{1}{128}(6435-3003x+165x^2-2x^3+\frac{1}{315}x^4)$	$\frac{1}{128}(6435-858x+22x^2-\frac{4}{35}x^3)$
$n = 10$	$\frac{1}{128}(12155-5720x+\frac{1001}{3}x^2-\frac{44}{9}x^3+\frac{1}{63}x^4)$	$\frac{1}{128}(12155-\frac{5005}{3}x+\frac{143}{3}x^2-\frac{22}{63}x^3+\frac{11}{2835}x^4)$

III. Electrotechnical applications

1. Equation of the circuit:

$$Z(I-\bar{I}) = E, \qquad \text{(I, § 27 and I, § 33)}$$

$$Z = Ls+R+\frac{1}{Cs}, \quad Z\bar{I} = LI(0)-\frac{Cs}{Q(0)} \text{ (a simple system)} \qquad \text{(I, § 26 and I, § 27)}$$

$$Z = Z_1+Z_2, \; Z\bar{I} = Z_1\bar{I}_1+Z_2\bar{I}_2 \text{ (connection in series)} \qquad \text{(I, § 33)}$$

$$\frac{1}{Z} = \frac{1}{Z_1}+\frac{1}{Z_2}, \; \bar{I} = \bar{I}_1+\bar{I} \text{ (connection in parallel)}$$

2. Stationary current:

$$E = \frac{E_1 s-E_2\omega}{s^2+\omega^2}, \; I_u = \frac{I_1 s-I_2\omega}{s^2+\omega^2} \qquad \text{(I, § 34)}$$

$$I_1+iI_2 = \frac{E_1+iE_2}{Z(\omega i)}.$$

$Z_0 = |Z(\omega i)|$ (apparent resistance)

$0 = \arg Z(\omega i)$ (phase translation).

3. Table of simple quadripoles and their matrices.

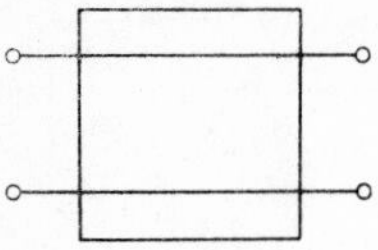	$\begin{bmatrix}1 & 0\\0 & 1\end{bmatrix}$	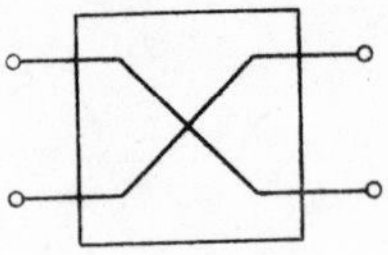	$\begin{bmatrix}-1 & 0\\0 & -1\end{bmatrix}$
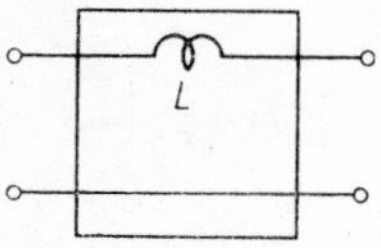	$\begin{bmatrix}1 & Ls\\0 & 1\end{bmatrix}$	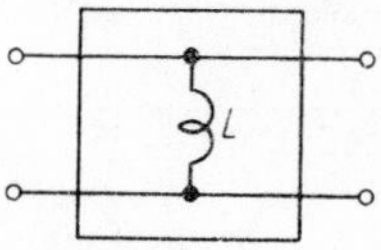	$\begin{bmatrix}1 & 0\\\frac{1}{Ls} & 1\end{bmatrix}$
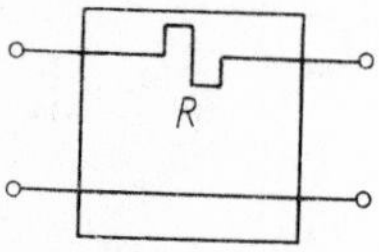	$\begin{bmatrix}1 & R\\0 & 1\end{bmatrix}$	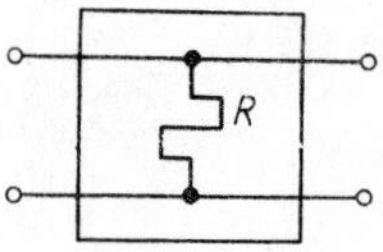	$\begin{bmatrix}1 & 0\\\frac{1}{R} & 1\end{bmatrix}$
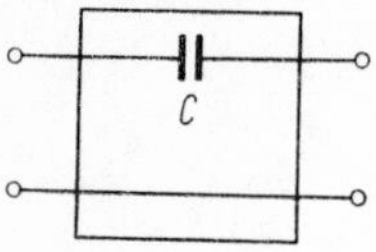	$\begin{bmatrix}1 & \frac{1}{Cs}\\0 & 1\end{bmatrix}$	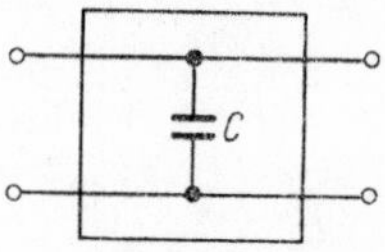	$\begin{bmatrix}1 & 0\\Cs & 1\end{bmatrix}$
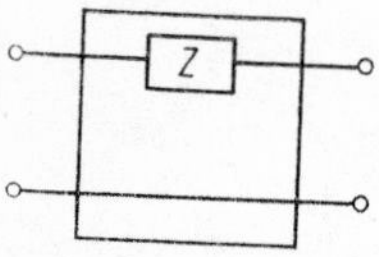	$\begin{bmatrix}1 & Z\\0 & 1\end{bmatrix}$	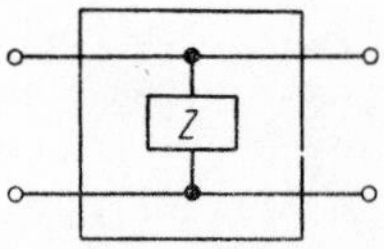	$\begin{bmatrix}1 & 0\\\frac{1}{Z} & 1\end{bmatrix}$
	$\begin{bmatrix}\frac{L_1}{M} & \frac{(L_1 L_2 - M^2)s}{M}\\\frac{1}{Ms} & \frac{L_2}{M}\end{bmatrix}$		

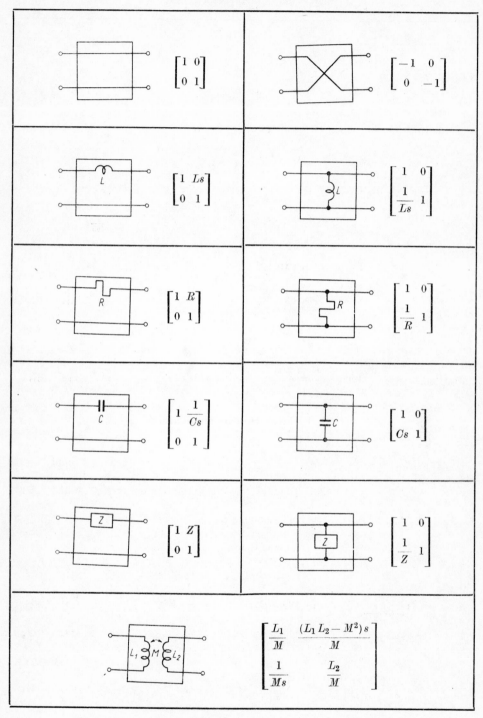

IV. Tables of functions

1. Gamma function of Euler $\Gamma(\lambda)$

	0	1	2	3	4	5	6	7	8	9
2,0	1,0000	0043	0086	0131	0176	0222	0269	0316	0365	0415
1	0465	0516	0568	0621	0675	0730	0786	0842	0900	0959
2	1018	1078	1140	1202	1266	1330	1395	1462	1529	1598
3	1667	1738	1809	1882	1956	2031	2107	2184	2262	2341
4	2422	2503	2586	2670	2756	2842	2930	3019	3109	3201
5	3293	3388	3483	3580	3678	3777	3878	3981	4084	4190
6	4296	4404	4514	4625	4738	4852	4968	5085	5204	5325
7	5447	5571	5696	5824	5953	6084	6216	6351	6487	6625
8	6765	6907	7051	7196	7344	7494	7646	7799	7955	8113
9	8274	8436	8600	8767	8936	9108	9281	9457	9636	9817

Other values one gets by formula

$$\Gamma(\lambda+1) = \lambda\Gamma(\lambda).$$

2. Error function erfλ

	0	1	2	3	4	5	6	7	8	9
0,0	0,0000	0113	0226	0338	0451	0564	0676	0789	0901	1013
1	1125	1236	1348	1459	1569	1680	1790	1900	2009	2118
2	2227	2335	2443	2550	2657	2763	2869	2974	3079	3183
3	3286	3389	3491	3593	3694	3794	3893	3992	4090	4187
4	4284	4380	4475	4569	4662	4755	4847	4937	5027	5117
5	5205	5292	5379	5465	5549	5633	5716	5798	5879	5959
6	6039	6117	6194	6270	6346	6420	6494	6566	6638	6708
7	6768	6847	6914	6981	7047	7112	7175	7238	7300	7361
8	7421	7480	7538	7595	7651	7707	7761	7814	7867	7918
9	7969	8019	8068	8116	8163	8209	8254	8299	8342	8385
1,0	8427	8468	8508	8548	8586	8624	8661	8698	8733	8768
1	8802	8835	8868	8900	8931	8961	8991	9020	9048	9076
2	9103	9130	9155	9181	9205	9229	9252	9275	9297	9319
3	9340	9361	9381	9400	9419	9438	9456	9473	9490	9507
4	9523	9539	9554	9569	9583	9597	9611	9624	9637	9649
5	9661	9673	9684	9695	9706	9716	9726	9736	9745	9755
6	9763	9772	9780	9788	9796	9804	9811	9818	9825	9832
7	9838	9844	9850	9856	9861	9867	9872	9877	9882	9886
8	9891	9895	9899	9903	9907	9911	9915	9918	9922	9925
9	9928	9931	9934	9937	9939	9942	9944	9947	9949	9951
2,	0,9 9532	9702	9814	9886	9931	9959	9976	9987	9993	9996
3,	0,99 9978	9988	9994	9997	9998	9999				

3. Bessel function $J_0(\lambda)$

	0	1	2	3	4	5	6	7	8	9
0	+1	+0,998	990	978	960	938	912	881	846	808
1	+0,765	720	671	620	567	512	455	398	340	283
2	224	167	110	056	003	−048	−097	−142	−185	−224
3	−0,260	292	320	344	364	380	392	399	403	402
4	397	389	377	361	342	321	296	269	240	210
5	178	144	110	076	041	007	+027	+060	+092	+122
6	+0,151	177	202	224	243	260	274	285	293	298
7	300	299	295	288	279	266	252	235	215	194
8	172	148	122	096	069	042	015	−013	−039	−065
9	−0,090	114	137	158	177	194	209	222	232	240
10	246	249	250	248	243	237	228	216	203	188
11	171	153	133	112	090	068	045	021	+002	+025
12	+0,048	070	091	111	130	147	163	177	189	199
13	207	213	217	218	218	215	210	203	194	184
14	171	157	141	125	107	088	068	048	027	006
15	−0,014	035	054	074	092	109	125	140	153	165
16	175	183	189	194	196	196	195	191	186	179
17	170	159	147	134	119	103	086	069	051	032
18	013	+005	+204	+042	+060	+077	+093	+109	+123	+135
19	+0,147	156	165	171	176	179	180	179	177	173
20	167	160	150	140	128	115	101	086	070	054

4. Bessel function $J_1(\lambda)$

	0	1	2	3	4	5	6	7	8	9
0	+0,000	050	100	148	196	242	287	329	369	406
1	440	417	498	522	542	558	570	578	582	581
2	577	568	556	540	520	497	471	442	410	375
3	339	301	261	221	179	137	095	054	013	−027
4	−0,066	103	139	172	203	231	257	279	289	315
5	328	337	343	346	345	341	334	324	331	295
6	277	256	233	208	182	154	125	095	065	035
7	005	+025	+054	+083	+110	+135	+159	+181	+201	+219
8	+0,235	248	258	266	271	273	273	270	264	256
9	245	232	217	200	182	161	140	117	093	068
10	043	018	−007	−031	−055	−079	−101	−122	−142	−160
11	−0,177	191	204	214	222	228	232	233	232	229
12	223	216	206	194	181	165	149	131	111	091
13	070	049	027	005	+017	+038	+059	+079	+098	+117
14	+0,133	149	163	175	185	193	200	204	207	207
15	205	201	196	188	178	167	154	140	125	108
16	090	072	053	034	014	006	−025	−044	−063	−081
17	−0,098	114	128	141	153	163	172	179	184	187
18	188	187	184	181	174	167	157	146	134	120
19	106	090	074	056	039	021	003	+015	+033	+050
20	+0,067	083	098	112	125	136	146	155	162	167

5. Functions $J_0(i\lambda)$ and $-iJ_1(i\lambda)$

λ	$J_0(i\lambda)$	$-iJ_1(i\lambda)$	λ	$J_0(i\lambda)$	$-iJ_1(i\lambda)$
0,0	1,000	0,000	5,0	27,24	24,34
1	003	050	1	29,79	26,68
2	010	101	2	32,58	29,25
3	023	152	3	35,65	32,08
4	040	204	4	39,01	35,18
5	064	258	5	42,69	38,59
6	092	314	6	46,74	42,33
7	126	372	7	51,17	46,44
8	167	433	8	56,04	50,95
9	213	497	9	61,38	55,90
1,0	266	565	6,0	67,23	61,34
1	326	637	1	73,66	67,32
2	394	715	2	80,72	73,89
3	469	797	3	88,46	81,10
4	553	886	4	96,98	89,03
5	647	982	5	106,29	97,73
6	750	1,085	6	116,54	107,30
7	864	196	7	127,79	117,82
8	990	317	8	140,14	129,38
9	2,128	448	9	153,70	142,08
2,0	280	591	7,0	168,6	156,0
1	446	745	1	185,0	171,4
2	629	914	2	202,9	188,3
3	830	2,098	3	222,7	206,8
4	3,049	298	4	244,3	227,2
5	290	517	5	268,2	249,6
6	553	755	6	294,3	274,2
7	842	3,016	7	323,1	301,3
8	4,157	301	8	354,7	331,1
9	503	613	9	389,4	363,9
3,0	881	953	8,0	427,6	399,9
1	5,294	4,326	1	469,5	439,5
2	747	734	2	515,6	483,0
3	6,243	5,181	3	566,3	531,0
4	785	670	4	621,9	583,7
5	7,378	6,206	5	683,2	641,6
6	8,028	793	6	750,5	705,4
7	739	7,436	7	824,4	775,5
8	9,517	8,140	8	905,8	852,7
9	10,369	913	9	995,2	937,5
4,0	11,30	9,76	9,0	1093,6	1030,9
1	12,32	10,69	1	1201,7	1133,6
2	13,44	11,71	2	1320,7	1246,7
3	14,67	12,82	3	1451,5	1371,0
4	16,01	14,05	4	1595,3	1507,9
5	17,48	15,39	5	1753	1658
6	19,09	16,86	6	1927	1824
7	20,86	18,48	7	2119	2006
8	22,79	20,25	8	2329	2207
9	24,91	22,20	9	2561	2428

ANSWERS TO PROBLEMS

PART ONE

CHAPTER I

p. 8

(α) and (β) t;

(γ) and (δ) $\frac{2}{3}[\sqrt{(1+t)^3}-1]$;

(ε) and (ζ) $\frac{1}{2}(\operatorname{sh} t-\sin t)$;

p. 8

$\frac{1}{t+1}$ belongs to class $\mathcal{C}$ because $t+1>0$.

$\frac{1}{t-1}$ does not belong to class $\mathcal{C}$ (being discontinuous for $t=1$).

$\frac{1}{t-i}$ belongs to class $\mathcal{C}$ because $t \neq i$.

$\frac{1}{e^t+e^{-t}}$ belongs to class $\mathcal{C}$ because $e^t>0$ and $e^{-t}>0$.

$\frac{1}{e^t-e^{-t}}$ does not belong to class $\mathcal{C}$ (being discontinuous for $t=0$).

$\frac{1}{\cos t}$ does not belong to class $\mathcal{C}$ (being discontinuous for $t=\frac{1}{2}(2k+1)\pi$, $k=0,1,2,\ldots$).

$\frac{1}{1+\cos t}$ does not belong to class $\mathcal{C}$ (being discontinuous for $t=(2k+1)\pi$, $k=0,1,2,\ldots$).

$\frac{1}{2+\cos t}$ belongs to class $\mathcal{C}$ because $2+\cos t>0$.

$\frac{1}{i+\cos t}$ belongs to class $\mathcal{C}$ because $\cos t \neq i$ for a real t.

p. 13

2. (α) $\{\frac{1}{2}t^2\}$; (β) $\{2\sin t-2\cos t+2\}$.

p. 14

1. (α) $\left\{t-\frac{1}{n}\sin nt\right\}$; (β) $\left\{t+\frac{1}{n}e^{-nt}-\frac{1}{n}\right\}$;

(γ) $\left\{\left(-\frac{t}{n}-\frac{3}{n^2}\right)e^{-nt}+\frac{3}{n^2}-\frac{2t}{n}+\frac{t^2}{2}\right\}$.

CHAPTER III

p. 38

1. (α) $\{\frac{1}{3}e^{t/2}\sin\frac{3}{2}t\}$; (β) $\{e^{3t}+2e^{-2t}\}$; (γ) $s+1+\{2e^{2t}+3e^{-t}\}$;

(δ) $\{4+t+2\cos t-\sin t\}$;

(ε) $\left\{1-e^{-t/2}\cos\frac{\sqrt{3}}{2}t-\frac{1}{\sqrt{3}}e^{-t/2}\sin\frac{\sqrt{3}}{2}t\right\}$; (ζ) $s^2-1+\{\sin t\}$;

(η) $\{4\operatorname{ch}2t+\cos 2t+\frac{3}{2}\sin 2t\}$; ϑ) $\left\{\frac{2}{3}e^{-t/2}\left[\frac{2}{\sqrt{3}}\sin\frac{\sqrt{3}}{2}t-t\cos\frac{\sqrt{3}}{2}t\right]\right\}$.

CHAPTER IV

p. 45

1. (α) $x=\left\{\frac{e^{\alpha t}}{\beta}\sin\beta t\right\}$; (β) $x=\{\frac{1}{3}\sin t-\frac{1}{6}\sin 2t\}$;

(γ) $x=\{-\frac{1}{2}+\frac{1}{10}e^{2t}+\frac{2}{5}\cos t-\frac{1}{5}\sin t\}$; (δ) $x=\{\frac{1}{3}t^3+2+2e^{-t}\}$;

(ε) $x=\{\frac{1}{2}\gamma t^2+(1-\gamma)(t-1)+\frac{1}{2}(-\gamma)e^{-t}+\frac{1}{2}\cos t-\frac{1}{2}\sin t\}$;

(ζ) $x=\{e^t\}$; (η) $x=\{\frac{1}{4}(t^2-\operatorname{sh}t\sin t)\}$;

(ϑ) $x=\left\{\frac{1}{(a^2+1)^2}\operatorname{ch}t+\left[1-\frac{1}{(a^2+1)^2}+\frac{t}{2}\right]\cos t+\left[\frac{1}{2a}-\frac{a^3}{2(a^2+1)}t\right]\sin at\right\}$;

(ι) $x=\{\beta-2\alpha+\frac{1}{2}\alpha t^2+(2\alpha-\beta-\frac{3}{8}\gamma t+\frac{1}{8}\beta t^2)\cos t+$

$+(\frac{3}{5}\gamma+\frac{1}{8}(4\alpha-5\beta)t-\frac{1}{8}\gamma t^2)\sin t\}$;

(κ) $x=\{\frac{83}{80}\operatorname{ch}2t-\frac{1}{10}\cos t+\frac{1}{16}\cos 2t\}$.

p. 46

2. (α) $x=\{2-2e^{-t}-2te^{-t}\}$, $y=\{2-t-2e^{-t}-2te^{-t}\}$;

(β) $x=\{e^t(\cos t-2\sin t)\}$, $y=\{e^t(\cos t+3\sin t)\}$;

(γ) $x=\{-\frac{5}{4}+\frac{13}{4}\cos 2t-3\sin 2t\}$, $y=\{\frac{3}{2}t+3\cos 2t+\frac{13}{4}\sin 2t\}$;

(δ) $x=\{-\frac{1}{2}+e^t-\frac{11}{34}e^{4t}-\frac{3}{17}\cos t+\frac{5}{17}\sin t\}$,

$y=\{-\frac{2}{3}e^t+\frac{22}{51}e^{4t}+\frac{4}{17}\cos t-\frac{1}{17}\sin t\}$;

(ε) $x=\left\{-\frac{1}{2}e^t+\frac{1}{4}e^{2t}-\frac{3}{4}e^{t/2}\cos\frac{\sqrt{23}}{2}t+\frac{11}{4\sqrt{23}}e^{t/2}\sin\frac{\sqrt{23}}{2}t\right\}$,

$y=\left\{-\frac{1}{2}e^t-\frac{1}{8}e^{2s}+\frac{5}{8}e^{t/2}\cos\frac{\sqrt{23}}{2}t-\frac{73}{8\sqrt{23}}e^{t/2}\sin\frac{\sqrt{23}}{2}t\right\}$;

(ζ) $x = \left\{-6-4t-t^2+\frac{100}{17}e^{t/2}+\frac{2}{17}\cos 2t+\frac{1}{34}\sin 2t\right\}$,

$y = \left\{-1-t-\frac{1}{2}t^2+\frac{25}{17}e^{t/2}+\frac{1}{34}\cos 2t+\frac{9}{68}\sin 2t\right\}$;

(η) $x = \{2-e^t\}$, $y = \{-2+4e^t-te^t\}$,

$z = \{-2+5e^t-te^t\}$;

$$(\vartheta)\quad x = \left\{-11e^{2t}+20e^{13t/2}\operatorname{ch}\frac{\sqrt{97}}{2}t-\frac{212}{\sqrt{97}}e^{13t/2}\operatorname{sh}\frac{\sqrt{97}}{2}t\right\},$$

$$y = \left\{-11e^{2t}+16e^{13t/2}\operatorname{ch}\frac{\sqrt{97}}{2}t-\frac{144}{\sqrt{97}}e^{13t/2}\operatorname{sh}\frac{\sqrt{97}}{2}t\right\},$$

$$z = \left\{-17e^{2t}+24e^{13t/2}\operatorname{ch}\frac{\sqrt{97}}{2}t-\frac{216}{\sqrt{97}}e^{13t/2}\operatorname{sh}\frac{\sqrt{97}}{2}t\right\}.$$

CHAPTER V

p. 65

1. For fig. 16:

$$I = \frac{E(Ls+2R)(R_1Cs+1)}{R_1(R+R_2)LCs^2+[(R+R_1+R_2)L+RR_1(R+2R_2)C]s+R(R+2R_1+2R_2)}.$$

For fig. 17:

$$I = \frac{E}{2}\left(\frac{1}{R_1}+\frac{1}{R_2}\right)+\frac{E}{2R_2}\cdot\frac{(2R_2^2C-L)s-2R_2}{R_2LCs^2+Ls+2R^2}.$$

2. We assume that $\frac{1}{C_1}\neq 0$, $\frac{1}{C_2}\neq 0$, $\frac{1}{C_3}\neq 0$, $L\neq 0$, $R_1\neq 0$, $R_2\neq 0$, $R_3\neq 0$.

Then $R_2 = R_1$, $R_3 = \frac{C_1}{C_2}R_1$, $L = C_3R_1^2$.

3. $I-I_1-I_2 = 0$,

$I_1-I_3-I_7 = 0$,

$I_2-I_4-I_8 = 0$,

$I_3-I_5+I_8 = 0$,

$I_4-I_6+I_7 = 0$,

$\frac{1}{Cs}(I-\bar{I})+R_1I_1+R_3I_3+\frac{1}{Cs}(I_5-\bar{I}_5) = E$,

$\frac{1}{Cs}(I-\bar{I})+R_2I_2+R_4I_4+\frac{1}{Cs}(I_6-\bar{I}_6) = E$,

$R_3I_3+\frac{1}{Cs}(I_5-\bar{I}_4)-\frac{1}{Cs}(I_6-\bar{I}_6)-\frac{1}{Cs}(I_7-\bar{I}_7) = 0$,

$R_4I_4+\frac{1}{Cs}(I_6-\bar{I}_6)-\frac{1}{Cs}(I_5-\bar{I}_5)-\frac{1}{Cs}(I_8-\bar{I}_8) = 0$.

p. 70

1. For fig. 29:

$$Z = Z_1+Z_2+Z_3, \quad \bar{I} = \frac{Z_1\bar{I}_1+Z_2\bar{I}_2+Z_3\bar{I}_3}{Z_1+Z_2+Z_3}.$$

For fig. 30:

$$Z = \frac{Z_1Z_2Z_3}{Z_2Z_3+Z_1Z_3+Z_1Z_2}, \quad \bar{I} = \bar{I}_1+\bar{I}_2+\bar{I}_3.$$

2. For fig. 31:

$$Z = \frac{(Z_1Z_2+Z_1Z_4+Z_2Z_4)(Z_3Z_5+Z_3Z_6+Z_5Z_6)}{(Z_1+Z_2)(Z_3Z_5+Z_3Z_6+Z_5Z_6)+(Z_5+Z_6)(Z_1Z_2+Z_1Z_4+Z_2Z_4)},$$

$$\bar{I} = \frac{Z_1Z_2(\bar{I}_1+\bar{I}_2)+Z_4(Z_1+Z_2)\bar{I}_4}{Z_1Z_2+Z_1Z_4+Z_2Z_4} + \frac{Z_3(Z_5+Z_6)\bar{I}_3+Z_4Z_6(\bar{I}_5+\bar{I}_6)}{Z_3Z_5+Z_3Z_6+Z_5Z_6}.$$

For fig. 32:

$$Z = \frac{Z_1Z_2Z_3}{Z_2Z_3+Z_1Z_3+Z_1Z_3} + \frac{Z_4Z_5Z_6}{Z_5Z_6+Z_4Z_6+Z_4Z_5},$$

$$\bar{I} = \frac{Z_1Z_2Z_3(Z_5Z_6+Z_4Z_6+Z_4Z_5)(\bar{I}_1+\bar{I}_2+\bar{I}_3)+Z_4Z_5Z_6(Z_2Z_3+Z_1Z_3+Z_1Z_2)(\bar{I}_4+\bar{I}_5+\bar{I}_6)}{Z_1Z_2Z_3(Z_5Z_6+Z_4Z_6+Z_4Z_5)+Z_4Z_5Z_6(Z_2Z_3+Z_1Z_3+Z_1Z_2)}.$$

For fig. 33:

$$Z = Z_2+\frac{Z_1Z_3}{Z_1+Z_3}+\frac{Z_4Z_5Z_6}{Z_5Z_6+Z_4Z_6+Z_4Z_5},$$

$$\bar{I} = \frac{(Z_5Z_6+Z_4Z_6+Z_4Z_5)[Z_2(Z_1+Z_3)\bar{I}_2+Z_1Z_3(\bar{I}_1+\bar{I}_3)]+Z_4Z_5Z_6(Z_1+Z_3)(\bar{I}_4+\bar{I}_5+\bar{I}_6)}{(Z_1Z_2+Z_2Z_3+Z_1Z_3)(Z_5Z_6+Z_4Z_6+Z_4Z_5)+Z_4Z_5Z_6(Z_1+Z_3)},$$

3.

$$Z = \frac{Z_1Z_2Z_3+Z_1Z_2Z_4+Z_1Z_3Z_4+Z_1Z_3Z_5+Z_1Z_4Z_5+Z_2Z_3Z_4+Z_2Z_3Z_5+Z_2Z_4Z_5}{Z_1Z_2+Z_1Z_4+Z_1Z_5+Z_2Z_3+Z_2Z_5+Z_3Z_4+Z_3Z_5+Z_4Z_5}.$$

4.

$$L_1 = \tfrac{1}{5},\ L_2 = L_3 = \tfrac{3}{5},$$

$$R_1 = 1,\ R_2 = \tfrac{6}{5},\ R_3 = \tfrac{9}{5},\ C_1 = \tfrac{6}{5}.$$

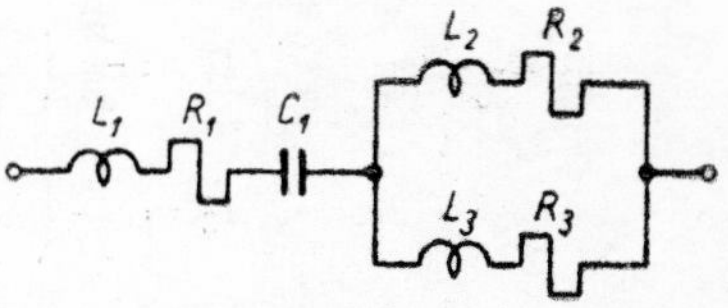

Fig. 172

(This solution can be understood in an arbitrarily adopted system of units. e. g.: Henry, Ohm, Farad.) The solution is not unique since, as has been seen on p. 67, every ohm resistance can be replaced by the equivalent system represented in fig. 22.

p. 72

For fig. 35:

$$I_0 = \frac{E_0}{R_1}\sqrt{\frac{L^2\omega^2+(R_1+R_2)^2}{L^2\omega^2+R_2^2}}, \qquad \psi = \varphi+\operatorname{arc\,tg}\frac{R_1L\omega}{L^2\omega^2+R_2(R_1+R_2)}.$$

For fig. 36:

$$I_0 = E_0 C_1 \omega \sqrt{\frac{R^2 C_2^2 \omega^2 + 1}{R^2 (C_1 + C_2)^2 \omega^2 + 1}}, \qquad \psi = \varphi - \operatorname{arc\,tg}\left(\frac{R^2 C_2^2 \omega^2 + 1}{R C_1 \omega} + R C_2 \omega\right).$$

For fig. 37:

$$I_0 = \frac{E_0}{R L \omega} \sqrt{\frac{R^2 (L C \omega^2 - 2)^2 + \omega^2 (L + R^2 C)^2}{R^2 C^2 \omega^2 + 4}}, \qquad \psi = \varphi + \operatorname{arc\,tg} \frac{R (4 - L C \omega^2 + R^2 C^2 \omega^2)}{L \omega (2 + R^2 C^2 \omega^2)}.$$

p. 77

For fig. 41:

Introduce the notation:

$$D = (L_1 R_1 C_1 s^2 + L_1 s + R_1)(L_2 R_2 C_2 s^2 + L^2 s + R_2) - M^2 s^2 (R_1 C_1 s + 1)(R_2 C_2 s + 1).$$

Then

$$I_1 = \frac{E}{D}(R_1 C_1 s + 1)(L_2 R_2 C_2 s^2 + L_2 s + R_2),$$

$$I_2 = \frac{E}{D} R_1 C_1 s (L_2 R_2 C_2 s^2 + L_2 s + R_2),$$

$$I_3 = \frac{E}{D}(L_2 R_2 C_2 s^2 + L_2 s + R_2),$$

$$I_4 = \frac{E}{D} M s (R_1 C_1 s + 1)(R_2 C_2 s + 1),$$

$$I_5 = \frac{E}{D} M R_2 C_2 s^2 (R_1 C_1 s + 1),$$

$$I_6 = \frac{E}{D} M s (R_1 C_1 s + 1).$$

For fig. 42: Write

$$D = s(Ms + R_1)(Ms - L_2 s - R_2) - \left(L_1 s^2 - M s^2 + \frac{1}{C}\right)(L_2 s + R_1 + R_2).$$

Then

$$I_1 = \frac{E}{D}\left(2 M s^2 - L_1 s^2 - L_2 s^2 - R_2 s - \frac{1}{C}\right),$$

$$I_2 = \frac{E}{D}\left(M s^2 - L_1 s^2 - \frac{1}{C}\right),$$

$$I_3 = \frac{E}{D}(M s^2 - L_2 s^2 - R_2 s).$$

p. 82

$$(\alpha) \quad \begin{bmatrix} 1 & Ls \\ 0 & 1 \end{bmatrix} \begin{bmatrix} 1 & 0 \\ Cs & 1 \end{bmatrix} = \begin{bmatrix} 1 + LCs^2 & Ls \\ Cs & 1 \end{bmatrix};$$

$$(\beta) \quad \begin{bmatrix} 1 & 0 \\ \frac{1}{R_1} & 1 \end{bmatrix} \begin{bmatrix} 1 & R_2 \\ 0 & 1 \end{bmatrix} = \begin{bmatrix} 1 & R_2 \\ \frac{1}{R_1} & \frac{R_2}{R_1} + 1 \end{bmatrix};$$

(γ) $\begin{bmatrix} -1 & 0 \\ 0 & -1 \end{bmatrix}\begin{bmatrix} 1 & 0 \\ Cs & 1 \end{bmatrix} = \begin{bmatrix} -1 & 0 \\ -Cs & -1 \end{bmatrix};$

(δ) $$\begin{bmatrix} 1 & \frac{1}{Cs} \\ 0 & 1 \end{bmatrix}\begin{bmatrix} \frac{L_1}{M} & \frac{(L_1L_2-M^2)s}{M} \\ \frac{1}{Ms} & \frac{L_2}{M} \end{bmatrix} = \begin{bmatrix} \frac{L_1}{M}+\frac{1}{CMs^2} & \frac{(L_1L_2-M^2)s}{M}+\frac{L_2}{CMs} \\ \frac{1}{Ms} & \frac{L_2}{M} \end{bmatrix}.$$

p. 84

(α) $$\begin{bmatrix} 1 & 0 \\ \frac{1}{R_1} & 1 \end{bmatrix}\begin{bmatrix} 1 & \frac{1}{Cs} \\ 0 & 1 \end{bmatrix}\begin{bmatrix} 1 & 0 \\ \frac{1}{R_2} & 1 \end{bmatrix} = \begin{bmatrix} 1+\frac{1}{R_2Cs} & \frac{1}{Cs} \\ \frac{1}{R_1}+\frac{1}{R_1R_2Cs}+\frac{1}{R_2} & \frac{1}{R_1Cs}+1 \end{bmatrix};$$

(β) $$\begin{bmatrix} 1 & 0 \\ C_1s & 1 \end{bmatrix}\begin{bmatrix} 1 & Ls \\ 0 & 1 \end{bmatrix}\begin{bmatrix} 1 & 0 \\ C_1s & 1 \end{bmatrix} = \begin{bmatrix} LC_2s^2+1 & Ls \\ C_1s+LC_1C_2s^3+C_2s & LC_1s^2+1 \end{bmatrix};$$

(γ) $$\begin{bmatrix} 1 & \frac{1}{Cs} \\ 0 & 1 \end{bmatrix}\begin{bmatrix} \frac{L_1}{M} & \frac{(L_1L_2-M^2)s}{M} \\ \frac{1}{Ms} & \frac{L_2}{M} \end{bmatrix}\begin{bmatrix} -1 & 0 \\ 0 & -1 \end{bmatrix}$$

$$= \begin{bmatrix} -\frac{L_1}{M}-\frac{1}{MCs^2} & -\frac{(L_1L_2-M^2)s}{M}-\frac{L_2}{MCs} \\ -\frac{1}{Ms} & -\frac{L_2}{M} \end{bmatrix}.$$

p. 86

For short-circuited ends:

(α) $I_1 = \left(\frac{1}{R_1}+Cs\right)E_1,\ I_2 = CsE_1;$

(β) $I_1 = \left(C_1s+\frac{1}{Ls}\right)E_1,\ I_2 = \frac{E_1}{Ls};$

(γ) $I_1 = \frac{L_2Cs}{(L_1L_2-M^2)Cs^2+L_2}E_1,\ I_2 = -\frac{MCs}{(L_1L_2-M^2)Cs^2+L_2}E_1.$

For free ends:

(α) $I_1 = \frac{(R_1+R_2)Cs+1}{R_1(R_2Cs+1)}E_1, \quad E_2 = \frac{R_2Cs}{R_2Cs+1}E_1;$

(β) $I_1 = \frac{LC_1C_2s^2+(C_1+C_2)s}{LC_2s^2+1}E_1, \quad E_2 = \frac{E_1}{LC_2s^2+1};$

(γ) $I_1 = \frac{Cs}{L_1Cs^2+1}E_1, \quad E_2 = -\frac{MCs^2}{L_1Cs^2+1}E_1.$

CHAPTER VI

p. 102

1. (α) $x = e^{at}(A+Bt+Ct^2+\frac{1}{6}t^3)$; (β) $x = Ae^{-2t}+(B\sin t+C\cos t)e^{2t}$;

(γ) $x = Ae^{-\sqrt{6+2\sqrt{6}}t}+Be^{\sqrt{6+2\sqrt{6}}t}+Ce^{-\sqrt{6-2\sqrt{6}}t}+De^{\sqrt{6-2\sqrt{6}}t}+e^{2t}$;

(δ) $x = A+Be^{t/2}+Ce^{t}+De^{3/2t}+\frac{18}{65}\sin t-\frac{14}{65}\cos t$;

2. (α) $x = 3t^2-t-1+(2-\beta)\sin t+(1+\alpha)\cos t$,

$y = t^2+2+(1+\alpha)\sin t+(\beta-2)\cos t$;

(β) $x = -\frac{93}{17}+\frac{31}{26}e^{t}-(\alpha+\beta+\frac{1803}{442})e^{-4t}\sin t+(\alpha+\frac{1891}{442})e^{-4t}\cos t$,

$y = \frac{6}{17}-\frac{2}{13}e^{t}+(2\alpha+\beta+\frac{1847}{221})e^{-4t}\sin t+(\beta-\frac{44}{221})e^{-4t}\cos t$;

(γ) $x = 44A+Be^{5t}+3Ce^{-17t}$,

$y = -26A-4Be^{5t}-Ce^{-17t}$,

$z = -75A-10Be^{5t}+3Ce^{-17t}$.

p. 104

1. (α) $x = \dfrac{\operatorname{sh} t}{\operatorname{sh} 2\pi}$;

(β) Unsolvable.

2. $x = e^{t-\pi/2}\sin t$.

p. 105

(α) $x = A+Be^{2t}+Ce^{-2t}+\frac{1}{96}e^{4t}-\frac{1}{160}e^{4t}\sin 2t$, where:

$A = \frac{1}{160}e^{6}(-2\sin 2-4\cos 2+5)+\frac{3}{4}$,

$B = \dfrac{64}{e^2}(\sin 2+\cos 2-2)+\dfrac{3}{8e^2}$,

$C = \frac{1}{960}e^{6}(3\sin 2+9\cos 2-10)-\frac{1}{8}e^{2}$;

(β) $x = 2e^{6(2-t)}[\cos(t-2)-\sin(t-2)]$,

$y = 2e^{6(2-t)}\cos(t-2)$.

CHAPTER VII

p. 107

(α) One discontinuity point for $t = 0$;

$$\int_0^t \frac{d\tau}{\tau^\lambda} = (1-\lambda)t^{1-\lambda}.$$

(β) Discontinuity points only for $t = k\pi$ $(k = 0, \pm 1, \pm 2, \ldots)$;

$$\int_{2k\pi}^{(2k+1)\pi}\frac{d\tau}{\sqrt{\sin\tau}} = \int_{(2k+1)\pi}^{(2k+1)\pi}\frac{d\tau}{\sqrt{-\sin\tau}} = 2\int_0^{\pi/2}\frac{d\tau}{\sqrt{\sin\tau}} < 8\int_0^{\pi/2}\frac{d}{2\sqrt{\tau}} = 8\sqrt{\frac{\pi}{2}}.$$

(γ) One discontinuity point for $t = 1$:

$$\int_0^1 \frac{d\tau}{\sqrt[3]{|\tau-1|}} = \int_0^1 \frac{d\tau}{\sqrt[3]{\tau}} = \frac{3}{2}; \quad \int_0^t \frac{d\tau}{\sqrt[3]{\tau-1}} = \frac{3}{2}(t-1)^{2/3}.$$

(δ) One discontinuity point for $t = 1$; $f(t) = -1$ for $0 \leqslant t < 1$ and $f(t) = 1$ for $t > 1$, whence

$$\int_0^t |f(\tau)|\, d\tau = t.$$

p. 114

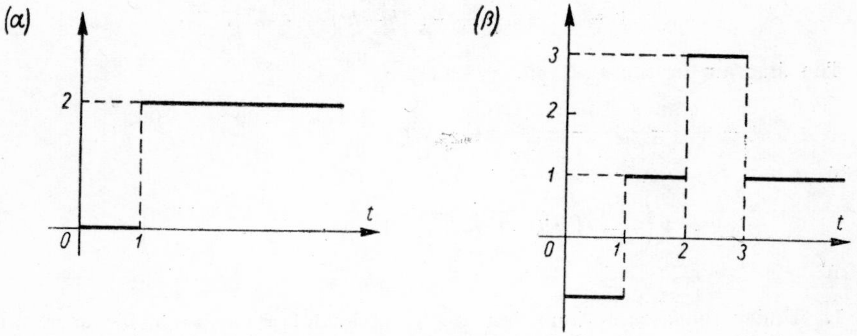

Fig. 173

p. 129

(α) $F = -20 + \dfrac{20}{s}(h - h^2) + 30sh^3$;

(β) $F = -100 + \dfrac{400}{3s^2}(1 - h^3) - \dfrac{400}{s}h^3 - 150s(h + h^2) - 500h^3$.

p. 132

The diagram in the example.

$$Q = -\frac{20}{s} + \frac{30}{s^2}(1-h) - 15h^2 - \frac{10}{s}h^3,$$

$$M = -\frac{20}{s^2} + \frac{30}{s^3}(1-h) - \frac{15}{s}h^2 - \frac{10}{s^2}h^3.$$

The diagram in exercise (α):

$$Q = -\frac{20}{s} + \frac{20}{s^2}(h - h^2) + 30h^3,$$

$$M = -\frac{20}{s^2} + \frac{20}{s^3}(h - h^2) + \frac{30}{s}h^3.$$

The diagram in exercise (β).

$$Q = -\frac{100}{s} + \frac{400}{3s^3}(1-h^3) - \frac{400}{s^2}h^3 - 150(h+h^2) - \frac{500}{s}h^3,$$

$$M = -\frac{100}{s^2} + \frac{400}{3s^4}(1-h^3) - \frac{400}{s^3}h^3 - \frac{150}{s}(h+h^2) - \frac{500}{s^2}h^3.$$

p. 135

The diagram in the example.

$$y = \varkappa\left(\frac{5}{s^2} - \frac{20}{s^4} + \frac{30}{s^5}(1-h) - \frac{15}{s^3}h^2 - \frac{10}{s^4}h^3\right).$$

The diagram in exercise (β).

$$y = \varkappa\left(-\frac{160}{3s^2} - \frac{100}{s^5} + \frac{400}{s^6}(1-h^3) - \frac{300}{s^5}h^3 - \frac{50}{s^3}(1+h^2) - \frac{500}{s^4}h^3\right).$$

The diagram in exercise (α).

$$y = \varkappa\left(-\frac{20}{s^4} + \frac{20}{s^5}(h-h^3) + \frac{30}{s^3}h^3\right).$$

The diagram in the example.

$$y = \varkappa\left(\frac{50}{s^3} - \frac{100}{s^4} + \frac{300}{s^5}(h-h^2) - \frac{100}{s^4}h^2 - \frac{200}{s^3}h^3 - \frac{100}{s^4}h^4\right).$$

p. 136

$$y = \varkappa\left(\frac{300}{s^4}(1+h+h^4) - \frac{450}{s^4}(h+h^3) - \frac{1275}{2s^2} + \frac{1175}{2s}\right).$$

p. 140

1. Under the assumption that the total load is $112f$ we have the following reactions on the supports:

$$11f, \quad 32f, \quad 26f, \quad 32f, \quad 11f.$$

Deflection curve:

$$y = \varkappa f\left(\frac{112}{s^5}(1-h^4) - \frac{1}{s^4}(11+32h+26h^2+32h^3+11h^4) + \frac{8}{3s^2}\right).$$

2. Deflection curve (fig. 174):

for a horizontal beam

$$y = \frac{\varkappa P}{3}\left(\frac{1}{s^4}(-2+3h-h^3) + \frac{10}{9s^3}(1-h^3)\right),$$

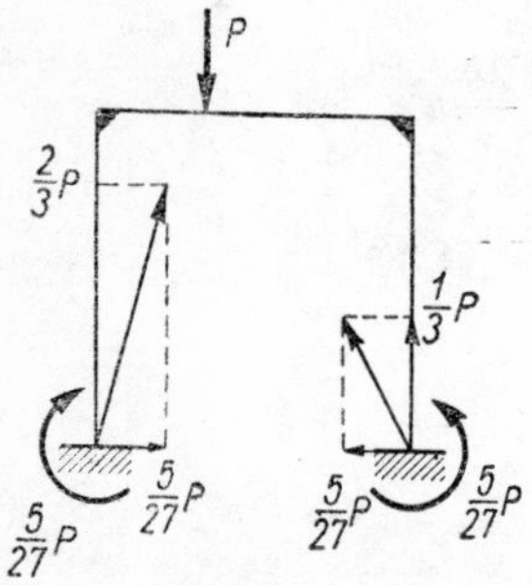

Fig. 174

i. e.

$$y(t) = \begin{cases} \frac{1}{9}\varkappa P(-t^3+\frac{5}{3}t^2) & \text{for } 0 \leqslant t \leqslant 1, \\ \frac{1}{6}\varkappa P(\frac{1}{3}t^3 - \frac{17}{9}t^2 + 3t - 1) & \text{for } 1 \leqslant t \leqslant 3; \end{cases}$$

for the left-hand vertical beam

$$y = \frac{5\varkappa P}{27}\left(\frac{1-h^3}{s^4} - \frac{1+2h^3}{s^3}\right),$$

i. e.

$$y(t) = \frac{5}{27}\varkappa P(\tfrac{1}{3}t^3 - \tfrac{1}{2}t^2) \quad \text{for} \quad 0 \leqslant t \leqslant 3.$$

The deflection curve equation for the right-hand vertical beam is like the one for the left-hand beam with the opposite sign.

PART TWO

CHAPTER I

p. 144

1. $\left|\dfrac{\cos nt}{n}\right| \leqslant \dfrac{1}{n} \to 0.$

2. Let $\varepsilon_n = \begin{bmatrix} 1 \text{ for } n \leqslant t_0 \\ 0 \text{ for } n > t_0 \end{bmatrix}.$

Then $\varepsilon_n \to 0$ and $|H_n(t) - 0| \leqslant \varepsilon_n$ for $0 \leqslant t \leqslant t_0$.

p. 146

1. $\lim\limits_{n\to\infty} \{\cos nt\} = \lim\limits_{n\to\infty} s\left\{\dfrac{\sin nt}{n}\right\} = s \cdot 0 = 0,$

$$\lim_{n\to\infty} \{n \sin nt\} = \lim_{n\to\infty} s^2\left\{t - \frac{\sin nt}{n}\right\} = s^2\{t\} = 1,$$

$$\lim_{n\to\infty} \{n^2 \cos nt\} = \lim_{n\to\infty} s^3\left\{t - \frac{\sin nt}{n}\right\} = s^2(t) = s.$$

2. $\lim\limits_{n\to\infty} h^n = \lim\limits_{n\to\infty} sH_n = s \cdot 0 = 0$ (see exercise 2, p. 000)

p. 144

3. (α) $a^n = \{ne^{-nt}\} = s^2\left\{-\dfrac{1}{n} + t + \dfrac{1}{n}e^{-nt}\right\} = s^2 f_n.$

Since $f \rightrightarrows \{t\}$ in the interval $0 \leqslant t < \infty$, we have $a_n \to s^2\{t\} = 1$. (A double arrow $\rightrightarrows$ denotes the uniform convergence of a sequence of functions, a single arrow $\to$ denotes the convergence of a sequence of operators in the sense of the definition of § 12 (p. 144) or else the ordinary convergence of a numerical sequence).

$$(\beta) \quad a_n = \{n^2 te^{-nt}\} = s^2\left\{te^{-nt} + \frac{2}{n}e^{-nt} + t - \frac{2}{n}\right\} = s^2\{f_n(t)\}.$$

The function $\{f_n(t) - t\}$ has the derivative $\{-nte^{-nt} - e^{-nt}\}$, i. e. it is decreasing; consequently

$$|f_n(t) - t| \leqslant |f_n(t_0) - t_0| = \left| t_0 e^{-nt_0} + \frac{2}{n}e^{-nt_0} - \frac{2}{n}\right| \to 0 \qquad (0 \leqslant t \leqslant t_0).$$

Hence $f_n \rightrightarrows \{t\}$ in every interval $0 \leqslant 1 \leqslant t_0$ and thus $a_n \to s^2\{\,\} = 1$.

$$(\gamma) \quad a_n = \{n - n^2 t + |n - n^2 t|\} = \begin{Bmatrix} 2n - 2n^2 t & \text{for} & 0 \leqslant t \leqslant \dfrac{1}{n} \\ 0 & \text{for} & \dfrac{1}{n} \leqslant t \leqslant \infty \end{Bmatrix}$$

$$= s^2 \begin{Bmatrix} nt^2 - \dfrac{n^2}{3}t^3 & \text{for} & 0 \leqslant t \leqslant \dfrac{1}{n} \\ -\dfrac{1}{3n} + t & \text{for} & \dfrac{1}{n} \leqslant t < \infty \end{Bmatrix} = s^2 \cdot \{f_n(t)\}.$$

Since

$$|f_n(t)-t| = \begin{bmatrix} \left|-t+nt^2-\frac{n^2}{3}t^2\right| & \text{for} \quad 0\leqslant t\leqslant \frac{1}{n} \\ \frac{1}{3n} & \text{for} \quad \frac{1}{n}\leqslant t<\infty \end{bmatrix}$$

$$\leqslant \begin{bmatrix} t+nt^2+\frac{n^2}{3}t^3 & \text{for} \quad 0\leqslant t\leqslant \frac{1}{n} \\ \frac{1}{3n} & \text{for} \quad \frac{1}{n}\leqslant t<\infty \end{bmatrix} \leqslant \begin{bmatrix} \frac{1}{n}+\frac{1}{n}+\frac{1}{3n} & \text{for} \quad 0\leqslant t\leqslant \frac{1}{n} \\ \frac{1}{3n} & \text{for} \quad \frac{1}{n}\leqslant t<\infty \end{bmatrix}$$

$$\leqslant \frac{7}{3n} \quad \text{for} \quad 0\leqslant t<\infty$$

we have $f_n \rightrightarrows \{t\}$ in the whole interval $0\leqslant 1<\infty$ and consequently $a_n \to s^2\{t\} = 1$.

$$(\delta) \quad a_n = \left\{\frac{1}{n}t^{1/n-1}\right\} = s^2\left\{\frac{n}{n+1}t^{1/n+1}\right\} = s^2\{f_n(t)\}.$$

The function $\{f_n(t)-t\}$ is negative and decreasing in the interval $(0, 1)$; at point $t=1$ it has its minimum equal to the number $-\frac{1}{n+1}$, and for $t>1$ it is increasing. Thus in every interval $0\leqslant t\leqslant t_0$ we have

$$|f_n(t)-t| \leqslant \frac{1}{n+1}+|f_k(t_0)-t_0| = \frac{1}{n+1}+\left|\frac{n}{n+1}t_0^{1/n+1}-t_0\right| = \varepsilon_n.$$

Since $\varepsilon_n \to 0$, we have $f_n \rightrightarrows \{t\}$ and $a_n \to s^2\{t\} = 1$.

4. $$a_n = \{n^3\sin nt+n^4 t\cos nt\} = s^5\left\{\frac{4}{n^2}\cos nt+\frac{t}{n}\sin nt+t^2-\frac{4}{n^2}\right\} = s^2\{f_n(t)\}.$$

Since $|f_n(t)-t^2| = \frac{8}{n^2}+\frac{t_0}{n}$ for $0\leqslant t\leqslant t_0$, we have $f_n \rightrightarrows \{t\}$ in the interval

$$0\leqslant t\leqslant t_0 \text{ and } a_n \to s^5\{t^2\} = s^5\cdot 2l^3 = 2s^2.$$

5. $$a+bh^n = a+bs\cdot\begin{Bmatrix} 0 & \text{for} \quad 0\leqslant t<n \\ 1 & \text{for} \quad n<t<\infty \end{Bmatrix} = a+bs\{H_n(t)\}.$$

Since $\{H_n(t)\} \rightrightarrows 0$ in the interval $0\leqslant t\leqslant t_0$ (see exercise 2 on p. 144) we have $s\{H_n(t)\} \to 0$ and consequently $a+bh^n \to a+b\cdot 0$.

CHAPTER II

p. 154

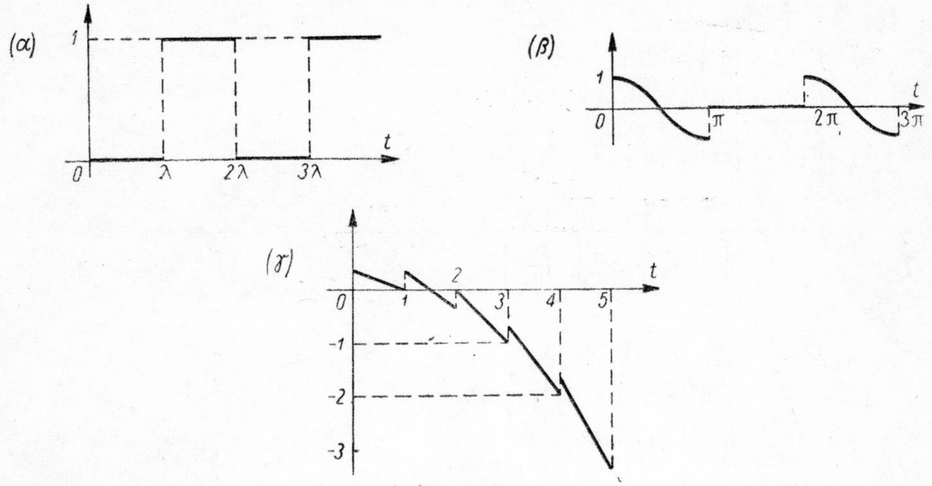

Fig. 175

p. 157

The periodic part of the current has a period λ; in the time interval $0 \leqslant t < \lambda$ it consists of an impulse 1 and a current

$$\frac{\mu e^{\lambda}}{e^{\lambda}-1}\, e^{-t} - \frac{2\mu e^{2\lambda}}{e^{2\lambda}-1}\, e^{-2t}.$$

The turbulent part has the shape

$$\frac{\mu}{e^{\lambda}-1}\, e^{-t} - \frac{2\mu}{e^{2\lambda}-1}\, e^{-2t}.$$

(The existence of impulses in the periodic part is due to the impulses in the potential difference and the absence of resistance in the lower branch of the network).

The periodic part of the current has a period 1: in the time interval $0 \leqslant t < 1$ it has the shape $[Rt - L - (L+A)e^{-at}]/R^2$, where

$$A = \frac{1}{L}\,\frac{(1-a)e^{a}-a}{a^2(e-1)}.$$

The turbulent part is Ae^{-at}.

CHAPTER III

p. 163

$$\xi_n = \frac{1}{\sqrt{5}}\left[\left(\frac{1+\sqrt{5}}{2}\right)^{n+1} - \left(\frac{1-\sqrt{5}}{2}\right)^{n+1}\right].$$

CHAPTER IV

p. 171

$$\sin\frac{1}{s} = \frac{1}{1!}\,\frac{1}{s} - \frac{1}{3!}\,\frac{1}{s^3} + \frac{1}{5!}\,\frac{1}{s^5} - \ldots = \left\{\frac{1}{1!}\cdot 1 - \frac{1}{3!}\,\frac{t^2}{2!} + \frac{1}{5!}\,\frac{t^4}{4!} - \ldots\right\}.$$

PART THREE

CHAPTER I

p. 187

(α) $f'(\lambda) = \{2\lambda\} = 2l\lambda;$

(β) $f'(\lambda) = \{4\lambda^3 + 2\lambda t^2\} = 4l\lambda^3 + 4l^3\lambda;$

(γ) $f'(\lambda) = \{\cos(\lambda + t)\} = \dfrac{1}{1+s^2}(s\cos\lambda - \sin\lambda);$

(δ) $$f'(\lambda) = \frac{\{-2\lambda\}}{\left\{\lambda^4 t + \frac{2}{3}\lambda^2 t^3 + \frac{1}{30}t^5\right\}} = \frac{-2\lambda}{l(\lambda^2 + 2l^2)^2}.$$

p. 188

(α) $f''(\lambda) = \{2\} = 2l, \; f'''(\lambda) = 0;$

(β) $f''(\lambda) = \{12\lambda^2 + 2t^2\} = 12l\lambda^2 + 4l^3,$

$f'''(\lambda) = \{24\lambda\} = 24l\lambda;$

(γ) $f''(\lambda) = \{-\sin(t+\lambda)\} = \dfrac{1}{s^2+1}(-s\sin\lambda - \cos\lambda);$

$f'''(\lambda) = \{-\cos(t+\lambda)\} = \dfrac{1}{s^2+1}(-s\cos\lambda + \sin\lambda);$

(δ) $$f''(\lambda) = \frac{2(3\lambda^2 - 2l^2)}{l(\lambda^2+2l^2)^3}, \quad f'''(\lambda) = \frac{-24\lambda(\lambda^2 - 2l^2)}{l(\lambda^2+2l^2)^4}.$$

CHAPTER II

p. 195

(α) $$\frac{1}{\sqrt{s}}e^{-\lambda/s} = \sum_{n=0}^{\infty}(-1)^n \frac{\lambda^n l^{n+1/2}}{n!} = \left\{\sum_{n=0}^{\infty}(-1)^n \frac{\lambda^n t^{n-1/2}}{n!\,\Gamma\left(n+\frac{1}{2}\right)}\right\}$$

$$= \left\{\sum_{n=0}^{\infty}(-1)^n \frac{\lambda^n t^{n-1/2}}{n(n-1)\ldots 1\cdot\left(n-\frac{1}{2}\right)\left(n-\frac{3}{2}\right)\ldots\frac{1}{2}\cdot\Gamma\left(\frac{1}{2}\right)}\right\}$$

$$= \left\{\sum_{n=0}^{\infty}(-1)^n \frac{2^{2n}\lambda^n t^{n-1/2}}{(2n)(2n-1)\ldots 1\cdot\sqrt{\pi}}\right\}$$

$$= \left\{\frac{1}{\sqrt{\pi t}}\sum_{n=0}^{\infty}(-1)^n \frac{(2\sqrt{\lambda t})^{2n}}{(2n)!}\right\} = \left\{\frac{1}{\sqrt{\pi t}}\cos 2\sqrt{\lambda t}\right\}.$$

(β) The procedure is the same as before but the factor $(-1)^n$ must be omitted.

(γ) $$\frac{1}{s^2}e^{-\lambda/s} = \sum_{n=0}^{\infty}(-1)^n \frac{\lambda^n l^{n+2}}{n!} = \left\{\sum_{n=0}^{\infty}(-1)^n \frac{\lambda^n t^{n+1}}{n!\,(n+1)!}\right\}$$

$$= \left\{\sqrt{\frac{t}{\lambda}}\sum_{n=0}^{\infty}(-1)^n \frac{(2\sqrt{\lambda t})^{2n+1}}{2^{2n+1}n!\,(n+1)!}\right\} = \left\{\sqrt{\frac{t}{\lambda}}J_1(2\sqrt{\lambda t})\right\}.$$

CHAPTER IV

p. 208

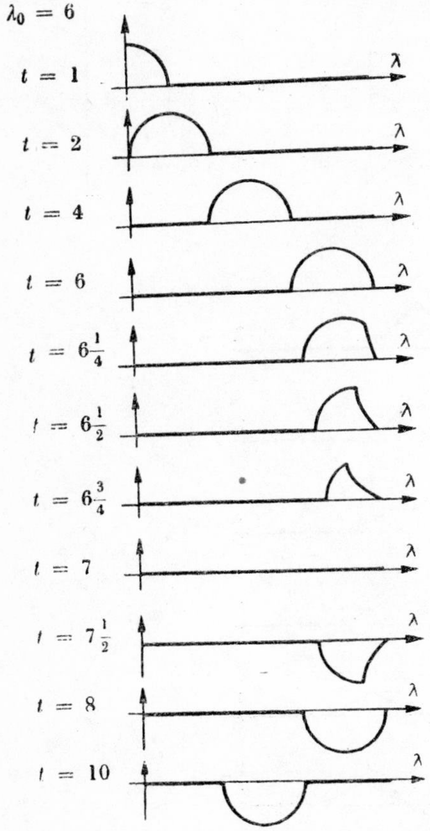

Fig. 177

Construction method for $t = 6\frac{3}{4}$:

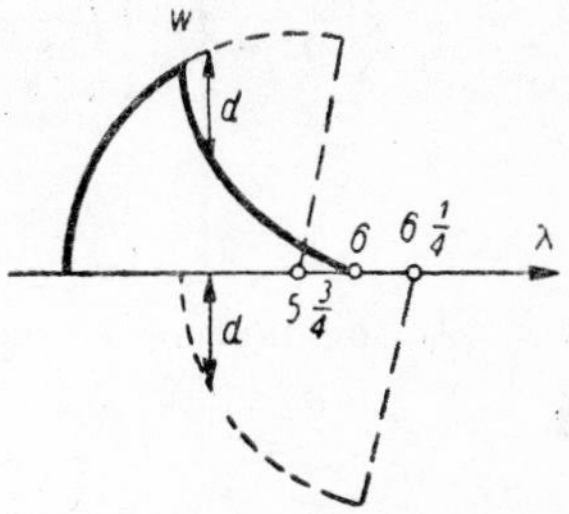

Fig. 176

(The arc whose end-points are denoted in the figure by w and 6 is not that of a circle but of a fourth degree curve).

p. 209

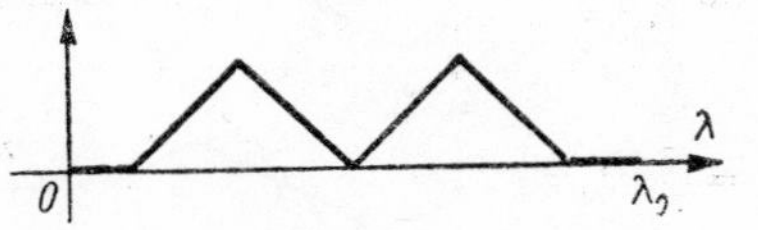

Fig. 178

p. 217

1. If $0 \leqslant t \leqslant \frac{1}{2}a\lambda_0$, then

$$x(\lambda, t) = \begin{bmatrix} \mu\lambda\left(\lambda_0 - \dfrac{2t}{a}\right) & \text{for} \quad 0 \leqslant \lambda \leqslant \dfrac{t}{a} \\ \mu\lambda\left(\lambda_0 - \dfrac{t^2}{a^2}\right) & \text{for} \quad \dfrac{t}{a} \leqslant \lambda \leqslant \lambda_0 - \dfrac{t}{a} \\ \mu(\lambda_0 - \lambda)\left(\lambda_0 - \dfrac{2t}{a}\right) & \text{for} \quad \lambda_0 - \dfrac{t}{a} \leqslant \lambda \leqslant \lambda_0 \end{bmatrix};$$

and if $\frac{1}{2}a\lambda_0 \leqslant t \leqslant a\lambda_0$, then

$$x(\lambda, t) = \begin{bmatrix} \mu\lambda\left(\lambda_0 - \dfrac{2t}{a}\right) & \text{for} \quad 0 \leqslant \lambda \leqslant \lambda_0 - \dfrac{t}{a} \\ \mu\left[\left(\lambda_0 - \dfrac{t}{a}\right)^2 - \lambda(\lambda_0 - \lambda)\right] & \text{for} \quad \lambda_0 - \dfrac{t}{a} \leqslant \lambda \leqslant \dfrac{t}{a} \\ \mu(\lambda_0 - \lambda)\left(\lambda_0 - \dfrac{2t}{a}\right) & \text{for} \quad \dfrac{t}{a} \leqslant \lambda \leqslant \lambda_0 \end{bmatrix}.$$

For $t > a\lambda_0$ the motion is repeated periodically.

2.

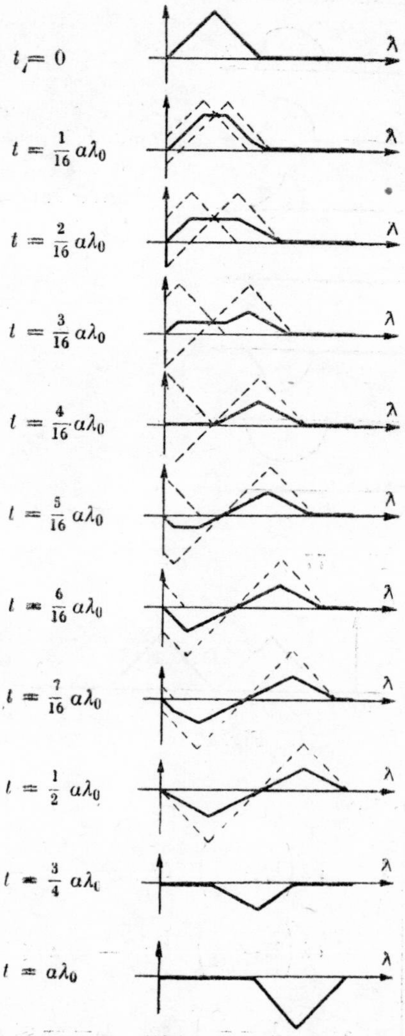

Fig. 179

CHAPTER V

p. 226

(α) $\dfrac{1}{s^2+a^2} = \left\{\dfrac{1}{a}\sin at\right\}, \quad \left|\dfrac{1}{a}\sin at\right| < \dfrac{1}{a}.$

(β) $\dfrac{1}{\sqrt{s}}\, e^{-\lambda\sqrt{s}} = \left\{\dfrac{1}{\sqrt{\pi t}}\exp\left(-\dfrac{\lambda^2}{4t}\right)\right\}$. The function in braces has at point $t = \dfrac{\lambda^2}{2}$ its maximum equal to $\dfrac{1}{\lambda}\sqrt{\dfrac{2}{\pi e}}$.

p. 242

1. $X''(\lambda) = svx''(\lambda).$

$$X''(\lambda) - a^2 sX(\lambda) = svx''(\lambda) - a^2 s^2 vx(\lambda) = sv[x''(\lambda) - a^2 sx(\lambda)] = 0.$$

$$X(0) = sv\cdot x(0) = sv\cdot\frac{1}{s} = v.$$

$$X'(\lambda) = sv\cdot x'(\lambda).$$

$$X'(\lambda_0) = sv\cdot x'(\lambda_0) = sv\cdot 0 = 0.$$

The function $X(\lambda) = \{X(\lambda, t\}$ represents temperature changes in a bar which at the instant $t = 0$ had temperature 0 everywhere and to whose one end we impart temperature $v = \{v(t)\}$ insulating at the same time the other end $\lambda = \lambda_0$.

2. $X(\lambda) = \left\{\dfrac{2\pi}{a^2\lambda_0^2}\sum_{n=1}^{\infty}(n-\tfrac{1}{2})\sin\dfrac{(n-\frac{1}{2})\pi\lambda}{\lambda_0}\int_0^t v(t-\tau)\exp\left(-\dfrac{(n-\frac{1}{2})^2\pi^2}{a^2\lambda_0^2}\tau\right)d\tau\right\}.$

p. 244

1. $X''(\lambda) = -sv\cdot x''(\lambda).$

$$X''(\lambda) - a^2 s\cdot x(\lambda) = -sv[x''(\lambda) - a^2 s\cdot x(\lambda)] = 0.$$

$$X'(0) = -sv\cdot x'(0) = -sv\cdot\left(-\frac{1}{s}\right) = v.$$

$$X(\lambda_0) = -sv\cdot x(\lambda_0) = 0.$$

The function $X(\lambda) = \{X(\lambda, t)\}$ represents temperature changes in a bar for which the outflow of heat through the point $\lambda = 0$ is defined by the function $v = \{v(t)\}$ while the end $\lambda = \lambda_0$ is constantly kept at temperature 0; at the instant $t = 0$ the whole bar has temperature 0.

2. $X(\lambda) = -\left\{\dfrac{2}{a^2\lambda_0}\sum_{n=1}^{\infty}\cos\dfrac{(n-\frac{1}{2})\pi\lambda}{\lambda_0}\int_0^t v(t-\tau)\exp\left(-\dfrac{(n-\frac{1}{2})^2\pi^2}{a^2\lambda_0^2}\tau\right)d\tau\right\}.$

PART FOUR

CHAPTER I

p. 272

(α) $x = ce^{-4\lambda s}$; (β) $x = ce^{-\lambda s}$; (γ) $x = c_1 e^{\lambda s} + c_2 e^{-\lambda s}$;

(δ) $x = c_1 e^{-\lambda} + c_2 e^{-\lambda s} + ce^{-\lambda/s}$; (ε) $x = 0$.

p. 282

(α) $x(\lambda) = \dfrac{1}{s} e^{-4\lambda s}$; (β) $x(\lambda) = e^{(1-\lambda)s}$;

(γ) $x(\lambda) = \dfrac{s}{1+e^{-s}} (e^{(\lambda-1)s} + e^{-\lambda s})$; (δ) $x(\lambda) = -e^{-\lambda} + 2e^{-\lambda/s}$.

The solutions are unique.

CHAPTER II

p. 285

(α) $x_0(\lambda) = \dfrac{1}{s}(a\lambda + b)$; (β) $x_0(\lambda) = -\dfrac{6}{s^4} + \dfrac{3}{s^2}\lambda^2 + \dfrac{1}{s}\lambda^3$;

(γ) $x_0(\lambda) = \dfrac{s^2-4}{2s^4}\lambda^2 + \dfrac{1}{6s^2}\lambda^4$.

p. 286

(α) $x_0(\lambda) = \dfrac{1}{s^2} e^{-\lambda s}$; (β) $x_0(\lambda) = \dfrac{\lambda^2}{2} e^{-\lambda s}$; (γ) $x_0(\lambda) = \dfrac{\lambda}{s} e^{-\lambda s}$.

p. 287

(α) $x_0(\lambda) = \left(\dfrac{4(1+5s)}{s^3(s-1)^4} + \dfrac{8}{s^2(s-1)^3}\lambda + \dfrac{1}{s^2(s-1)^2}\lambda^2\right) e^{-\lambda s}$;

(β) $x_0(\lambda) = \left(\dfrac{3\lambda^2}{16s^2} + \dfrac{\lambda^3}{12s\sqrt{s}} + \dfrac{\lambda^4}{48s}\right) e^{-\lambda\sqrt{s}}$.

p. 288

(α) $x_0(\lambda) = \dfrac{s^2}{1} + \dfrac{\lambda}{s} + \dfrac{e^{\lambda}}{1-s+s^2}$; (β) $x_0(\lambda) = \dfrac{\lambda}{3s^2} e^{-s\lambda} + \dfrac{1}{2s^3} e^{s\lambda}$;

(γ) $x_0(\lambda) = 1 - \dfrac{e^{-\lambda}}{(s-1)^2} - \dfrac{e^{2\lambda}}{s(2s+1)(s+2)}$.

p. 289

(α) $x_0(\lambda) = \left(\dfrac{\lambda}{4s^3} - \dfrac{\lambda^3}{6s}\right)\cos\lambda s + \dfrac{\lambda^2}{4s^2}\sin\lambda s$;

(β) $x_0(\lambda) = \dfrac{-\lambda}{s(s-1)}\cos\lambda s + \dfrac{2}{s(s-1)^2}\sin\lambda s -$

$$- [2s\cos\lambda s + (s^2 - s - 1)\sin\lambda s]\frac{e^{\lambda}}{s^4 - 2s^3 + 3s^2 + 2s + 1};$$

(γ) $x_0(\lambda) = -\dfrac{1}{s^2} - \dfrac{\lambda}{2s\sqrt{s}}\sin\lambda\sqrt{s}$.

p. 290

(α) $x(\lambda) = \frac{1}{\varepsilon^3}(6e^{-2s\lambda} - 5e^{-3s\lambda} + 1)$;

(β) $$x(\lambda) = \left[\frac{1}{1-e^{-s}}\left(\frac{1}{2}e^{-s} - \frac{4}{s^3} + \frac{12}{s^2} - \frac{23}{3s} + \frac{13}{6} - s\right) + \right.$$

$$\left. + \left(\frac{4}{s^2} - \frac{10}{s^2} + \frac{2}{s}\right)\lambda + \left(-\frac{2}{s^3} + \frac{5}{s} - \frac{1}{2}\right)\lambda^2 + \left(\frac{2}{3s} - \frac{5}{3} + s\right)\lambda^2\right] e^{-2\lambda s} +$$

$$+ \frac{1}{1-e^{-s}}\left(\frac{4}{s^3} - \frac{12}{s^2} + \frac{23}{3s} - \frac{8}{3} + s\right)e^{-2\lambda s};$$

(γ) $x(\lambda) = e^{\lambda/s} + \sin\lambda\sqrt{s}$;

(δ) $$x(\lambda) = \left[\frac{1}{s} - \frac{\lambda}{4\sqrt{2}(s^2-1)}\right]\cos\lambda\sqrt{2} +$$

$$+ \left[\frac{1}{s\sin 2\sqrt{2}} - \left(\frac{1}{s} - \frac{1}{2\sqrt{2}(s^2-1)}\right)\operatorname{ctg} 2\sqrt{2}\right]\sin\lambda\sqrt{2};$$

(ε) $$x(\lambda) = e^{\lambda\sqrt{2}} + \frac{\sin\lambda\sqrt{2}}{8(s^2+1)}.$$

CHAPTER III

p. 297

(α) $x(\lambda, t) = \lambda + \sin\lambda \operatorname{sh} t$;

(β) $x(\lambda, t) = e^{-\lambda}[(2-t^2)\sin t - 2t\cos t + 2\lambda(\sin t - t\cos t) + \lambda^2 \sin t) + \frac{2}{t^2}$;

(γ) For $0 \leqslant t < \lambda$:

$$x(\lambda, t) = e^{\lambda}(t^2 - 2t - 4 - \frac{1}{2}e^{-t} + \frac{9}{2}\cos\frac{1}{\sqrt{3}}t + \frac{3}{2}\sqrt{3}\sin\frac{1}{\sqrt{3}}t,$$

for $0 \leqslant \lambda < t$:

$$x(\lambda, t) = e^{\lambda}\left(t^2 - 2t - 4 - \frac{1}{2}e^{-t} + \frac{9}{2}\cos\frac{1}{\sqrt{3}}t + \frac{3}{2}\sqrt{3}\sin\frac{1}{\sqrt{3}}t\right) -$$

$$-(t-\lambda)^2 - 2(t-\lambda) - 4 - \frac{1}{2}e^{-(t-\lambda)} + \frac{9}{2}\cos\frac{1}{\sqrt{3}}(t-\lambda) + \frac{3}{2}\sin\frac{1}{\sqrt{3}}(t-\lambda).$$

BIBLIOGRAPHY

1. Berg, E. J., *Heaviside's operational calculus as applied to Engineering and Physics*, New York 1936.

1. Bochner, S., *Integration von Funktionen, deren Werte die Elemente eines Vektorraumes sind*, Fund. Math. 20 (1933), p. 262-276.

1. Carslaw, H. and Jaeger, J., *Operational methods in applied mathematics*, New York 1941.

1. Carson, J. R., *Electric circuit theory and operational calculus*, New York 1926.

1. Churchill, R. V., *Modern operational Mathematics in Engineering*, New York 1944.

1. Comrie, L. J., *Mathematical Tables*, London 1949.

1. Crum, M. M., *On the resultant of two functions*, The Quarterly Journal of Mathematics, Oxford Series 12, nº 46 (1941), pp. 108-111.

1. Dahr, K., *A course of integrational and operational calculus with applications to problems of physics and electrotechnics*, Stockholm 1935.

1. Dieudonné, J. et Schwartz, L., *La dualité dans les espaces* (*F*) *et* (*LF*), Annales de l'Institut Fourier 1 (1950), p. 61-101.

1. Диткин, В. А., *Операционное исчисление*, Успехи математических наук, т. II, вып. 6 (22) (1947), pp. 72-158.

1. Диткин В. А. и Кузнецов П. И., *Справочник по операционному исчислению*, Москва-Ленинград 1951.

1. Doetsch, G., *Tabellen zur Laplace-Transformation und Anleitung zum Gebrauch*, Berlin-Göttingen 1947.

2. — *Theorie und Anwendung der Laplace-Transformation*, Berlin 1937.

3. — *Handbuch der Laplace-Transformation*, *I-III*, Basel-Stuttgart 1950-1956.

1. Drobot, S., *Uwagi o zastosowaniu rachunku operatorów do statyki konstrukcji*, Archiwum Mechaniki Stosowanej VI (1954), pp. 93-100.

1. Drobot, S. et Mikusiński, J. G.-, *Sur l'unicité des solutions de quelques équations différentielles dans les espaces abstraits*, Studia Mathematica 11 (1950), pp. 38-40.

2. (Дробот, С. и Микусинский, Я.), *Об операторе сдвига и его применении к статике балок*, Успехи Мат. Наук 13 (1958), p. 73-92.

1. Dufresnoy, J., *Sur le produit de composition de deux fonctions*, Comptes Rendus de l'Académie des Sciences 225 (1947), pp. 857-859.

2. — *Autour du théorème de Phragmén-Lindelöf*, Bulletin des Sciences Mathématiques 72 (1948), pp. 17-22.

1. Эфрос, А. М. и Данилевский, А. М., *Операционное исчисление и контурные интегралы*, Харков 1937.

1. Gardner, M. and Barnes, I., *Transients in Linear Systems*, vol. 1, New York 1942.

1. Heaviside, O., *Electromagnetic theory*, London 1899.

1. Hirschman, I. (Jr) and Widder, D., *Generalized Bernstein polynomials*, Duke Math. Journal 16 (1949), p. 433-438.

1. Humbert, P., *Le calcul symbolique*, Actualités scientifiques et industrielles 147 (1934).
1. Jahnke, E. und Emde, E., *Funktionentafeln*, 3 Auflage, Leipzig-Berlin 1938.
1. Jeffreys, H., *Operational methods in mathematical physics*, 2nd edition, Cambridge Tracts 23 (1931).
1. Kamke, E., *Differentialgleichungen, Lösungsmethoden und Lösungen*, 2. Auflage, Leipzig 1943.
1. Kuratowski, K., *Wykłady rachunku różniczkowego i całkowego*, część I, Warszawa 1948.
1. Leja, F., *Rachunek różniczkowy i całkowy*, wydanie V, Warszawa 1956.
1. Lerch, M., *Sur un point de la théorie des fonctions génératrices d'Abel*, Acta Mathematica 27 (1903), pp. 339-352.
1. Лурье, A. H., *Операционное исчисление*, Москва 1950.
1. Łuszczki, Z., Mikusiński, J., Urbanik, K., Wloka, J. und Zieleźny, Z., *Einige Bemerkungen über Hirschman-Widderschen Funktionen* $H_{n,k}(x)$, Coll. Math. 4 (1956), p. 30-32.
1. Magnus, W. und Oberhettinger F., *Formeln und Sätze für die Speziellen Funktionen der Mathematischen Physik*, Berlin 1943.
1. Mazur, S. et Orlicz, W., *Sur les espaces métriques linéaires (I)*, Studia Math. 10 (1948), p. 184-208.
1. Mc Lachlan, N. W., *Complex Variable and Operational Calculus with technical applications*, Cambridge 1939.
2. — *Modern Operational Calculus*, London 1948.
1. Mikusiński, J. G., *Remarks on the moment problem and a theorem of Picone*, Colloquium Mathematicum II, 2 (1951), pp. 138-141.
2. — *Sur les équations différentielles du calcul opératoire et leurs applications aux équations aux dérivées partielles*, Studia Mathematica 12 (1951), pp. 227-270.
3. — *Sur les fonctions exponentielles du calcul opératoire*, Studia Mathematica 12 (1951), pp. 208-224.
4. — *Sur les fondements du calcul opératoire*, Studia Mathematica II (1950), pp. 41-70.
5. — *Sur l'unicité des solutions de quelques équations différentielles dans les espaces abstraits*, Annales de la Société Polonaise de Mathématique 22 (1949), pp. 157-160.
6. — *Sur un déterminant*, Studia Mathematica 25 (1952), pp. 27-29.
7. — *Un théorème d'unicité pour quelques systèmes d'équations différentielles considérées dans les espaces abstraits*, Studia Mathematica 12 (1951), pp. 80-83.
8. — *Une nouvelle justification du calcul opératoire*, Atti della Academia Nazionale dei Lincei 2 (1950), pp. 113-121.
9. — *Sur la croissance de la fonction opérationnelle* $\exp(-s^{\alpha}\lambda)$, Bull. Ac. Pol. Sci. IV, 7 (1956), p. 423-425.
10. — *On the function whose Laplace transform is* $e^{-s^{\alpha}}$, Studia Math. (in print).
11. — *Sur les notions de distribution et d'opérateur*, Bull. Pol. Sci. (in print).
12. — *Sur un type de conditions mixtes pour les équations aux dérivées partielles*, Studia Math. 13 (1953), p. 277-286.
13. — *Sur les solutions linéairement indépendantes des équations différentielles à coefficients constants*, Studia Math. 16 (1957), p. 41-47.
14. — *Sur les théorèmes d'unicité et le nombre de solutions linéairement indépendantes*, Studia Math. 16 (1957), p. 95-98.
15. — *Sur l'espace linéaire avec dérivation*, Studia Math. 16 (1957), p. 113-123.
16. — *Extensions de l'espace linéaire avec dérivation*, Studia Math. 16 (1957), p. 156-172.

17. — (Микусинский, Я.), *О работах польских математиков по теории обобщенных функций и операционному исчислению*, Успехи Мат. Наук 11 (1956), p. 169-172.
18. — *Sur la méthode de généralisation de M. Laurent Schwartz et sur la convergence faible*, Fund. Math. 35 (1948), p. 235-239.
19. — *Une définition de distribution*, Bull. Ac. Pol. Sci., Cl. III, 3 (1955), p. 589-591.
20. — *Rachunek operatorów na tle aktualnych kierunków matematyki*, Roczniki Polskiego Tow. Mat., Prace Matem. I, 2 (1955), p. 344-370.
1. Mikusiński, J. G. et Ryll-Nardzewski C., *Sur le produit de composition*, Studia Mathematica 12 (1951), pp. 52-57.
2. — *Sur l'opérateur de translation*, Studia Mathematica 12 (1951), pp. 205-207.
3. — *Sur un type de conditions mixtes pour les équations aux dérivées partielles*, Studia Mathematica 13 (1953), pp. 277-286.
4. — *O rachunku operatorów*, Zastosowania Matematyki I (1953), pp. 28-40.
5. — *Sur la dérivée algébrique*, Fundamenta Mathematicae 40 (1953), pp. 99-105.
1. Mikusiński, J. and Sikorski, R., *The elementary theory of distributions*, Rozprawy Matemat. 12, Warszawa 1957.
1. Phragmén, E., *Sur une extension d'un théorème classique de la théorie des fonctions*, Acta Mathematica 28 (1904), pp. 331-368.
1. Picone, M., *Nouvelles méthodes de recherche pour la détermination des intégrales des équations linéaires aux dérivées partielles*, Annales de la Société Polonaise de Mathematique 19 (1946), pp. 36-61.
2. — *Nuovi metodi d'indagine per la teoria delle equaziani a derivate parziali*, Rendiconti del Seminario Matematico e Fisico di Milano 18 (1939).
1. Pogorzelski, W., *Rachunek operatorowy i przekształcenie Laplace'a*, Warszawa 1950.
1. Ryll-Nardzewski, C., *Sur la convergence des séries d'opérateurs*, Studia Mathematica 13 (1953), pp. 37-40.
2. — *Sur le séries de puissances de l'operateur différentiel*, Studia Mathematica 13 (1953).
1. Schwartz, L., *Théorie des distributions I, II*, Paris 1950 and 1951.
1. Sikorski, R., *On Mikusiński's algebraical theory of differential equations*, Studia Math. 16 (1957), p. 230-236.
1. Soboleff, S., *Méthode nouvelle à résoudre le problème de Cauchy pour les équations hyperboliques normales*, Recueil Math. 1 (1936), p. 39-71.
1. Temple, G., *Theories and applications of generalized functions*, Journal Lond. Math. Soc. 28 (1953), p. 134-148.
1. Titchmarsh, E. C., *The zeros of certain integral functions*, Proceedings of the London Mathematical Society 25 (1926) pp. 283-302.
2. — *Introduction to the theory of Fourier Integrals*, Oxford 1948.
1. Tychonoff, A., *Théorèmes d'unicité pour l'équation de la chaleur*, Математический Сборник 42, pp. 199-216.
1. Urbanik, K., *Sur la structure non-topologique du corps des opérateurs*, Studia Math. 14 (1954), p. 243-246.
1. Wagner, K. W., *Operatorrechnung*, 2. Auflage, Leipzig 1950.
1. Węgrzyn, S., *Stany nieustalone w układach pobudzanych periodycznie*, Archiwum elektrotechniki 3 (1954), pp. 481-498.
2. — *Rachunek operatorowy*, Warszawa 1955.
1. Włodarski, L., *Sur une formule de Efros*, Studia Math. 13 (1953), p. 183-187,
2. — *Une remarque sur une classe de fonctions exponentielles du calcul opérationnel*. Studia Math. 13 (1953), p. 188-189.

INDEX

CONTENTS

CHAPTER VII. **The algebraic derivative**

PART FOUR

AN OUTLINE OF THE GENERAL THEORY OF LINEAR DIFFERENTIAL EQUATIONS WITH CONSTANT COEFFICIENTS

CHAPTER I. **Homogeneous equations**

CHAPTER II. **Non-homogeneous equations**

CHAPTER III. **Applications to partial differential equations**

PART FIVE

INTEGRAL OPERATIONAL CALCULUS

PART SIX

APPENDIX

IV. Tables of functions

MISLEADING ERRORS

Page line	Instead of	should be
9^{12}	$=\int_0^t\left[\int_0^t\right.$	$=\int_0^t\left[\int_0^{t-\tau}\right.$
9^{14}	$=\int_0^t\left[\int_0^t\right.$	$=\int_0^t\left[\int_\tau^t\right.$
23^9	$tg = 0$	$fg_1 = 0$
25^2	be identical,	be identical to 0,
33_5	$=\left\{\int_0^t e^{a(t+\tau)}\right.$	$=\left\{\int_0^t e^{a(t-\tau)}\right.$
42_{14}	$x' = x(2t-1)e^{t^2}$	$x' - x = (2t-1)e^{t^2}$
44_4	$2x''+y''+z'' =$	$2x''+y''+z''+z =$
59	Fig. 7, scheme 3	$I_1+I_2+I_3+I_4 = 0$
84^5	$E = 0$	$E_2 = 0$
85^{10}	$I_0 e^{i\varphi}$	$I_0 e^{i\psi}$
95^{11}	$A_{12} = 0$	$A_{12} \neq 0$
104_2	s''	s^2
114^7	$sa' =$	$sa =$
120_6	$\frac{3}{5} -$	$\frac{3}{s} -$
128_8	$F = g+$	$F = q+$
130^5	$M = \frac{Q}{s} = \frac{F}{s}$	$M = \frac{Q}{s} = \frac{F}{s^2}$
133_5	$-8h^4$	$-Bh^4$
134^{11}	$F = \frac{100}{s^2}$	$F = \frac{100}{s}$
145^8	$q_n = a_n/r$	$g_n = a_n/r$
154_3	$f = Q_1/P$	$f = Q/P$
159^3	$\frac{1}{h}$	$\frac{1}{h^2}$
162^2	$\ldots+\frac{a_k-1}{h}$	$\ldots+\frac{a_{k-1}}{h}$
169_1	$\left(\frac{0}{2}\right)^n$	$\left(\frac{\varrho}{2}\right)^n$

Page line	Instead of	should be
172^7	$\left(-\frac{\beta}{\nu}\right)$	$\binom{-\beta}{\nu}$
174_{10}	$a = 2/\sqrt{Lc}$	$a = 2/\sqrt{LC}$
181^9	$\{h_1(t)\}$	$\{h_1(\lambda, t)\}$
193^{17}	$[\psi(\lambda f)]$	$[\psi(\lambda f)]'$
199_{15}	$= 2wx(\lambda)x'(\lambda)x''(\lambda) =$	$2wx(\lambda)x'(\lambda) - 2x'(\lambda)x''(\lambda) =$
237_8	$\exp\left(-\frac{n^2\pi^2}{a^2\lambda_0^2}\right)$	$\exp\left(-\frac{n^2\pi^2}{a^2\lambda_0^2}t\right)$
239^2	$= \lambda(\xi)$	$= g(\xi)$
241_7	λ^2	λ_0^2
242_{14}	λ^2	λ_0^2
256^4	$= \frac{as+\beta}{Ls+R}e^{-(as+a)\lambda} =$	$= \frac{as+\beta}{Ls+R}e^{-(a\lambda+a)\lambda}E =$
256_{15}	$T''(\lambda) =$	$U''(\lambda) =$
258_{16}	$= s\sqrt{LC+a}$	$= s\sqrt{LC}+a$
259_{12}	$a = \frac{1}{2}\left(\frac{R}{4}+\frac{G}{C}\right)$	$a = \frac{1}{2}\left(\frac{R}{L}+\frac{G}{C}\right)$
264^6	$t\cos\beta^2$	$t\cos\beta t$
280_{12}	$x(0) = 1/s$	$x(0) = -1/s$
284_{10}	$(28c_2 + bc_3\lambda)+$	$(2c_2 + 6c_3\lambda)+$
291_5	$a^{\nu-\varkappa-1}$	$a_{\mu\nu}s^{\nu-\varkappa-1}$
292^8	$\sum_{\varkappa'=0}^{n=1}\sum_{\nu'=0}^{\varkappa'-1}$	$\sum_{\varkappa'=0}^{n-1}\sum_{\nu'=1}^{\varkappa'-1}$
294_6	$= \frac{s}{s^2-1} =$	$= \frac{s}{s^2-1} -$
295_6	$s^2 -$	$u^2 -$
297_2	$-x_{t^3}$	$-x_{t^2}$
298^5	$-x_{\lambda t}(\lambda, 0) - x(\lambda, 0)]$	$-x_{\lambda t}(\lambda, 0) - x_t(\lambda, 0) - x(\lambda, 0)]$
298^7	$x_{\lambda^2}(\lambda, 0) = x_{\lambda^2}(\lambda, 0) = 0$	$x_{\lambda^2}(\lambda, 0) = x_{\lambda^3}(\lambda, 0) = 0$
298_8	$x^{(\lambda)} =$	$x(\lambda) =$
323^{10}	$= \int_\gamma^\beta f(\lambda)\,d\lambda.$	$+ \int_\gamma^\beta f(\lambda)\,d\lambda.$